PROBA

RANDO

PROBABILITY AND RANDOM PROCESSES

Using MATLAB with Applications to Continuous and Discrete Time Systems

Donald G. Childers
University of Florida

IRWIN

Chicago • Bogotá • Boston • Buenos Aires • Caracas
London • Madrid • Mexico City • Sydney • Toronto

Irwin Book Team

Publisher: *Tom Casson*
Senior sponsoring editor: *Scott Isenberg*
Director of marketing: *Kurt L. Strand*
Project supervisor: *Karen J. Nelson*
Senior production supervisor: *Laurie Sander*
Designer: *Larry J. Cope*
Cover Designer: *Annette Rapier/A.M. Design*
Director, Prepress Purchasing: *Kimberly Meriwether David*
Compositor: *Interactive Composition Corporation*
Typeface: *10/12 Times Roman*
Printer: *R. R. Donnelley & Sons Company*

Library of Congress Cataloging-in-Publication Data

Childers, Donald G.
    Probability and random processes using MATLAB : with applications to continuous and discrete time systems / Donald G. Childers.
        p. cm.
    Includes index.
    ISBN 0–256–13361–1
    1. Probabilities—Data processing.   2. Stochastic processes—Data processing.   3. MATLAB.   I. Title.
QA273.19.E4C47 1997
519.2'078—dc20   96–35875

Printed in the United States of America
1 2 3 4 5 6 7 8 9 0 DO 3 2 1 0 9 8 7 6

This book is dedicated to my wife, Barbara, to whom I have been wed for 43 years, and to our two children, Dawn and Darin. Thank you one and all for your sacrifices while putting up with me, for your love, and for the memories from the past and for those yet to come.

Donald G. Childers

PREFACE

The purpose of this book is to bring theory and practice into closer contact when teaching probability theory, and random processes. Many books in this area teach only or mostly theory. The practice is left for other courses or omitted completely. More emphasis is placed on analyzing data in today's engineering world, than was true in years past. This is because it is easier to collect data and to analyze it. In fact many engineers will spend hours analyzing data, rather than thinking about the results or the design or the purpose of their project. They substitute frenetic programming activity for contemplative cognitive activity. This book strives to strike a balance between theory and practice. The goal is for the student to understand the basic concepts of the theory as well as its assumptions and limitations, yet also be able to analyze data and discuss how the analysis results are related to the basic theory. It is my belief that a close coupling of theory and practice facilitates the understanding of both, especially enhancing the understanding of the theory.

In order to achieve the above goal, this book has features that distinguish it from others in this area. The text strives to blend probability theory, random processes, and data (signal) processing. MATLAB is used extensively throughout the book, beginning in Chapter 1. The use of MATLAB is not reserved for the problems only. It is used in examples as well as in demonstration software for probability and for calculating spectra, correlation functions, and other factors. There are two software "games" that allow the student to practice simple probability problems in Chapters 1 and 2. There is also a software package introduced in Chapter 6 that lets the student explore the calculation of spectra and correlation functions without having to write programs. The software is used with a PC and a mouse to point and click on data and the desired program. Several data sets are included for the student to analyze, including some speech files. The purpose of this software is to facilitate learning, not programming.

Another feature of the book is the use of quizzes at key points throughout the text. Most of the quizzes are simple, but a few are more extensive. The purpose of the quizzes is to (hopefully) have the student stop at these key points and solve a simple problem or answer a question about the material he/she has just read, rather than go on to additional material. So the quizzes are to help the student focus on new material before proceeding to additional material. Each chapter has problems that tend to focus on the use of theory as well as MATLAB problems that tend to focus on applications and simulations. The solutions manual is extensive and provides MATLAB programs for all of the MATLAB problems along with example solutions, including figures. The text has numerous applications that cover communications, aspects of statistics, speech, radar, Markov processes, spectral analysis, correlation functions, data modeling, and so on.

Some additional features of the text are that random sequences are used extensively so that the use of data does not confuse the student. Vector random variables and vector random processes are studied. Ensemble averaging is separated from time averaging and ergodic random processes. Elementary statistics is introduced and related to the analysis of data and the evaluation of analysis techniques. Various spectral analysis techniques are introduced. Random number generation is examined. The response of linear systems to signals plus noise is studied, and discrete matched filters are presented along with discrete Wiener filters. Several appendices provide review material so that the student does not need to go to other sources.

This book consists of eight chapters and six appendices and a bibliography. The material is suitable for a Senior or Graduate level one semester course and has been used in a first course on probability and random processes at the University of Florida. The prerequisites include an understanding of the basics of linear algebra, such as vectors and matrices. The reader should also be acquainted with Fourier, Laplace, and Z-transforms, and sampling theory.

The material is designed to be taught in sequence, covering elementary probability theory in the first two chapters, then random variables in Chapter 3, followed by the theory of expectation in Chapter 4. Chapter 5 introduces random processes and Markov random processes. The theoretical concepts of correlation functions and the power spectrum are covered in Chapter 6. A software package designed for this book for analyzing data is also introduced in Chapter 6. Chapter 7 introduces selected concepts on estimation, statistics, and simulation. The theory of ergodicity is discussed at the beginning of the chapter. While Chapter 7 emphasizes practice, it shows how practice is related to theory and modeling. Finally, Chapter 8 covers the theory and practice of random processes and linear systems. The emphasis is on discrete time systems, including discrete matched filters and Wiener filters. However, the theory of optimum continuous time matched filters and Wiener filters is covered in Appendices 4 and 5. Appendix 1 reviews unit step and delta functions. Appendix 2 provides some examples of typical time functions and their correlation functions, power spectrum, and other properties. Fundamentals of Fourier, Laplace, and Z-transforms and the fast Fourier transform (FFT) are reviewed in Appendix 3. Appendix 6 contains two practice examinations for the material covered in Chapters 1 through 4 and one practice examination covering the material in Chapters 5 through 8. The solutions to these exams are contained in the solutions manual.

The publisher plans to make the solutions manual and the software available on their home site on the World Wide Web,

http://www.irwin.com

The solutions manual is typed in Microsoft Word, version 7. The electronic version of the solutions to the MATLAB problems can be copied to an ASCII editor such as Notepad, saved in a subdirectory and executed under MATLAB. No typing of the m-files should be required.

Many people have provided assistance for the development of this book. The most notable are former doctoral students. I am particularly indebted to the following (listed in alphabetical order): Chieteuk Ahn, Keun Sung Bae, Minsoo Hahn, Yung-Sheng (Albert) Hsiao, Yu-Fu Hsieh, Hwai-Tsu Hu, Ajit L. Lalwani, Kyosik Lee, Minkyu (MK) Lee, Pedro P. L. Prado, Yean-Jen (James) Shue, Yuan-Tzu Ting, John M. White, Chun-Fan Wong, Changshiann (John) Wu, Ching-Jang (Charles) Wu, Ke Wu and others of years past. These individuals contributed to the completion of this book in various ways, such as; making corrections, offering suggestions, and working examples and problems.

I would also like to thank the reviewers of this manuscript, whose comments and recommendations helped me to improve the book through the various drafts and stages of development.

In-Soo Ahn
Bradley University

Jon Bredeson
University of Alabama

Mark A. Clements
Georgia Institute of Technology

George R. Davis
Arizona State University

John R. Deller
Michigan State University

Leonard Gould
Massachusetts Institute of Technology

Alfred Hero
University of Michigan at Ann Arbor

Ben H. Jansen
University of Houston

Kurt Kosbar
University of Missouri at Rolla

David Landgrebe
Purdue University

Darryl Morrell
Arizona State University

Kizhakke V. Ravi
GMI Engineering and Management Institute

Marvin Siegel
Michigan State University

Wayne E. Stark
University of Michigan

Saibun Tjuatja
University of Texas at Arlington

Steven A. Tretter
University of Maryland

Douglas B. Williams
Georgia Institute of Technology

The editorial team at Irwin provided guidance and responsiveness throughout the development and production of the book. I appreciate the efforts of Scott Isenberg, Senior Sponsoring Editor; Carrie Berkshire, Tricia Howland, Anne O'Day, and Marc Mattson, Editorial Assistants; Karen Nelson, Project Editor; Larry Cope, Designer; and Laurie Sanders, Production Manager.

Finally, I would also like to thank my wife, who helped assemble the solutions manual. She often reminded me she had no idea what the solution meant, but she said she could make it presentable. Alas, I have no secretary to thank for help on this book. I myself typed the entire manuscript, its numerous revisions, and the solutions manual.

CONTENTS

PROBABILITY AND
RANDOM PROCESSES

chapter

1

Introduction

1.1 GOALS

The purpose of this book is to introduce the concepts of probability and random processes and to illustrate these concepts with engineering applications. To achieve this goal we will find it necessary to introduce many new definitions. After each definition we will generally give an example that will illustrate an application of the definition. While in the first few chapters it may appear that there is not enough emphasis on applications to engineering problem solving, this changes as we progress through the book. The theory is important and must be mastered so that you will become adept at interpreting the results of both experimental studies and theoretical derivations.

Some of the applications that will be examined include the design of filters and systems that will enhance a signal and suppress interference, such as noise. Such applications occur in communication systems and signal processing. Other problems include pattern recognition procedures applied to speech recognition. We will also encounter optimization techniques, such as maximization of signal-to-noise ratio (S/N) and error minimization. Often these applications will require procedures for correlation and spectral analysis of signals. We will examine both continuous-time and discrete-time signals and systems. The emphasis is on methods for processing digital signals in noise. The analytical tools to be introduced will include methods for solving differential and integral equations as well as linear algebra (matrix theory) for solving simultaneous-difference equations.

1.2 APPLICATIONS

The range of fields that use the theory and practice of random processes is very extensive and includes communications, electrical and electronic engineering, acoustics and digital audio, geoscience, instrumentation, systems reliability, ocean and environmental systems, computer engineering, physics, chemical and mechanical engineering, radio astronomy, and numerous other disciplines.

Some typical application areas include systems simulation and testing. The electronics consumer industry uses the concepts in microwave ovens, high fidelity audio systems, and the design of compact disc systems. The electronics industry studies electronic emissions, recombinations, ionizing collisions, carrier life time, physical constants of materials and electronic devices, and integrated-circuit testing. The concepts are used in image and speech processing, circuit modeling, biological and medical applications, and for generating test signals for numerous applications, including antenna systems, communications, electronic countermeasures, and signal detection.

To illustrate the range of potential uses of the material we will examine in this book, let us consider several simple examples. One is speech recognition, a topic of considerable interest today. Many researchers are working on methods to achieve computer recognition of speech. One application is to recognize commands spoken to a computer (see Figure 1.1). Such systems are presently available from several vendors. A simple speech recognition system might use a procedure called template matching, which may be described as follows. We define a vocabulary, or a set of possible words for a computerized dictionary. This restricts the number of possible alternatives that must be recognized. Then a template for each word is obtained by digitizing the word as it is spoken. The template may be the time waveform, or the spectrum of the word, or a vector of selected features of the word. Common features are the envelope of the time waveform, the energy, the number of zero crossings within a specified interval, and the like.

For our example we will use the time waveform (see Figure 1.2). Here we have a vocabulary of four words and their respective waveforms versus time as spoken by an adult male. We store each template on disk. Now imagine we want the computer to recognize the spoken word hello and have it printed on the screen of the computer. We ask someone to speak hello. The word is digitized and stored in a file on disk as a test template. This test template is then compared with each of the stored templates as in Figure 1.3.

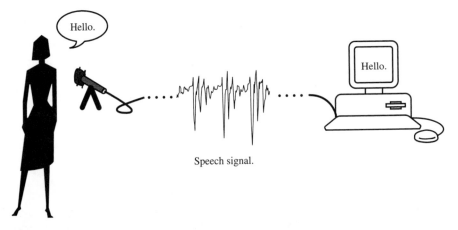

Speech signal.

Figure 1.1   A simple speech recognition system

One way to make such a comparison is by correlating the test template with each stored template. If the templates are aligned and of the same duration, then we calculate the crosscorrelation between each stored template and the test template to obtain the value of the crosscorrelation for zero shift between the two templates. (Crosscorrelation of two digitized signals is similar to a vector product of the two signals.) Denote this number as $R_{rt}(0)$. This number will vary for each reference template. The reference template that gives the largest $R_{rt}(0)$ is the best match, and we decide that that particular reference word is the test word. We then print that word on the screen.

In Chapter 6 you will study in detail the methods of correlation and how these methods may be applied. Speech recognition is a complicated task and this example has greatly simplified the problem. Factors that make the task so difficult include interference from the surroundings, variability in the amplitude and duration of the spoken word, changes in other characteristics of the spoken word such as the speaker's pitch, the size of the dictionary, and other factors. We have illustrated some of the variability that may occur when various talkers speak the same word in Figure 1.4. Here we see that

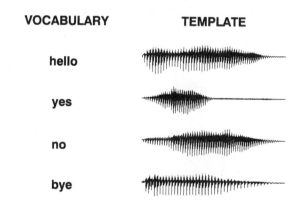

Figure 1.2   Vocabulary for speech recognition

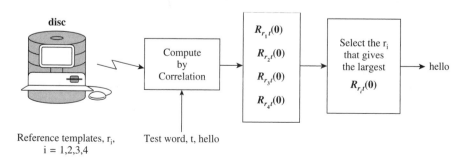

Figure 1.3   Recognition of test word hello

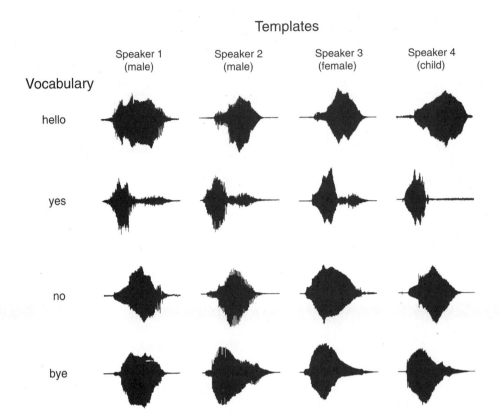

Figure 1.4   Vocabulary for speech recognition

the waveform templates may vary considerably from speaker to speaker. This variability may be described by the theory of probability and random processes, which in turn may be used to develop models for speech production and recognition. Such models may then be used to design systems for speech recognition.

Another example is the improvement of the signal-to-noise ratio (S/N) by filtering. Suppose an image is being transmitted by facsimile (fax). During transmission lightning interference (noise) occurs, corrupting the desired signal. It is possible to improve the S/N through filtering (see Figure 1.5). The filter is designed to remove portions of the noise to improve the picture reception. One criterion for such filter design is the maximization of the S/N. We will study such design procedures in Chapters 7 and 8.

In communications, audio, and imaging systems, noise or adjacent-channel interference may cause errors in the transmitted data. To combat data corruption these systems use data coding that adds redundancy to the data. This redundancy provides the basis for designing error correction coding schemes, which are used in compact disk (CD) players. Every CD player, whether in an automobile, or a home stereo, has a Reed-

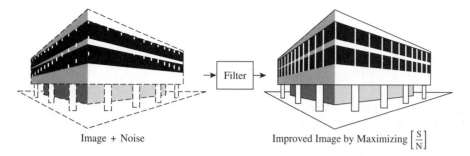

Image + Noise   Improved Image by Maximizing $\left[\frac{S}{N}\right]$

Figure 1.5   A filter designed to improve S/N

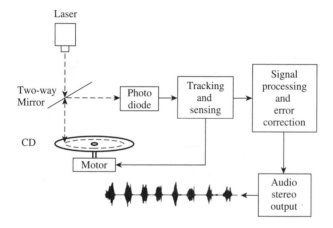

Figure 1.6   Simple schematic of a CD player

Solomon decoder. A CD player is like a communications channel (see Figure 1.6), wherein errors may occur because of imperfections in the CD, possibly due to dirt or perhaps caused by a scratch. All (or nearly all) of these errors are found and corrected because of redundancy built into the recording format using the powerful Reed-Solomon coding and decoding schemes. The decoding algorithm is capable of correcting as many as 4,000 consecutive bit errors. This is approximately 1/20 sec of music assuming 16 bits/sample and 44.1 k samples/sec. The design of some codes, such as Huffman codes, and some decoding algorithms is based on probability theory and correlation, which we cover in Chapters 2, 3, 4, and 6.

These three simple examples provide illustrations of the diversity of problems that probability and random processes may model, thereby assisting in the development of design solutions.

The remainder of this chapter will review the prerequisites for understanding the material to be presented in this book and will provide a short survey of set theory, which is the basic foundation for probability theory.

1.3 BACKGROUND MATERIAL

We assume that the reader is familiar with linear system concepts, including circuit theory; convolution; filtering; response of linear systems to signals; Fourier, Laplace, and Z-transforms; set theory; and linear algebra. Thus, the concepts of both continuous and discrete linear systems are presumed to be familiar. However, as the need arises we will review some of this material in the text or in an appendix. In the next chapter we will use some elementary concepts from set theory to introduce the concept of probability. Let us review those principles that we will need.

1.4 SET THEORY

The purpose for reviewing set theory is to provide a mathematical structure for organizing methods for counting and grouping objects. Set theory may be used to define the probabilities of possible outcomes of experiments. Note that experiments may be performed in the laboratory, or they may be thought experiments, or they may represent models for a theory.

There are two common methods for defining a set.

Definition 1.1. A set may be defined by listing its elements, provided this is possible. This method is known as the roster method. Synonyms for set include class, aggregate, and collection. We will denote sets by capital letters

$$A, B, C, \ldots$$

The elements or objects of a set will be indicated by lower case letters, such as

$$a, b, c, \ldots$$

If a is an object (or element or member or point) of A, then we denote this as a $\in$ A. If a is not an object of A, this is denoted as a $\notin$ A.

Definition 1.2. A second way of defining a set is called the property method, which describes some property held by all elements of the set, but is not held by elements that do not belong to the set.

Example 1.1 | Suppose we number the faces of a die as 1 through 6. If we toss such a die, the possible numbers that may appear on the uppermost face of the die are elements of the set {1, 2, 3, 4, 5, 6}, which is the roster method for defining the set. We may also define the set by the property method as {n | n is an integer $\geq$ 1 and $\leq$ 6}, which is read as the set of all numbers (elements) n given that n is an integer from 1 to 6 inclusively. The vertical line | is read as "given that" or "such that."

Example 1.2 | The set {t | t is a triangle in a plane} is the set of all triangles in a plane. The rosterbe used to define this set, since we are unable to list all the members of the set.

"ROSTERBE" ⇒ "ROSTER METHOD CAN'T BE"

Quiz 1.1   Define the set of all vowels in the English alphabet by both the roster and property methods.

If A is the set of all dogs, then a terrier called Whiskers is a member of A. A cat named Twink is not a member of A. | **Example 1.3**

If N is the set of integers, then 3 is an element of the set, while the number 1.1 is not. | **Example 1.4**

Definition 1.3. We may have sets contained within sets, which may be denoted as $A \subset B$ or $B \supset A$. This means that every element of A belongs to B. The symbols $\subset$ and $\supset$ are read as **is contained in** and **contains,** respectively. Note also that the open end of the symbol is toward the larger set. We may also say that A is a **subset** of B. The two sets A and B are said to be equal if and only if they contain the same elements, that is, $A \subset B$ and $B \subset A$ simultaneously. This definition, as simple as it seems, has the important consequence that the only way to prove that two sets are equal is to show, in two steps (proofs), that every element in either set belongs to the other as well. We will illustrate the use of this definition in one of the problems.

If B is the set of all books and A is the set of mystery books, then $A \subset B$ or $B \supset A$. | **Example 1.5**

If B is the set of integers from zero to ten and A is the set of integers from ten to zero, then A and B are equal. Note that the order of the elements is not important here. | **Example 1.6**

Definition 1.4. There are two other sets that are important. These are the universal set and the null set. The former is the set of all objects under consideration in a given problem. The latter is the set that contains no elements, which is also called the **empty set.** We shall denote the **universal set** as S, which is the same symbol we shall use in the next chapter to denote the sample space. The **null set** will be denoted as $\varnothing$.

Note that for a set A, then $A \subset S$ and A is not contained in $\varnothing$. For all sets A, then $\varnothing \subset A \subset S$, and $A \subset A$. If $A \subset B$ and $B \subset C$, then $A \subset C$.

Example 1.7 | Suppose we toss a numbered die as in Example 1.1. Then the set of possible outcomes is $S = \{1, 2, 3, 4, 5, 6\}$. No other outcomes are possible. Thus, $\overline{S} = \varnothing$.

1.4.1   THE ALGEBRA OF SETS

Definition 1.5. For any two sets A and B we define their **sum** (or **union**) as the set C $= A + B$, which consists of all elements belonging to A or B or both. The union is sometimes denoted as $A \cup B$. For any two sets A and B we define their **product** as the set $D = A \bullet B = AB$, which consists of all elements belonging to both A and B. The term **intersection** is synonymous with product and is denoted with the symbol $\cap$; for example, $D = A \cap B$. For any set A we define its **complement** (in S) as the set $\overline{A}$ consisting of all elements of S that do not belong to A. If $A \subset B$ we define the difference set $B - A$ as the set of elements in B that do not belong to A. These concepts are illustrated in Figure 1.7. The set A is contained within the thick solid line, the set B within the dashed line, the set $A + B$ is the union of sets A and B, and the set AB is the intersection of sets A and B. The set $\overline{A + B}$ is the complement of the set $A + B$. Also note that the difference set $B - AB = \overline{AB}$.

1.4.2   LAWS OF ALGEBRA FOR SET OPERATIONS

The following laws are consequences of the definitions we have just introduced. The reader should verify these laws to gain familiarity with the algebra of sets.

- Idempotent: $A + A = A; A \bullet A = AA = A$ for all sets A.
- Commutative: $A + B = B + A; A \bullet B = B \bullet A$ for all sets A and B.
- Associative: $A + (B + C) = (A + B) + C = A + B + C$; $A \bullet (B \bullet C) = (A \bullet B) \bullet C = A \bullet B \bullet C$ for all sets A, B, and C.
- Distributive: $A \bullet (B + C) = (A \bullet B) + (A \bullet C), A + (B \bullet C) = (A + B) \bullet (A + C)$

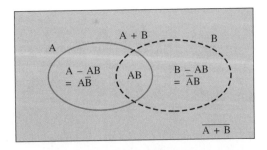

Figure 1.7   A Venn diagram illustrating some of the concepts of sets

- Consistency: The three conditions $A \subset B$, $A \cdot B = A$, and $A + B = B$ are consistent or mutually equivalent.
- Universal bounds: $\varnothing \subset A \subset S$ for all sets A.
- Product: $\varnothing \cdot A = \varnothing$; $S \cdot A = A$ for all sets A.
- Sum: $\varnothing + A = A$; $S + A = S$ for all sets A.
- Involution: $\overline{(\overline{A})} = \overline{\overline{A}} = A$ for all sets A.
- Complementarity: $A + \overline{A} = S$; $A \cdot \overline{A} = \varnothing$ for all sets A.
- De Morgan's first law: $\overline{A + B} = \overline{A} \cdot \overline{B}$ for all sets A and B.
- De Morgan's second law: $\overline{A \cdot B} = \overline{A} + \overline{B}$ for all sets A and B.

De Morgan's laws may be stated in the following way. To find the complement of an expression replace each set by its complement and interchange additions with multiplications and multiplications with additions.

$$\overline{\overline{A} \cdot \overline{B}} = \overline{\overline{A}} + \overline{\overline{B}} = A + B$$

| **Example 1.8**

The algebra of sets is important in the subject of logic and in the design of switching circuits and computers. We already know that Boolean operations can be visualized by means of Venn diagrams (see Figure 1.7), where for convenience we have removed the dot that denotes the "and" operation; that is, $AB = A \cdot B$. The usefulness of these diagrams is, unfortunately, limited to relatively simple expressions.

A numbered die is rolled and the outcome is observed. The set of possible outcomes is denoted as $S = \{1, 2, 3, 4, 5, 6\}$ corresponding to the uppermost face of the die. Let A be the set of possible outcomes $\{1, 2, 3\}$ and B be the set of possible outcomes $\{2, 4, 6\}$. Then we have the following sets:

| **Example 1.9**

- $\overline{A} = \{4, 5, 6\} = S - A$
- $\overline{B} = \{1, 3, 5\}$
- $A + B = \{1, 2, 3, 4, 6\}$
- $A \cdot B = \{2\}$
- $A \cdot \overline{A} = \varnothing$
- $A + \overline{A} = S$
- $\overline{A + B} = \{5\}$
- $A \cdot \overline{B} = \{1, 3\}$
- $\overline{A} \cdot \overline{B} = \{5\} = \overline{A + B}$
- $A \cdot B + A \cdot \overline{B} = A \cdot (B + \overline{B}) = A \cdot S = A$
- $(A \cdot B) \cdot (A \cdot \overline{B}) = \varnothing$

Quiz 1.2   Illustrate the above sets with a figure showing the integers on the real line.

The previous examples have been ones with countable sets. We will also encounter uncountable sets, such as the points on the real line.

Example 1.10   If a and b are two real numbers such that $a < b$, then two possible subsets are $\{x \mid a \leq x \leq b\}$ and $\{x \mid a < x < b\}$ on the real line. The first set is called a closed interval, while the second set is an open interval. We may also have half open (or half closed) sets such as $\{x \mid a \leq x < b\}$ and $\{x \mid a < x \leq b\}$.

Quiz 1.3   Suppose that the universal set is the set of all real numbers, x. Describe the set of real numbers such that $x^2 = -1$.

Definition 1.5. Two sets are said to be **mutually exclusive,** or **disjoint,** if and only if they have no common elements. In such a case the set AB is the null set; that is, $AB = \{\varnothing\}$. Thus, in Figure 1.7, if A and B are disjoint, then the set AB would have no elements.

Definition 1.6. The collection of sets $A_1, A_2, \ldots, A_N$ is said to be **collectively exhaustive** if and only if the union of the sets is the universal set; that is, $A_1 + A_2 + \ldots + A_N = S$. The sets $A_1, A_2, \ldots, A_N$ are collectively exhaustive if each element in the universal set is included in at least one of the sets, $A_1, A_2, \ldots, A_N$. In no case may there be any element in the universal set that is not included in at least one of the sets, $A_1, A_2, \ldots, A_N$.

A collection of sets $\{A, B, C, \ldots\}$ may be mutually exclusive, collectively exhaustive, both, or neither.

Example 1.11   A numbered die is rolled and the outcome is observed. The set of possible outcomes is denoted as $S = \{1, 2, 3, 4, 5, 6\}$ corresponding to the uppermost face of the die. Let several sets of possible outcomes be the following: $A = \{1, 2, 3\}$, $B = \{2, 4, 6\}$, $C = \{3, 5\}$, and $D = \{5\}$. Then the sets $\{A + B + C\}$, $\{A + B + C + D\}$, and $\{A + B + D\}$ are all collectively exhaustive, while the sets A and D are mutually exclusive, as are the sets B and D.

1.5   FUNCTIONS

Functions and sets are perhaps the very basis of mathematics, and we will, of course, find use for them in the chapters that follow.

Definition 1.7. A function, f, is a rule that assigns or maps every element of a given set, D, to a specific object. The set D is called the domain of the function. Thus, f is a function of D. If x is an element of D, then f(x) denotes the object assigned to x by f(x), which is called the value of f at x. The set, R, of all objects

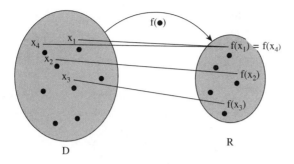

Figure 1.8 The domain and range of a function

f(x) is called the range of f. Thus, f is a mapping of the elements of D to the set (range) of f. This is illustrated in Figure 1.8. Typically the range, R, will be the real numbers and, thus, R will be the real line. Note that f(x) may be an element of D; that is, the domain and the range may be the same (e.g., the real line).

Let D be the set of students in your class on random processes. Let f(x) be the age of each student measured to the nearest year. Then the range of f consists of the positive integers, which is probably confined to the range 18 to 30. | **Example 1.12**

A coin is tossed once and we observe the outcome. The set of possible outcomes is a head (H) or a tail (T). Let this set be the domain. Define a function, f, that maps the elements H and T of D to the range R consisting of the integers 0 and 1, respectively. We will have occasion to use functions such as this many times in the chapters that follow. | **Example 1.13**

Quiz 1.4 A coin is tossed twice and we observe the outcomes. Define the domain. Define a function that maps the possible outcomes to an appropriate number of points on the real line.

1.6 QUIZZES AND PRACTICE EXAMINATIONS

As already noted, each chapter will present quizzes on the material presented prior to that point. These quizzes will be simple and are intended to help the reader focus on important concepts. The answers to these quizzes should be worked out by the reader without the aid of the book or other sources.

Practice examinations will also be given from time to time at the end of selected chapters. These examinations are intended to help the reader determine if he or she is assimilating the material. Sometimes these examinations will be closed book and other times they will be open book.

Quiz 1.5   Define a set A, the universal set, and the null set.

Quiz 1.6   A die has six faces, which are numbered 1 to 6. Two identical dice are tossed. The numbers on the two exposed faces of the dice are read after they come to rest. Form the set that consists of the sum of the numbers on the two exposed faces. How many distinct elements are in this set? In how many ways can each distinct element be formed?

1.7   MATLAB®

MATLAB is a registered trade mark of the MathWorks, Inc. It is a technical software computing environment. Our purpose for introducing computer-based examples and problems is to expand our armamentarium so that we may solve problems that might be too tedious to do via hand calculations. Furthermore, MATLAB has plotting capabilities that can greatly assist the visualization of data. We include MATLAB examples and problems in each chapter.

Example 1.14   This example is a partial implementation of Example 1.9 using MATLAB, version 4.2c or higher. A sample of the display for this example is shown in Figure 1.9. The software is available with this book and is contained in subdirectory Ch 1. The program is executed by running the m file

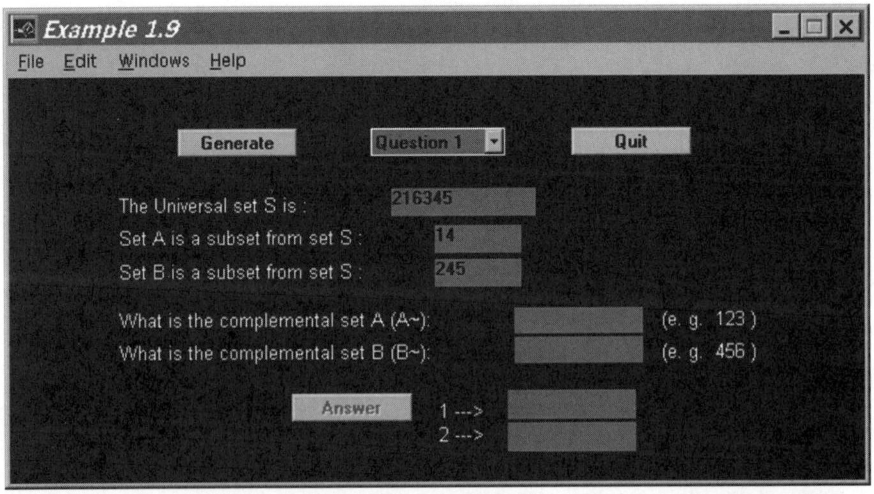

Figure 1.9   Software program for MATLAB

ex1_9. Once the program is running, three boxes appear, labeled generate, question 1, and quit. When the box labeled question 1 is selected, a menu appears showing additional question boxes that the user can select. After a question is selected, the question is printed on the screen. The user then selects generate and the program generates a sequence of numbers that are displayed in the Universal set S box. The manner in which these numbers are generated will be discussed in Chapter 7. For this example the user is to consider these numbers as the universal set. The boxes immediately below the universal set display the elements in subsets of the universe. These subsets change with each question. The user is to answer the questions displayed concerning the various subsets by typing in the appropriate answers in the format shown. The user can then select the answer box to see the answer. The user can move on to other questions or generate a new universal set and subsets for the same question. The entire set of questions for Example 1.9 is not implemented in this software program. The reader is encouraged to add additional questions and modifications.

1.8   SUMMARY

The purpose of this chapter was to describe the goals of the book, to provide some illustrative examples of application areas, and to review aspects of set theory. Many new terms were introduced. You should review the algebra of set operations and Venn diagrams. The reader should know the definitions of the following terms:

- Set.
- Universal set.
- Null set.
- Intersection, sum, and complement of two or more sets.
- Functions, domain, and range.

This chapter has also introduced the format for the book, namely, the headings, subheadings, definitions, examples, and quizzes. This format is intended to help the reader review the material and quickly spot the major topics. Not all definitions will be clearly designated by the **definition** heading, only the ones of major importance. However, we will use bold to call the reader's attention to many of the new terms. Watch for these items.

PROBLEMS

1.1 Draw a Venn diagram for Example 1.9. Be as complete as possible.

1.2 Prove the distributive law $A + (BC) = (A + B)(A + C)$. Draw a Venn diagram to illustrate the proof. The Venn diagram is not the proof.

1.3 Suppose the universal set S is the set of 14 golf clubs, consisting of the pitching wedge (w), sand wedge (s), irons 1 through 9, the driver (d), the 3 wood (3w), and a putter (p). Let the set $A = \{d, 3w\}$, $B = \{1, 2, 3, 4, 5, 6, 7, 8, 9\}$, $C = \{w, s\}$,

D = {p}, E = {s, p, 5}, F = {d, 9, w, p}. Determine the elements of the following sets: (a) S, (b) AB, (c) A$\overline{B}$, (d) $\overline{C}$, (e) $\overline{C}$ − B, (f) F − DE, (g) AD, (h) $\overline{AD}$, (i) $\overline{A}$ − CF. Which collections of sets are mutually exclusive and which are collectively exhaustive?

1.4 Prove De Morgan's first law.

1.5 Consider two basketball teams, Grant and Harper. Each team has 12 members. The union of the two teams forms the universal set. Only five members of each team may play at a time. Denote the playing team members as PG and PH for Grant and Harper, respectively. Draw a Venn diagram that illustrates these sets.

1.6 Suppose that a light bulb company conducts an experiment that measures the lifetimes of their light bulbs. Let the measured parameter be denoted as t, the time in hours until a light bulb fails. Assume that a light bulb can last no longer than 10,000 hours. Describe the set of light bulb lifetimes for this problem.

1.7 Let the set A = {x | x^2 = 36}. Describe this set by the roster method.

1.8 Let the universal set S be given as {π, 0, 7, 3/4, $\sqrt{2}$}. Define the following subsets of S as A = {π, 0}, B = {0, 7, 3/4}, C = {0, $\sqrt{2}$, 7}. Determine A • B, A ∩ C, A + B, A + C, $\overline{A}$, $\overline{A + B}$, A − B. Which collection of sets is mutually exclusive and which is collectively exhaustive?

1.9 Discuss whether or not {7} = 7.

1.10 Describe the set of solutions to the equation x^2 − 5x + 6 = 0 in at least two ways.

1.11 Classify the positive decimal integers according to whether they are (a) odd, (b) even, and (c) their last digit is a seven. Draw a Venn diagram. Give an example of each possible case.

1.12 Suppose a set consists of three elements, say {a, b, c}. How many subsets of this set are there? List them. Now suppose a set consists of n elements. How many subsets of this set are there?

1.13 A coin is tossed twice and the outcomes are observed. Denote the possible outcomes as (H, H), (H, T), (T, H), and (T, T). Define a function that maps these possible outcomes to the corners of a square in two dimensional space with the lower left corner of the square located at the origin.

1.14 The faces of a die are numbered 1 through 6. The die is rolled once. Define the domain of possible outcomes. Let a function be defined that maps the possible even outcomes to 0 and the possible odd outcomes to 1. Draw a diagram that illustrates this mapping.

1.15 The faces of a die are numbered 1 through 6. The die is rolled twice. Define the domain of possible outcomes as the sum of the outcomes of the two rolls. How many elements are in D? Let a function be defined that maps the sum if it is even to 0 and the sum if it is odd to 1. Draw a diagram that illustrates this mapping.

1.16 Define a function for D being the set of all integers and R the set of all even integers.

1.17 Let D be the set of six colored marbles. Each marble is unique in color with the colors being black, white, blue, yellow, green, and red. Let the range R be 0 and 1. Define a function that maps the colors to the range.

1.18 Some students in Electrical Engineering are registered for the following courses:

Number of students	Course
30	Communications
27	Control
31	Computers
10	Communications and Computers
8	Control and Communications
7	Computers and Control
5	Communications, Computers, and Control

Draw a Venn diagram that illustrates these sets and subsets with the numbers given. How many students take Control but not Computers? How many students take Communications but not Control nor Computers?

MATLAB PROBLEMS

1.1M Expand on the MATLAB software provided in subdirectory Ch 1 by adding additional questions and the appropriate answers in the same manner as that used in the program.

1.2M Modify the MATLAB software provided in subdirectory Ch 1 to change the Universal set S. The present program always generates the six numbers 1 to 6 in a different order each time. Change the number generation so that multiple occurrences of the same number may occur, e.g., 661244 or 511123.

1.3M Repeat Problem 1.2M as follows. Keep the original problem but simply increase the size of the number set from 6 to 10 or 20 or 100. The display of the numbers will become a problem if the size of the number set is too large.

1.4M Repeat Problem 1.2M as follows. Keep the original problem but add a second set of six numbers generated in a second box and modify the questions so that the intersection and union of the numbers that appear in both boxes can be considered.

chapter
2

Introduction to Probability Theory

2.1   WHY STUDY PROBABILITY?

Many electrical engineering students have studied, analyzed, and designed systems from the point of view of steady-state and transient signals using time domain or frequency domain techniques. However, these techniques do not provide a method for accounting for variability in the signal nor for interference due to noise. We will see that the theory of probability and random processes is useful for modeling the uncertainty of various events (e.g., the arrival of telephone calls and the failure of electronic components). We also know that the performance of many communication systems and computer networks is adversely affected by noise, which may often be present in the form of an undesired signal that degrades the performance of the system. Thus, it becomes necessary to design systems that can discriminate against noise and enhance a desired signal.

How may we distinguish between a deterministic signal or function and a random phenomenon, such as noise? Usually noise is defined to be any undesired signal, which often occurs in the presence of a desired signal. This definition includes deterministic as well as nondeterministic signals. A deterministic signal is one that is perfectly predictable from its known past values, such as a sinusoid, which may be represented by a fixed amplitude and a time-varying phase angle of $2\pi ft$, where f is known. The amplitude and phase are known for past time and for any future time. Random signals, such as noise, do not have this property since, as we shall see in Chapter 5, random signals are described by properties of an ensemble. As we saw in Chapter 1, even the same word spoken by different speakers is not deterministic; there is a variability, which can be modeled as a random fluctuation. The amplitude and/or phase of a random signal cannot be calculated for any specified future time instant even though the entire past history of the signal may be known. However, the amplitude and/or phase of a random signal can be predicted to occur with a specified probability, provided certain factors are known. In this chapter we will begin our study of probability. We shall see that the theory of probability will be able to describe (model) phenomena that occur in many diverse fields, such as communications, control, and computers. Perhaps the major reason for studying probability and random processes is to be able to model complex systems and phenomena.

2.2   APPROACHES TO PROBABILITY

The relationship between probability and gambling has been known for some time. Over the years some famous scientists and mathematicians have devoted time to probability; Galileo wrote on dice games, Laplace worked out the probabilities of some gambling games, and Pascal and Bernoulli contributed to the basic theory of probability. Since the time of this early work, the theory of probability has become a highly developed branch of mathematics.

One approach to defining probability is to consider an experiment for which it is possible to specify certain outcomes as favorable. For our purposes we will consider an **experiment** to be a test or a trial to illustrate a known result, or to validate a hypothesis, or to determine the possibility of something previously untried. An experiment may be repeated many times. Assume that each trial of the experiment results in only one outcome, which may be favorable or unfavorable. We may repeat the experiment many times and form the ratio of the number of times a favorable outcome occurred to the number of times we performed the experiment. This ratio is called the **frequency ratio.** The probability of a favorable outcome is defined as the limit of the frequency ratio as the number of trials goes to infinity. This definition of probability, based upon experimental results, underlies a classical approach to probability.

We may also approach probability in another manner. For example, suppose we perform a thought experiment that involves flipping a fair coin (i.e., a coin that is not biased in weight to favor one side). What is the probability of obtaining a head on the first flip of the coin? Very likely, we would say 1/2. Our answer is not based upon the **frequency ratio** derived from an actual experiment because we have not performed such an experiment. How did we arrive at the number 1/2? We assumed that the coin is fair and, thus, the two possible outcomes (head or tail) are presumed to be **equally likely** or **equally probable** to occur. Therefore, in our imagined example, or thought experiment, one-half of the time the result will be heads and the probability must, therefore, be 1/2. Consider another example. What is the probability of obtaining a 2 for one roll of a numbered die? We have every reason to believe that each face of the die is equally likely to appear. Thus, the desired probability is 1/6. Probabilities obtained without the aid of physical experiments are called **a priori** (before the fact). Philosophically, this differs from defining a probability by observing the outcomes of an experiment, or **a posteriori** (after the fact). Perhaps a convenient way of distinguishing these two terms is to recall a little poem by Edward Carpenter, quoted by W. Grey Walter in his book "The Living Brain" (W.W. Morton and Co.: New York, 1953). In the poem Carpenter was speaking of a huge beast known as diplodocus, which weighed 40 tons, had web feet and a tail that was 30 feet long. It was a vegetarian and the greatest of the dinosaurs. This creature had **two** sets of brains,

One in his head, the usual place, the other at the spinal base.
Thus he could reason **a priori** as well as **a posteriori**.

The frequency ratio and the equally likely approaches to probability have disadvantages. The former bases its calculations on experimental outcomes, while the latter assumes that the outcomes are equally likely to occur. Another way of introducing probability that avoids these faults is the axiomatic approach, which will be discussed briefly later in the chapter. However, one convenient and illuminating way of introducing probability that also overcomes these faults is to consider the concept of a **sample space.**

2.3   THE SAMPLE SPACE

Definition 2.1. The collection or set of "all possible" distinct (collectively exhaustive and mutually exclusive) outcomes of an experiment is called **the sample space of the experiment.** The sample space, denoted by the symbol S, is the universal set of outcomes for the experiment. For the present an experimental outcome is considered to be a single outcome, not a set of outcomes. We sometimes call a single outcome a **simple** outcome. A subset of outcomes will be defined later as an event.

The reason we have placed quotes about the words *all possible* in Definition 2.1 is explained by the following imaginary situation. Suppose that we conduct the experiment of flipping a coin. It is conceivable that the coin may land on its edge. But experience has shown us that such a result is highly unlikely to occur. Therefore, our sample space for such experiments typically excludes such unlikely outcomes. We also require for the present that the outcomes all be distinct (i.e., we do not allow repeated outcomes to be included in our set of outcomes). Consequently, we are for the present considering only the set of simple outcomes that are collectively exhaustive and mutually exclusive.

2.4   EXAMPLES OF SIMPLE EXPERIMENTS AND THEIR SAMPLE SPACES

Example 2.1 | Consider the experiment of flipping a fair coin once, where *fair* means that the coin is not biased in weight to favor a particular side. There are two possible outcomes, namely, a head or a tail. Thus, the sample space, S, consists of two outcomes, one labeled H to indicate that a head occurred as a result of flipping the coin, one labeled T to indicate that a tail occurred.

Example 2.2 | A die with numbered faces is rolled and the result is observed. The sample space S consists of six possible outcomes that may be labeled 1, 2, 3, 4, 5, 6 indicating the possible faces of the die that may be observed.

As a third example, consider the experiment of flipping a coin twice and observing the results. The sample space consists of four outcomes, which may be labeled by the ordered pairs (H, H), (H, T), (T, H), and (T, T); the first component in the ordered pair indicates the result of the first flip, and the second component indicates the result of the second flip. An alternative way to consider this experiment is to imagine that we conduct two distinct experiments, with each experiment consisting of flipping a single coin once. The sample spaces, (S_1 and S_2) for each of these experiments are the same, namely, the same as Example 2.1 (i.e., H and T). We may now consider the sample space S of the original experiment to be the combination of the sample spaces S_1 and S_2, which consists of all possible combinations of the elements of both S_1 and S_2, namely, the pairs (H, H), (H, T), (T, H), and (T, T). This is an example of a combined sample space. For this example the order in which we conducted the experiments S_1 and S_2 is not important. Consequently, we need not distinguish between the results of S_1 and S_2. This is not always the case.

Example 2.3

For our fourth experiment let us flip a coin until a tail occurs. The experiment is then terminated. The sample space S consists of a collection of sequences of outcomes. Label these sequences as x_n. The final outcome in any particular sequence is a tail and terminates the sequence. The preceding outcomes prior to the occurrence of the tail must be heads. The possible sequences that may occur are:

$x_1 : (T)$

$x_2 : (H, T)$

$x_3 : (H, H, T,)$

$x_n : (H, H, \dots, H, T)$, where there are $(n - 1)$ heads followed by a tail.

Note that n can extend to infinity. This is another example of a combined sample space resulting from conducting independent, but identical experiments. In this example the sample space is countably infinite, while the previous sample spaces are finite.

Example 2.4

As a last example select a number in some arbitrary manner from the closed interval $[0, 1]$. The sample space S consists of all real numbers x for which $0 \leq x \leq 1$. This is an example of a continuous sample space. Other examples of continuous sample spaces include the measurement of the voltage of random noise and the (x, y, z) position of an oxygen molecule in the atmosphere. Examples 2.1 to 2.4 illustrate discrete sample spaces.

Example 2.5

2.5   DISCRETE AND CONTINUOUS SAMPLE SPACES

Therefore, we have the following definition.

> **Definition 2.2.** A sample space is called **discrete** if it is a finite or a countably infinite set. It is called **continuous** or a **continuum** otherwise. Recall that when a set of objects can be put in a one-to-one correspondence with the positive integers, the set is said to be countable or denumerable.

There are also infinite sets that are uncountable and that are not continuous, but these sets are beyond the scope of this book. So for our purposes we will consider only the above two types of sets or sample spaces. While it is possible to have a sample space that is a mixture of discrete and continuous sample spaces, we shall restrict ourselves to the study of discrete sample spaces for the present.

2.6   THE SAMPLE SPACE IS NOT UNIQUE

A particular experiment can often be represented by more than one sample space. The choice of a particular sample space depends upon the questions that are to be answered concerning the experiment. This is perhaps best explained by recalling Example 2.2. Suppose we are asked to record after each roll of the die only whether the face was even or odd, not the exact number. The sample space could then be represented by two outcomes only, for example, even and odd, which occur if the faces (2, 4, 6) and (1, 3, 5) appear, respectively. However, the original sample space is, in some way, more fundamental, since the outcomes even and odd can be determined from the original sample space. If the second (even, odd) representation is used, then knowing that an even (or odd) number occurred is not sufficient to determine which specific number appeared. However, if we know the exact value of the face that appeared, then we may determine whether the face value was odd or even.

2.7   FUNCTIONS ON A SAMPLE SPACE

In a manner analogous to that used in Chapter 1 we may define a function on a sample space. Such definitions often have geometrical interpretations as well. However, as we discussed above, the function and geometrical interpretation may not be unique and often depends upon the purpose for which it is introduced.

Consider the examples of Section 2.4 again.

| **Example 2.6** | For Example 2.1, the sample space S consisted of the elements H and T. Define a function, f, that maps the domain S to 0 and 1, respectively. Then, the range of f consists of the two points 0 and 1 on the real line |

and is one-dimensional. It is sometimes convenient to consider the range of f as a new sample space that is numerical rather than symbolic, such as (H, T).

| **Example 2.7** | For Example 2.2 the domain of S may be mapped to a range with the same set of numbers, which may be thought of as a one-dimensional sample space that may be constructed by putting the faces of the die in one-to-one correspondence with the integers 1 through 6 on the real line. In this example the definition of a function is implicit, |

since the domain is already numerical and the domain and the range are the same.

In Example 2.3, the domain of S is mapped to a two dimensional space. Define a function whose range consists of the four points (0, 0), (0, 1), (1, 0), and (1, 1), which can be represented in a two dimensional plane. | **Example 2.8**

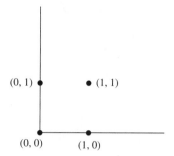

On the other hand, we may map (H, H) to (0, 0), which may be interpreted as a binary number. And similarly (H, T) may be mapped to (0, 1), (T, H) to (1, 0), and (T, T) to (1, 1). These binary numbers can then be mapped to their decimal equivalent, which in turn may be mapped onto the real line (e.g., (0, 0):0, (0, 1):1, (1, 0):2 and (1, 1):3) so that the sample space may be represented as four points on the real line, which is a one-dimensional representation.

Because of the possible geometrical representation for a sample space, we sometimes refer to the outcomes as points. The outcomes may also be called elements or members of the sample space.

Quiz 2.1   Define a sample space.

Quiz 2.2   Define a function that yields a geometrical representation for the sample space in Example 2.4.

Quiz 2.3   Define a function that maps the domain of S in Example 2.5 to a geometrical sample space.

2.8   THE PROBABILITY FUNCTION

We now define the probability of an outcome of an experiment.

> **Definition 2.3.** To each outcome, x_n, in our (discrete) sample space, S, we associate a non-negative number $P_n = P(x_n)$ such that $0 \leq P_n \leq 1$ and $\Sigma P(x_n) = 1$, where x_n is in S. The summation is over all elements x_n in S. The set of outcomes $X = \{x_n\}$ is collectively exhaustive and mutually exclusive. The number P_n is called the **probability of the outcome,** x_n. We will usually drop the subscript n on P_n, since it will generally be clear which outcome we are referring to.

What is the number that one associates with each outcome in the sample space? Provided each outcome of an experiment is **equally likely** to occur, we say that each outcome in the sample space is considered to be **equally probable** to occur in the performance of the experiment. For such a case, the probability we shall associate with each outcome of the sample space will be the reciprocal of the total number of outcomes in the sample space. In this case we are also assuming that each outcome of the experiment is unique. However, just because the outcomes are unique does not imply that the outcomes are equally likely or equally probable, as we shall illustrate in Example 2.10.

> **Definition 2.4.** The **probability of an equally likely outcome** is $P(x_n) = 1/N$, $N \geq 1$ where N is finite and nonzero and is the total number of unique (collectively exhaustive and mutually exclusive) outcomes in S. We also require that $\sum_1^N P(x_n) = 1$, where $x_n \in S$.

2.9   EXAMPLES OF PROBABILITY FUNCTIONS

Consider once again the examples of Section 2.4.

Example 2.9 | Consider Example 2.1 with a fair coin. The total number of equally likely outcomes in the sample space is 2. These outcomes are collectively exhaustive and mutually exclusive.

$$S : x_1 = H, x_2 = T$$

$$P_1 = P(x_1) = 1/2$$

$$P_2 = P(x_2) = 1/2$$

$$\sum_{k=1}^{2} P_k = P_1 + P_2 = 1$$

Example 2.10 | Consider Example 2.2 with a fair die. There are six equally likely outcomes, which are collectively exhaustive and mutually exclusive.

$$S : x_1 = 1, x_2 = 2, x_3 = 3, x_4 = 4, x_5 = 5, x_6 = 6$$

$$P_k = P(x_k) = 1/6 \qquad k = 1, 2, 3, 4, 5, 6$$

$$\sum_{k=1}^{6} P_k = P_1 + P_2 + P_3 + P_4 + P_5 + P_6 = 1/6 + 1/6 + 1/6 + 1/6 + 1/6 + 1/6$$

$$= 1$$

Next consider Example 2.2 with an unfair (loaded) die such that the unfair die shows 2 one-third of the time and 5 two-thirds of the time on average.

$$S : \text{Same as above}$$

Note that this is an example of an unfair die, that is, one with two possible outcomes, namely, 2 and 5. However, we are told that these two outcomes are not equally probable to occur. While we do not yet have a method for establishing the probability of the possible outcomes for this example, let us try to use an intuitive approach, and apply Definition 2.3. Since the faces (1, 3, 4, 6) cannot appear, then their probability should be zero, that is:

$$P_1 = P_3 = P_4 = P_6 = 0$$

We know from Definition 2.3 that $P_1 + P_2 + P_3 + P_4 + P_5 + P_6 = 1$. Then using the above, we conclude that $P_2 + P_5 = 1$. Furthermore, we are told the frequency ratio of the occurrence of these two outcomes. Consequently, we may conclude that

$$P_2 = \frac{1}{3} \text{ and } P_5 = \frac{2}{3}$$

Another solution to this example is to redefine the sample space such that only the two outcomes 2 and 5 appear in the sample space. However, since we are told that the outcomes in this sample space are not equally likely, we must calculate the probabilities in a manner different from that specified in Definition 2.4. We will discuss non-equally likely sample spaces more fully later.

From Example 2.3:   **Example 2.11**

$$S : x_1 = (H, H), x_2 = (H, T), x_3 = (T, H), x_4 = (T, T)$$

$$P_k = P(x_k) = \frac{1}{4} \quad k = 1,2,3,4$$

$$\sum_{k=1}^{4} P_k = 1$$

This example has a sample space with four equally likely outcomes that are collectively exhaustive and mutually exclusive.

From Example 2.4:   **Example 2.12**

$$S : x_n = (H, H, \ldots, H, T) \, n = 1,2,3,\ldots$$

$$P_n = P(x_n) = 1/2^n \, n = 1,2,3,\ldots$$

$$\sum_{n=1}^{\infty} P_n = \sum_{n=1}^{\infty} (1/2)^n = \frac{1/2}{1 - 1/2} = 1$$

Why does $P_n = 1/2^n$? Hint: Consider the set of all possible outcomes for flipping a coin n times. Then x_n is just one outcome for each n. What is the total number of such outcomes for each n? Again, the outcomes in S are equally likely, and, furthermore, the outcomes are collectively exhaustive and mutually exclusive.

We cannot consider Example 2.5. Why?   **Example 2.13**

Quiz 2.4   Define an equally likely (or equally probable) outcome in a sample space.

Quiz 2.5   Three coins, a nickel, a dime, and a quarter are inside a container. The coins cannot be seen. An experiment consists of selecting a coin from the container in such a manner that the size and value of the coin cannot be determined a priori. What is the sample space? Are the outcomes in the sample space equally likely to occur? What is the probability of selecting the quarter?

2.10   EVENTS

Definition 2.5. Any set or collection of outcomes in the sample space constitutes an **event**. When the experiment is performed, and if the observed outcome is an outcome in the event, we say that the event **occurred**.

Definition 2.6. A **simple event** is an event that cannot be decomposed. Thus, a simple event is a simple outcome or a single sample point in the sample space. A **compound event** is a set of simple events.

Example 2.14	As an example reconsider the experiment of rolling a die. We already know the sample space. However, let A be the event that the face of the die that appears is less than 4, and B be the event that an even face shows. List the outcomes in the sample space that comprise A (answer 1, 2, 3). Name the outcomes in the sample space that comprise B (answer 2, 4, 6). Other possible events for this example will be considered after some additional terminology is introduced.

Let A + B (read as "A or B" or "A plus B") denote the event that A has occurred *or* B has occurred, or that both A and B have occurred. Let AB (read as "A *and* B") denote the event that both A and B have occurred; this is often referred to as the **joint** event AB. Let $\overline{A}$ (read as "the complement of A") denote the event that A has *not* occurred, or said another way, $\overline{A}$ is the opposite event of A. Variations of the above terminology are used in logic, set theory, and Boolean algebra.

Example 2.14 concluded	Let us now return to Example 2.14 and seek an interpretation of A + B. This event consists of the outcomes that the face observed is either less than 4, or an even face, or both.

We now define the probability of an event.

2.11   PROBABILITY OF AN EVENT AND SOME OF ITS PROPERTIES

Definition 2.7. The **probability of occurrence of an event A**, denoted by P (A), will be defined as the sum of the probabilities of the outcomes that constitute the event A. In symbols we have

$$P(A) = \sum_{x_k \in A} P(x_k).$$ [2.11.1]

This definition is valid for both equally likely and non-equally likely samples spaces.

Quiz 2.6   What is another way of defining the probability of occurrence of an event A that will be valid only for equally likely events in a sample space?

As an example let us calculate P(A) for Example 2.14. There are three outcomes in A. Each outcome is equally probable with $P(x_k) = 1/6$. Thus $P(A) = 1/6 + 1/6 + 1/6 = 1/2$. |**Example 2.15**

The probability of a **certain event** is always equal to one; that is, $P(S) = 1$. Why? By a certain event we mean an event that occurs at each and every performance of the experiment. Thus, each outcome in the sample space belongs to the certain event. A consequence of this fact is that $0 \le P(A) \le 1$ for every A.

The probability of an **impossible event** is zero; that is, $P(\varnothing) = 0$. Why? By an impossible event we mean one that can never occur during the performance of the experiment. Thus, no outcomes in the sample space belong to the impossible event. Note that this does not mean that the sample space is void.

Suppose that we have two sets, A and B; then the probability of A + B is given by the **addition formula**

$$P(A + B) = P(A) + P(B) - P(AB)$$ [2.11.2]

for every set A and every set B. P(AB) is the probability of the occurrence of the joint event AB.

Remember, to calculate probabilities we must keep track of the number of outcomes in each set. The outcomes can only be counted once. It should be apparent that $P(A + B) \le P(A) + P(B)$.

Quiz 2.7   Derive [2.11.2] from [2.11.1]. Hint: Consider the Venn diagram in Figure 2.1, which is a replication of Figure 1.7.

As an example let us calculate P(A + B) for Example 2.14 of Section 2.10. The outcomes that |**Example 2.16**
comprise A are (1, 2, 3) and those of B are (2, 4, 6). There are three outcomes in each event. Thus $P(A) = P(B) = 1/2$. How many outcomes comprise the joint event AB? The outcome 2 is in both events and is the only such outcome. Thus $P(AB) = 1/6$. Therefore, using [2.11.2], $P(A + B) = 1/2 + 1/2 - 1/6 = 5/6$.

A check of this calculation will be demonstrated in our next example after we discuss mutually exclusive events.

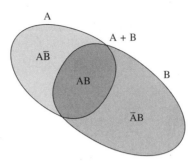

Figure 2.1   Illustration of several sets

Definition 2.8. Two events A and B are called **mutually exclusive,** or **disjoint,** events if they have no common outcomes or sample points. In such a case the event AB is an impossible event, so that $P(AB) = P(\varnothing) = 0$. Therefore [2.11.2] becomes

$$P(A + B) = P(A) + P(B) \qquad\qquad [2.11.3]$$

Thus, for mutually exclusive events the event $A + B$ occurs only if either A or B occur but not both. We say that a collection of events is **collectively exhaustive** if and only if the union (sum) of the sets in the collection is the sample space. Thus, each sample point in the sample space is included in at least one of the sets in the collection. In no case may there be a sample point that is not included in at least one of the sets in the collection. A collection of events may be mutually exclusive, collectively exhaustive, both, or neither.

A particular case of mutually exclusive events is when $B = \overline{A}$, or B is the opposite of, or complement event to, A. Then $A + B = A + \overline{A} = S$ is the certain event. Thus, the collection of A and $\overline{A}$ is collectively exhaustive and mutually exclusive. Therefore

$$P(A + \overline{A}) = P(A) + P(\overline{A}) = 1 \qquad\qquad [2.11.4]$$

The sum of the probability of any event and its complement event is always equal to unity. An important consequence of this is that the probability of an event, A, need not be calculated directly. We may first calculate the probability of an event A by calculating the probability of the complement event, $\overline{A}$, which is sometimes easier, and then subtract $P(\overline{A})$ from unity, yielding $P(A)$. Thus, from [2.11.4] we have $P(A) = 1 - P(\overline{A})$.

Example 2.17   As an example let us consider the calculation of $P(A + B)$, where A and B are still the events of Example 2.14. What is the complement (opposite) event to $A + B$? We have seen earlier in this section that $A + B$ is the event that all faces on the die can occur except one, namely, the face 5. Thus $\overline{A + B}$ is the event that the face 5 appears. Therefore, $P(\overline{A + B}) = 1/6$. Note now that by [2.11.4] $P(A + B) + P(\overline{A + B}) = 1$, or that $P(A + B) = 1 - P(\overline{A + B}) = 5/6$. This is the check that was promised earlier when we calculated $P(A + B)$ in Example 2.16.

Two other properties are

$$P(A) = P(AB) + P(A\overline{B}) \qquad\qquad [2.11.5]$$

and

$$P(A + B) = P(A\overline{B}) + P(\overline{A}B) + P(AB)$$ [2.11.6]

These properties are illustrated in Figure 2.1 as well. As we previously mentioned, the key to these relationships is that we must be careful to count the outcomes or elements in an event (set) only once. Note that [2.11.5] implies that AB and $A\overline{B}$ are mutually exclusive. This is true for all A, B. We may prove this as follows.

$$(AB)(A\overline{B}) = A[B(A\overline{B})] = A[(BA)\overline{B}] = A[(AB)\overline{B}] = A[A(B\overline{B})] = A[A\varnothing] = A\varnothing = \varnothing$$

Return to Example 2.14 once again. In this experiment we roll a die once and observe the outcome. The universal set is S = {1,2,3,4,5,6}. The event A is that the outcome is less than 4, or A = {1,2,3}, while the event B is that the face showing is an even number, or B = {2,4,6}. We assume that each possible outcome is equally likely to occur. We may now calculate the probabilities of several events. | **Example 2.18**

$$P(A) = P(1) + P(2) + P(3) = 3/6 = 1/2$$

$$P(B) = P(2) + P(4) + P(6) = 3/6 = 1/2$$

$$P(A + B) = P(1) + P(2) + P(3) + P(4) + P(6) = 5/6$$

Note that in calculating P(A + B), we only counted the outcome 2 once. We may illustrate this more specifically as follows:

$$P(A + B) = P(A) + P(B) - P(AB)$$

$$= [P(1) + P(2) + P(3)] + [P(2) + P(4) + P(6)] - [P(2)]$$

We see that the outcome 2 is counted once in computing P(A) and once in computing P(B). Thus, the outcome 2 has been counted twice. Consequently, we must remove one of these counts by subtracting the probability P(AB). We continue with this example to find

$$P(\overline{A + B}) = 1 - P(A + B) = 1/6 = P(5)$$

$$P(\overline{B}) = P(1) + P(3) + P(5) = 1/2 = 1 - P(B)$$

$$P(\overline{A}) = P(4) + P(5) = P(6) = 1/2 = 1 - P(A)$$

$$P(A) = P(AB) + P(A\overline{B}) = P(2) + [P(1) + P(3)] = 1/2$$

Sometimes we need to calculate the probability of compound events greater than two. The addition formula may be extended accordingly:

$$P(A+B+C) = P(A) + P(B) + P(C) - P(AB) - P(BC) - P(CA) + P(ABC)$$ [2.11.7]

Quiz 2.8   Draw a Venn diagram illustrating [2.11.7]

We will now briefly discuss the axioms of probability.

2.12   THE AXIOMS OF PROBABILITY

In the previous section we discussed and determined various properties of the probability function. However, all of the properties are not independent. In fact, all of these properties can be derived from the following three conditions, which are known as the **axioms of probability**:

1. $P(A) \geq 0$ for every event A.   **[2.12.1]**
2. $P(S) = 1$ for the certain event S.   **[2.12.2]**
3. $P(A + B) = P(A) + P(B)$, if two events A and B are mutually exclusive.   **[2.12.3]**

Axiom 3 must be augmented to account for infinite sequences of mutually exclusive events for infinite sample spaces.

With these axioms as a foundation it is possible to build a complete structure of probability. However, the sample space approach is considered by many as more illuminating for an introduction to probability.

2.13   CONDITIONAL PROBABILITIES

Often the occurrence of one event may be dependent upon the occurrence of another. For example, suppose an urn contains four white balls and five blacks balls. If two balls are removed successively without replacement, what is the probability that they are both white? If we denote by A the event of selecting a white ball first and by B the event of selecting a white ball second, then we must find P(AB). Clearly, the event B depends upon the occurrence of event A, since we are withdrawing balls without replacement.

As an aside, it is uncertain how an urn came to be used as one of the most popular containers for objects used in examples illustrating probability. Possibly, it is because an urn is a narrow necked jar that is usually opaque. Consequently, when we reach inside the urn to grasp an object we are unable to see into the urn because our hand and arm fill the neck. We will use a box instead of an urn from time to time. However, we will assume that we cannot see the objects in the box as we remove one or more of the objects.

Returning to our urn example, we know that the probability of selecting a white ball on the first draw is 4/9. If we replace that ball and repeat the same experiment the answer is the same. However, if we withdraw a white ball on the first draw and discard it, we now have three white balls and five black balls left in the urn. Now the probability of selecting a white ball on the next (second) draw is 3/8. Thus, the probability of drawing a white ball on the second draw depends (is conditional) on the outcome of the first draw.

Definition 2.9. We denote by $P(B \mid A)$ the **conditional probability** of B given that the event A has occurred. We show below that $P(B \mid A) = P(AB)/P(A)$.

The manner by which we calculate the conditional probability is the following. Since we are given the event A, we may contract or reduce the sample space S to the sample space A. We then redefine the outcomes in A in such a way that the ratio of the old probability (using the sample space S) to the new probability (using the sample space A) is constant and that the sum of the newly assigned probabilities totals unity. The conditional probability is then computed by considering only those outcomes of B in A. Suppose an outcome a is in S and has a probability of P(a). Also let P(A) be greater than zero. Then the **new** probability is given by $P_{new}(a) = P(a)/P(A)$ for all a $\in$ A. Note that

$$\sum_{a \in A} P_{new}(a) = \sum_{a \in A} \frac{P(a)}{P(A)} = \frac{1}{P(A)} \sum_{a \in A} P(a) = \frac{P(A)}{P(A)} = 1 \qquad [2.13.1]$$

Furthermore, the relative frequencies of $P(a)/P(b) = P_{new}(a)/P_{new}(b)$ are unchanged for all outcomes a and b in A. Now the conditional probability is given by

$$P(B|A) = \sum_{a \in AB} P_{new}(a) = \sum_{a \in AB} \frac{P(a)}{P(A)} = \frac{1}{P(A)} \sum_{a \in AB} P(a) = \frac{P(AB)}{P(A)} \qquad [2.13.2]$$

We may write the above equation as the **multiplication theorem**, a formula that relates conditional and joint probabilities:

$$P(AB) = P(B|A)P(A) = P(A|B)P(B) \qquad [2.13.3]$$

The form

$$P(A|B)/P(A) = P(B|A)/P(B) \qquad [2.13.4]$$

for P(A) and P(B) both not equal to zero, is known as **Bayes' theorem**. This theorem may be rewritten as

$$P(A|B) = P(B|A)P(A)/P(B) \qquad [2.13.5]$$

For three events A, B, C we have

$$P(ABC) = P(C|AB)P(AB) = P(C|AB)P(B|A)P(A) \qquad [2.13.6]$$

which can be extended to more events.

By using the relationships that $A = AS = A(B + \bar{B}) = AB + A\bar{B}$, and $(AB)(A\bar{B}) = \varnothing$, we may derive another useful formula for any events A and B in the same sample space as

$$P(A) = P(AB + A\bar{B}) = P(AB) + P(A\bar{B})$$
$$= P(A|B)P(B) + P(A|\bar{B})P(\bar{B}) \qquad [2.13.7]$$

If we have a situation where there are numerous mutually exclusive and collectively exhaustive events A_i, i = 1, 2, ..., M, then by [2.13.5] and [2.13.7] we have a more general form of **Bayes' theorem:**

$$P(A_i|B) = [P(B|A_i)P(A_i)]/[P(B|A_1)P(A_1)$$
$$+ ... + P(B|A_M)P(A_M)] \qquad [2.13.8]$$

2.14   EXAMPLES OF CONDITIONAL PROBABILITIES

Example 2.19 | Suppose an urn contains five white and seven red balls. Two balls are withdrawn at random from the urn without replacement.

   a. What is the probability that both balls are white?

   b. What is the probability that the second ball is red?

Solution:

   We note that the sample space is composed of equally likely outcomes.

   a. Let A be the event that the first ball withdrawn is white. Let B be the event that the second ball withdrawn is white. The answer to question *a* is P(AB). From [2.13.3] we have

$$P(AB) = P(B|A)P(A) = (4/11) \cdot (5/12) = 5/33.$$

   b. Let A be the event that the second ball withdrawn is red and B be the event that the first ball withdrawn is white. The answer to question *b* is P(A). From [2.13.7] we have

$$P(A) = P(A|B)P(B) + P(A|\overline{B})P(\overline{B})$$

$$= \frac{7}{11} \cdot \frac{5}{12} + \frac{6}{11} \cdot \frac{7}{12} = \frac{77}{132} = \frac{7}{12}$$

   It is interesting to note that the answer to part *b* does not depend on the color of the first ball that is withdrawn. In fact, the answer is the same as if we were withdrawing a red ball on the first draw. Why is this so? If a ball is withdrawn and discarded without observing its color, then we have gained no information that could influence our calculation of the probability of selecting a specific colored ball on the second draw. However, we might wonder, what if we sneak a look at the first ball? We would then assign a different probability to the event A. This is illustrated in the solution to part *a*.

This paradox has led us to the heart of the concept of probability. The theory of probability has as its ultimate goal the ability to **predict** the frequency of occurrence of an event when there is an element of uncertainty in the process of the generation of the event, or when there is incomplete information concerning the event or its generation.

It seems apparent that the more we know about a particular process, then the better we should be able to predict a particular outcome. This has been illustrated above. If we carry this thought process to the extreme, such that there is no uncertainty about the generation of an event, then prediction becomes perfect and probability is trivial. When this happens, such an event is either certain to occur or is impossible.

2.15   INDEPENDENT EVENTS

Definition 2.10. Two events A and B are said to be **statistically independent** if and only if either

$$P(B \mid A) = P(B) \qquad \text{[2.15.1a]}$$

or

$$P(A \mid B) = P(A) \qquad \text{[2.15.1b]}$$

It then follows from [2.13.3] that

$$P(AB) = P(A) \cdot P(B) = P(A)P(B) \qquad \text{[2.15.1c]}$$

which could also be used to define two statistically independent events.

Suppose in Example 2.19 (both parts) that the first ball withdrawn is replaced before the second ball is withdrawn. Then the two events A and B are statistically independent. The solution for question *a* now becomes

$$P(AB) = P(A)P(B) = (5/12)(5/12) = 25/144$$

and the solution for question *b* is

$$P(A) = 7/12$$

which may be calculated from [2.13.7] as follows:

$$P(A) = P(A \mid B)P(B) + P(A \mid \overline{B})P(\overline{B})$$

$$= \frac{7}{12} \cdot \frac{5}{12} + \frac{7}{12} \cdot \frac{7}{12} = \frac{7}{12}$$

Example 2.20

Consider the experiment of throwing two numbered dice and observing the numbers that appear on the two upper faces. For convenience let the two dice be distinguished by color, with the first die tossed being red and the second die being white. Let A denote the event that the set of possible outcomes for the red die are less than or equal to 2 and B denote the event that the set of outcomes for the second die are greater than or equal to 4. What is the probability that the joint event AB occurs when both dice are tossed? There are several ways by which we may calculate this probability. One way is to determine the elements that are contained in the joint event. We do this by finding the number or ordered pairs (n, m) that are in the joint event. This is 6. The total number of possible outcomes (ordered pairs) is 36. Since each possible outcome (ordered pair) is equally likely to occur, then P(AB) = 6/36. Now note that since P(A) = 2/6 and P(B) = 3/6, then P(AB) = P(A)P(B) = 6/36, and P(A | B) = P(A) and P(B | A) = P(B). Thus, the two events, A and B, are statistically independent, or simply independent.

Example 2.21

2.16   FACTORIALS AND THE GAMMA FUNCTION

We will shortly see that sometimes the numbers we calculate for the number of elements in an event may become quite large. Furthermore, they are often related to one another in a very special way, such as in permutations and combinations of elements in a set. We will define these terms shortly. To help us make such calculations it is convenient to have a special notation, called factorial.

Definition 2.11. Let n be any positive integer. We denote by the symbol n! (read **n factorial**) the number

$$n! = n(n-1)(n-2)\ldots(2)(1) = \prod_{k=1}^{k=n} k \qquad [2.16.1]$$

From the definition we have

$$n! = n(n-1)! \qquad [2.16.2]$$

$$n! = n(n-1)\ldots(n-r+2)(n-r+1)[(n-r)!] \text{ for } r < n \qquad [2.16.3]$$

Equations [2.16.2] and [2.16.3] are known as recursion relations for n!. It is convenient to extend the definition to n = 0, which we can do by means of [2.16.2] with n = 1. Thus

$$1! = 1 = (1)(0!) \qquad [2.16.4]$$

So we conclude that

$$0! = 1 \qquad [2.16.5]$$

Definition 2.12. The factorial function has been extended to noninteger values by means of the **gamma function** defined by the complex integral

$$\Gamma(\alpha+1) = \int_0^\infty e^{-x} x^\alpha dx \quad \text{for the real part of } \alpha > -1 \qquad [2.16.6]$$

where α may be complex. By integration by parts, we may show that

$$\Gamma(\alpha+1) = \alpha\Gamma(\alpha) \qquad [2.16.7]$$

which is the recursion relation for the gamma function. From [2.16.7] and the fact that $\Gamma(1) = 1$, which is obtainable from [2.16.6] with $\alpha = 0$, we obtain

$$\Gamma(n+1) = n! \quad \text{for } n = 1, 2, 3, \ldots \qquad [2.16.8]$$

Definition 2.13. An asymptotic relation of some importance is **Sterling's formula** for factorials,

$$n! \approx \sqrt{2\pi}\, n^{n+1/2}\, e^{-n} \left(1 - \frac{1}{12n}\right) \qquad [2.16.9]$$

2.17   PERMUTATIONS

Very often it is an extremely laborious task to list all the outcomes or the events in a sample space for a particular experiment or even to count all the outcomes in a particular event. For this reason we shall discuss in the next few sections some enumeration formulas that are useful for calculating probabilities of various events.

Definition 2.14. If n objects are arranged in a particular order, then this ordering is called a **permutation** of the n objects. Each possible arrangement of the n objects corresponds to a different permutation.

How many different permutations are there of n distinct objects taken r ($0 \leq r \leq n$) at a time? Another way of putting this question is: If from n distinct objects one selects r, how many different permutations can be made? A convenient way of obtaining the answer is to imagine that r boxes are available into which one object of the total of n is to be placed. Thus, for the first selection n objects are available from which the contents of the first box may be selected. Having selected an object to fill the first box, there are $n - 1$ objects to choose from to fill the second box, and so on. In general there are ($n - r + 1$) ways in which the contents of the *r*th box can be selected. This is illustrated pictorially in Figure 2.2.

Definition 2.15. We denote the number of possible permutations of n distinct objects taken r at a time by

$$(n)_r = (n)(n-1)\cdots(n-r+1)$$
$$= n!/(n-r)! \qquad \text{[2.17.1]}$$

Note that $(n)_n = n!$ and $(n)_0 = 1$.

Often the n objects are not distinct. For n objects, let n_1 be of one kind, n_2 be of a second kind, ..., and n_k be of a kth kind with $\sum_{j=1}^{k} n_j = n$. How many *distinct* permutations of the n objects are possible? If the n objects are distinct, then there are n! permutations. But since n_1 are alike, then $n_1!$ of the permutations are indistinguishable for each fixed permutation of the other objects. This argument may be expanded to a number of different objects. Thus, we have the result that the number of distinct permutations of n objects with n_1 of one kind, n_2 of a second kind, ..., and n_k of a kth kind is

$$(n)_{n_1,n_2,\ldots,n_k} = \frac{n!}{n_1!n_2!\ldots n_k!} \quad \text{where} \quad \sum_{j=1}^{k} n_j = n \qquad \text{[2.17.2]}$$

Before we consider some examples, let us first discuss another enumeration technique.

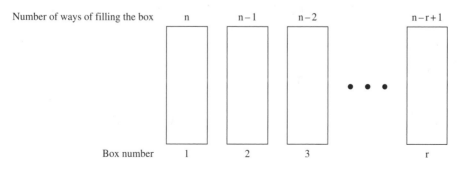

Figure 2.2

2.18   COMBINATIONS

Definition 2.16. On occasion we may not be concerned with the arrangement or ordering among a particular selection of objects. For such cases we define a **combination** of n objects as any collection of the n objects immaterial of the order.

How many different combinations are there of n objects taken r at a time? This question is answered by recalling that the number of permutations is $(n)_r = \frac{n!}{(n-r)!}$. For permutations, however, each collection of r objects is counted r! times. We are not interested in the permutations of the r objects; only the combinations are of interest.

Definition 2.17. Thus, the number of **combinations** of n objects taken r at a time is denoted as:

$$\binom{n}{r} = \frac{(n)_r}{(r)_r} = \frac{n!}{r!(n-r)!}$$

[2.18.1]

It is interesting to note that $\binom{n}{0} = 1$, $\binom{n}{n} = 1$, and $\binom{n}{1} = n$.

The numbers $\binom{n}{r}$ are also known as the **binomial coefficients** that appear in the **binomial theorem**:

$$(x + y)^n = \binom{n}{0} x^n y^0 + \binom{n}{1} x^{n-1} y^1 + \ldots + \binom{n}{n} x^0 y^n$$

$$= \sum_{r=0}^{n} \binom{n}{r} x^{n-r} y^r$$

[2.18.2]

Some interesting relationships that can be derived from [2.18.1] and [2.18.2] are:

$$\binom{n}{r} = \binom{n}{n-r}$$

[2.18.3]

$$\sum_{r=0}^{n} \binom{n}{r} = 2^n = (1+1)^n$$

[2.18.4]

$$\sum_{r=0}^{n} (-1)^r \binom{n}{r} = 0 = (1-1)^n$$

[2.18.5]

$$\sum_{r=1}^{n} r\binom{n}{r} = n2^{n-1}$$

[2.18.6]

$$\sum_{r=1}^{n} (-1)^r r\binom{n}{r} = 0$$

[2.18.7]

$$\binom{n}{r} + \binom{n}{r+1} = \binom{n+1}{r+1}$$

[2.18.8]

2.19   SOME EXAMPLES OF PERMUTATIONS AND COMBINATIONS

How many permutations of the four letters A,B,C,D are possible, taking them three at a time? In this example $n = 4$ and $r = 3$; thus | **Example 2.22**

$$(n)_r = (4)_3 = \frac{4!}{(4-3)!} = 4! = 24$$

These are listed below:

ABC	ABD	ACD	BCD
ACB	ADB	ADC	BDC
BAC	BAD	CAD	CBD
BCA	BDA	CDA	CDB
CAB	DAB	DAC	DBC
CBA	DBA	DCA	DCB

How many combinations of the letters A,B,C,D are possible taking them three at a time? This calls for the calculation of | **Example 2.23**

$$\binom{n}{r} = \binom{4}{3} = \frac{4!}{3!(4-3)!} = 4$$

From Example 2.22 these are seen to be (ABC), (ABD), (ACD), (BCD). Note that the order is not important.

How many distinct permutations of the word *sleek* are possible? For this case $n = 5$, $n_1 = 1(s)$, $n_2 = 1(l)$ $n_3 = 2(e)$, and $n_4 = 1(k)$. Then | **Example 2.24**

$$(5)_{1,1,2,1} = \frac{5!}{1!1!2!1!} = 5 \cdot 4 \cdot 3 \cdot = 60$$

We will not list these. However, consider the following simpler example.

How many distinct permutations are there for the word *see*? Here $n = 3$, $n_1 = 1$ (s), $n_2 = 2(e)$, then | **Example 2.25**

$$(3)_{1,2} = \frac{3!}{1!2!} = 3$$

These are (see), (ese), and (ees).

What is the probability of a poker player's obtaining the two-pair hand of two aces and two kings? | **Example 2.26**
The total number of possible poker hands is $\binom{52}{5}$. The number of combinations of two aces is $\binom{4}{2}$,

as is the number of combinations of two kings. The fifth remaining card must come from $52 - 8 = 44$. It can be selected in any of $\binom{44}{1}$ ways. Thus the probability of obtaining this hand is

$$\text{Probability of hand} = \frac{\binom{4}{2}\binom{4}{2}\binom{44}{1}}{\binom{52}{5}}$$

An alternative way to arrive at the same answer is as follows: The first ace (or king) may be selected in 4 out of 52 ways, the second ace in 3 out of 51 ways; the first king may then be selected in 4 out of 50 ways, and the second king in 3 out of 49 ways. The final and fifth card may be selected in 44 out of 48 ways. The answer is thus

$$\frac{4}{52} \cdot \frac{3}{51} \cdot \frac{4}{50} \cdot \frac{3}{49} \cdot \frac{44}{48}$$

This is the probability of (A, A, K, K, X) in this order, where X denotes any other card. If we compare the two answers, we find that they are *not* the same. Why? The last computation does not account for all the distinct permutations that can occur. The problem calls for *any* two-pair hand of aces and kings. There are $(5)_{2,2,1}$ such hands; therefore the answer becomes

$$\text{Probability of hand} = (5)_{2,2,1,}\frac{4}{52} \cdot \frac{3}{51} \cdot \frac{4}{50} \cdot \frac{3}{49} \cdot \frac{44}{48} = \frac{5!}{2!2!1!}\frac{4}{52} \cdot \frac{3}{51} \cdot \frac{4}{50} \cdot \frac{3}{49} \cdot \frac{44}{48}$$

$$= \frac{\binom{4}{2}\binom{4}{2}\binom{44}{1}}{\binom{52}{2}}$$

Example 2.27 | In communications, pulse amplitude modulation (PAM) is a method for coding information. A PAM "word" consists of a sequence of pulses, where each pulse is one amplitude level out of a given number of amplitude levels. For example, suppose a PAM word is three pulses long and that the possible number of amplitude levels is four. Then the number of distinct PAM words for this case is $(4)(4)(4) = (4)^3 = 64$.

Example 2.28 | A special case of PAM is pulse code modulation (PCM), where the possible number of amplitude levels is two, which are typically designated to be 0 and 1. In PCM each pulse is called a binary digit, or bit. Thus, a PCM word consists of a sequence of bits of 1s and 0s. Suppose a PCM word is three bits long. How many distinct words are there? The answer is $(2)(2)(2) = 2^3 = 8$. These are, of course, the eight binary numbers (0,0,0), (0,0,1), . . . , (1,1,1).

Quiz 2.9   Suppose we have three boxes that contain football tickets for seats on the 50-yard line and in the end zone distributed as follows:

where A denotes one 50-yard line ticket and B denotes one end zone ticket. Select a box at random. (This means that each box is equally likely or equally probable to be selected.) Without looking into the box, select a ticket from that box. Now look at the ticket. If the ticket selected is a 50-yard line ticket, what is the probability that there is another 50-yard line ticket in that box? (Hint: The solution requires the application of Bayes' theorem.)

Quiz 2.10   Four friends are playing a card game, where each is dealt 13 cards. What is the probability that each player will be dealt one ace each?

Quiz 2.11   Two urns are available. One contains two white balls and two black balls. The second urn contains two white balls and four black balls. If an urn is selected at random and two balls are withdrawn without replacement, what is the probability that the two balls are the same color?

2.20   MATLAB

Figure 2.3 shows a display from a MATLAB software program provided with this book in subdirectory ch2. This program is similar to that introduced in Chapter 1 and is initiated by running the m file ch2, which is in subdirectory ch2. This program illustrates probabilities, including conditional probabilities. The initial options are the same as those for Chapter 1, but it also provides a new option called normal. This option generates a set of numbers for both box 1 and box 2 using one of two methods called normal and uniform, respectively. Both of these methods will be discussed in the following chapter. When the *generate* button is pressed, numbers and blanks will appear in both boxes. The blank spaces are not to be considered as numbers; rather, they control the number of numbers that can appear in each box. There are three questions that the user may select and provide answers for. The correct answer is available upon request by the user. New numbers can be generated for the same question or for each new question. This program allows the user to repeatedly practice calculating some simple probabilities.

2.21   SUMMARY

This chapter has introduced many new terms, some of which we list below. Memorize the definitions for these terms and any appropriate equations.

Frequency ratio.

Sample space: discrete and continuous.

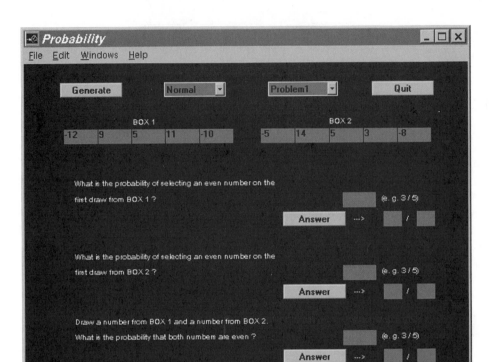

Figure 2.3   A MATLAB example

A priori.

A posteriori.

Event.

Compound event.

Probability function.

P(A+B), addition formula.

P(AB), probability of joint event.

Mutually exclusive and collectively exhaustive.

Axioms of probability.

Conditional probability.

Multiplication theorem.

Independent events.

Permutations.

Combinations.

One way of expressing the theme of this chapter is that it involves counting. Probability involves counting the occurrence of a particular event or events. If the sample space consists of simple outcomes that are equally likely to occur, which means that the outcomes are equally probable to occur, then we may calculate the probability of an event by counting the number of all the outcomes in the event and then divide that number by the total number of outcomes in the sample space. However, sometimes such a listing is not practical because there are too many events. So we may apply the counting formulas for permutations and combinations. These formulas may be used to count the events in an experiment or a sample space.

When solving the problems, try imaginatively to draw a picture of the sample space. Then try to count the number of outcomes in the sample space that belong to the event defined in the problem. Remember that on occasion, it may be easier to count the number of outcomes in the complement event.

PROBLEMS

2.1   What is the sample space for the experiment for flipping two coins simultaneously and observing the outcome? In what way does this sample space differ from the one for flipping one coin twice?

2.2   What is the sample space for rolling two dice simultaneously? Find a way of determining the number of ways that the *sum* of the two faces of the dice can occur. Do this by employing the sample space.

2.3   What is the sample space for the roll of a die that has three blank faces and 1,2, and 3 on the remaining faces? Is this an equally likely sample space?

2.4   What is the probability of obtaining a blank face for the above die? What is the probability of obtaining a 3?

2.5   What is the probability of obtaining exactly one head in two flips of a perfect coin? What is the probability of obtaining at least one head in two flips of a perfect coin?

2.6   We are given a number of darts. When we throw a dart at a target, we have a probability of 1/4 of hitting the target. What is the probability of obtaining a hit if three darts are thrown simultaneously? Calculate this probability two ways. Hint: Construct the sample space. How many outcomes are in the sample space? Is the sample space an equally likely space?

2.7   Two balls are selected sequentially (without replacement) from an urn containing three red, four white, and five blue balls.
a. What is the probability that the first is red and the second blue?
b. What is the probability of selecting a white ball on the second draw if the first ball is replaced before the second is selected?

2.8   A die is rolled six times. What is the probability of obtaining the ordered sequence 1,2,3,4,5,6? What is the probability of obtaining any specific ordered sequence of length six?

2.9   A box of 30 diodes is known to contain five defective ones. If two diodes are selected at random without replacement, what is the probability that at least one of these diodes is defective?

2.10   How many distinct permutations of the words *peeper* and *noon* are possible?

2.11   There are four players in bridge and each player is dealt 13 cards from the deck of 52 cards. What is the probability of a bridge player obtaining exactly 11 cards of one suit?

2.12   A particular computer circuit is designed so that if any 2 or fewer of a total of 10 connections between the input and output fail, the computation is still correct. What is the number of ways in which a correct calculation can be made if exactly two connections have failed? What is the number of ways in which exactly two connections can fail and a correct computation still be made?

2.13   What is the probability that a poker hand withdrawn from a deck will contain three jacks and two nonjacks?

2.14   A computer memory has the capability of storing 10^6 words. Due to outside forces, portions of the memory are often erased. Therefore, words are stored redundantly in various areas of the memory. If a particular word is stored in n different places in the memory, what is the probability that this word cannot be recalled if one-half of the memory is erased by electromagnetic radiation? Hint: Consider each word to be stored in a particular cell (or box). These cells (boxes) may be located anywhere, geometrically speaking, in memory. The contents of each cell may be either erased or not erased. Assume n is small compared to the memory capacity.

2.15   A monkey is playing with ten colored marbles and three empty boxes. If he puts the ten marbles into the three boxes at random, what is the probability that he puts three marbles in one box, three in another box, and four in the third box?

2.16   Three friends are cutting a normal deck of cards to determine who will buy lunch. The deck is reformed after each cut. What is the probability that the first ace is cut by the third individual?

2.17   If two events A and B can occur and P(A) is not zero and P(B) is not zero, what combinations of independent (I), not independent ($\bar{\text{I}}$), mutually exclusive (M), and not mutually exclusive ($\bar{\text{M}}$) are permissible? In other words, which of the four combinations (I, M), (I, $\bar{\text{M}}$), ($\bar{\text{I}}$, M), ($\bar{\text{I}}$, $\bar{\text{M}}$) are permissible? Construct an example for those combinations that are permissible.

2.18   In pulse code modulation (PCM), a PCM word consists of a sequence of binary digits (bits) of 1s and 0s. Suppose the PCM word length is n bits long. How many distinct words are there?

2.19   If each PCM word, three bits long, is equally likely to occur, what is the probability of a word with exactly two 1s to occur? Solve this problem in two ways. First, consider all words in a sample space. Second, suppose each bit is equally likely.

2.20   In pulse amplitude modulation (PAM), a PAM word consists of a sequence of pulses, where each pulse may take on a given number of amplitude levels. Suppose a PAM word is n pulses long and each pulse may take on m different levels. How many distinct PAM words are there?

2.21   Manufacturer X produces personal computers (PCs) at two different locations in the world. 15 percent of the PCs produced at location A are delivered to a single retail outlet defective, while 5 percent of the PCs produced at location B are delivered defective to the same retail store. If the manufacturing plant at A produces 1,000,000 PCs per year and the plant at B produces 150,000 PCs per year, find the probability of purchasing a defective PC.

2.22 Show the following:

a. $\int_{-\infty}^{\infty} e^{-t^2} dt = (\pi)^{\frac{1}{2}}$

b. $\Gamma(1/2) = (\pi)^{\frac{1}{2}}$

Then

c. determine the value of $\Gamma(13/2)$.

2.23 Four different resistors, three capacitors, and two inductors are available to construct a tuned circuit. How many different tuned circuits can be built? Does it matter whether the circuits are parallel or serial?

2.24 Let the sample space consist of the integers from 1 to 5; that is, S = {1, 2, 3, 4, 5}. Suppose we define a subset A = {2, 3}. Now show that equation [2.13.1] is valid. Also calculate the conditional probability P(2 | A) using equation [2.13.2].

2.25 Prove equations [2.18.3] through [2.18.8].

MATLAB PROBLEMS

2.1M Write and execute a MATLAB program to calculate n! in general, and then calculate 64!. Note that there is a gamma function defined in MATLAB where n! = gamma(n + 1). Compare your answer, which can also be found in tables, to the approximate value obtained using Sterling's formula, which can also be implemented with a MATLAB program. Your implementation of Sterling's formula might use logarithms.

2.2M One way that the MATLAB software program provided with this chapter can be extended is to add a third box, allowing numbers to be moved from one or more boxes to another. Write such an extension.

2.3M Another way to extend the MATLAB program is to increase the number of elements (or containers or positions) within each box. This could be done in a fixed manner; that is, the number of elements is always the same. It could also be done by changing the possible number of elements each time the *generate* button is pushed. Write such a change for the program.

2.4M Another way to modify the MATLAB program is to increase the size of the two boxes that contain the numbers generated by the program. Write such a change for the program.

chapter
3

Random Variables

3.1 INTRODUCTION

In this chapter we expand the concept of events by mapping the sample space to the
real line. Such a mapping provides a numerical designation for events so that we may
use numerical valued functions instead of event (or set) functions. Thus, we will define a random variable to be a real numerical valued function defined over a sample
space. Recall that probabilities are assigned to events in the sample space. Therefore,
we will need to represent events in the range of the random variable. We will define
the probability that a random variable is equal to, or less than, or greater than a specific value, as well as the probability that a random variable falls within a range of
values. We will also illustrate how probability theory can be applied to various
engineering situations.

3.2 RANDOM VARIABLES

Definition 3.1. A **random variable** is a real numerical valued function defined
over a sample space. If the sample space for the random experiment is denoted as
S, then a function X that assigns a real number X(s) to every outcome or point
$s \in S$ is called a random variable. Thus, X is a function whose domain is the sample space and whose range is the set of real numbers. This definition is illustrated
in Figure 3.1. We will denote the random variable by an upper-case letter (e.g., X),
and any specific value of the random variable with a lower-case letter (e.g., x). On
occasion we will subscript the lower-case letter to distinguish between two or
more specific values. Furthermore, the notation $\{X = x\}$ will denote the subset of
S consisting of all outcomes in S such that $X(s) = x$. The notation $\{X \leq x\}$ denotes the subset of S consisting of all outcomes in S such that $X(s) \leq x$. Therefore, $\{X \leq x\}$ becomes a set of experimental outcomes. As part of the definition
of a random variable we require that the set $\{X \leq x\}$ is an event for every x. We

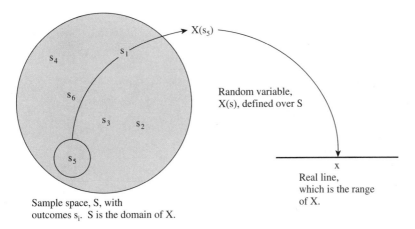

Figure 3.1   A random variable X mapping the experimental outcome s_5 to a value x on the real line

will also require that the probabilities of the events $\{X = \infty\}$ and $\{X = -\infty\}$ be equal to zero. Thus, $P(X = \infty) = 0$ and $P(X = -\infty) = 0$.

Note that the random variable is not the probability of a sample point (or an event) in the sample space. The random variable is a real numerical valued function that assigns a number to an outcome (point) or set of outcomes (points) in the sample space. One advantage of a random variable is that we may define events in the range of the random variable (i.e., over intervals on the real line). We can then define a probability for such events over the interval on the real line.

Recall from Definition 2.2 in Chapter 2 that a sample space is discrete if it is a finite set or a countably infinite set and is continuous otherwise. With this in mind, we offer the following definitions.

Definition 3.2. A **discrete random variable** is a random variable that has a range with only a finite or a countably infinite number of values on the real line. A discrete random variable is usually, but not necessarily, defined over a finite set or a countably infinite set of outcomes (points) in the sample space.

A discrete random variable may be defined for the random experiment of flipping a perfect coin. The outcome of a particular flip is H or T. Define the random variable X to be $X(H) = 1$ and $X(T) = 2$. The set of outcomes in S is $\{H, T\}$. However, these are mapped to the set $\{1, 2\}$ by the random variable X. Thus, assuming the coin is fair, then $P(X = 1) = 1/2$ and $P(X = 2) = 1/2$.   **Example 3.1**

Another example, more detailed, of a discrete random variable is to consider the above experiment and observe the number of heads that occur if the experiment is performed n times. Define a random variable X to be the number of times a head occurs in n trials. Clearly, $0 \le X \le n$, where X is an integer. Thus, the range of X is $[0, n]$ where X is an integer in this range. The probability that   **Example 3.2**

$X \le n$ is 1, while the probability that $X = 0$ is $1/2^n$. Verify this last result. Note that this example is one that combines a number of experiments, since the basic experiment is performed n times.

Example 3.3 | Again let the experiment be the same as that of Example 3.1, but let the trials continue until a head has occurred for the first time. Define a random variable X to be the number of trials until the experiment ends (i.e., a head appears). For this case $1 \le X < \infty$ where X is an integer. Thus, X is a discrete random variable. This example is also one that combines a number of experiments, since the basic experiment is performed n times.

Example 3.4 | We may define a discrete random variable on a continuous sample space. For example, suppose the sample space is the closed interval [0, 1] on the real line, which has an uncountably infinite number of points for the domain of the random variable. Define a random variable that maps [0, 1/2] to 0 and maps (1/2, 1] to 1. Then the range of the random variable is finite and, therefore, the random variable is discrete. This example illustrates that the size of the sample space, or domain of X, does not determine whether or not the random variable is discrete or continuous; rather, it is the range that matters.

We have not discussed the probabilities for events for Examples 3.3 and 3.4 because this is more easily done after we introduce the concept of probability distribution functions and probability density functions, which we will define in the next section.

Definition 3.3. A continuous random variable is a random variable that has a range with an uncountably infinite number of values on the real line. A continuous random variable is usually, but not necessarily, defined over an uncountably infinite number of outcomes (points) in the sample space.

Example 3.5 | An example of a continuous random variable is the voltage across the output terminals of a noise generator. The range of values that the voltage can assume is continuous, as contrasted with the previous examples. If the random variable is a function of time, then, as we will see in Chapter 5, such functions are called random processes.

Example 3.6 | This example maps a discrete sample space to a continuous random variable on the real line over the interval from 0 to 1. Suppose a sample space consists of the outcomes of flipping a coin (i.e., an H or a T is the sample space for each flip). If an H occurs, then select a number in the interval [0, 1/2] on the real line, and if a T occurs, then select a number in the interval (1/2, 1].

Quiz 3.1   A die is tossed and the value of the outcome is observed. A random variable is defined that is an integer in the range from one to the value of the face of the die that is observed. What is the sample space? What type of random variable is this?

In order to discuss the probability of certain events for examples with a continuous random variable, it is convenient to define the probability distribution and density functions.

It should be clear that for any particular sample space, many different random variables can be defined. The important point is that we may select a random variable that permits us to focus our attention on values on the real line. Many more examples of random variables will appear throughout this chapter and those that follow.

Quiz 3.2   Each week a state lottery draws six distinct numbers in sequence from the set of numbers 1 to 49; that is, a specific number in the range 1 to 49 may occur only once for each six-number draw. What is the sample space? Define a random variable for this sample space. Note that this quiz introduces the notion of mapping numbers to numbers, which is often just a formality. Thus, we can have events that are defined on the real line that are also mapped to the real line with a random variable.

Quiz 3.3   Can a random variable be defined that maps the points of a sample space to complex numbers?

3.3   PROBABILITY DISTRIBUTION FUNCTIONS FOR DISCRETE RANDOM VARIABLES

Definition 3.4. A probability distribution function for a discrete random variable is a function that assigns a probability to each value of the random variable. The probability that the random variable X assumes a specific value x is the value of the probability distribution for x. This definition assumes that the events in the sample space are **simple events;** that is, each event is only one experimental outcome. There is only one value assigned to the random variable for each outcome, or sample point, in the sample space. We may assign various sample points of the sample space to the same value of the random variable, as we will illustrate below.

We may expand on the above definition as follows. Let the events in a discrete sample space be denoted as E_i. Let the random variable be defined as X, which may assume specific values x. Then the probability distribution is denoted as $P_X(X = x)$, or more simply as $P_X(x)$. If we sum $P_X(x)$ over all values of x, then this is the same as the sum of the probabilities of all sample points in the sample space, since the random variable represents mutually exclusive events. Consequently, we may conclude that

$$0 \leq P_X(x) \leq 1 \qquad\qquad [3.3.1]$$

$$\sum_{\text{all x}} P_X(x) = 1 \qquad\qquad [3.3.2]$$

Note that since the probability distribution function is a probability, we use an upper-case P to denote this function. The subscript is an upper-case X denoting the random variable. The argument is a lower-case x denoting a specific value for the random variable.

Example 3.7

Perform the experiment of flipping a coin twice and observe the outcomes. The sample space may be represented as (H, H), (H, T), (T, H), (T, T), which we define as events E_i. Define a random variable, X, that is the number of tails that occur on any one outcome. Then we may tabulate the events E_i, their probability, and the random variable as follows.

Event	Outcome Flip 1	Outcome Flip 2	$P(E_i)$	Random Variable, X
E_1	H	H	1/4	0
E_2	H	T	1/4	1
E_3	T	H	1/4	1
E_4	T	T	1/4	2

Note that we have assigned to the two events E_2 and E_3 the same value of the random variable. The value of the probability for each value of the random variable X may be calculated by adding the probabilities of the corresponding outcomes, or sample points, in the sample space. The value X = 0 corresponds to one outcome, X = 1 to two outcomes, and X = 2 to one outcome. We may construct the probability distribution for X as follows.

Probability Distribution for X, Where X Denotes the Number of Tails		
Random Variable, X	Outcomes in X	$P_X(x)$
0	E_1	1/4
1	E_2, E_3	1/2
2	E_4	1/4

$$\sum_{x=0}^{2} P_X(x) = 1$$

Example 3.8

Consider the experiment of rolling two dice and observing the sum of the faces that appear (see Problem 2.2). What is the probability distribution for this experiment? From the solution of Problem 2.2, we found that there were 36 points in the sample space; that is, there were 36 **equally likely (equally probable)** outcomes. Thus, the probability of each simple event or outcome was 1/36. For this experiment we define the random variable, X, to be the sum of the two faces that appear. We tabulate X and its probability distribution below.

X, Sum of the Two Faces	Number of Ways that X Can Occur	Probability Distribution, $P_X(x)$
2	1	1/36
3	2	2/36
4	3	3/36
5	4	4/36
6	5	5/36
7	6	6/36
8	5	5/36
9	4	4/36
10	3	3/36
11	2	2/36
12	1	1/36

Therefore, $P_X(x)$ can be plotted as shown in Figure 3.2.

Definition 3.5. Another interesting and useful function is the **cumulative probability distribution function** for discrete random variables. This function is defined as

$$P_X(X \le x_k) = \sum_{j=-\infty}^{k} P_X(X = x_j)u(x - x_j) \qquad \text{[3.3.3]}$$

where $P_X(X = x_k)$ is the probability distribution defined in Definition 3.4. Stated in words, the cumulative probability distribution function is the probability that the random variable X is less than or equal to some specific value x_k on the real line. The unit step function, $u(x)$, is defined to be unity for $x \ge 0$ and zero otherwise. Equation [3.3.3] produces a stairstep type of function, which we illustrate in the following example.

Some authors define a function $F_X(x) = P_X(X \le x)$. Such a definition does tend to help distinguish between $P_X(X = x)$ and $P_X(X \le x)$. However, we believe that the distinction between $P_X(X = x)$ and $P_X(X \le x)$ will be clear, and that the function $F_X(x)$ is

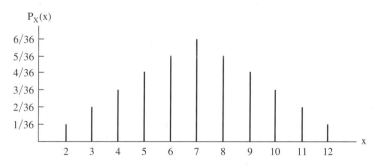

Figure 3.2   The probability distribution for rolling two dice and observing the sum of the faces

a further abstraction, Nevertheless, we will use both notations in this chapter. Note once again that the upper-case P denotes probability, in this case the cumulative probability. The subscript is the random variable and the argument is the random variable, X, less than or equal to the specific value, x.

Example 3.9 | What is the cumulative probability distribution function for Example 3.8? This is shown in Figure 3.3. At each point x, there is a step equal to $P_X(X = x)$ at that point.

Definition 3.6. The probability that a random variable falls between two specific values can be readily defined through the use of the probability distribution function, that is,

$$P_X(x_i < X \le x_j) = \sum_{k=-\infty}^{j} P_X(X = x_k)[u(x - x_k) - u(x - x_j)]$$ [3.3.4]

$$- \sum_{k=-\infty}^{i} P_X(X = x_k)[u(x - x_k) - u(x - x_i)]$$

$$= \sum_{k=i+1}^{j} P_X(X = x_k)[u(x - x_k) - u(x - x_j)]$$

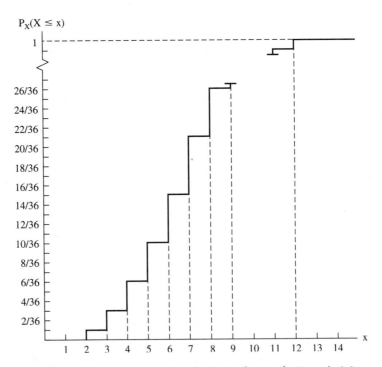

Figure 3.3   Cumulative probability distribution function for Example 3.9

where we have used subscripts to denote the various discrete values that the random variable, X, may assume and we require that $x_i \leq x_j$, $i < j$. This definition may be extended to define the probabilities for $x_i < X < x_j$, $x_i \leq X \leq x_j$, and so on.

What is the probability that the outcome of the experiment of Example 3.8 is less than or equal to seven (i.e., the sum of the two faces of the dice is less than or equal to seven). The answer is readily obtained from Figure 3.3 and is 21/36. What is the probability that the sum of the faces of the two dice is less than or equal to nine, but greater than or equal to four? This is answered by referring to Figure 3.2 and is 27/36. The answer can also be obtained from Figure 3.3 by finding $P_X(X \leq 9) = 30/36$ and subtracting $P_X(X < 4) = 3/36$ which becomes $P_X(4 \leq X \leq 9) = P_X(X \leq 9) - P_X(X < 4) = 27/36$.

| Example 3.10

3.4   EXAMPLES OF PROBABILITY DISTRIBUTION FUNCTIONS FOR DISCRETE RANDOM VARIABLES

BINOMIAL

Imagine an experiment is performed for which the only possible outcomes are a success with probability p or a failure with probability q. Thus, $p + q = 1$. We denote each performance of the experiment as a trial, where each trial has one outcome. The outcomes and, therefore, the trials are assumed to be independent (see Definition 2.10); that is, the outcome of any one trial does not depend on the outcome of any other trial. Sequences of such trials are called **Bernoulli trials.** Let the random variable X be the number of times a success occurs in n trials. It is clear that $0 \leq X \leq n$. What is the probability that you will observe $X = r$ consecutive successes followed by $n - r$ consecutive failures? The probability of such an event is $p^r q^{n-r}$. If we now ask for the probability of exactly $X = r$ successes out of n trials, then $p^r q^{n-r}$ must be multiplied by the number of ways these r successes can occur, that is, the number of combinations of r successes in n trials. Thus, we have

$$P_X(r) = \binom{n}{r} p^r q^{n-r} = \frac{n!}{(n-r)!r!} p^r q^{n-r} \qquad [3.4.1]$$

binomial probability distribution func

where we have used a result from Chapter 2 to obtain the form on the right. This probability distribution function for the discrete random variable is known as the **binomial probability distribution function.** Note that

$$\sum_{r=0}^{n} \binom{n}{r} p^r q^{n-r} = (p + q)^n = 1 \qquad [3.4.2]$$

In MATLAB gamma(n) = (n − 1)!. Thus, in MATLAB

$\binom{n}{r}$ = round(gamma(n + 1)./(gamma(r + 1).*gamma(n − r + 1)))

MULTINOMIAL

The binomial function can be generalized to k random variables, X_i, $i = 1, 2, \ldots, k$, as follows. Denote all the possible outcomes of an experiment as A_i, $i = 1, 2, \ldots, k$, with respective probabilities of p_i, $i = 1, 2, \ldots, k$, where the A_i are events and $\sum_{i=1}^{k} p_i = 1$. If the trials are independent and one performs n trials, what is the probability that A_j occurs r_j times, where $j = 1, 2, \ldots k$ and $\sum_{j=1}^{k} r_j = n$? This event (occurring in any particular order) has probability $p_1^{r_1} p_2^{r_2} \ldots p_k^{r_k}$ and the number of different permutations is $\frac{n!}{r_1! r_2! \ldots r_k!}$. The random variable, X_i, indicates the number of times, r_i, that the outcome, A_i, occurs. Thus, the probability distribution is

$$P_{X_1 X_2 \ldots X_k}(r_1, r_2, \ldots, r_k) = \frac{n!}{r_1! r_2! \ldots r_k!} p_1^{r_1} p_2^{r_2} \ldots p_k^{r_k} \qquad \text{[3.4.3]}$$

$$\text{where } 0 \le r_j \le n \text{ and } \sum_{j=1}^{k} r_j = n$$

This is called the **multinomial probability distribution function.** Note that

$$P_{X_1 X_2 \ldots X_k}(r_1, r_2, \ldots, r_k)$$

is an extension to multiple random variables of the notation used for the binomial probability distribution function. It can be shown that

$$\sum \frac{n!}{r_1! r_2! \ldots r_k!} p_1^{r_1} p_2^{r_2} \ldots p_k^{r_k} = (p_1 + p_2 + \ldots + p_k)^n = 1 \qquad \text{[3.4.4]}$$

where

$$0 \le r_j \le n$$

and

$$\sum_{j=1}^{k} r_j = n$$

Thus, [3.4.3] is a generalization of [3.4.1].

Note that if $k = 2$, then $A_1 = A$ and $A_2 = \overline{A}$, $p_1 = p$ and $p_2 = 1 - p$, $r_1 = r = X$, $r_2 = n - r$, and then [3.4.3] becomes [3.4.1].

GEOMETRIC

As another example consider an experiment for which a possible outcome is the event A, the probability of which is p. Perform the experiment until the event A occurs for the first time. Define a random variable, X, to be the number of trials until the experiment ends. Here $1 \le X < \infty$ where X is an integer. Since p is the probability of A occurring, then $(1 - p)$ is the probability of A not occurring. Therefore, the probability of obtaining $(r - 1)$ events other than A followed by the event A, or a total number of events $X = r$, is

$$P_X(r) = (1 - p)^{r-1} p, \ 1 \le r < \infty \qquad \text{[3.4.5]}$$

$$= 0 \text{ otherwise}$$

Note that

$$\sum_{r=1}^{\infty} (1-p)^{r-1}p = \frac{p}{1-(1-p)} = 1 \qquad \text{[3.4.6]}$$

GENERALIZED GEOMETRIC

The geometric probability distribution function can be generalized to the case where the event A occurs exactly a times, where a $\geq$ 1 in r trials (r $\geq$ a). For this to happen A must occur (a $-$ 1) times in (r $-$ 1) trials and then A must occur on the rth trial. The probability of (a $-$ 1) As in (r $-$ 1) trials in any order is

$$\binom{r-1}{a-1}p^{a-1}(1-p)^{(r-1)-(a-1)}$$

and the probability of A on the rth trial is p. Thus, the distribution for the random variable X $=$ a As in r trials in any order is

$$P_Xr(a) = \binom{r-1}{a-1}p^a(1-p)^{r-a}, \; a \leq r < \infty \qquad \text{[3.4.7]}$$

$$= 0, \quad \text{otherwise}$$

HYPERGEOMETRIC

Suppose one has a set of J elements, K of which belong to a particular class A. Withdraw n elements without replacement. If each element is assumed equally likely to occur, and if the random variable X $=$ r is the number of elements of A that are withdrawn, then

$$P_X(r) = \frac{\binom{K}{r}\binom{J-K}{n-r}}{\binom{J}{n}} \qquad \text{[3.4.8]}$$

where $0 \leq X = r \leq K$, $0 \leq r \leq n$, and $0 \leq n - r \leq J - K$. This is known as the **hypergeometric** probability distribution function, which is often useful for problems that involve a deck of cards.

POISSON

As our final example, we consider the Poisson probability distribution function. This particular function has many applications since it describes the behavior of many physical phenomena, some examples of which will be given in a later chapter.

The Poisson function is the limiting case of the binomial function when the probability, p, of a success in a single trial approaches zero as the number of trials, n, approaches infinity such that $\alpha = np = $ constant. The **Poisson probability distribution function** is given as

$$P_X(r) = \frac{\alpha^r}{r!}e^{-\alpha} \qquad \text{[3.4.9]}$$

where $\alpha > 0$ and r $=$ 0, 1, ..., ∞.

The random variable is still X, which is the number of times a success occurs in n trials.

Example 3.11

Ten thousand raffle tickets for a charity are sold at $1 each. The raffle prize is $2,000, and the holder of 1 and only 1 of the 10,000 tickets will be the winner. John White buys three tickets. What is the probability distribution for his gain?

The random variable X is Mr. White's gain, which has two possible values. Either Mr. White will lose $3 or he will win $2,000 and thereby gain $1,997. In the first case his gain is negative, or -3. In the second case his gain is positive and is $1,997. The probability for these two values of the gain are 9,997/10,000 and 3/10,000, respectively, since we assume that the sample space consists of 10,000 tickets, any one of which is equally likely to be the winner. Consequently, the probability distribution for the gain is

Random Variable X Gain	$P_X(x)$
$-$ $3.00	9,997/10,000
$1,997.00	3/10,000

Example 3.12

A golfer has learned from past experience that on the average she can make a putt from 10 feet only once in 10 times. Let X be the number of putts she takes until she makes her first putt. Assume that the putts are independent events, even though in practice this is probably not the case. Find $P_X(X = 1)$. Find $P_X(X \leq 2)$.

The probability that the putter will make the first putt is 1/10. Thus, $P_X(1) = 1/10$. The probability that the putter requires two putts before she makes the putt is given by the geometric probability distribution; that is, she must miss the first putt and then make the second putt. This probability is $(9/10)(1/10) = 9/100 = P_X(2)$. Thus, $P_X(X \leq 2) = P_X(1) + P_X(2) = 1/10 + 9/100 = 19/100$. (Note that the random variable must be greater than or equal to unity, since the putter must take at least one putt.)

Example 3.13

A woodpecker has a territory that it patrols for food each day without fail. On any given day the probability that a birdwatcher will spot the woodpecker is 0.9. If five equally skilled birdwatchers are present, what is the probability that exactly four birdwatchers will spot the same woodpecker (i.e., X = 4)? What is the probability that at least one birdwatcher spots the woodpecker (i.e., $X \geq 1$)? Assume that the birdwatchers operate independently of each other.

The solution to this problem is determined by the binomial distribution, where the random variable is the number of birdwatchers that spot the woodpecker. Thus,

$$P_X(4) = \binom{5}{4}(.9)^4(.1)^1 = 0.32805$$

The probability that at least one birdwatcher spots the woodpecker is $P(X \geq 1)$, which is

$$P_X(X \geq 1) = \sum_{k=1}^{5} \binom{5}{k}(.9)^k(.1)^{5-k} = 0.99999$$

We may calculate this latter result more simply by noting the following

$$P_X(X \geq 1) = 1 - P(X = 0) = 1 - (.1)^5 = 0.99999$$

Another way to solve this problem is to construct the sample space as follows. This is the manner by which Problem 2.6 was solved. Imagine each birdwatcher is represented by a box. Each birdwatcher either spots the woodpecker or doesn't spot it. Thus, each box may be filled in one of two ways, either with an "s" for spotting or "n" for not spotting the woodpecker. Thus, one particular outcome for the experiment is a particular sequence of s's and n's. The sample space consists of all such sequences of length five, that is,

sssss

ssssn

sssns

. . .

nnnnn

There are $2^5 = 32$ such sequences in the sample space. Note, however, that each sequence or outcome in this experiment is not equally likely to occur, since the probability of spotting is (.9) which is not the same as not spotting, which is (.1). Thus, the outcome sssss has a probability of $(.9)^5$ while the outcome snnnn has a probability $(.9)(.1)^4$. Now, to calculate $P_X(4)$ we need to count all the sequences with four s's. There are five such sequences, or outcomes. They each have a probability of $(.9)^4(.1)$. Thus, $P_X(4) = 5(.9)^4(.1) = 0.32805$, which is the same as we calculated above. Similarly we may calculate $P_X(X \geq 1)$ by counting the number of sequences with at least one s. There are 31 such outcomes. We must then calculate the probability for each sequence and then add all of these probabilities to obtain our final answer. A simpler approach is to observe that there is only one sequence that does not contain an s, namely nnnnn. If we subtract the probability of this sequence from one, then we obtain the probability that at least one bird-watcher spots the woodpecker. This is the same answer we calculated above.

Quiz 3.4   Suppose that 90 percent of the students that take a course using this book pass the course. What is the probability that only 1 student will fail the course, if there are 50 students in the class? What is the probability that at least two students will fail the course? Assume each student does his/her own work, that is, that each student's performance is independent from all others. Set up the formula first, then calculate the exact number for the probability.

Assume that telephone calls to a stockbroker in an interval from 0 to t have a Poisson probability distribution function and that they are made randomly and independently in time with an average rate of calls per second denoted as λ. (We will define the term *average* in the next chapter. For this example think of λ as a constant.) Determine the probability that exactly one call is | **Example 3.14** made in an interval that is $10/\lambda$ long. We may use the Poisson probability distribution function with $\alpha = \lambda t$

$$P_X(k) = \frac{(\lambda t)^k}{k!} e^{-\lambda t}$$

where $\lambda t > 0$ and $k = 0, 1, \ldots, \infty$.
   Then for $t = 10/\lambda$ and $k = 1$ we have

$$P_X(1) = \frac{(10)^1}{1!} e^{-10} = 10e^{-10}$$

Quiz 3.5   What is the probability that no calls are placed in the same interval as above?

Quiz 3.6   What is the probability that at least two calls are placed in a three second interval if the average rate of calls is 0.1?

3.5   CUMULATIVE PROBABILITY DISTRIBUTION AND PROBABILITY DENSITY FUNCTIONS FOR CONTINUOUS AND MIXED RANDOM VARIABLES

The word *continuous* means uninterrupted or unbroken. Mathematically, a function $f(x)$ defined on some interval containing $x = b$ is continuous at $x = b$ if and only if for every $\varepsilon > 0$ there is a $\delta > 0$ such that if $|x - b| < \delta$, then $|f(x) - f(b)| < \varepsilon$. Consequently, to identify continuous random variables, we seek a random variable that maps the sample space onto the real line such that it will satisfy this definition. Some examples of continuous random variables are how much people weigh, the musical aptitude of students, and the distance that athletes can throw the javelin. Because our measurement of these random variables is usually imprecise, we often represent the exact value with a rounded value, say, to the nearest tenth or to the nearest integer. For example, we might measure the length of life of a workstation to the nearest day or perhaps the nearest hour depending on the accuracy of the records available. Despite this coarse measurement, we would still regard the life of the workstation as a continuous random variable.
   Recall Definitions 3.2 and 3.3, which define discrete and continuous random variables. Recall that the critical feature in these definitions is the range of the random variable. If the range is finite or countably infinite, then the random variable is discrete. If the range is uncountably infinite, then the random variable is continuous.

Quiz 3.7   Are the following random variables discrete or continuous?

1. The number of telephone calls one can receive during a 10-minute interval, neglecting the time it takes to answer a call and to hang up.
2. The amount of rainfall in Los Angeles in the month of June.

3. The number of spelling errors in this book.
4. The time to complete this quiz.
5. The number of bad tomatoes in a dozen at the local grocery store.

For a continuous random variable, we are unable to assign a probability to the sample point or experimental outcome in the same manner as we did for a discrete random variable, because the range contains an uncountably infinite number of values. Consequently, we need to define a different approach for determining the probability of a continuous random variable. The approach we shall take is to define the cumulative probability distribution function for a continuous random variable.

> **Definition 3.7.** The **cumulative probability distribution function** for a **continuous random variable,** X, is defined as $P_X(X \leq x)$, which is the probability that X is less than or equal to a specific value x. For this definition we will assume that the cumulative probability distribution is not only continuous but also differentiable with a continuous derivative everywhere. (We will relax this condition shortly.) The cumulative probability distribution is a bounded, nondecreasing function. Furthermore, as the random variable approaches its smallest value, the cumulative probability distribution approaches zero, while as the random variable approaches its largest value, the cumulative probability distribution approaches unity. Thus, we say that the cumulative probability distribution is a monotonically, nondecreasing function of X, which increases from zero to unity as X ranges over its set of values in an increasing manner. Any function that satisfies these properties may be considered a cumulative probability distribution function. Note once again that the upper-case P denotes probability. This definition will be modified below for mixed random variables (e.g., a random variable that is the sum of both a continuous and a discrete random variable).

Now suppose we have a **mixture of continuous and discrete random variables,** such as a sum of a continuous random variable and a discrete random variable. We assume that a point in the sample space is mapped either to a value of the continuous random variable or to a value of the discrete random variable, but not to both. The discrete random variable will have a nondecreasing cumulative probability distribution consisting of a stairstep function with jump discontinuities at the values of the random variable X, for which $P_X(X = x) > 0$, similar to that shown in Figure 3.3. The continuous random variable will have a nondecreasing cumulative probability distribution that is continuous everywhere, as defined above. In general for a random variable that is a mixture of continuous and discrete random variables, one may show that any bounded, nondecreasing cumulative probability distribution may be composed of two parts: one part being a stairstep function with jump discontinuities at the values of the random variable X, for which $P_X(X = x) > 0$, and another part that is continuous everywhere. The first part corresponds to a cumulative probability distribution for a discrete random variable, while the second part corresponds to a cumulative distribution for a continuous random variable. Consequently, we may have a cumulative probability distribution that represents a mixture of continuous and discrete random variables. Furthermore, one can imagine that any cumulative probability distribution for a continuous random variable may be approximated by a cumulative probability distribution for a discrete random variable. Thus, any continuous random variable may be approximated by a discrete random variable.

Figure 3.4(a) is one example of a cumulative probability distribution for a continuous random variable. However, if we have a mixture of continuous and discrete random variables, then, as we have discussed, the distribution need not be continuous, and in fact the distribution function may have jumps as illustrated by Figure 3.4(c). The plot of $P_X(X \leq x)$ may extend over the infinite real line depending on the mapping from the sample space to the real line, or the plot may extend over only a short interval as shown

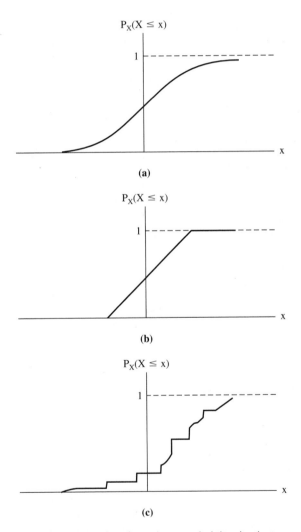

Figure 3.4 Examples of cumulative probability distribution functions for (a) and (b) continuous random variables, and (c) both continuous and discrete random variables

in Figure 3.4(b). The cumulative probability distributions shown in Figures 3.4(b) and 3.4(c) are not differentiable at the discontinuities. We will discuss this further when we define probability density functions.

The value of $P_X(X \le x)$ for any specific x is the probability that the random variable X is less than or equal to x. This value can be read directly from the cumulative probability distribution curve. Sometimes we are not interested in the cumulative probability distribution; instead, we need to know how the random variable is distributed as a "density," that is, the probability per unit of measure. This may be described most easily for discrete random variables for which we may define a number known as the **relative frequency** of an event. For example, suppose we consider the weight of all students at a particular university. Rather than letting the measured weights be a continuous random variable, we classify the measured weights into classes, or intervals, of, say, 10 pounds. Our scale of measurements is then quantized into intervals of (0–9), (10–19), . . . , (290–299). For convenience we terminate the weight scale at 299 and arbitrarily say that any weight greater than 299 pounds will be counted as being in the range (290–299). Now suppose there are 3,000 students and we measure the weight of each. Each weight is quantized to one of the specified 10-lb. intervals, where we designate the first interval to be (0–9). The fraction of the total number of measurements falling within a specified class or interval is called the **frequency ratio.** For example, if there are 100 weights, out of the total of N = 3,000, that fall in the 10th interval, (90–99), then the relative frequency for this interval is f_i/N, where f_i is the number of weights in the interval (90–99). Thus, we have that $i = 10, f_{10} = 100, N = 3,000$, so that $f_{10}/N = 1/30$. If we plot a tabulation of frequency ratios, then such a plot is called a **frequency histogram** or simply a **histogram,** which might appear as in Figure 3.5. For a discrete random variable, a histogram represents a measured probability distribution function. The histogram is a bar graph with rectangles constructed over each interval. The height of each rectangle is equal to the number of measurements f_i that fall in each class interval divided by the total number of measurements. If we adjust the total area under the relative frequency histogram such that the total area is unity, then the areas under the frequency histogram represent the probabilities of the measured weights for a given interval. As the number of measurements becomes large and the intervals become small, the histogram approximates a smooth curve and the discrete random variable approximates a continuous

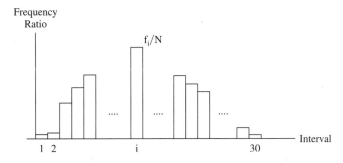

Figure 3.5   An example of a histogram

random variable. For a continuous random variable, such a curve is known as the **probability density function** because the probability of the random variable being less than or equal to a specific value is represented by the area under the probability density function for all values of $X \le x$. The relative frequency associated with a particular interval in the set of all measurements is the fraction of measurements of the total that falls in that interval, and it is also the probability of obtaining a measurement in that interval for an arbitrary measurement. We may conclude that the probability density function describes characteristics of a random variable. We will be more specific about these characteristics as we progress through the book.

MATLAB has a statistical toolbox that includes numerous probability density and distribution functions for both discrete and continuous random variables. If you have access to this statistical toolbox, you should run the demonstration program. However, MATLAB has a number of functions we will use that do not require the statistical toolbox. We will include examples from time to time that use MATLAB and we will assign homework problems that will require the use of MATLAB or a similar software package.

Definition 3.8. Following the discussion given above, we define the **probability density function** for continuous random variables as

$$p_X(x) = \frac{d}{dx} P_X(X \le x) \qquad \text{[3.5.1]}$$

where the **cumulative probability distribution function** is defined above. Accordingly, the cumulative probability distribution function is related to the probability density function by

$$P_X(X \le x) = \int_{-\infty}^{x} p_X(t)\,dt \qquad \text{[3.5.2]}$$

Here we have used a lower case p to denote the probability density function of the random variable X. The argument, x, is the specific value of the random variable X. Thus, the probability of an event becomes the integral of the probability density over the appropriate range.

As we noted previously, some authors use the notation $F_X(x) = P_X(X \le x)$. A lower-case f is also used for the probability density, i.e., $f_X(x) = p_X(x)$. With this notation we have the following:

$$f_X(x) = \frac{d}{dx} F_X(x)$$

and

$$F_X(x) = \int_{-\infty}^{x} f_X(t)\,dt$$

We will use both notations in this book, since the f notation is a convenient shorthand that is used by some textbook authors and it is found in the technical literature.

The following properties of $f_X(x) = p_X(x)$ follow from [3.5.2] and the fact that $F_X(x) = P_X(X \leq x)$ is differentiable:

1. $\displaystyle \int_{-\infty}^{\infty} p_X(x)dx = \int_{-\infty}^{\infty} f_X(x)dx = 1$ [3.5.3a]

2. $\displaystyle F_X(x) = P_X(X \leq x) = \int_{-\infty}^{x} f_X(t)dt = 1 - \int_{x}^{\infty} f_X(t)dt$ [3.5.3b]

3. If $f_X(x)$ exists, then $F_X(x)$ is absolutely continuous.   [3.5.3c]

Note that there may exist continuous random variables that do not have a probability density function. This is a topic beyond the scope of this book.

We may consider some other properties of the probability density function by examining Figure 3.6. The probability that X is less than or equal to x_1 is the area under the curve from $-\infty$ to x_1; that is, $F_X(x_1) = \int_{-\infty}^{x_1} f_X(x)dx$. An alternative relationship is $F_X(x_1) = 1 - \int_{x_1}^{\infty} f_X(x)dx$. Similarly, the probability that X is greater than x_4 is $P_X(X > x_4) = \int_{x_4}^{\infty} f_X(x)dx$. The probability of $x_2 < X \leq x_3$ is $P_X(x_2 < X \leq x_3) = \int_{x_2}^{x_3} f_X(x)dx$. Thus, the area under the curve $p_X(x)$ for the interval x to $x + dx$ represents the probability that $P_X(x < X \leq x + dx)$. Later we will see that for bivariate (two) random variables, the probability density will be represented by a surface and the probability will be the volume under the surface.

We have already discussed the situation when we may have both a discrete and a continuous random variable, that is, **mixed random variables.** By using the properties of delta and step functions, we may show that the probability density function for a discrete random variable consists of a delta function with a weight $P_X(X = x)$ at each of the possible values, x, of the discrete random variable. (The properties of the delta function are discussed in Appendix 1.)

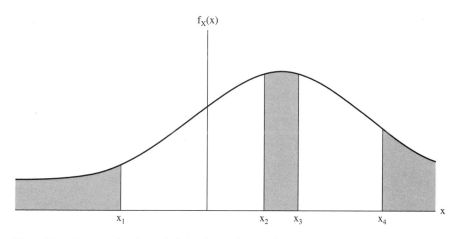

$f_X(x)$

Figure 3.6 An example of a probability density function for a continuous random variable

Definition 3.9. We define a **probability density function** for a **discrete random variable** in terms of its probability distribution function as follows:

$$f_X(x) = p_X(x) = \sum_{\text{all } x_i} P_X(x_i)\delta(x - x_i) \qquad \textbf{[3.5.4]}$$

where $\delta(x)$ is the delta function. Then the **cumulative probability distribution** can be determined as follows:

$$F_X(x) = P_X(X \le x) = \sum_{\text{all } x_i} P_X(x_i) \int_{-\infty}^{x} \delta(t - x_i)\,dt \qquad \textbf{[3.5.5]}$$

$$= \sum_{\text{all } x_i} P_X(x_i)u(x - x_i)$$

where $u(x)$ is the unit step function.

Definition 3.10. The **probability density function for mixed random variables** is the sum of the probability density functions for the discrete and continuous random variables. This definition is actually a result of the fact that we require a sample point of a sample space to be mapped to a value of the continuous random variable or to a value of the discrete random variable, but not both. The probability density function for mixed random variables must, of course, satisfy the various properties we have discussed. The **cumulative probability distribution function for mixed random variables** is the integral of the probability density function, as previously defined. Properties $[3.5.3a,b,c]$ are also satisfied.

Note that Definitions 3.9 and 3.10 are essentially equivalent to our definition for the probability distribution function for discrete random variables. We may use the same representation for the probability density function for both continuous and discrete random variables. Consequently, the probability density function for mixed random variables may be used as a general representation. The reason this approach was not taken earlier is that the probability distribution function is a natural and frequently used procedure for introducing the concept of a probability distribution without delta functions, and many authors take this approach. Therefore, we decided to introduce these concepts in this manner. However, through the use of delta functions we see that we may unify the concept of probability distribution and density functions. The cumulative probability distribution function is useful for mixed random variables and will continue to be used throughout the text. Therefore, we will use the probability density function and the cumulative probability distribution function to represent discrete, continuous, and mixed random variables.

Quiz 3.8   Suppose a probability density function has no delta functions. What is the probability that the random variable X will assume a specific value, say x_0?

3.6   EXAMPLES OF PROBABILITY DENSITY FUNCTIONS

Example 3.15 | What is the probability density function representation for Bernoulli trials? Recall that the binomial probability distribution is

$$P_X(r) = \binom{n}{r} p^r q^{n-r} = \frac{n!}{(n-r)!r!} p^r q^{n-r}$$

Then we may write the probability density function as follows:

$$p_X(x) = \sum_{r=0}^{n} \binom{n}{x} p^x q^{n-x} \delta(x-r) = \sum_{r=0}^{n} \frac{n!}{(n-x)!x!} p^x q^{n-x} \delta(x-r)$$

$$= \sum_{r=0}^{n} \frac{n!}{(n-r)!r!} p^r q^{n-r} \delta(x-r)$$

Quiz 3.9   What is the binomial cumulative probability distribution for the above example?

Consider the example of pulse code modulation (PCM), which we examined in the Examples at the end of Chapter 2. Assume the occurrence of a one to be as equally probable as the occurrence of a zero. Let the random variable X be X = 1 if a PCM one occurs and X = 0 if a PCM zero occurs. Then | **Example 3.16**

$$P_X(X = 1) = \frac{1}{2}$$

and

$$P_X(X = 0) = \frac{1}{2}$$

We may write the probability density function as

$$f_X(x) = p_X(x) = P_X(X=0)\delta(x) + P_X(X=1)\delta(x-1) = \frac{1}{2}\delta(x) + \frac{1}{2}\delta(x-1)$$

The cumulative probability distribution is obtained by integrating the probability density, which is

$$F_X(x) = P_X(X \le x) = \int_{-\infty}^{x} p_x(t)dt = \int_{-\infty}^{x} \left[\frac{1}{2}\delta(t) + \frac{1}{2}\delta(t-1) \right] dt = \frac{1}{2}u(x) + \frac{1}{2}u(x-1)$$

We may plot $f_X(x)$ and $F_X(x)$ as in Figure 3.7

Perhaps one of the simplest examples of a continuous probability density function is the **equiprobable,** or **uniform, probability density function.** It is expressed as $f_X(x) = \frac{1}{b-a}[u(x-a) - u(x-b)]$, where b > a and u(x) is the unit step function, and is illustrated in Figure 3.8. Note that this function satisfies all of the properties of a probability density function that we have discussed. | **Example 3.17**

Quiz 3.10   Can either a or b be negative in Example 3.17? Can both a and b be negative?

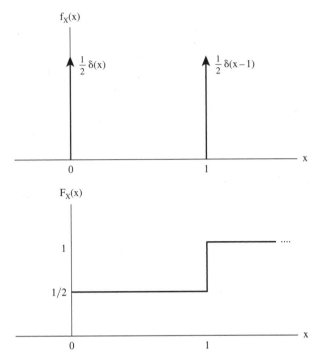

$f_X(x)$

$\frac{1}{2}\delta(x)$ $\frac{1}{2}\delta(x-1)$

0   1   x

$F_X(x)$

1

1/2

0   1   x

Figure 3.7   Probability density function and cumulative probability distribution function for PCM example

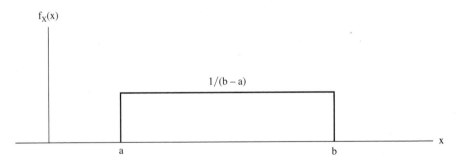

$f_X(x)$

$1/(b-a)$

a   b   x

Figure 3.8   The uniform (or equiprobable) probability density function

---

Example 3.18 | Another example is the **Gaussian,** or **normal probability, density function,** which is written as

$$f_X(x) = \frac{1}{\sqrt{2\pi}\,\sigma_X} e^{-(x-\mu_X)^2 / 2\sigma_X^2}$$ **[3.6.1]**

where $\sigma_X > 0$ and where μ_X is the mean and σ_x the standard deviation of the random variable.
These terms will be defined and discussed in the next chapter. For the moment simply interpret
them as constants. Figure 3.9 is a plot of $f_X(x)$.

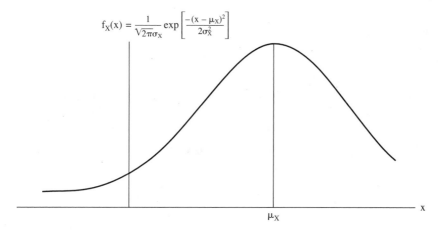

$$f_X(x) = \frac{1}{\sqrt{2\pi}\sigma_X} \exp\left[\frac{-(x - \mu_X)^2}{2\sigma_X^2}\right]$$

Figure 3.9   The Gaussian (or normal) probability density function

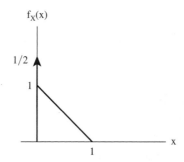

Figure 3.10   Probability density function
for Example 3.19

Figure 3.10 shows an example of a probability density function with both a discrete and a continuous random variable. The probability density function is expressed as | **Example 3.19**

$$f_X(x) = \frac{1}{2}\delta(x) + (1 - x)[u(x) - u(x - 1)]$$

Quiz 3.11   Determine the cumulative probability distribution function for Example 3.19.

3.7   JOINT PROBABILITY DENSITY AND DISTRIBUTION FUNCTIONS

Many engineering problems involve two or more random variables. For example, we may
study the distribution of rainfall within a state, or the frequency of occurrence of thunder-
storms along the Atlantic coast, or the pollution index within the Los Angeles city limits,

or the dissipation of heat on a sound board in a personal computer (PC), or the measurement of noise in an image, or the occurrence of earthquakes at the San Andreas fault. These problems may frequently involve two independent spatial (coordinate) variables. It is also possible that we may have a problem that has both temporal and spatial variables. When such problems involve two independent variables, they are often referred to as **two-dimensional, joint probability,** or **bivariate** problems. If there are more than two independent variables, then we call such problems **multivariate**. In this section we shall consider two-dimensional, or joint probability, density and distribution functions.

Definition 3.11. The **joint probability density function** for two continuous random variables is defined in a manner analogous to [3.5.1] as

$$p_{XY}(x, y) = \frac{\partial^2 P_{XY}(X \le x, Y \le y)}{\partial x \, \partial y} \qquad [3.7.1]$$

where $P_{XY}(X \le x, Y \le y)$ is the **joint cumulative probability distribution,** which is defined as

$$P_{XY}(X \le x, Y \le y) = P_{XY}(-\infty < X \le x, -\infty < Y \le y) \qquad [3.7.2]$$

$$= \int_{-\infty}^{x} \int_{-\infty}^{y} p_{XY}(s, t) ds dt$$

The joint probability density function is always nonnegative; that is, $p_{XY}(x,y) \ge 0$. Any discontinuities of $P_{XY}(X \le x, Y \le y)$ correspond to discrete probabilities at those discontinuities in an analogous manner to that discussed for mixed random variables. Again the f notation is often used where $F_{XY}(x, y) = P_{XY}(X \le x, Y \le y)$ and $f_{XY}(x, y) = p_{XY}(x, y)$. For this section we will use the p notation.

Definition 3.12. The probability that an experimental outcome, or a sample point s, falls in region C of the sample space is given by the integral of the joint probability density function over that region; that is

$$P_{XY}(s \in C) = \int_C \int p_{XY}(x, y) dx dy \qquad [3.7.3]$$

Consequently, it follows that

$$\int_{-\infty}^{\infty} \int_{-\infty}^{\infty} p_{XY}(x, y) dx dy = 1 \qquad [3.7.4]$$

More specifically, the probability that the joint random variable (X,Y) lies in the area defined by $x_1 < X \le x_2$ and $y_1 < Y \le y_2$ is

$$P_{XY}(x_1 < X \le x_2, y_1 < Y \le y_2) = P_{XY}(-\infty < X \le x_2, -\infty < Y \le y_2) \quad [3.7.5]$$
$$- P_{XY}(-\infty < X \le x_2, -\infty < Y \le y_1)$$
$$- P_{XY}(-\infty < X \le x_1, -\infty < Y \le y_2)$$
$$+ P_{XY}(-\infty < X \le x_1, -\infty < Y \le y_1)$$
$$= \int_{x_1}^{x_2} \int_{y_1}^{y_2} p_{XY}(s, t) ds dt$$

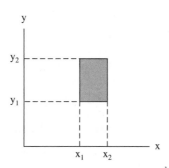

Figure 3.11   An interpretation for the joint cumulative distribution function for Equation [3.7.5]

This is illustrated in Figure 3.11.

Definition 3.13. The probability density function for the random variable X is calculated from the joint probability density function as

$$p_X(x) = \int_{-\infty}^{\infty} p_{XY}(x, y)\, dy \qquad\qquad \textbf{[3.7.6]}$$

and similarly for $p_Y(y)$. The probability densities $p_X(x)$ and $p_Y(y)$ are also known as the **marginal probability density functions** for the random variables X and Y, respectively.

If $p_{XY}(x,y) = c\, e^{-(x+y)}$ for $x > 0$ and $y > 0$, then $p_X(x) = c\, e^{-x}$, and, of course, $c = 1$. | **Example 3.20**

Definition 3.14. If the joint random variables are discrete, then we use delta functions, as we did for the single random variable case. Thus, the **joint probability density function for two discrete random variables** is also known as the **bivariate probability density function** and is given as

$$p_{XY}(x_j, y_k) = \sum_{\text{all } j,k} P_{XY}(X = x_j, Y = y_k)\delta((x - x_j), (y - y_k)) \qquad \textbf{[3.7.7]}$$

$$= \sum_{\text{all } j,k} P_{XY}(X = x_j, Y = y_k)\delta(x - x_j)\delta(y - y_k)$$

The cumulative probability distribution function for two discrete random variables is defined the same as for [3.7.2].

Definition 3.15. The **joint probability density function for two mixed random variables** is defined as the sum of the joint probability density functions for the discrete and continuous random variables. The probability density function for mixed random variables must, of course, satisfy the various properties we have discussed. In particular, the integral of the probability density function for the mixed random variables over their entire range must be unity. The **cumulative probability distribution function for any two mixed random variables** is the integral of the joint probability density function for the two mixed random variables, as previously defined. Once again we note that we may from now on use joint probability density function to represent both discrete and continuous random variables.

One may also introduce **multivariate probability distribution and density functions,** i.e., functions of more than two random variables. Such functions are natural extensions of the joint distribution and density functions we have defined above.

3.8   EXAMPLES OF JOINT PROBABILITY DENSITY FUNCTIONS

Example 3.21   One of the simplest examples of a joint probability density function is the **uniform** joint probability density function, which is illustrated in Figure 3.12.
Mathematically, we have

$$p_{XY}(x, y) = \frac{1}{x_1 y_1} [u(x) - u(x - x_1)][u(y) - u(y - y_1)] \qquad [3.8.1]$$

where for this example $x_1, y_1 > 0$. Note, however, that either or both x_1 and y_1 may be negative, in which case we use $1/|x_1| |y_1|$. The reader will note that this function can be separated into the product of an "x-density" function with a "y-density" function, that is, the product of the two marginal probability density functions. When we can factor a joint density function into the product of two marginal density functions, we say that the random variables are statistically independent. We will discuss this again shortly.

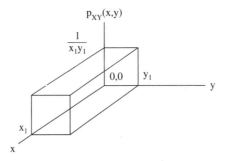

Figure 3.12   Two-dimensional uniform joint probability density function

Example 3.22

Another example is the **joint Gaussian probability density function.** This function is expressed as

$$p_{XY}(x, y) = \frac{1}{2\pi\sigma_X\sigma_Y \sqrt{1 - \rho_{XY}^2}} \exp$$

$$\left\{ -\frac{1}{2(1 - \rho_{XY}^2)} \left[\frac{(x - \mu_X)^2}{\sigma_X^2} - \frac{2\rho_{XY}(x - \mu_X)(y - \mu_Y)}{\sigma_X\sigma_Y} + \frac{(y - \mu_Y)^2}{\sigma_Y^2} \right] \right\} \qquad \text{[3.8.2]}$$

where μ_X and μ_Y are the means, σ_X and σ_Y are the standard deviations, which satisfy $\sigma_X, \sigma_Y > 0$, and ρ_{XY} is the correlation coefficient of the random variables, such that $|\rho_{XY}| < 1$. The mean, standard deviation, and correlation coefficient are discussed in the next chapter. For the present consider these parameters as numbers. A plot of [3.8.2] appears in Figure 3.13.

Example 3.23

A fire has destroyed a local electronics store. However, some of the merchandise is saved. The owner runs an advertisement announcing a lottery for the merchandise. To be eligible for the lottery, one must purchase a ticket. The price of the ticket varies with the type of merchandise; for example, to be eligible for amplifiers and receivers requires a ticket costing $50. To be eligible for two speakers requires a ticket costing $25. The holder of a ticket is guaranteed to win some merchandise. Ann decides to try to win two new speakers for her hi-fi system. The rules of the lottery are that the speakers will be selected two at a time but not necessarily in matched pairs. There are three speakers of type A and five of type B. Ann's ticket is selected first. Find the joint probability density function for the two types of speakers. This problem may be modeled as an urn problem as follows.

A box contains three white balls and five black balls, corresponding to type A and type B speakers, respectively. Two balls are withdrawn without replacement. Let the random variable X denote the number of white balls withdrawn and the random variable Y denote the number of black balls withdrawn. Find $p_{XY}(x,y)$, the joint probability density function of x and y.

Solution:

The random variables are discrete, so the joint probability density function will be represented by weighted delta functions, where the weights will be equal to the probability of the appropriate

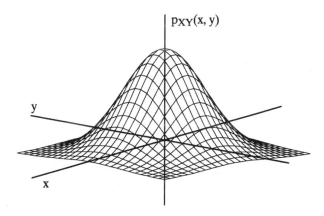

Figure 3.13   An example of a probability density function for the joint random variables (X, Y)

event. The random variables may take on specific values given by X = 0,1,2; Y = 0,1,2; and note that X + Y = 2. Denote the events of withdrawing a white ball (black ball) on the ith (i = 1,2) draw as $w_i(b_i)$. Then we have

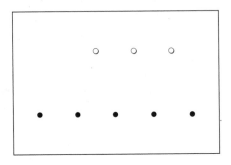

$$p_{XY}(2, 0) = P(w_1w_2)\delta[(x - 2),(y)] = P(w_1)P(w_2 \mid w_1)\delta[(x - 2), (y)]$$

$$= \frac{3}{8} \cdot \frac{2}{7}\delta[(x - 2), (y)] = \frac{3}{28}\delta[(x - 2), (y)]$$

$$p_{XY}(1, 1) = [P(w_1b_2) + P(b_1w_2)]\,\delta[(x - 1),(y - 1)]$$

$$= \left[\frac{3}{8} \cdot \frac{5}{7} + \frac{5}{8} \cdot \frac{3}{7}\right]\delta[(x - 1), (y - 1)] = \frac{15}{28}\delta[(x - 1), (y - 1)]$$

$$p_{XY}(0, 2) = \left[\frac{5}{8} \cdot \frac{4}{7}\right]\delta[(x), (y - 2)] = \frac{10}{28}\delta[(x), (y - 2)]$$

$$p_{XY}(x, y) = 0 \text{ otherwise}$$

Note that $p_{XY}(x,y)$ is the sum of the above terms.
    Check:

$$\int_0^2\int_0^2 p_{XY}(x, y)\,dx\,dy = \frac{3}{28} + \frac{15}{28} + \frac{10}{28} = 1$$

To obtain the marginal probability density, $p_X(x)$, we integrate over all y. Thus

$$p_X(x) = \int_0^2 p_{XY}(x, y)\,dy = \int_0^2 [p_{XY}(2, 0) + p_{XY}(1, 1) + p_{XY}(0, 2)]dy$$

$$= \frac{10}{28}\delta(x) + \frac{15}{28}\delta(x - 1) + \frac{3}{28}\delta(x - 2)$$

Similarly we find $p_Y(y)$ to be

$$p_Y(y) = \int_0^2 p_{XY}(x, y)\,dx = \int_0^2 [p_{XY}(2, 0) + p_{XY}(1, 1) + p_{XY}(0, 2)]\,dx$$

$$= \frac{3}{28}\delta(y) + \frac{15}{28}\delta(y - 1) + \frac{10}{28}\delta(y - 2)$$

Quiz 3.12   Determine the probability that Ann obtains a matched pair of speakers.

While Hal is at the electronic store's lottery it is announced that video cassettes have been discov- | **Example 3.24**
ered in two separate boxes. The cassette types are 4-hour and 6-hour. There are three of each type in
one box, while the other box contains four 4-hour cassettes and five 6-hour cassettes. Hal buys a lottery ticket for $1, which entitles him to two cassettes. The rules of the lottery are that one cassette
will be withdrawn from each box. Hal is the first person eligible for the draw. He hopes to obtain two
6-hour video cassettes. Find the joint probability density function for the 4-hour and 6-hour video
cassettes. Again this problem may be modeled as an urn problem as follows.

   Two boxes, A and B, contain three white balls and three black balls and four white balls and
five black balls, where a white and a black ball corresponds to a four-hour and a six-hour cassette,
respectively. A ball is withdrawn from each box. Let $X = 1$ if a white ball is withdrawn and
$X = 0$ if a black ball is withdrawn from A. Use the same notation for Y being withdrawn from B.
Find $p_{XY}(x,y)$ the joint probability density function.

   The solution is similar to that given in the previous example. Here we have $X = 0,1$, and
$Y = 0,1$. We will denote the events of withdrawing a white (black) ball from box A as $w_A(b_A)$ and
similarly for box B as $w_B(b_B)$. We also note that the events are independent.

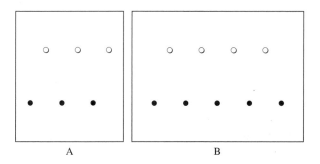

$$p_{XY}(0, 0) = P(b_A)P(b_B)\, \delta(x, y) = \frac{3}{6}\cdot\frac{5}{9}\delta(x, y) = \frac{5}{18}\delta(x, y)$$

$$p_{XY}(0, 1) = P(b_A)P(w_B)\, \delta(x, y - 1) = \frac{3}{6}\cdot\frac{4}{9}\delta(x, y - 1) = \frac{4}{18}\delta(x, y - 1)$$

$$p_{XY}(1, 0) = P(w_A)P(b_B)\, \delta(x - 1, y) = \frac{3}{6}\cdot\frac{5}{9}\delta(x - 1, y) = \frac{5}{18}\delta(x - 1, y)$$

$$p_{XY}(1, 1)= P(w_A)P(w_B)\, \delta(x - 1, y - 1) = \frac{3}{6}\cdot\frac{4}{9}\delta(x - 1, y - 1)= \frac{4}{18}\delta(x - 1, y - 1)$$

Check:

$$\int_0^1\int_0^1 p_{XY}(x, y)\, dx\, dy = \frac{5}{18} + \frac{4}{18} + \frac{5}{18} + \frac{4}{18} = 1$$

Note that in this example $p_{XY}(x,y)$ is formed by summing the four terms $p_{XY}(i,j), i,j = 0,1$.

Quiz 3.13   Determine the probability that Hal will obtain two 6-hour video cassettes. What is the probability that Hal will obtain two cassettes of the same duration?

Quiz 3.14   Plot the probability density functions for the two previous examples.

Quiz 3.15   Determine the marginal probability densities for the last example.

Example 3.25 | This example involves both a discrete random variable and a continuous random variable. Suppose the output voltage of a noise generator is either zero or positive. Suppose further that the voltage is zero with probability 1/2 and Gaussian distributed for positive values with $\mu_X = 0$. What is the probability density function for the voltage of the noise generator?

Solution:

$$P_X(X = 0) = \frac{1}{2}$$

Thus, for zero voltage, we have the probability density

$$p_X(x) = P_X(X = 0)\, \delta(x) = \frac{1}{2}\delta(x)$$

For $x > 0$, we also have

$$p_X(x) = \frac{1}{\sqrt{2\pi}\,\sigma_X} \exp\left(-\frac{x^2}{2\sigma_X^2}\right)$$

Therefore, the complete probability density is

$$p_X(x) = \frac{1}{2}\delta(x) + \frac{1}{\sqrt{2\pi}\,\sigma_X} \exp\left(-\frac{x^2}{2\sigma_X^2}\right), \quad x \geq 0$$

This function is plotted in Figure 3.14. Verify that

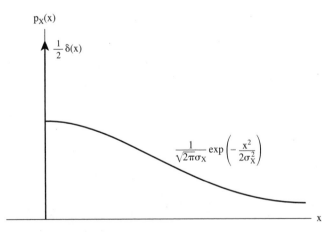

Figure 3.14   Example of a combination of a discrete random variable and continuous random variable being represented by a probability density function

$$\int_{-\infty}^{\infty} p_X(x)dx = 1$$

The errors committed by a computer system manufactured by Company A are found to be dependent upon two major factors: the time following *power-on* and the number of machine instructions per second executed. The computer system is found to have a high probability density for committing errors immediately after *power-on*. However, the probability density decreases gradually to no errors after eight hours. For some undetermined reason, the errors made by the computer system are also inversely proportional to the number of machine instructions executed per second. If the computer performs very few instructions, then the probability density for an error is large. However, as the number of machine instructions increases, the probability density function for an error decreases to zero at 100 million instructions per second (MIPS). Assume the probability density function $p_{XY}(x,y)$ for the computer system errors is as shown in Figure 3.15, where the x

Example 3.26

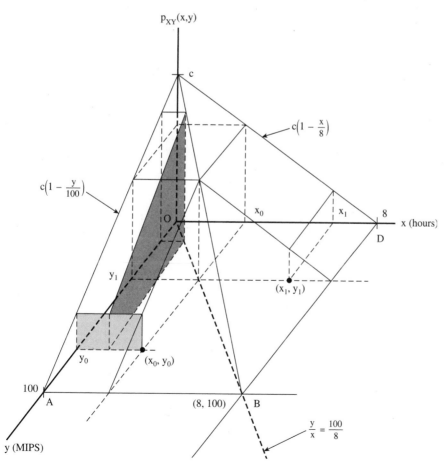

Figure 3.15 Probability density for Example 3.26

axis represents the time after *power-on;* that is, zero represents when the power is turned on. Let the y axis represent the number of MIPS. Find c. Determine the probability that a computer system error occurs between seven and eight hours after power-on. Also find the cumulative probability distribution function.

To find c we know that

$$\int_{-\infty}^{\infty}\int_{-\infty}^{\infty} p_{XY}(x, y) \, dy \, dx = 1$$

Note that this is the volume under the surface of the probability density function. To make the required calculation, we may break the integral into two parts as follows, where we use dummy variables of integration.

$$c\int_{0}^{8}\int_{100s/8}^{100}\left(1 - \frac{t}{100}\right) dt \, ds + c\int_{0}^{8}\int_{0}^{100s/8}\left(1 - \frac{s}{8}\right) dt \, ds = \frac{c400}{3} + \frac{c400}{3} = 1 \text{ or } c = \frac{3}{800}$$

We may check this calculation by recalling that the volume for a pyramid is one-third the area of the base times the height.

The probability of an error between seven and eight hours after *power-on* is

$$\frac{3}{800}\int_{7}^{8}\int_{100s/8}^{100}\left(1 - \frac{t}{100}\right) dt \, ds + \frac{3}{800}\int_{7}^{8}\int_{0}^{100s/8}\left(1 - \frac{s}{8}\right) dt \, ds = \frac{23}{1024}$$

This result can be checked using a combination of triangular prisms and pyramids. We will also check this calculation another way below.

The cumulative probability distribution function may be calculated as follows by referring to Figure 3.15. Consider two cases. First, consider an arbitrary point (x_0, y_0) in the triangle defined by OAB for which $y_0/x_0 \geq 100/8$. Then we have

$$P_{XY}(X \leq x_0, Y \leq y_0) = \int_{0}^{x_0}\int_{100/8\,x}^{y_0} c\left(1 - \frac{y}{100}\right) dy \, dx + \int_{0}^{x_0}\int_{0}^{100/8\,x} c\left(1 - \frac{x}{8}\right) dx \, dy$$

$$= c\left[x_0 y_0 - \frac{x_0 y_0^2}{200} - \frac{25}{96}x_0^3\right] \text{ for } \frac{y_0}{x_0} \geq \frac{100}{8}$$

Similarly, for the second case we consider an arbitrary point (x_1, y_1) in the triangle defined by OBD for which $y_1/x_1 \leq 100/8$. Then we have

$$P_{XY}(X \leq x_1, Y \leq y_1) = \int_{0}^{y_1}\int_{8/100y}^{x_1} c\left(1 - \frac{x}{8}\right) dx \, dy + \int_{0}^{y_1}\int_{0}^{8/100\,y} c\left(1 - \frac{y}{100}\right) dx \, dy$$

$$= c\left[x_1 y_1 - \frac{x_1^2 y_1}{16} - \frac{y_1^3}{7500}\right] \text{ for } \frac{y_1}{x_1} \leq \frac{100}{8}$$

The cumulative probability distribution function may also be easily found by using a combination of boxes, pyramids, and triangular prisms also illustrated in Figure 3.15. For the same arbitrary points we have

$$P_{XY}(X \leq x_0, Y \leq y_0) = \left[x_0\left(\frac{100}{8}x_0\right)c\left(1 - \frac{x_0}{8}\right)\right] + \left[\left(\frac{100}{8}x_0^2\right)\left(\frac{1}{3}\right)\left(\frac{x_0}{8}c\right)\right]$$

$$+ \frac{1}{2}\left[c\left(1 - \frac{x_0}{8}\right)x_0\left(100 - \frac{100}{8}x_0\right) - (100 - y_0)c\left(1 - \frac{y_0}{100}\right)x_0\right]$$

$$= c\left[x_0 y_0 - \frac{x_0 y_0^2}{200} - \frac{25}{96} x_0^3\right] \text{ for } \frac{y_0}{x_0} \geq \frac{100}{8}$$

and

$$P_{XY}(X \leq x_1, Y \leq y_1) = \left[y_1\left(\frac{8}{100} y_1\right) c\left(1 - \frac{y_1}{100}\right)\right] + \left[\frac{1}{3}\left(\frac{8}{100} y_1^2\right)\left(c \frac{y_1}{100}\right)\right]$$

$$+ \frac{1}{2}\left[c y_1\left(1 - \frac{y_1}{100}\right)\left(8 - \frac{8}{100} y_1\right) - y_1 c\left(1 - \frac{x_1}{8}\right)(8 - x_1)\right]$$

$$= c\left[x_1 y_1 - \frac{x_1^2 y_1}{16} - \frac{y_1^3}{7500}\right] \text{ for } \frac{y_1}{x_1} \leq \frac{100}{8}$$

These results may be checked at $x_1 = x_0 = 0$ and $y_1 = y_0 = 0$, where the cumulative probability distribution is 0, and at $x = 8$ and $y = 100$, where the cumulative probability distribution is 1. Another check is for $x_0 = 7$ and $y_0 = 100$. The volume, or probability, is 1001/1024. If we subtract this number from 1 we obtain 23/1024, which we calculated above in another manner. One of the problems is to plot the cumulative probability distribution using MATLAB.

Quiz 3.16   Verify all of the calculations made for Example 3.26.

3.9   CONDITIONAL PROBABILITY DENSITY AND DISTRIBUTION FUNCTIONS

The notion of conditional probability developed in Chapter 2 can be extended to the density and distribution functions introduced in this chapter.

Definition 3.16. The **conditional cumulative probability distribution** function of the random variable X given the event A has occurred is defined as follows:

$$P_{X|A}(X \leq x \,|\, A) = \frac{P_{XA}(X \leq x, A)}{P(A)} \qquad \text{[3.9.1]}$$

The probability distribution function $P_{XA}(X \leq x, A)$ is the joint probability of the events $\{X \leq x\}$ and A, that is, the intersection of the event $\{X \leq x\}$ and the event A. It is assumed that $P(A)$ does not equal zero. Note that if $x = \infty$, then the event $\{X \leq x\}$ is the certain event and, therefore, the intersection of $\{X \leq x\}$ with A is A. Consequently, $P_{X|A}(X \leq x \,|\, A) = 1$. A similar argument for $x = -\infty$ gives $P_{X|A}(X \leq x \,|\, A) = 0$. One can continue in this manner to show that $P_{X|A}(X \leq x \,|\, A)$ has all the properties of a distribution function. The subscripts $X|A$ and XA are sometimes omitted if the context is clear. Furthermore, the word *cumulative* is also frequently dropped, since the specification

{X ≤ x} on the random variable indicates that we are discussing a cumulative distribution.

Definition 3.17. The **conditional probability density function** of the random variable X given the event A is

$$p_{X|A}(x|A) = \frac{d}{dx} P_{X|A}(X \le x|A) \qquad [3.9.2]$$

Example 3.27 | The range of the absolute value of an amplitude modulated signal, X, is from 0 to 20 volts. Let M = | X | and suppose M has a uniform probability density over this range. Let the event A be {M ≤ 5}. The probability of this event is P(A) = P(M ≤ 5). Find $P_{M|A}(M \le m|A)$. $P_{MA}(M \le m, A) = P_{MA}(M \le m, M \le 5) = P_M(M \le m)$ since the event {M ≤ m} is a subset of the event {M ≤ 5} for m ≤ 5. Therefore, $P_{M|A}(M \le m|A) = P_M(M \le m)/P(M \le 5)$. However, if m ≥ 5, then the event {M ≤ 5} is a subset of the event {M ≤ m}. Thus, $P_{MA}(S \le s, A) = P_{MA}(M \le m, M \le 5) = P_M(M \le 5) = P(M \le 5)$, from which we determine that $P_{M|A}(M \le m|A) = 1$. This is illustrated in Figure 3.16.

Quiz 3.17   Determine the conditional probability density, $p_{M|A}(m|A)$ for the above example.

Suppose the probability of the event A in Definitions 3.16 and 3.17 goes to zero. In the last example this occurs if we replace the event {M ≤ 5} by {M ≤ 0}. Consequently, the conditional cumulative probability distribution is undefined. This situation leads us to consider a definition for the conditional probability density function. Suppose we have a special case of an event defined over a segment of the real line that extends from y to y + Δy and that Δy approaches zero, then P(A) in Definition 3.16 can be replaced by $p_Y(y)\Delta y$ as Δy goes to zero and similarly for the cumulative probability distribution functions. Under these conditions the Δy and Δx on both sides of the equation will cancel and we obtain the following result. However, we make this result a definition to give it the same significance as our previous definitions.

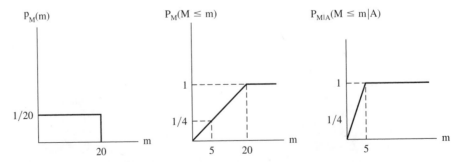

Figure 3.16   The various probability density and distribution functions for Example 3.27

Definition 3.18. The **conditional probability density function** is defined as

$$p_{X|Y}(x\,|\,y) = \frac{p_{XY}(x,y)}{p_Y(y)} \quad \text{and} \quad p_{Y|X}(y\,|\,x) = \frac{p_{XY}(x,\,y)}{p_X(x)} \qquad [3.9.3]$$

where we assume marginal probability densities $p_X(x)$ and $p_Y(y)$ are not zero. The conditional probability density function $p_{X|Y}(x\,|\,y)$ is read as the probability of x given that $Y = y$. Note that upon integrating both sides of [3.9.3] with respect to x or y, we have

$$\int_{-\infty}^{\infty} p_{X|Y}(x\,|\,y)dx = \frac{\int_{-\infty}^{\infty} p_{XY}(x,\,y)dx}{p_Y(y)} = 1 \quad \text{and} \quad \int_{-\infty}^{\infty} p_{Y|X}(y\,|\,x)dy = \frac{\int_{-\infty}^{\infty} p_{XY}(x,\,y)dy}{p_X(x)} = 1$$

Definition 3.19. The **conditional cumulative probability distribution function** for the random variable $X \leq x$ subject to the assumption that the random variable $Y = y$ is

$$P_{X|Y}(X \leq x\,|\,y) = \int_{-\infty}^{x} p_{X|Y}(s\,|\,y)ds \qquad [3.9.4]$$

Similarly, we define

$$P_{Y|X}(Y \leq y\,|\,x) = \int_{-\infty}^{y} p_{Y|X}(t\,|\,x)dt \qquad [3.9.5]$$

Example 3.28

The rainfall at a local airport for the month of July was recently measured over a section of land that extended from two to four miles along a runway. The joint probability density function for inches of rain and distance in miles was found to be approximated as follows:

$$p_{XY}(x, y) = \frac{1}{8}(6 - x - y)[u(x) - u(x - 2)][u(y - 2) - u(y - 4)]$$

where the random variable X is the amount of rainfall in inches and the random variable Y is the distance in miles. A sketch of this probability density function appears in Figure 3.17.

Find (1) the cumulative probability distribution function, (2) the probability that the amount of rainfall is greater than or equal to zero and less than or equal to unity for the distance in miles greater than or equal to three and less than or equal to four, (3) the marginal probability density and the cumulative probability distribution for x, (4) the conditional probability density for y given x, and (5) the conditional cumulative probability distribution that $x < 1$ given that $y < 3$.

Our solution proceeds as follows. For part (1) we have

$$P_{XY}(x, y) = \int_{-\infty}^{x}\int_{-\infty}^{y} p_{XY}(s, t)\, dt\, ds = \frac{1}{8}\int_0^x\int_2^y (6 - s - t)\, dt\, ds$$

$$= \frac{x}{16}(y - 2)(10 - x - y)[u(x) - u(x - 2)][u(y - 2) - u(y - 4)]$$

As a check we note that $P_{XY}(x,y) = 0$ for $x < 0$ and $y < 2$ and $P_{XY}(x,y) = 1$ for $x > 2$ and $y > 4$. Next, we have for part (2) that

$$P_{XY}(0 \leq X \leq 1, 3 \leq Y \leq 4) = \int_0^1\int_3^4 p_{XY}(s, t)\, dt\, ds = 1/4$$

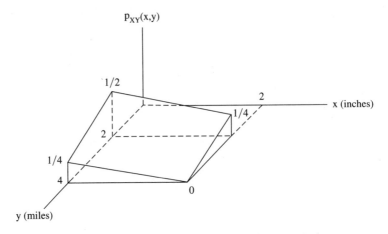

Figure 3.17   The joint probability density function for Example 3.28

For part (3) we find

$$p_X(x) = \int_{-\infty}^{\infty} p_{XY}(x, y)\, dy = \frac{1}{4}(3 - x)[u(x) - u(x - 2)]$$

As a check we see that the integral of $p_X(x)$ from 0 to 2 is unity. The cumulative probability distribution for part (4) is

$$P_X(X \le x) = P_X(x) = \int_{-\infty}^{x} p_X(s)\, ds = \frac{1}{8}x(6 - x)[u(x) - u(x - 2)]$$

which is zero for $x < 0$ and unity for $x > 2$. Next we find that

$$p_{Y|x}(y\,|\,x) = \frac{p_{XY}(x, y)}{p_X(x)} = \frac{1}{2}\frac{(6 - x - y)}{(3 - x)}[u(x) - u(x - 2)][u(y - 2) - u(y - 4)]$$

Finally, for part (5) we find that

$$P_{X|Y}(X < 1\,|\,Y < 3) = \frac{P_{XY}(X < 1, Y < 3)}{P_Y(Y < 3)}$$

$$P_{XY}(X < 1, Y < 3) = \frac{1}{8}\int_0^1 \int_2^3 (6 - s - t)\, dt\, ds = \frac{3}{8}$$

$$p_Y(y) = \int_{-\infty}^{\infty} p_{XY}(s, y)\, ds = \frac{1}{4}(5 - y)[u(y - 2) - u(y - 4)]$$

$$P_Y(Y < 3) = \int_2^3 p_Y(t)\, dt = \frac{5}{8}$$

$$P_{X|Y}(X < 1\,|\,Y < 3) = \frac{3/8}{5/8} = \frac{3}{5}$$

Quiz 3.18   Find the conditional probability density $p_{X|Y}(x\,|\,y)$ for the above example.

3.10   STATISTICAL INDEPENDENCE

Definition 3.20. Statistical independence for two joint random variables, X and Y, is defined in terms of the probability density function as follows. Two random variables are statistically independent if and only if

$$p_{XY}(x, y) = p_X(x)p_Y(y)$$ **[3.10.1]**

for all x and y. From this definition it follows that

$$p_{X|Y}(x|y) = p_X(x) \text{ and } p_{Y|X}(y|x) = p_Y(y)$$ **[3.10.2]**

In words, [3.10.1] says that if the joint probability density is separable into the product of the two marginal probability densities, then X and Y are statistically independent. Equation [3.10.2] may be interpreted as saying that the conditional probability density is equal to the marginal probability density, which in turn means that the two random variables are statistically independent of one another. We will often omit the word *statistically* for convenience. Furthermore, Definition 3.20 may be extended to more than two random variables, in which case we say that the random variables are **mutually independent.**

Another consequence of Definition 3.20 is that the cumulative probability distribution function for two independent random variables is

$$P_{XY}(X \le x, Y \le y) = P_X(X \le x)P_Y(Y \le y)$$ **[3.10.3]**

for all x and y. Furthermore, we have from [3.9.2] that

$$P_{X|Y}(X \le x | Y = y) = P_X(X \le x)$$ **[3.10.4]**

$$\text{and } P_{Y|X}(Y \le y | X = x) = P_Y(Y \le y)$$

One example of two statistically independent random variables is given in Example 3.21, which described the joint uniform probability density function.

Consider the joint probability density function for the two random variables X and Y given by   **Example 3.29**

$$p_{XY}(x, y) = ce^{-(ax + by)} \text{ where } x, y \ge 0 \text{ and } a, b, c > 0$$

The two random variables are statistically independent because we may write $p_{XY}(x, y)$ as the product of the two marginal probability densities as follows:

$$p_{XY}(x, y) = \{\sqrt{c}e^{-ax}\}\{\sqrt{c}e^{-by}\}$$

Quiz 3.19   Determine the constants (a, b, c) for the above example.

3.11   VECTOR RANDOM VARIABLES

We will find it convenient in later chapters to represent data in the form of a vector or a matrix. Such examples occur frequently in communications, digital signal processing, and image processing. Consequently, we introduce here the concept of a vector of random variables. If we have two random variables, $X_1(s)$ and $X_2(s)$, defined on a sample space, then specific values of $X_1(s)$ and $X_2(s)$, denoted as x_1 and x_2, respectively, may be considered as a random point in the (x'_1, x'_2) plane. Such a point may be considered a specific value of a **random vector** or of a **vector random variable.** We may illustrate the concept of generating a random vector in a manner similar to that used in Figure 3.1. Figure 3.18 shows that two experimental outcomes may be mapped via two random variables to the real plane, thereby, generating a random vector with respect to the origin. The random variable may also map events (or sets of experimental outcomes) to the real plane. Another way of generating a random vector is to use a single random variable, $X(s)$. Then we may form the elements of a random vector by assigning the value of the random variable for the first experimental outcome to one element of the random vector. Then another experiment is performed and the value of the random variable for that experimental outcome is assigned to the next component of the random vector, and so on. In this way we may form a random vector as $(X(s_1),X(s_2),. . . ,X(s_n))$. Note, however, that the components of the vector need not be generated in sequence, for instance, we may have $X(s_j)$ as the first component of the random vector if so desired.

> **Definition 3.21.** A **random vector** consists of a set or grouping of random variables that are considered as a single entity. We shall assume that the random vector has a defined probability distribution function and a defined probability density function such that if we denote the random vector as a column vector such that

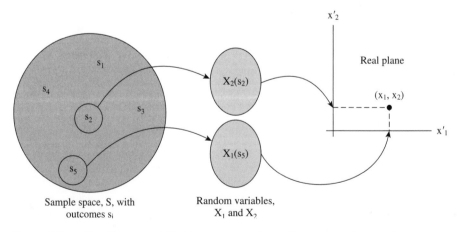

Figure 3.18   Two random variables mapping experimental outcomes to the real plane

$$\vec{X} = (X_1, X_2, \ldots, X_n)^T \qquad\qquad \text{[3.11.1]}$$

$$\vec{x} = (x_1, x_2, \ldots, x_n)^T \qquad\qquad \text{[3.11.2]}$$

and we further denote that a vector random variable is less than or equal to a specific vector as the following

$$(\vec{X} \leq \vec{x}) = (X_1 \leq x_1, X_2 \leq x_2, \ldots, X_n \leq x_n)^T \qquad\qquad \text{[3.11.3]}$$

Then we may write the cumulative probability distribution function as

$$P_{\vec{X}}(\vec{X} \leq \vec{x}) \qquad\qquad \text{[3.11.4]}$$

which may also be expressed in terms of the probability density function as

$$P_{\vec{X}}(\vec{X} \leq \vec{x}) = \int_{-\infty}^{x_n}\int_{-\infty}^{x_{n-1}} \cdots \int_{-\infty}^{x_1} p_{\vec{X}}(\vec{t})\, dt_1\, dt_2 \ldots dt_n = \int_{-\infty}^{\vec{x}} p_{\vec{X}}(\vec{t})\,d\vec{t} \quad \text{[3.11.5]}$$

The previous definitions for conditional, joint, and marginal probability distribution and density functions may be extended to random vectors as well. Note that the elements or components of a random vector may each be statistically independent, in which case we say that they are mutually independent. Similarly we may have random vectors that are each statistically independent, in which case we say that they are mutually independent.

A coin is flipped twice and the outcomes are observed. We form a random vector as follows: The first element of the random vector is generated from the outcome of the first toss such that if a head occurs, then the element is a one, while if a tail occurs then the element is a zero; that is, from the first toss of the coin we may have $X_1(H) = 1$ or $X_1(T) = 0$. Similarly, for the second toss of the coin we form the second element, that is, from the second toss we may have $X_2(H) = 1$ or $X_2(T) = 0$. Thus, we may generate four possible vectors, namely, $(0,0)^T$, $(1,0)^T$, $(0,1)^T$, $(1,1)^T$. All vectors are equally likely to occur with probability of 1/4. Note that this is similar to the joint probability of two outcomes (or events). If we have the vector $(0,0)^T$, are the elements independent? Yes, since we assume that the tosses of the coin are independent. We may also show that $P_{X1X2}(X_1 = 0, X_2 = 0) = P_{X1}(X_1 = 0)P_{X2}(X_2 = 0)$.

Example 3.30

An experiment consists of flipping a coin. The experiment is performed twice and the outcomes are observed. Let the sample space be that for both experiments. If at least one head occurs, then generate the first component of a random vector by mapping the event to a 1; that is, X_1 (at least 1 head) = 1. If at least one tail occurs, then the second component of the vector is formed in a similar manner by mapping that event to a zero; that is, X_2(at least 1 tail) = 0. There are several observations we may make about this example: $X_1 = 1$ if HH, HT, or TH occurs; similarly $X_2 = 0$ if TH, HT, or TT occurs. However, if HH occurs, then X_2 is undefined, and similarly if TT occurs, then X_1 is undefined. The only vector that is defined is $(1, 0)^T$. The probability that this vector occurs is 1/2, since it may be generated in two ways, either with the occurrence of HT or TH. If we have the vector $(1,0)^T$, are the two elements independent? To answer this we must find $P_{X1}(X_1 = 1)$, which is 3/4, and similarly $P_{X2}(X_2 = 0) = 3/4$, which means that $P_{X1}(X_1 = 1)P_{X2}(X_2 = 0) = 9/16 \neq P_{X1X2}(X_1 = 1, X_2 = 0) = 1/2$. Thus, the components of the vector are not independent. Another way of seeing this is to observe that if we

Example 3.31

have the vector $(1,0)^T$ and we consider one component as given, then we know the other component with certainty, since only this vector is possible.

Example 3.32 | A die is rolled twice and the outcomes are observed. We form a random vector by forming the first element from the outcome of the first roll, and the second element is formed from the outcome of the second roll. Let E_1 denote the event that the outcome is an even face on the first roll, and O_1 denote the event that the outcome is an odd face on the first roll. We have similar events for the second roll. We form the first element of the random vector as follows: $X_1(E_1) = 0$ or $X_1(O_1) = 1$, and similarly the second element is formed from the second roll as $X_2(E_2) = 0$ or $X_2(O_2) = 1$. What is the probability of the vector $(1,0)^T$ occurring? This can happen if an odd face occurs on the first roll and an even face occurs on the second roll, which is $(1/2)(1/2) = 1/4$.

Quiz 3.20   Are the elements of the above vector $(1,0)^T$ independent?

Quiz 3.21   Two dice are rolled and the sum of the faces of the outcomes is observed. We form the first element of a random vector by mapping the sum greater than or equal to 5 to zero. The second element is formed by mapping the sum of the faces less than or equal to 8 to one. What vectors are defined? Determine their probability of occurrence. If the vector $(0,1)^T$ is formed are the elements independent?

Example 3.33 | Let the position of a fly inside a circle of unity radius centered at the origin be given by the random vector

$$\vec{X} = (x, y)^T$$

Assume that the fly is equally likely to be anywhere within the circle at the time of observation. What is the probability that the fly is in the region inside a circle of radius 1/2? First we need to determine the probability density function, which is

$$p_{\vec{X}}(\vec{x}) = \frac{1}{\pi}, \text{ for } [x^2 + y^2]^{\frac{1}{2}} < 1$$

$$= 0, \text{ otherwise}$$

The probability we seek is found as follows:

$$I = \int_{-R}^{R}\int_{-\sqrt{R^2-x^2}}^{\sqrt{R^2-x^2}} p_{\vec{X}}(\vec{x}) \, dy \, dx = R^2$$

When $R = 1/2$, then $I = 1/4$.
Of course, for this problem we could have found the probability by simply forming the ratio of the areas of the two circles. The same solution can be obtained using polar coordinates. However, we wanted to illustrate a more general procedure.

3.12   MATLAB EXAMPLES

The purpose of introducing computer-based examples and problems is to expand our armamentarium so that we may solve problems that might be too tedious to do via hand calculations. Furthermore, as noted previously, MATLAB has plotting capabilities that can greatly assist the visualization of data. We include MATLAB examples and problems in each chapter.

Example 3.34

In this example we calculate the histogram for a random number generator. MATLAB has a function called *rand* that returns a scalar whose value changes each time *rand* is called. The function *rand* generates random numbers that are uniformly distributed in the interval [0,1] using a special algorithm. We will discuss random number generation in a later chapter. For the present, however, consider the algorithm to be a procedure that selects a number from a table in a random manner. To construct a histogram for the random numbers generated by *rand* we write a script that calls *rand* repeatedly. Since we can do this only a finite number of times, we quantize the range of the random numbers in increments of 0.1. We then calculate the number of times a random number falls in each quantized interval, divide by the total number of numbers generated for the example, and calculate the resulting histogram. The MATLAB script for this example is given in Figure 3.19 and the plot of the histogram is shown in Figure 3.20, where the total number of values generated is 10,000. The execution of the script in Figure 3.19 is slow because of the *for* loop. A faster implementation is given in the next example. Note that we use the function *hist* in MATLAB to generate the y values for a graph. However, before plotting the bar graph, we normalize the y values by the total number of values. This ratio is the frequency ratio we described in Chapter 2, and the bar graph is the histogram.

Example 3.35

In this example we compute the histogram for the amplitude of a sine function with a random phase angle. Let $Y = a \sin\Theta$, where a is any nonzero number and Θ is a random variable that is uniformly distributed from $-\pi/2$ to $\pi/2$; that is, $p_\Theta(\theta) = 1/\pi$ for Θ ranging from $-\pi/2$ to $\pi/2$. We will show in the next chapter that a function of a random variable is also a random variable; consequently, Y is a random variable. We are to calculate the histogram for $p_Y(y)$. Our task is to use the random number generator in MATLAB to provide a random phase for the specified interval. We do this as follows. First shift the interval of the random numbers provided by *rand* by

---

```
N=10,000;                          % do N times
x=zeros (1,N);                     % allocate storage
x=rand(1,N);                       % get N random numbers
bins=[0.05:0.1:0.95];              % create 10 bins, centers at 0.05,
                                   % 0.15, . . .
[yvalues,xvalues]=hist(x,bins);    % define xvalues and yvalues
yvalues=yvalues/N;                 % divide by N
bar(xvalues,yvalues);              % plot bar graph
```

Figure 3.19   MATLAB script for Example 3.34

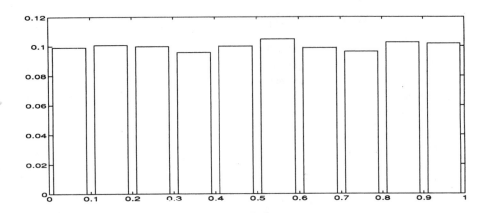

Figure 3.20   Histogram for Example 3.34

```
N = 100000;                          % do N times
theta = rand(1,N);                   % faster than generating N rands
theta = theta – 0.5;                 % shift
theta = theta*pi;                    % scale
theta = 100*theta;                   % these 3 steps quantize to 0.01
theta = round(theta);
theta = theta/100;
a = 10;                              % a can be any nonzero number
y = a*sin(theta);                    % find y
bins = a*[ − 0.995:0.01:0.995];      % bins with centers at 0.005,. . .
                                     % steps of 0.1 for a since a = 10
[yvalues,xvalues] = hist(y,bins);    % compute histogram
yvalues = yvalues/N;                 % normalize to N
bar(xvalues,yvalues);                % graph
```

Figure 3.21   MATLAB script for Example 3.35

subtracting 1/2 from each number generated. Then multiply the shifted numbers by π. Both shifting and scaling a random variable are examples of a function of a random variable. We can show that these operations do not change the basic probability density function for the resulting random variable. Consequently, the random numbers generated by *rand* that are shifted by 1/2 and scaled by π are uniformly distributed from $-\pi/2$ to $\pi/2$. We calculate the random variable Y for each random phase angle. Since we can only generate a finite number of phase angles, we quantize the phase Θ to intervals of 0.01, which in turn means that Y will be quantized. The MATLAB script for this problem is given in Figure 3.21. In Figure 3.22 the histogram obtained for 100,000 random phase angles is shown.

Note from Figure 3.22 that the probability for y's being near $\pm a$ (± 10) is considerably larger than for y's being any other value. This is reasonable since the derivative of $\sin\Theta$ is zero for $\Theta = \pm \pi/2$. Thus, the change in $\sin\Theta$ occurs slowly for Θ near $\pm \pi/2$, which in turn means

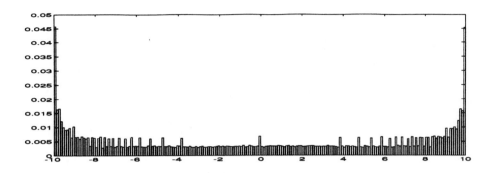

Figure 3.22   Histogram for Example 3.35

that the probability for y's being near the peak value is greater than any other value. We will discuss this problem again from a theoretical view point in the next chapter.

_____

This is an example of generating a sequence of Bernoulli trials using the random number generator *rand*. The reader can implement this MATLAB m file and experiment with variations in n and p (see Figure 3.23). One modification would be to plot the sequence. | **Example 3.36**

```
%bernou.m
%Bernoulli sequence
n = input('Enter the number of trials, n ')
p = input('Enter the probability of success for each trial, p ')
O = rand(n,1) <= p;        % generate ones for random numbers <= p
R = sum(O)/n;              % fraction of ones or relative frequency of ones
N = [1:n]';                % show results
disp(['n = ', num2str(n), '   p = ', num2str(p),])
disp(['R = ', num2str(R),])
SEQ = [N O];
disp([SEQ])
 > > bernou

Enter the number or trials, n 20
n =
    20
Enter the probability of success for each trial, p .8
p =
    0.8000
```

Figure 3.23   MATLAB program to generate a sequence of Bernoulli trials

n = 20   p = 0.8
R = 0.9

1	1
2	1
3	1
4	1
5	1
6	1
7	0
8	1
9	1
10	1
11	1
12	1
13	1
14	1
15	0
16	1
17	1
18	1
19	1
20	1

Figure 3.23 (continued)   MATLAB program to generate
a sequence of Bernoulli trials

3.13   SUMMARY

This chapter has introduced several new concepts. The most important of which is the definition of discrete, continuous, and mixed **random variables.** We then defined **probability density and distribution functions** for both discrete and continuous random variables, as well as the **cumulative probability distribution function.** The concept of **mixed random variables** was then defined along with the probability density and cumulative probability distribution functions. We pointed out that the probability density function could be used to represent discrete, continuous, and mixed random variables, thereby obviating the need for the probability distribution function for discrete random variables. Thus, we need only the probability density and cumulative probability distribution functions to represent discrete, continuous, and mixed random variables. Definitions were then given for the **joint probability density and cumulative probability distribution functions** for two random variables, where the random variables may be discrete, continuous or mixed. The concepts of **conditional probability density functions** and **statistical independence** were defined for two random variables. We showed that a **random vector** is a natural extension to multidimensions of a single dimensional random variable. We concluded the chapter by introducing MATLAB as a software tool that can be used to assist us in the solution of problems. All of the definitions will be used along with MATLAB and other concepts that will be introduced in the following chapters to solve design and analysis problems.

PROBLEMS

3.1   Consider the interval a $\leq$ x $\leq$ b and suppose that it is equally probable that any point can be picked in this interval. Then the probability density function is $f_X(x) = p_X(x) = \frac{1}{b-a}$, a $\leq$ x $\leq$ b; p(x) = 0 otherwise. What is the cumulative probability distribution function?

3.2   A random variable has the following exponential probability density function

$$f_X(x) = p_X(x) = a^{-bx}, x \geq 0$$

$$= 0, \text{ otherwise}$$

where a and b are constants.

a. Determine the required relation between a and b.

b. Determine the cumulative probability distribution function $P_X(X \geq x_0)$.

3.3   Given the probability distribution function $P_X(X = x) = \frac{a}{x!}$, x = 0,1,2, . . . and $P_X(X = x) = 0$, otherwise.

a. Determine the constant a.

b. What is the probability that X = 2?

c. What is the probability that X < 2?

3.4   Five cards are drawn from a deck. Let X be the random variable that denotes the number of queens and Y the random variable that denotes the number of kings drawn. Find an expression for $P_{XY}(x,y)$, the joint probability distribution function for obtaining x queens and y kings.

3.5   A digital voltmeter that provides an output reading of 0,1,2, . . . , or 9 is erratic (behaves in a random manner). The voltmeter is monitored 10 times. Let X denote the number of 1s and Y the number of 3s that are observed. Find an expression for the joint probability density $p_{XY}(x,y)$ for observing x 1s and y 3s. Plot this function. What is the *probability* that more 3s are observed than 1s? What is the probability density function for observing x 1s, no matter what y is? Are X and Y independent random variables? What is $p_{X|Y}(x \mid y)$?

3.6   Find and plot the cumulative probability distribution function $F_X(x) = P_X(X \leq x)$ if the probability density function is

a. $f_X(x) = p_X(x) = 1, 0 \leq x \leq 1$.

b. $f_X(x) = p_X(x) = x$ for $0 \leq x \leq 1$ and $p_X(x) = -x + 2$ for $1 < x \leq 2$.

3.7   If a joint probability density function is $p_{XY}(x,y) = xye^{-(x+y)}$ for $x \geq 0, y \geq 0$, what is the probability that jointly X < 1 and Y < 1? What is $p_{X|Y}(x \mid y)$?

3.8   A possible outcome of an experiment is the event A. The probability of this event is p. The experiment is performed n times, the outcome of any trial is not affected by the results of the previous trials. Define a random variable X to be the number of times the event A occurs in n trials. What is the probability distribution function $P_X(X = x)$? Show that

$$\sum_{x=-\infty}^{\infty} P_X(x) = 1$$

What is the name of this probability distribution function?

3.9   Under the conditions of Problem 3.8, let the trials continue until the event A has occurred for the first time. Define a random variable X to be the number of trials that occur until the experiment ends. Find the probability distribution function $P_X(X = x)$. Show that

$$\sum_{x=-\infty}^{\infty} P_X(x) = 1$$

What is the name of this probability distribution function?

3.10   Consider Example 3.23 again. For this problem replace the first ball before the second is withdrawn. Find the joint probability density function and the marginal probability density functions for x and y. Are the random variables independent? Determine the conditional probability density functions for x and y.

3.11   In Example 3.23 we found the joint and marginal probability density functions. Are the random variables independent? Determine the conditional probability density functions for x and y.

3.12   Is $f_X(x) = p_X(x) = ce^{-a|x|}$, $a > 0$ a valid probability density function? If so, then determine the relation between a and c. Determine the cumulative probability distribution function, $F_X(x) = P_X(X \le x)$. Plot $f_X(x)$ and $F_X(x)$ for $c = 1$.

3.13   Suppose X and Y are two discrete random variables each having two equally likely values, 0 and 1. Determine the joint probability density function for X and Y.

3.14   Imagine an audio amplifier contains six transistors. Harry has determined that two transistors are defective, but he does not know which two. Harry removes three transistors at random and inspects them. Let X be the number of defective transistors that Harry finds, where X may be 0, 1, or 2. Find the probability distribution for X. Plot a histogram for the results. Repeat the problem but find the probability density function for X and plot the function. Compare the histogram and the probability density function.

3.15   From past experience Jane has determined that she has a probability of 1/3 of catching a fish before the lure she uses must be replaced. She never uses the same lure to catch more than one fish. One day she is fishing and sees that she has three lures. Let X be the number of fish she catches before she exhausts the lures she has. Find the probability density function for X. What is the *probability* she will catch more than one fish?

3.16   A software manufacturer knows that 1 out of 10 software games that the company markets will be a financial success. The manufacturer selects 10 new games to market. What is the probability that exactly one game will be a financial success? What is the probability that at least two games will be a success?

3.17 For Example 3.24 determine if the joint random variables are independent. Find the conditional probability density functions.

3.18 As we saw in this chapter, we may model the arrival of telephone calls with a Poisson probability density function. Suppose that the average rate of calls is 10 per minute. What is the probability that less than three calls will be received in the first six seconds? in the first six minutes?

3.19 Roll a die once and observe the outcome. Define the events A = {1, 2, 3, 4, 5} and B = {3, 4, 5, 6}, where the numbers denote the possible outcomes. Form the random vector $(X_1(A) = 0, X_2(B) = 1)^T$. What is the probability of the vector $(0,1)^T$ occurring? Are the elements of the vector independent?

3.20 Suppose we flip a coin three times, thereby forming a sequence of heads and tails. Form a random vector by mapping each outcome in the sequence to 0 if a head occurs or 1 if a tail occurs. How many vectors may be generated? List them. Are the vectors independent of one another?

3.21 The voltage of communication signal S is measured. However, the measurement procedure is subject to error. Find the probability that for any particular measurement, the error will exceed ± 0.75 percent of the correct value if this value is 10 volts. The probability density function, $f_S(s)$, of the measurements is

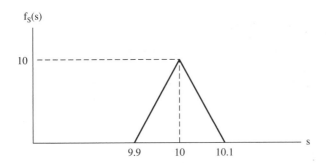

3.22 Determine the marginal probability density functions for Example 3.26.

3.23 The traffic managers of toll roads and toll bridges need specific information to properly staff the toll booths so that the queues are minimized (i.e., the waiting time is minimized).

   a. Assume that there is one toll booth on a busy interstate highway and that the number of cars per minute approaching the toll booth follows a Poisson probability distribution with $\alpha = 10$. The traffic manager wants you to determine the probability that exactly 11 cars approach this toll booth in the minute from noon to one minute past noon.

   b. Now assume that there are N toll booths at this location and that the number of cars per minute approaching each toll booth follows the same Poisson probability distribution with $\alpha = 30$. The traffic manager wants you to calculate the number of toll booths that need to be staffed if the probability is not to exceed 0.05 that no more than five cars approach each toll booth in one minute.

MATLAB PROBLEMS

3.1M Plot the cumulative probability distribution function calculated in Example 3.26. To give a smooth surface, let the y interval be 1 and the x interval be 0.2.

3.2M MATLAB has a Gaussian random number generator *randn* that is similar to *rand*. Determine a histogram for *randn* in a manner similar to that used for *rand* in Example 3.34. However, in this problem the range for the random variable could be quite large. Therefore, use quantization intervals of 0.1. Compare the histogram with the shape of the Gaussian probability density plotted in the text.

3.3M For the Gaussian probability density function plot $f_X(x)$ for $\mu_X = -2, 0, 2$. For each value of μ_X let $\sigma_X = 1/2, 1, 2, 4$. Let x take the following steps: $-\infty$ to -10, then go from -10 to $+10$ in steps of 0.2, then from $+10$ to ∞. Discuss the significance of μ_X and σ_X. Remember that the integral of $p_X(x)$ from $-\infty$ to ∞ is 1, regardless of the values of μ_X and σ_X, provided σ_X is not zero. Calculate and plot the cumulative probability distribution versus x for $\mu_X = 0$, and $\sigma_X = 1/2, 1, 2, 4$. Use the same step sizes as specified above. Use the same scales for the axes for each plot.

3.4M Data file P3_4M.d is part of the software that accompanies this book. This file is a sampled speech signal, namely, a sustained vowel /i/, as pronounced in the word b*ee*t. The data are sampled at 10 kHz. Determine the histogram for the amplitude of the signal. Use a step size of 100 for the data with bins ranging from $-15,000$ to $15,000$. Also determine the histogram of the time interval between the major peaks of the signal. The interval between the peaks is called the pitch period, and the reciprocal of the interval is the pitch, or the fundamental frequency of voicing. The random variation in the pitch period (or pitch) is called jitter. An adult male speaker, typically, has a pitch that falls in the range of 80 to 200 Hz with an average value of 125 Hz, while an adult female speaker has a pitch in the range 150 to 350 Hz, with an average value of 300 Hz. Determine if the speaker for the data provided is a male or female.

3.5M The data record P3_5M.d is part of the software that accompanies this book. This file is a sampled record of a noise voltage. The sampling frequency is 10 kHz. Determine the amplitude histogram for this data. Use the same step size and number of bins as for Problem 3.4M. What probability density function is a good model for this data?

3.6M Write a MATLAB function to calculate the binomial probabilities

$$P_X(r) = \binom{n}{r} p^r (1 - p)^{n-r}$$

You should consider if $p > 0.5$.

3.7M Modify the MATLAB program in Problem 3.6M to calculate the cumulative probability distribution.

3.8M Write a MATLAB function to calculate the Poisson probabilities

$$P_X(r) = \frac{\alpha^r}{r!} e^{-\alpha}$$

3.9M Modify the MATLAB program in Problem 3.8M to calculate the cumulative probability distribution.

3.10M Write a MATLAB program to calculate the probability $P_X(x_1 \leq X \leq x_2)$ for the Gaussian probability density function for arbitrary x_1 and x_2.

3.11M In Example 3.36 conduct the following experiment. Vary the number of trials from 1 to 50, keeping track of the relative frequency of the Bernoulli trials. Then plot the relative frequency versus the number of trials. Discuss the results.

3.12M Consider an urn that contains three balls numbered 1, 2, and 3. Select a ball from the urn and record its number. Replace the ball and shake the urn and withdraw another ball and record its number. Repeat this process many times. Define the outcome of each draw as the number of the ball chosen. Define the relative frequency of each ball as the number of times the number of the ball (1, 2, or 3) is selected in n trials, such as, N(i)/n, where N(i), i = 1, 2, 3 is the number of times that ball number i occurs in n trials. Simulate this experiment using *rand* in MATLAB. Vary the number of trials from 1 to 50, keeping track of the relative frequency of the three ball numbers. Then plot the relative frequency versus the number of trials. Discuss the results.

3.13M Implement Example 3.28 in MATLAB so that you can calculate the probability $P_{XY}(x_1 \leq X \leq x_2, y_1 \leq Y \leq y_2)$ for any x_i and y_i, i = 1, 2. You may have to consider several ranges of values for x_i and y_i, i = 1, 2.

chapter

4

Expectation (Averages)

4.1 INTRODUCTION

The theory of **expectation** of a random variable is of considerable importance, since it defines an average, as well as the mean square value and other expected values of a random variable. These expected values often represent important features, characteristics, or attributes of a random variable. Perhaps one of the most widely known averages is the mean value or expected value. We introduce this concept with the following example.

Example 4.1 Consider a sequence of PCM pulses, as discussed at the end of Chapter 2. The voltage level of each pulse is either zero or one with equal probability. Assume the pulses are mutually independent. Let the random variable be X, the voltage level observed after each pulse occurs. Then X = 0 or 1 with equal probability. Suppose 10^6 successive pulses are observed. Intuitively, we would expect to observe approximately $(0.5)\,10^6$ PCM zeros and $(0.5)\,10^6$ PCM ones. Assuming this to be the case, then the average value of X (i.e., the dc voltage level) would be

$$\frac{\sum_{\text{two voltage levels}} (\text{Number of measurements at each voltage level}) \times (\text{Voltage level})}{\text{Total number of measurements}}$$

$$= \frac{(0.5)\,10^6(0) + (0.5)\,10^6(1)}{10^6} = \frac{1}{2}$$

Thus, the average value is the anticipated (or expected) dc voltage level of 1/2 volt.

Definition 4.1. Let X be a random variable with probability density function $f_X(x) = p_X(x)$. Then we define the **expected value** of X to be E[X], that is:

$$E[X] = \int_{-\infty}^{\infty} x\, p_X(x)\, dx = \int_{-\infty}^{\infty} x\, f_X(x)\, dx = \mu_X \qquad [4.1.1]$$

where X may be any random variable with a well-defined probability density function.

The expected value is defined provided the integral is absolutely convergent. We will use this definition for **discrete, continuous,** and **mixed random variables.** The expected value is the **average** of the random variable weighted by the probability density function for the entire range of values of the random variable. The symbol μ_X is also used to denote the average or expected value. Since the probability density function describes the relative frequency of occurrence of each value of the random variable, then [4.1.1] may also be considered to be the **mean value** or **statistical average** of the random variable. Yet another view point is from mechanics. If we think of $p_X(x)$ as a mass distributed along the x axis, then [4.1.1] calculates the **centroid,** or the **center of gravity** of the mass, which is also known as the **first moment about the origin.** We will discuss this more fully below. In summary, several interchangeable names are given to the expected value of a random variable. These include average, statistical average, mean, centroid, center of gravity, first moment about the origin, and, of course, expected value. Throughout this chapter, when we denote the expected value of a random variable, we will generally use square brackets, such as [ ], to demarcate the random variable. There are a few exceptions to this notation, namely, for vector random variables and matrices of random variables. However, the random variable will be clear in these situations. In the following chapters we may on occasion use other brackets to demarcate the random variable, but this too will be clear. In this chapter we will use the *p* notation for the probability density function.

Example 4.2

The geometric random variable was given in Chapter 3 and is the number of trials, X, until an experiment ends. The experiment was defined as follows. A successful outcome is the event A, which occurs with probability p. The experiment is repeated until the event A occurs (i.e., until a success occurs). Thus, we have r − 1 trials followed by 1 trial, where on the last trial the event A occurs. Since r is greater than or equal to unity, the probability density function is the following:

$$p_X(x) = \sum_{r=1}^{\infty} (1-p)^{x-1} p\, \delta(x-r) = \sum_{r=1}^{\infty} (1-p)^{r-1} p\, \delta(x-r) \qquad [4.1.2]$$

Then the expected value of the random variable is

$$E[X] = \int_{-\infty}^{\infty} x\, p_X(x)\, dx = \sum_{r=1}^{\infty} \int_{-\infty}^{\infty} x(1-p)^{x-1} p\, \delta(x-r)\, dx \qquad [4.1.3]$$

$$= \sum_{r=1}^{\infty} r(1-p)^{r-1} p = p \sum_{r=1}^{\infty} r(1-p)^{r-1} = p \cdot \frac{1}{p^2} = \frac{1}{p}$$

Note, to arrive at the above result, we interchanged the order of integration and summation. This is allowed provided the summation of the terms in the series converges uniformly on the closed interval containing the limits of integration.

For this example the mean of the random variable is the reciprocal of the probability of success. This says that on the average the number of trials before a success occurs is the reciprocal of the probability of success. This is not true for other random variables, as we shall soon see.

Quiz 4.1   Show that

$$\sum_{r=1}^{\infty} r\,(1-p)^{r-1} = \frac{1}{p^2}$$

Example 4.3 | For Bernoulli trials find the expected value of exactly $X = r$ successes. The probability density function is the binomial probability density, which is

$$p_X(x) = \sum_{r=0}^{n} \binom{n}{x}\, p^x q^{n-x}\, \delta(x-r) = \sum_{r=0}^{n} \binom{n}{r}\, p^r q^{n-r}\, \delta(x-r) \qquad \textbf{[4.1.4]}$$

where n is the number of trials performed, r is the number of successes in n trials, and p is the probability of success. A success occurs with probability p, and a failure occurs with probability $q = 1 - p$. The expected value is calculated as follows:

$$E[X] = \int_{-\infty}^{\infty} x\, p_X(x)\, dx = \sum_{r=0}^{n} \int_{-\infty}^{\infty} x\, \binom{n}{x} p^x q^{n-x} \delta(x-r)\, dx \qquad \textbf{[4.1.5]}$$

$$= \sum_{r=0}^{n} r\binom{n}{r} p^r q^{n-r} = np$$

This says that the mean value is n times the probability p of success. The average number of successful trials that occur within n trials is np, or on the average, if n trails are performed, then the average number of successes is expected to be np.

Quiz 4.2   Show how the result of [4.1.5] is derived. Hint: Rewrite the factorial inside the summation in the form $\binom{n\,-\,1}{r\,-\,1}$. Change the limits of summation appropriately. Then use the identity about the summation of the binomial distribution from Chapter 3.

Example 4.4 | Find the mean value for the Poisson random variable, with the probability density function given as

$$p_X(x) = \sum_{r=0}^{\infty} \frac{\alpha^x}{x!} e^{-\alpha} \delta(x-r) \qquad \textbf{[4.1.6]}$$

The mean is calculated as follows:

$$E[X] = \int_{-\infty}^{\infty} x\, p_X(x)\, dx = \sum_{r=0}^{\infty} \int_{-\infty}^{\infty} x\, \frac{\alpha^x}{x!} e^{-\alpha} \delta(x-r)\, dx \qquad \textbf{[4.1.7]}$$

$$= \sum_{r=0}^{\infty} r\, \frac{\alpha^r}{r!} e^{-\alpha} = \sum_{r=1}^{\infty} \frac{\alpha^r e^{-\alpha}}{(r-1)!} = \alpha \sum_{r=0}^{\infty} \frac{\alpha^r e^{-\alpha}}{r!} = \alpha$$

Example 4.5 | Assume your personal computer has a mean time between failures (MTBFs) of 1,000 hours and that the time between failures has a Poisson probability density function. Determine the probability that at least one failure occurs in a 100 hour interval. What is the average number of failures per hour? The probability of at least one failure in time t is

$$P_F(F \geq 1) = 1 - P_F(F = 0) = 1 - \left[\frac{(\lambda t)^k}{k!} e^{-\lambda t} \right]_{k=0} = 1 - e^{-\lambda t}$$

The average number of failures per hour is the reciprocal of the MTBF or $\lambda = 1/1,000$. Thus,

$$P_F(F \geq 1) = 1 - e^{-\frac{1}{1,000}} = 1 - e^{-\frac{100}{1,000}} = 1 - e^{-0.1} \approx 0.095$$

Example 4.6

Recall Example 3.11. Ten thousand raffle tickets for a charity are sold at $1 each. The raffle prize is $2000, and the holder of 1 and only 1 of the 10,000 tickets will be the winner. John White buys three tickets. In Chapter 3 we calculated the probability distribution for Mr. White's gain. Here we find his expected gain.

The random variable, X, is Mr. White's gain, which has two possible values. Either Mr. White will lose $3 or he will win $1997. In the first case his gain is negative, or $-\$3$. In the second case his gain is positive, $1997. The probability for these two values of the gain are 9997/10,000 and 3/10,000, respectively, since we assume that the sample space consists of 10,000 tickets, any one of which is equally likely to be the winner. Consequently, we may write the probability density function for the gain as

Random Variable, X, Gain	$p_X(x)$
$-\$3$	$9997/10,000\ \delta(x+3)$
$\$1997$	$3/10,000\ \delta(x-1997)$

Now the expected value of Mr. White's gain is

$$\int_{-\infty}^{\infty} x\, p_X(x)\ dx = (-3)\,\frac{9997}{10,000} + (1997)\,\frac{3}{10,000} = -\$2.40$$

The expected value is the result we would expect if the lottery were repeated an infinite number of times. If such an experiment were conducted, then Mr. White's average or expected gain per lottery would be a loss of $2.40.

4.2   MOMENTS

We can extend the definition of expected value to encompass polynomials of the random variable as follows:

Definition 4.2. The **nth moment** of the random variable X about a point x_0 is defined as

$$E[(X - x_0)^n] = \int_{-\infty}^{\infty} (x - x_0)^n p_X(x)\ dx \qquad \textbf{[4.2.1]}$$

Note that the expansion of $(X - x_0)^n$ is an nth order polynomial of the random variable. We will soon define the expectation of a general function of a random variable.

Some authors use the following notation for the expected value:

$$E[(X - x_0)^n] = \overline{(X - x_0)^n} \qquad \textbf{[4.2.2]}$$

This notation is particularly useful for classroom work on the blackboard. However, we will generally use E to denote expected value rather than the overbar notation. Note that the moments are defined for n as an integer greater than or equal to zero. We can define the expected value of a random variable raised to a negative power or a noninteger power. However, the expected value in these cases is not called a moment.

Definition 4.3. A special case of Definition 4.2 is the **nth moment about the origin,** which is

$$E[(X)^n] = E[X^n] = \int_{-\infty}^{\infty} x^n p_X(x)\, dx \qquad [4.2.3]$$

Definition 4.4. Another special case is the **nth central moment,** which is the nth moment about the mean, that is:

$$E[(X - \mu_X)^n] = \int_{-\infty}^{\infty} (x - \mu_X)^n\, p_X(x)\, dx \qquad [4.2.4]$$

Example 4.7

Two special cases of the last definition are the following:

$$E[(X - \mu_X)] = \int_{-\infty}^{\infty} (x - \mu_X)\, p_X(x)\, dx = \mu_X - \mu_X \int_{-\infty}^{\infty} p_X(x)\, dx = \mu_X - \mu_X = 0 \quad [4.2.5]$$

$$E[(X - \mu_X)^2] = \int_{-\infty}^{\infty} (x - \mu_X)^2\, p_X(x)\, dx = E[(X)^2] - 2\mu_X \int_{-\infty}^{\infty} x\, p_X(x)\, dx + (\mu_X)^2$$

$$= E[(X)^2] - (\mu_X)^2 = \sigma_X^2 \qquad [4.2.6]$$

The second moment about the origin $E[X^2]$ is known as the **mean-square value** of the random variable. The expression $(\mu_X)^2$ is called the **square of the mean,** the term $(\sigma_X)^2$ is the **variance** of the random variable, while σ_X is the **standard deviation.** Thus, the **second central moment** is the variance, and the standard deviation is the positive square root of the variance.

The moments have some interesting interpretations. As mentioned earlier, if $p_X(x)$ is considered as a mass density function, then the mean is the centroid, or center of gravity of the mass distribution, with respect to the origin. The second moment about the origin is the moment of inertia of the mass distribution. The second central moment (or variance) is the central moment of inertia of the distribution of mass about the mean (center of gravity) and is equivalent to the parallel axis theorem for moments of inertia. This value represents a minimum inertia of the mass distribution. Therefore, the variance is often considered a measure of the **width,** the **spread,** or the **dispersion** of the random variable measured in squared units. The third central moment is a measure of **symmetry** of the random variable and is sometimes considered a measure of **skewness** of the random variable. The fourth central moment is called the **kurtosis** and is a measure of **peakedness** of the random variable near the mean. The higher moments have no simple physical interpretations. Table 4.1 gives a summary of the moments for n = 0, 1, 2, 3, 4. Note that not all random variables have finite moments. We give an example of this later for the Cauchy random variable.

Definition 4.5. The **coefficient of skewness** is

$$c_s = \frac{E[(X - \mu_X)^3]}{\sigma_X^3} \qquad [4.2.7]$$

Table 4.1   Summary of first five moments and central moments

n	n^{th} moment about the origin	n^{th} central moment
0	$E[X^0] = 1$	$E[(X - \mu_X)^0] = 1$
1	$E[X] = \mu_X$ = the mean.	$E[(X - \mu_X)] = 0$
2	$E[X^2]$ = the mean square value.	$E[(X - \mu_X)^2] = \sigma_X^2$ = the variance. σ_X is the standard deviation and is a measure of the width of $p_X(x)$.
3	$E[X^3]$	$E[(X - \mu_X)^3]$ = the skewness, which is a measure of the symmetry of $p_X(x)$. If $p_X(x)$ is symmetric about the mean, then all odd ordered central moments are zero.
4	$E([X^4]$	$E[(X - \mu_X)^4]$ = the kurtosis, which is a measure of the peakedness of $p_X(x)$ near μ_X.

which is dimensionless. This coefficient is positive if the random variable has a probability density that is skewed to the right and negative if skewed to the left. The **coefficient of kurtosis** is also dimensionless and is given as

$$c_k = \frac{E[(X - \mu_X)^4]}{\sigma_X^4}$$ [4.2.8]

The more values of the random variable concentrated near the mean of a probability density function, the larger the coefficient of kurtosis. This means the density will have a large peak near the mean. We will illustrate these definitions after introducing some additional material.

The expected value and the higher order moments are often used as statistical descriptors or features of the random variable and, therefore, of the probability density function of the random variable. In fact a Gaussian random variable is described by the mean and the variance. We will soon discuss this more thoroughly. Thus, the moments may be considered as a parametric representation of the random variable. However, such parametric representations are often only approximations; nevertheless, they may have practical value for certain applications such as pattern recognition and filter design. There are other parameters that one may use to describe the features of a random variable. We define two of these:

Definition 4.6. The value of the random variable, X, for which the probability density is maximum is called the mode. The **mode** may not have a unique value, as for a random variable with the uniform probability density function.

Definition 4.7. The **median** is that value of the random variable, X, for which one-half the area under the probability density function is to the left of the median and one-half is to the right.

These two definitions are illustrated in Figure 4.1 along with the mean.

Quiz 4.3   Verify the values for the mean, median, and mode shown in Figure 4.1 for $p_X(x) = xe^{-x}u(x)$. First show that $p_X(x)$ is a valid probability density function.

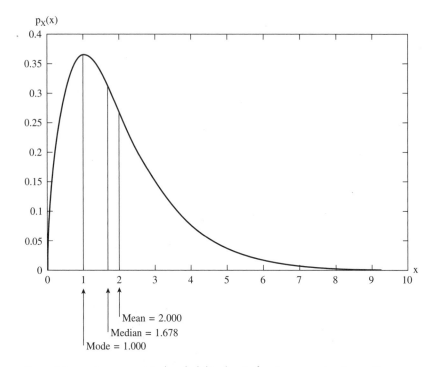

Figure 4.1   An asymmetrical probability density function, x exp(−x), x ≥ 0

The mean, mode, and median are often referred to as measures of **central tendency,** since they describe, to some extent, the tendency of the random variable to cluster around a particular value. Statistical analysis uses all three of these parameters. The median is often encountered in situations that involve percentiles (e.g., grading). The mode represents the **most probable value.** Sometimes the mean, median, and mode are the same value. The median and mode, however, are often not very satisfactory parametric representations of a random variable, since they do not lend themselves very well to mathematical operations, and often they cannot be determined analytically.

Quiz 4.4   Name a random variable for which the mean, mode, and median are the same value.

4.3   EXAMPLES

Example 4.8 | In this example we calculate the second moment about the origin as well as the variance for the binomial random variable. These are

$$E[X^2] = \sum_{r=0}^{n} \int_{-\infty}^{\infty} x^2 \binom{n}{x} p^x q^{n-x} \delta(x - r) \, dx$$

$$= \sum_{r=0}^{n} r^2 \binom{n}{r} p^r q^{n-r} = np[1 + (n-1)p] = np(np + q) \qquad [4.3.1]$$

The variance is given by

$$\sigma_X^2 = E[X^2] - \mu_X^2 = npq \qquad [4.3.2]$$

Example 4.9

Reconsider the Poisson random variable and find the mean square value and the variance. The second moment about the origin is

$$E[X^2] = \sum_{r=0}^{\infty} \int_{-\infty}^{\infty} x^2 \frac{\alpha^x}{x!} e^{-\alpha} \delta(x - r) \, dx = \sum_{r=0}^{\infty} r^2 \frac{\alpha^r}{r!} e^{-\alpha} = \alpha^2 + \alpha \qquad [4.3.3]$$

Consequently, the variance is

$$\sigma_X^2 = E[X^2] - \mu_X^2 = \alpha \qquad [4.3.4]$$

Quiz 4.5 Work out the details of finding the solutions for [4.3.1] and [4.3.3]. Hint: Consider the solutions for Examples 4.3 and 4.4 and Quiz 4.2.

Example 4.10

Consider a random variable with a uniform or rectangular probability density function given as

$$p_X(x) = \frac{1}{a}, \quad 0 \le x \le a \qquad [4.3.5]$$

$$= 0, \quad \text{otherwise}$$

The mean is

$$E[X] = \int_{-\infty}^{\infty} x \, p_X(x) \, dx = \int_0^a x \frac{1}{a} \, dx = \frac{a}{2} \qquad [4.3.6]$$

The second moment about the origin is

$$E[X^2] = \int_{-\infty}^{\infty} x^2 \, p_X(x) \, dx = \int_0^a x^2 \frac{1}{a} \, dx = \frac{a^2}{3} \qquad [4.3.7]$$

The variance is

$$\sigma_X^2 = E[X^2] - \mu_X^2 = \frac{a^2}{3} - \left(\frac{a}{2}\right)^2 = \frac{a^2}{12} \qquad [4.3.8]$$

See Figure 4.2 for a geometrical interpretation of this example.

The centroid (mean value for the x component) is $a/2$. This is the line of symmetry of the uniform or rectangular area; $a^2/3$ is the moment of inertia of the rectangle (unit mass) about the vertical (y axis); and $a^2/12$ is the moment of inertia of the rectangle about the centroid or line $x = a/2$.

Quiz 4.6 Determine the median and mode for Example 4.10. Compare these values to the mean.

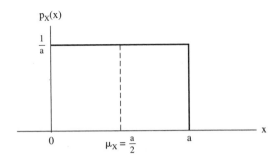

Figure 4.2   The uniform probability density

Quiz 4.7   Find the coefficient of skewness, c_s, and the coefficient of kurtosis, c_k, for a random variable with the uniform probability density function given in Example 4.10.

Quiz 4.8   Determine the coefficient of skewness, c_s, and the coefficient of kurtosis, c_k, for $p_X(x) = xe^{-x}u(x)$. Do the results agree with the descriptions given in the definitions?

4.4   EXPECTATION OF A FUNCTION OF A RANDOM VARIABLE

We now generalize the concepts of expected value and moments to functions other than polynomials.

> **Definition 4.8.** If X is a random variable with a probability density function $p_X(x)$, and if $g(X)$ is a function of the random variable, then the **expectation,** or **expected value** of the function $g(X)$, is defined as

$$E[g(X)] = \int_{-\infty}^{\infty} g(x)\, p_X(x)\, dx \qquad \text{[4.4.1]}$$

Special cases obviously include the mean and the moments of the random variable of order n, as we defined in Definitions 4.3 and 4.4. For example, we may have

$$g(X) = X^n$$

Then

$$E[g(X)] = \int_{-\infty}^{\infty} x^n\, p_X(x)\, dx = E[X^n] \qquad \text{[4.4.2]}$$

Similarly, if

$$g(X) = (X - x_0)^n$$

then

$$E[g(X)] = \int_{-\infty}^{\infty} (x - x_0)^n\, p_X(x)\, dx = E[(X - x_0)^n] \qquad \text{[4.4.3]}$$

It should be mentioned that E[g(X)] may not exist. However, such cases are rare and will be ignored here, except for the Cauchy random variable, which will be defined later.

Perhaps the most useful property of expectation is **linearity; that is, the mean of the sum is the sum of the means.** Suppose we have a number of functions of a random variable X. Denote these functions as $g_i(X)$. Then

$$E\left[\sum_{\text{all i}} g_i(X)\right] = \sum_{\text{all i}} E[g_i(X)] \qquad \textbf{[4.4.4]}$$

Note, that since E denotes integration as defined in [4.4.1], then by the linearity property we can **interchange expectation (integration) and summation.** As mentioned before, this is allowed provided the series summation is uniformly convergent over a closed interval containing the limits of integration.

A special case of linearity is the following. The **expected value** or **average of a constant is the constant,** that is, if

$$g(X) = a \qquad \textbf{[4.4.5]}$$

then

$$E[g(X)] = E(a) = a$$

Note, that we have already used this property in earlier examples.

Another special case of linearity is the **expected value of a constant times a random variable is the constant times the expected value of the random variable,** that is:

$$E[ag(X)] = a\,E[g(x)] \qquad \textbf{[4.4.6]}$$

The proof of [4.4.4] and of [4.4.5] and [4.4.6] is left as an exercise but is quite straight forward if one employs the appropriate definitions.

It is now possible to use linearity to derive [4.2.6] again, using the algebra of expected values. Thus, we have

$$\sigma_X^2 = E[(X - \mu_X)^2] = E[(X^2 - 2X\mu_X + \mu_X^2)] \qquad \textbf{[4.4.7]}$$

$$= E[X^2] + E[-2X\,\mu_X] + E[\mu_X^2]$$

$$= E[X^2] - 2\mu_X^2 + \mu_X^2 = E[X^2] - \mu_X^2$$

Example 4.11

Suppose that a function of a random variable X is $g(X) = aX + bX^2$. Find the mean and variance of g(X) in terms of the mean and variance of X. This is done as follows:

$$E[g(X)] = E[aX + bX^2] = aE(X) + bE(X^2) = a\mu_X + b\sigma_X^2 + b\mu_X^2 = a\mu_X + b\mu_X^2 + b\sigma_X^2$$

And

$$E\{[g(X)]\}^2 = E\{[aX + bX^2]\}^2 = E[a^2X^2 + 2abX^3 + b^2X^4]$$

$$= a^2E[X^2] + 2abE[X^3] + b^2E[X^4] = a^2(\sigma_X^2 + \mu_X^2) + 2abE[X^3] + b^2E[X^4]$$

$$\sigma_{g(X)}^2 = E[g(X)^2] - \{E[g(X)]\}^2$$

These expressions are not easily reduced to a simpler form unless more is known about the third and fourth moments. A special case is that when g(X) = aX, then

$$\sigma^2_{g(X)} = E[(aX)^2] - \{E[aX]\}^2 = a^2E[X^2] - a^2\mu_X^2 = a^2\sigma_X^2$$

Sometimes we need to calculate the probability that a random variable may deviate by a specified amount from its mean value, μ_X. The **Chebyshev inequality** gives a bound on the probability of deviation of a random variable from its mean value, μ_X. This inequality may be expressed in two forms, where one form is

$$P(|X - \mu_X| \geq \epsilon) \leq \frac{\sigma_X^2}{\epsilon^2} \qquad [4.4.8]$$

where ϵ is the value of the absolute deviation of the random variable from μ_X. The other form expresses ϵ as the product of a constant k and σ_X:

$$P(|X - \mu_X| \geq k\sigma_X) \leq \frac{1}{k^2}, \text{ where } \epsilon = k\sigma_X \qquad [4.4.9]$$

We illustrate the application of Chebyshev's inequality with the following quiz.

Quiz 4.9   The water temperature at a local spring fluctuates over time due to a random disturbance. Limited measurements show that the average temperature is 72°F with a standard deviation of 1°F. Determine the fraction of time during which the temperature can exceed 77°F. Hint: Use Chebyshev's inequality.

Often we will want to estimate characteristics or features of a random variable, say we may want an estimate of the mean. One estimate of the mean is simply the outcome of a single experiment of the random variable. We conduct an experiment involving the random variable and observe the outcome, which is that X = x. This outcome is one estimate of the mean value of X because the expected value of X is μ_X. However, this particular estimate of the mean is not a very good estimate because the variance of this estimate is the same as the variance of the random variable, which may be large. Consequently, another estimate of the mean value of a random variable is often used.

Definition 4.9. The **sample mean** is an estimate of the mean and is defined as

$$\hat{\mu}_X = \frac{1}{N}\sum_{i=1}^{N} X_i \qquad [4.4.10]$$

where each X_i is a random variable that represents one outcome for each repetition of an experiment and N is the total number of experiments performed. We may also perform one experiment with N random variables, which are all observed when the experiment is performed. The sample mean is also known as the **arithmetic mean.**

The **weak law of large numbers,** which is a result of Chebyshev's inequality, says that the sample mean approaches the true mean as N→ ∞, that is:

$$\lim_{N\to\infty} P[|\hat{\mu}_X - \mu_X| \geq \epsilon] = 0, \quad \epsilon > 0 \qquad [4.4.11]$$

Quiz 4.10.   Show that the mean of the sample mean is μ_X, and that the variance of the sample mean is $(\sigma_X)^2/N$.

Quiz 4.11.   As we mentioned above, another estimate of the mean is the value of the random variable for any particular experimental outcome, or $\hat{\mu}_X = X = x$. Compare the mean and the variance of this estimator of the mean with their counterparts in Quiz 4.10.

We will discuss estimators more thoroughly in another chapter; however, for the moment it is instructive to discuss the significance of the results of the two previous quizzes. First, we point out that an estimator of a random variable is a function of a random variable and is itself, therefore, a random variable. Thus, $\hat{\mu}_X$ is a random variable. Next, if we are estimating the mean value of a random variable, then it seems reasonable that the expected value of the estimator should be the true mean value. What is the significance of the variance of the estimator in this case? A desirable property is that the variance of the estimator should be small; in other words, we want the value of the estimator to always be close to the true value of the parameter that is being estimated. For convenience, denote the sample mean as Estimator I and the estimator in Quiz 4.11 as Estimator II. The variance of Estimator II is always the same value, namely, $(\sigma_X)^2$. However, the variance of Estimator I decreases as N increases. This means that Estimator I deviates less from the true value as N increases; that is to say, the sample mean will deviate less and less from the true value of the mean as more and more experimental outcomes are observed. This is illustrated in Figure 4.3 for a particular value of σ_X and N, which shows that the variance for Estimator I is smaller than that for Estimator II.

There are three other "means" that are useful in various situations.

Definition 4.10. The **geometric mean** is the nth root of the product of n numbers, that is:

$$m_g = \left[x_1\, x_2 \ldots x_n \right]^{\frac{1}{n}} \qquad \textbf{[4.4.12]}$$

The geometric mean is often used to estimate the center frequency of a filter that does not have a symmetric frequency response. For example, suppose a bandpass filter has one 3-dB frequency at 100 Hz and the other 3-dB frequency at 175 Hz, then the geometric mean frequency is $(17,500)^{1/2} = 132.29$, while the arithmetic mean is 137.5. Other uses for the geometric mean are in the rate-of-growth problems to give an average measure of change.

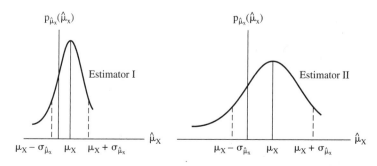

Figure 4.3   Probability density functions for two estimators for the mean

Example 4.12   Find the geometric mean of the numbers 2, 4, 8. This is

$$m_g = [(2)(4)(8)]^{\frac{1}{3}} = [64]^{\frac{1}{3}} = 4$$

The sample mean is $(1/3)(2 + 4 + 8) = 14/3 = 4.67$.

Definition 4.11. The **harmonic mean,** m_h, is the reciprocal of the arithmetic mean of the reciprocals of the numbers, that is:

$$m_h = \frac{1}{\frac{1}{n}\sum_{i=1}^{n}\frac{1}{x_i}} = \frac{n}{\sum_{i=1}^{n}\frac{1}{x_i}} \qquad [4.4.13]$$

The harmonic mean is often used for computing a statistical measure for situations where the values x_i represent rates such as miles per hour, pounds per linear foot, or similar cases. It is also sometimes used as a performance criterion for filters that are designed to improve the signal-to-noise ratio from the input to the output while also improving the resolution of two signals as well as to average spectra calculated in various applications.

Example 4.13   Using the same numbers as before, we find the harmonic mean to be

$$m_h = \frac{3}{\frac{1}{2} + \frac{1}{4} + \frac{1}{8}} = \frac{3}{\frac{7}{8}} = 3.43$$

We note that from these examples that $m_h \le m_g \le \hat{\mu}_X$. This is generally true with the equality holding if all the numbers are the same.

Definition 4.12. The **root mean square (RMS)**, or **quadratic mean**, of a set of numbers is

$$RMS = \sqrt{\frac{1}{n}\sum_{i=1}^{n}(x_i)^2} \qquad [4.4.14]$$

Example 4.14   The RMS of 2, 4, 8 is

$$RMS = \sqrt{\frac{1}{3}(4 + 16 + 64)} = \sqrt{\frac{1}{3}(84)} = 5.29$$

The RMS is used in many engineering problems, particularly those concerning energy or power.

The sample variance is used in statistics to estimate the variance of data. It is defined as

$$s^2 = \hat{\sigma}_X^2 = \frac{1}{N-1} \sum_{i=1}^{N} (X_i - \hat{\mu}_X)^2 \qquad \text{[4.4.15]}$$

where each X_i is a random variable that represents one outcome for each repetition of an experiment, N is the total number of experiments performed, and $\hat{\mu}_X$ is the sample mean. The sample standard deviation is s. If we calculate the sample standard deviation for the data used in the last example, we obtain s = 3.63. We shall discuss the sample variance at more length, as well as other estimators, in a later chapter.

4.5   THE CHARACTERISTIC FUNCTION

Definition 4.13. The **characteristic function** of a random variable is defined as the expected value of e^{juX}, that is:

$$\phi_X(u) = E[e^{juX}] = \int_{-\infty}^{\infty} e^{juX} p_X(x)\, dx \qquad \text{[4.5.1]}$$

Note that the characteristic function is similar to the Fourier transform of $p_X(x)$. The difference is in the sign of the exponent. Thus, the characteristic function and the probability density function of a random variable form a "Fourier" transform pair (the quotes are placed about Fourier to call attention to the fact that the exponent is of a different sign). Consequently we have the "transform" pair

$$\phi_X(u) = \int_{-\infty}^{\infty} e^{juX} p_X(x)\, dx \qquad \text{[4.5.1]}$$

$$p_X(x) = \frac{1}{2\pi} \int_{-\infty}^{\infty} e^{-juX} \phi_X(u)\, du \qquad \text{[4.5.2]}$$

The characteristic function may be written as an infinite series expansion as follows:

$$\phi_X(u) = \int_{-\infty}^{\infty} p_X(x)\, e^{juX}\, dx \qquad \text{[4.5.3]}$$

$$= \int_{-\infty}^{\infty} p_X(x) \left[1 + jux + \frac{1}{2!}(jux)^2 + \ldots\right] dx$$

which becomes

$$\phi_X(u) = \int_{-\infty}^{\infty} p_X(x)\,dx + ju \int_{-\infty}^{\infty} x\, p_X(x)\,dx + \ldots + \frac{(ju)^n}{n!} \int_{-\infty}^{\infty} x^n\, p_X(x)\, dx + \ldots \qquad \text{[4.5.4]}$$

Note the integrals in [4.5.4] may not exist. However, if they do, then they are the moments about the origin. Thus, we have

$$\phi_X(u) = 1 + juE[X] + \ldots + \frac{(ju)^n}{n!} E[X^n] + \ldots = \sum_{n=0}^{\infty} \frac{(ju)^n}{n!} E[X^n] \qquad \text{[4.5.5]}$$

where $\phi_X(0) = 1$. Therefore, we conclude that the coefficients of $(ju)^n/n!$ are the moments about the origin of the random variable.

Definition 4.14. We define a related function called the **moment generating function** of a random variable as

$$\Psi_X(u) = E[e^{uX}] \qquad [4.5.6]$$

then

$$\Psi_X(u) = \sum_{n=0}^{\infty} \frac{u^n}{n!} E[X^n] \qquad [4.5.7]$$

With this definition the coefficients of $u^n/n!$ are the moments of the random variable about the origin.

It is also interesting to note that the moments of the random variable are related to the MacLaurin series expansion of the characteristic function, $\phi_X(u)$; that is:

$$\phi_X(u) = \phi_X(0) + \sum_{n=1}^{\infty} \frac{u^n}{n!} \phi_X^{(n)}(0) = 1 + \sum_{n=1}^{\infty} \frac{(ju)^n}{n!} E[X^n] \qquad [4.5.8]$$

where we assume the characteristic function exists, and that the kth derivative with respect to u of the characteristic function, evaluated at u = 0, is

$$\phi_X^{(k)}(0) = j^k E[X^k] \qquad [4.5.9]$$

An important relation useful in communications, signal processing, and spectral estimation is the **Chernoff bound,** which is

$$P[e^{juX} \geq \epsilon] \leq \frac{E[e^{juX}]}{\epsilon} = \frac{\phi_X(u)}{\epsilon}, \qquad \epsilon > 0 \qquad [4.5.10]$$

Example 4.15 | The characteristic function for the binomial random variable is

$$\phi_X(u) = \int_{-\infty}^{\infty} \sum_{r=0}^{n} \binom{n}{x} p^x q^{n-x} e^{jux} \delta(x - r) \, dx \qquad [4.5.11]$$

$$= \sum_{r=0}^{n} \binom{n}{r} (pe^{ju})^r q^{n-r}$$

$$= (pe^{ju} + q)^n$$

The mean value can be found by evaluating the first derivative of $\phi_X(u)$ with respect to u at u = 0; that is, if [4.5.9] is used, then

$$E[X] = -j\phi^{(1)}(0) = -jn \left. (pe^{ju} + q)^{n-1} jp \, e^{ju} \right|_{u=0} = np$$

Quiz 4.12   Determine the second moment of the binomial random variable using the characteristic function in (4.5.11). Then find the variance of the binomial random variable.

Example 4.16 | For this example we find the characteristic function for a random variable with a uniform probability density function. Let

$$p_X(x) = \frac{1}{a}[u(x) - u(x - a)]$$

Then

$$\phi_X(u) = \int_0^a \frac{1}{a} e^{jux} \, dx = \frac{1}{aju}(e^{jua} - 1) \qquad \text{[4.5.12]}$$

$$= \frac{1}{jua} \sum_{n=0}^{\infty} \frac{(jua)^{n+1}}{(n+1)!} = \sum_{n=0}^{\infty} \frac{1}{(n+1)} \frac{(jua)^n}{n!}$$

$$= \sum_{n=0}^{\infty} \frac{(ju)^n}{n!} \left(\frac{a^n}{n+1} \right)$$

Thus the nth moment about the origin is

$$\frac{a^n}{n+1}, \quad n = 0, 1, 2, \ldots \qquad \text{[4.5.13]}$$

Quiz 4.13　Verify the above result in [4.5.13] as follows:

$$E[X^n] = \int_0^a x^n p_X(x) \, dx \qquad \text{[4.5.14]}$$

One of the most important random variables is the **Gaussian,** or **normal,** random variable, whose **|Example 4.17**
probability density function is given as

$$p_X(x) = \frac{1}{\sqrt{2\pi}\sigma_X} \exp\left[-\frac{(x - \mu_x)^2}{2\sigma_X^2} \right] \qquad \text{[4.5.15]}$$

where μ_X is the mean and σ_X^2 is the variance. This probability density function was introduced in Chapter 3, however, the parameters were not defined at that time. The characteristic function is found as follows:

$$\phi_X(u) = \frac{1}{\sqrt{2\pi}\sigma_X} \int_{-\infty}^{\infty} \exp\left[-\frac{(x - \mu_x)^2}{2\sigma_X^2} + jux \right] dx \qquad \text{[4.5.16]}$$

If we complete the square in the exponent, then

$$\phi_X(u) = \frac{\exp\left[ju\,\mu_X - \frac{u^2}{2}\sigma_X^2 \right]}{\sqrt{2\pi}\sigma_X} \int_{-\infty}^{\infty} \exp\left\{ -\frac{1}{2\sigma_X^2}[x - (\mu_X + ju\sigma_X^2)]^2 \right\} dx \qquad \text{[4.5.17]}$$

Next, change the variable, such that

$$y^2 = \frac{1}{\sigma_X^2}[x - (\mu_X + ju\sigma_X^2)]^2$$

then

$$\phi_X(u) = \frac{\exp\left[ju\mu_X - \frac{u^2}{2}\sigma_X^2 \right]}{\sqrt{2\pi}} \int_{-\infty}^{\infty} e^{-\frac{1}{2}y^2} \, dy$$

However

$$\frac{1}{\sqrt{2\pi}} \int_{-\infty}^{\infty} e^{-\frac{1}{2}y^2} \, dy = 1$$

Thus, we finally obtain the characteristic function as

$$\phi_X(u) = \exp\left[ju\,\mu_x - \frac{u^2}{2}\sigma_X^2\right] = 1 + ju\mu_X + \frac{(ju)^2}{2!}E[X^2] + \cdots \qquad \textbf{[4.5.18]}$$

It is important to note that the characteristic function of a Gaussian random variable is also a Gaussian random variable because any linear operation on a Gaussian random variable is also a Gaussian random variable.

Quiz 4.14   Verify that the first three terms of the series expansion of the characteristic function [4.5.18] are the ones shown. Note that if you expand the first exponential on the right of [4.5.18] then you will obtain terms involving both μ_X and σ_X. Show that when these terms are rewritten we obtain the second series on the right of [4.5.18].

Often the logarithm of the characteristic function yields a very descriptive display of the properties of the random variable.

Definition 4.15. In general we can write a series expansion of $\ln[\phi X(u)]$ as

$$\ln[\phi_X(u)] = \sum_{n=1}^{\infty} \lambda_n \frac{(ju)^n}{n!} \qquad \textbf{[4.5.19]}$$

where the coefficients, λ_n, are called the **cumulants** and are given as

$$\lambda_n = \frac{d^n}{d(ju)^n}\{\ln[\phi_X(u)]\}_{u=0}, \quad n = 1, 2, 3, \cdots \qquad \textbf{[4.5.20]}$$

The cumulants can be shown to be related to the moments of the random variable by taking the derivatives specified in [4.5.20]. By doing so we obtain

$$\lambda_0 = 0 \quad \text{since} \quad \phi_X(0) = 1 \qquad \textbf{[4.5.21]}$$

$$\lambda_1 = \mu_x$$

$$\lambda_2 = E[X^2] - \mu_X^2 = \sigma_X^2$$

$$\lambda_3 = E[X^3] - 3\mu_X E[X^2] + 2\mu_X^3 = E[(x - \mu_x)^3]$$

Thus, λ_1, the first cumulant, is the first moment about the origin or the mean; λ_2 is the second moment about the mean; and λ_3 is the third moment about the mean. However, the higher ordered λ_n's are not as simply related to the central moments.

Table 4.2 summarizes some of the moments of several of the random variables that we have considered previously, including the Gaussian.

We now consider a few of the properties of the normal or Gaussian random variable. If

$$p_X(x) = \frac{1}{\sqrt{2\pi}\sigma_x} e^{-\frac{1}{2}\left(\frac{x-\mu_x}{\sigma_x}\right)^2}$$

then a sketch of this function is shown in Figure 4.4. As mentioned previously, the Gaussian random variable is completely specified by two parameters, its mean, μ_X, and its standard deviation, σ_X. It is often useful to know the probability that a Gaussian random variable is bounded by $\pm c\sigma_X$, where c is a positive constant. Let us calculate the situations where c = 1, and 2. To do this we must find the area under the Gaussian probability density function between $\mu_X \pm c\sigma_X$. We do this as follows.

Table 4.2 Summary of the mean, the second moment about the origin, and the variance of random variables with the following probability density functions

Probability Density Function	Mean	Second Moment About the Origin	Variance
Geometric $$\sum_{r=1}^{\infty} (1-p)^{x-1} p\, \delta(x-r)$$	$\dfrac{1}{p}$	$\dfrac{2}{p^2} - \dfrac{1}{p}$	$\dfrac{1}{p^2} - \dfrac{1}{p}$
Binomial $$\sum_{r=0}^{n} \binom{n}{x} p^x q^{n-x}\, \delta(x-r)$$	np	$np(np+q)$	npq
Poisson $$\sum_{r=0}^{\infty} \frac{e^{-\alpha}\alpha^x}{x!}\, \delta(x-r)$$	α	$\alpha^2 + \alpha$	α
Uniform (rectangular) $$\frac{1}{a}[u(x) - u(x-a)]$$	$\dfrac{a}{2}$	$\dfrac{a^2}{3}$	$\dfrac{a^2}{12}$
Gaussian $$\frac{e^{-\frac{1}{2}\left(\frac{x-\mu_X}{\sigma_X}\right)^2}}{\sqrt{2\pi}\sigma_X}$$	μ_X	$\sigma_X^2 + \mu_X^2$	σ_X^2

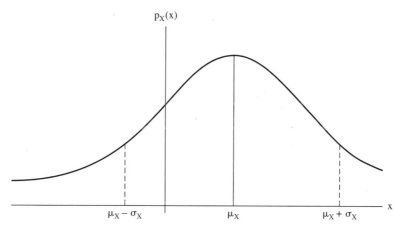

$$p_X(x)$$

Figure 4.4 The Gaussian probability density function

The area between $\mu_X \pm \sigma_X$ is

$$\int_{\mu_X - \sigma_X}^{\mu_X + \sigma_X} \frac{1}{\sqrt{2\pi}\sigma_X} e^{-\frac{1}{2}\left(\frac{x-\mu}{\sigma_X}\right)^2} dx = \frac{1}{\sqrt{2\pi}} \int_{-1}^{1} e^{-\frac{1}{2}t^2}\, dt \cong 0.68 \qquad \textbf{[4.5.22]}$$

and the area between $\mu_X \pm 2\sigma_X$ is

$$\int_{\mu_x-2\sigma_x}^{\mu_x+2\sigma_x} \frac{1}{\sqrt{2\pi}\sigma_X} e^{-\frac{1}{2}\left(\frac{x-\mu_x}{\sigma_x}\right)^2} dx = \frac{1}{\sqrt{2\pi}} \int_{-2}^{2} e^{-\frac{1}{2}t^2} dt \cong 0.95 \qquad \textbf{[4.5.23]}$$

These results are listed in Table 4.3. A more complete listing of values for the Gaussian probability density function is given in Table 4.4, where erf(x) denotes the error function,

Table 4.3   The area under the Gaussian probability density

Region	Area
$\mu_x - \sigma_x \leq X \leq \mu_x + \sigma_x$	68.3%
$\mu_x - 2\sigma_x \leq X \leq \mu_x + 2\sigma_x$	95.4%
$\mu_x - 3\sigma_x \leq X \leq \mu_x + 3\sigma_x$	99.6%

Table 4.4   Area under the Gaussian probability density

$$p_X(x) = \frac{1}{\sqrt{2\pi}} e^{-\frac{x^2}{2}}$$

$$erf(x) = \int_0^x p_X(t)\, dt$$

x	$p_X(x)$	erf(x)	x	$p_X(x)$	erf(x)
0.00	.39894	.00000	2.00	.05399	.47725
0.10	.39695	.03983	2.10	.04398	.48214
0.20	.39104	.07926	2.20	.03547	.48610
0.30	.38139	.11791	2.30	.02833	.48928
0.40	.36827	.15542	2.40	.02239	.49180
0.50	.35207	.19146	2.50	.01753	.49379
0.60	.33322	.22575	2.60	.01358	.49534
0.70	.31225	.25804	2.70	.01042	.49653
0.80	.28969	.28814	2.80	.00792	.49744
0.90	.26609	.31594	2.90	.00595	.49813
1.00	.24197	.34134	3.00	.00443	.49865
1.10	.21785	.36433	3.10	.00327	.49903
1.20	.19419	.38493	3.20	.00238	.49931
1.30	.17137	.40320	3.30	.00172	.49952
1.40	.14973	.41924	3.40	.00123	.49966
1.50	.12952	.43319	3.50	.00087	.49977
1.60	.11092	.44520	3.60	.00061	.49984
1.70	.09405	.45543	3.70	.00042	.49989
1.80	.07895	.46407	3.80	.00029	.49993
1.90	.06562	.47128	3.90	.00020	.49995

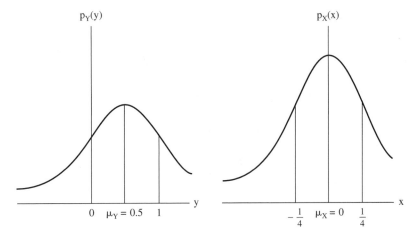

Figure 4.5   Illustration for Example 4.18

which is the integral of the Gaussian probability density function from 0 to x. It will become more clear in the following chapters why this integral is called the error function.

From the symmetry of the Gaussian probability density function we know that all odd central moments are zero. All even central moments can be expressed in terms of σ_X. The proofs of the following properties are left as problems:

$$E[(x - \mu_X)^{2n+1}] = 0 \text{ for } n = 1, 2, \ldots \qquad \textbf{[4.5.24]}$$

$$E[(x - \mu_X)^{2n}] = 1 \cdot 3 \cdot \cdot \cdot (2n - 1)\sigma_X^{2n} \text{ for } n = 1, 2, \ldots \qquad \textbf{[4.5.25]}$$

Quiz 4.15   Show that the coefficient of kurtosis is 3 for a Gaussian random variable.

Example 4.18

Suppose we have a Gaussian random variable Y such that $\mu_Y = 0.5$ and $\sigma_Y = 2$. Determine the probability that the random variable is in the interval $0 \le Y \le 1$. This is most easily solved with the use of Table 4.4 as follows. Normalize the random variable Y such that $X = (Y - \mu_Y)/\sigma_Y = (Y - 0.5)/2$. Then $\mu_X = 0$ and $(\sigma_X)^2 = (\sigma_Y)^2/4 = 1$. When $Y = 0$, $X = -1/4$, and when $Y = 1$, $X = 1/4$. Thus, the probability that $0 \le Y \le 1$ is found from Table 4.4 as 0.19717. This value is determined by linearly interpolating the tabular values for erf(x) between 0.2 and 0.3 to give erf(x) for $x = 0.25$. This value of erf(x) is the probability that X will occur in the interval $0 \le X \le 1/4$. We then double this value because we need the probability for $-1/4 \le X \le 1/4$. This is illustrated in Figure 4.5.

Before we consider expectations of two random variables with a joint probability density function, we tabulate in Table 4.5 some of the characteristic functions we have calculated along with some others.

Quiz 4.16   Show that the probability density function for the Cauchy random variable is a proper probability density function. Show that none of the moments of a Cauchy random variable exist. For simplicity, let $a = 1$ and $b = 0$.

Table 4.5 Characteristic functions for several random variables with the following probability density functions

	$p_X(x)$	$\phi_X(u)$
Binomial:	$\displaystyle\sum_{r=0}^{n} \binom{n}{x} p^x q^{n-x}\, \delta(x-r)$	$(p\,e^{ju} + q)^n$
Poisson:	$\displaystyle\sum_{r=0}^{\infty} \frac{\alpha^x}{x!} e^{-\alpha}\, \delta(x-r)$	$e^{\alpha(e^{ju}-1)}$
Uniform:	$\dfrac{1}{b-a}[u(x-a) - u(x-b)]$	$\dfrac{e^{jbu} - e^{jau}}{j(b-a)u}$
Cauchy:	$\dfrac{1}{\pi}\dfrac{a}{a^2 + (x-b)^2},\, a > 0;$	$e^{-a|u| + jbu}$
Laplace:	$\dfrac{1}{2a} e^{-\frac{|x-b|}{a}},\, a > 0;$	$(1 + a^2 u^2)^{-1} e^{jbu}$
Gaussian (normal):	$\dfrac{1}{\sqrt{2\pi}\sigma_X} e^{-\frac{1}{2}\left(\frac{x - \mu_X}{\sigma_X}\right)^2};$	$e^{\left(ju\mu_X - \frac{u^2}{2}\sigma_x^2\right)}$
Chi-Square with one degree of freedom:		
	$\dfrac{1}{\sqrt{2\pi}\sqrt{x^2}} e^{-\frac{1}{2}x^2} u(x)$	$(1 - 2ju)^{-\frac{1}{2}}$
Rayleigh:	$\dfrac{x}{b} e^{-\frac{x^2}{2b}} u(x), b > 0$	$\sqrt{2b\pi}\,(1 - 2bju)^{-\frac{3}{2}}$

4.6 EXPECTATION OF A FUNCTION OF TWO RANDOM VARIABLES

Definition 4.16. The **expected value** of a function of two random variables is given as

$$E[g(X, Y)] = \int_{-\infty}^{\infty}\int_{-\infty}^{\infty} g(x, y) p_{xy}(x,y)\, dx\, dy \qquad [4.6.1]$$

Definition 4.17. The **moments** are defined as

$$E[X^m Y^n] = \int_{-\infty}^{\infty}\int_{-\infty}^{\infty} x^m y^n p_{XY}(x, y)\, dx\, dy \qquad [4.6.2]$$

Note that the first moment for X remains as before, namely:

$$E[X] = \int_{-\infty}^{\infty}\int_{-\infty}^{\infty} x\, p_{XY}(x, y)\, dx\, dy = \int_{-\infty}^{\infty} x\, p_X(x)\, dx \qquad [4.6.3]$$

and similarly for the second moment,

$$E[X^2] = \int_{-\infty}^{\infty}\int_{-\infty}^{\infty} x^2 p_{XY}(x, y)\, dx\, dy = \int_{-\infty}^{\infty} x^2 p_X(x)\, dx \qquad [4.6.4]$$

The higher order moments also remain the same as previously defined.
The second central moments (variances) are defined as before and are denoted as

$$\sigma_X^2 = E[(X - \mu_X)^2] = E[X^2] - \mu_X^2 \qquad [4.6.5]$$
$$\sigma_Y^2 = E[(Y - \mu_Y)^2] = E[Y^2] - \mu_Y^2$$

Definition 4.18. The **mean cross product** of X and Y is a special case of Definition 4.16 and is

$$E[XY] = \int_{-\infty}^{\infty}\int_{-\infty}^{\infty} x\, y\, p_{XY}(x, y)\, dx\, dy \qquad [4.6.6]$$

Definition 4.19. The **covariance** is defined as

$$cov[X, Y] = E[(X - \mu_X)(Y - \mu_Y)] = E[XY] - \mu_X \mu_Y \qquad [4.6.7]$$

Definition 4.20.* The **correlation coefficient** is the normalized covariance and is defined as

$$\rho_{XY} = \frac{cov[X, Y]}{\sigma_X\sigma_Y} = \frac{E[XY] - \mu_X \mu_Y}{\sigma_X\sigma_Y}, \quad |\rho_{XY}| \le 1 \qquad [4.6.8]$$

The correlation coefficient ρ_{XY} is a measure of the correlation between the random variables X and Y; for instance, when $\rho_{XY} = 0$, then X and Y are said to be **uncorrelated,** and if $|\rho_{XY}| = 1$, that is, $\rho_{XY} = +1$ or -1, then X and Y are said to be **perfectly correlated** or **linearly correlated.** We illustrate these situations in the following two examples.

Example 4.19

Suppose random variable X is **linearly related** to random variable Y such that X = aY, where "a" is a positive constant, then

$$\rho_{XY} = \frac{E[XY] - \mu_X \mu_Y}{[(E[X^2] - \mu_X^2)(E[Y^2] - \mu_Y^2)]^{\frac{1}{2}}} = \frac{aE[Y^2] - a\mu_Y^2}{[(a^2E([Y^2] - a^2\mu_Y^2)(E[Y^2] - \mu_Y^2)]^{\frac{1}{2}}} = 1$$

Quiz 4.17   If $X = -aY, a > 0$, then show $\rho_{XY} = -1$.

Example 4.20

If x and y are independent random variables, then

$$p_{XY}(x, y) = p_X(x)\, p_Y(y)$$

In this case

$$\sigma_X\sigma_Y \rho_{XY} = E[XY] - \mu_X \mu_Y = \int_{-\infty}^{\infty}\int_{-\infty}^{\infty} x\, y\, p_X(x)p_Y(y)\, dx\, dy - \mu_X \mu_Y$$

$$= \int_{-\infty}^{\infty} x\, p_X(x)\, dx \int_{-\infty}^{\infty} y\, p_Y(y)\, dy - \mu_X \mu_Y = \mu_X \mu_Y - \mu_X \mu_Y = 0$$

*The double subscript indicates that two random variables are involved. In Chapter 6 we will find it convenient to use a double subscript on the variances as well.

Thus, the random variables are uncorrelated ($\rho_{XY} = 0$), provided σ_X and σ_Y are not zero. However, the converse is not generally true; that is, if the random variables are uncorrelated they need not be independent.

Quiz 4.18   Suppose two random variables X and Y have the joint probability density function

$$p_{XY}(x, y) = (x + y)[u(x) - u(x - 1)][u(y) - u(y - 1)]$$

Show that σ_X, σ_y, and ρ_{XY} are equal to $\sqrt{11}/12$, $\sqrt{11}/12$, $-1/11$, respectively.

Definition 4.21. The **characteristic function** for two random variables with a joint probability density function $p_{XY}(x,y)$ is

$$\phi_{XY}(u, v) = \int_{-\infty}^{\infty}\int_{-\infty}^{\infty} e^{j(ux+vy)}p_{XY}(x, y)\, dx\, dy \qquad \text{[4.6.9]}$$

Thus, $\phi_{XY}(u, v)$ is a two-dimensional "Fourier" transform of $p_{XY}(x,y)$. If X and Y are **independent,** then

$$\phi_{XY}(u, v) = \int_{-\infty}^{\infty} e^{jux}p_X(x)\, dx \int_{-\infty}^{\infty} e^{juy}\, p_Y(y)\, dy = \phi_X(u)\phi_Y(v) \qquad \text{[4.6.10]}$$

Thus, the **joint characteristic function of two independent random variables is the product of their characteristic functions.**

Example 4.21
(MATLAB)

The **joint Gaussian probability density function** for two random variables was introduced in Chapter 3 without defining the various parameters. We have now defined these parameters and can discuss the probability density function more fully. The joint Gaussian probability density function is given by

$$p_{XY}(x, y) = \frac{1}{2\pi\,\sigma_X\sigma_Y\sqrt{1 - \rho_{XY}^2}}\, \exp$$

$$\left\{-\frac{1}{2(1 - \rho_{XY}^2)}\left[\frac{(x - \mu_X)^2}{\sigma_X^2} - \frac{2\rho_{XY}(x - \mu_X)(y - \mu_Y)}{\sigma_X\sigma_Y} + \frac{(y - \mu_Y)^2}{\sigma_Y^2}\right]\right\} \qquad \text{[4.6.11]}$$

where σ_X, σ_Y, and ρ_{XY} have been previously defined. The joint probability density function is sometimes called a **two-dimensional** probability density function.

The **characteristic function** is also Gaussian and is given by

$$\phi_{XY}(u, v) = \exp[j\,(u\mu_X + v\mu_Y) - \frac{1}{2}\,(\sigma_X^2 u^2 + 2\rho_{XY}\sigma_X\sigma_Y\, uv + \sigma_Y^2 v^2)] \qquad \text{[4.6.12]}$$

Suppose we equate the portion of the exponent of [4.6.11] that is within square brackets to a constant, that is:

$$\left[\frac{(x - \mu_X)^2}{\sigma_X^2} - \frac{2\rho_{XY}(x - \mu_X)(y - \mu_Y)}{\sigma_X\sigma_Y} + \frac{(y - \mu_Y)^2}{\sigma_Y^2}\right] = c^2 \qquad \text{[4.6.13]}$$

This is the equation for an ellipse. Thus, the probability density function appears similar to that shown in Figure 3.13, but the shape of the probability density function may be nonsymmetric depending on the values of σ_X, σ_Y, and ρ_{XY}. We illustrate this in Figure 4.6 using the contour plot

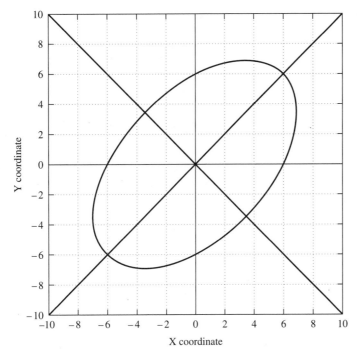

Figure 4.6   Contour plot for Example 4.21

function provided in MATLAB with $\mu_X = \mu_Y = 0$, $\sigma_X = \sigma_Y = 3$, $\rho XY = 1/2$, and $c^2 = 4$. The program for determining this plot is given in Figure 4.7. The contour section of the probability density function is ellipsoid, as we noted above, with its center located at $x = \mu_X = 0$ and $y = \mu_Y = 0$. If $\sigma_X = \sigma_Y$ and $\rho_{XY} = 0$, then the contour is circular. One of the problems asks you to plot other contours (loci of points) for various values of σ_X, σ_Y, ρ_{XY}, and c^2.

PROPERTIES

Below are listed two important **properties of Gaussian random variables**:

1. If n Gaussian random variables are mutually uncorrelated, then they are also mutually independent.
2. A linear transformation (e.g., differentiation, integration, or linear algebraic transformation) of Gaussian random variables yields Gaussian random variables.

Note that the converse of property 1 is true for all random variables; that is, **if two or more random variables are mutually independent, then they are mutually uncorrelated.**

Definition 4.22. Let two random variables X and Y have a joint probability density function, then the **conditional expectation of X given that Y = y** is defined as

$$E[X \mid Y = y] = \int_{-\infty}^{\infty} x \, p_{X|Y}(x \mid y) \, dx \qquad \textbf{[4.6.14]}$$

```
%MATLAB Example 4.21 by cjw
clear
clg
[X, Y]=meshgrid(-10:0.1:10);          % Generate X & Y array for the evaluation of function
                                      % with two variables.
mx=0;                                 % Set mean of x equal to zero
my=mx;                                % Set mean of x equal to mean of y
stdx=3;                               % Set standard deviation of x = 3
varx=stdx*stdx;                       % Set variance of x = 9
                                      % Note: In this example std dev of x = std dev of y
                                      % and the Correlation coef = 0.5
Z=(1/varx)*((X-mx).^2-(X-mx).*(Y-my)+(Y-my)+(Y-my).^2);
v=[0 4]                               % Set this vector to select the desired contour, c^2=4
contour(X,Y,Z,v)                      % Contour plot for this function with c^2=4
hold on;
grid;
v=[-10 10];                           % Set the vector u & v for the plot of X-axis & Y-axis
u=[0 0];
plot(u,v);                            % Plot the Y-axis
plot(v,u);                            % Plot the X-axis
w=[10 -10];                           % Set the vector for the plot of the minor axis
plot(v,v)                             % Plot the major axis for the ellipse
plot(v,w)                             % Plot the minor axis for the ellipse
xlabel('X coordinate')
ylabel('Y coordinate')
hold off;
```

Figure 4.7   MATLAB program for Example 4.21

We note that

$$E[X] = \int_{-\infty}^{\infty}\int_{-\infty}^{\infty} x\, p_{XY}(x, y)\, dx\, dy$$

Then

$$E[X] = \int_{-\infty}^{\infty} p_Y(y)\, dy \int_{-\infty}^{\infty} x\, p_{X|Y}(x\,|\,y)\, dx \qquad [4.6.15]$$

$$= \int_{-\infty}^{\infty} E[X\,|\,Y = y]p_Y(y)\, dy$$

Example 4.22 | Suppose the joint probability density function for two random variables is

$$p_{XY}(x, y) = 8xy[u(x) - u(x - 1)][u(y) - u(y - x)]$$

Then the marginal density for Y is

$$p_Y(y) = 4y(1 - y^2)[u(y) - u(y - 1)]$$

and the conditional probability density is

$$p_{X|Y}(x|y) = \frac{2x}{(1 - y^2)}[u(x - y) - u(x - 1)][u(y) - u(y - 1)], y > 0$$

Then

$$E[X|Y=y] = \int_y^1 x\left[\frac{2x}{(1-y^2)}\right]dx = \frac{2(1-y^3)}{3(1-y^2)} = \frac{2(1+y+y^2)}{3(1+y)}[u(y) - u(y - 1)]$$

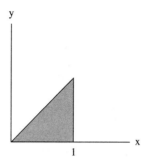

Quiz 4.19   Verify the results given in Example 4.22.

Quiz 4.20   For Example 4.22 find E[X] using [4.6.15]. Check your result. Find E[Y | X = x]. Then find E[Y] by two methods.

One may define the other conditional expectation moments in a manner similar to our earlier definitions for single and joint random variables.

4.7   THE EXPECTATION OF RANDOM VECTORS

The expectation of a random vector is similar to the expected value of a function of two random variables. We will find expectations of random vectors to be very useful when we deal with data in later chapters. Furthermore, the probability density function for a random vector is a convenient way to introduce multivariate, or multidimensional, probability density functions.

> **Definition 4.23.** The expectation of a random vector is taken with respect to each component of the random vector. We will use column vector notation and let T denote the transpose. If
>
> $$\vec{X} = (X_1, X_2, \ldots, X_n)^T \qquad \text{[4.7.1]}$$
>
> then the mean vector is
>
> $$\vec{\mu}_{\vec{X}} = (\mu_1, \mu_2, \ldots, \mu_n)^T \qquad \text{[4.7.2]}$$

where μ_i is an element of the vector of mean values of the elements of the random vector. We determine the mean vector by calculating each component of the mean vector one at a time as follows:

$$\mu_i = \int_{-\infty}^{\infty} \int_{-\infty}^{\infty} \cdots \int_{-\infty}^{\infty} x_i \, p_{\vec{X}}(x_1, x_2, \ldots, x_n) \, dx_1 \, dx_2 \ldots dx_n, \quad \text{for } i = 1, 2, \ldots, n \quad \textbf{[4.7.3]}$$

This calculation, of course, reduces to that using the marginal probability density function, that is,

$$\mu_i = \int_{-\infty}^{\infty} x_i \, p_{X_i}(x_i) \, dx_i, \quad \text{for } i = 1, 2, \ldots, n \quad \textbf{[4.7.4]}$$

Example 4.23 | **A** random variable has a uniform probability density function, such that

$$p_X(x) = 1, \quad -\frac{1}{2} \le x \le \frac{1}{2}$$

$$= 0, \quad \text{otherwise}$$

A three-element vector is formed by conducting three separate experiments such that the random variable is selected three times. Thus, $\vec{X} = (X_1, X_2, X_3)^T$. Determine the mean vector. This may be found from the marginal probability density function in [4.7.4]. Thus, $\vec{\mu}_{\vec{X}} = (0, 0, 0)^T$.

Quiz 4.21   Three random variables have the following probability density functions.

$$p_{X_1}(x) = 1, \quad -\frac{1}{2} \le x \le \frac{1}{2}, \; p_{X_2}(x) = 1, \; -1 \le x \le 0, \; p_{X_3}(x) = 1, \; 0 \le x \le 1$$

$$= 0, \quad \text{otherwise} \qquad = 0, \quad \text{otherwise} \qquad = 0, \quad \text{otherwise}$$

Determine the mean vector.

Quiz 4.22   A coin is flipped and the outcome is mapped to one if a head occurs and zero if a tail appears. This random variable is the first component of a random vector. Perform the experiment two more times with the random variables becoming the next two components of the random vector, respectively; thereby, obtaining a three component random vector. List all possible random vectors. Determine the mean vector. Determine the probability of occurrence of each vector.

The higher order moments of the random vector may be calculated as we did for functions of a random variable. However, it is convenient to use a matrix formulation, since we will find this is useful in later chapters. We have already introduced the covariance of two random variables. We generalize that concept now by defining the covariance matrix.

Definition 4.24. The **covariance matrix** $C_{\vec{X}\vec{X}^T}$ for a real random vector $\vec{X}$ is the expected value of the matrix formed by the vector product, $(\vec{X} - \vec{\mu}_{\vec{X}})(\vec{X} - \vec{\mu}_{\vec{X}})^T$, which is given as

$$C_{\vec{X}\vec{X}^T} = E[(\vec{X} - \vec{\mu}_{\vec{X}})(\vec{X} - \vec{\mu}_{\vec{X}})^T] \qquad \textbf{[4.7.5]}$$

$$= E\left\{ \begin{bmatrix} X_1 - \mu_1 \\ X_2 - \mu_2 \\ \vdots \\ X_n - \mu_n \end{bmatrix} [X_1 - \mu_1, X_2 - \mu_2, \ldots, X_n - \mu_n] \right\}$$

$$= E\begin{bmatrix} (X_1 - \mu_1)(X_1 - \mu_1) & (X_1 - \mu_1)(X_2 - \mu_2) & \cdots & (X_1 - \mu_1)(X_n - \mu_n) \\ (X_2 - \mu_2)(X_1 - \mu_1) & (X_2 - \mu_2)(X_2 - \mu_2) & \cdots & (X_2 - \mu_2)(X_n - \mu_n) \\ & \vdots & & \\ (X_n - \mu_n)(X_1 - \mu_1) & (X_n - \mu_n)(X_2 - \mu_2) & \cdots & (X_n - \mu_n)(X_n - \mu_n) \end{bmatrix}$$

$$= \begin{bmatrix} c_{11} & c_{12} & \cdots & c_{1n} \\ c_{21} & c_{22} & \cdots & c_{2n} \\ & \vdots & & \\ c_{n1} & c_{n2} & \cdots & c_{nn} \end{bmatrix}$$

where $c_{ij} = E[(X_i - \mu_i)(X_j - \mu_j)]$. The subscript $\vec{X}\vec{X}^T$ for $C_{\vec{X}\vec{X}^T}$ is sometimes denoted as $\vec{X}\vec{X}$ for convenience; that is, the T denoting **transpose** on the second random vector $\vec{X}$ is dropped. Yet a further simplification is to use $C_{\vec{X}}$. The c_{ij} are called the covariances or the covariance coefficients for the individual components of the random vector, i.e., the individual random variables X_i, $i = 1, 2, \ldots, n$. Since we are assuming that the random vector $\vec{X}$ is real, then the c_{ij} are all real. Furthermore, the covariance matrix $C_{\vec{X}\vec{X}^T}$ is symmetric; that is, $c_{ij} = c_{ji}$ for $i \neq j$. When $i = j$, then the covariances become the variances of the individual random variables; that is, $c_{ii} = E[(X_i)^2] - (\mu_i)^2 = (\sigma_i)^2$.

Definition 4.25. The correlation matrix is defined for a real random vector as

$$R_{\vec{X}\vec{X}^T} = E[(\vec{X})(\vec{X})^T] \qquad \text{[4.7.6]}$$

Then we have

$$R_{\vec{X}\vec{X}^T} = E[(\vec{X})(\vec{X})^T]$$

$$= E\left\{ \begin{bmatrix} X_1 \\ X_2 \\ \vdots \\ X_n \end{bmatrix} [X_1, X_2, \ldots, X_n] \right\}$$

$$= E\begin{bmatrix} (X_1)(X_1) & (X_1)(X_2) & \cdots & (X_1)(X_n) \\ (X_2)(X_1) & (X_2)(X_2) & \cdots & (X_2)(X_n) \\ & \vdots & & \\ (X_n)(X_1) & (X_n)(X_2) & \cdots & (X_n)(X_n) \end{bmatrix}$$

$$= \begin{bmatrix} r_{11} & r_{12} & \cdots & r_{1n} \\ r_{21} & r_{22} & \cdots & r_{2n} \\ & \vdots & & \\ r_{n1} & r_{n2} & \cdots & r_{nn} \end{bmatrix}$$

where $r_{ij} = E[(X_i)(X_j)]$. The r_{ij} are called the correlations or the correlation coefficients for the individual components of the random vector, that is, for the individual random variables X_i, $i = 1, 2, \ldots, n$. Since we are assuming that the random vector $\vec{X}$ is real, then the r_{ij} are all real. Furthermore, the correlation matrix $R_{\vec{X}\vec{X}^T}$ is symmetric that is, $r_{ij} = r_{ji}$ for $i \neq j$. When $i = j$, then the correlations become the expected value of the square of the random variables.

In the chapters that follow we will study methods for designing linear systems to improve the estimation of data and to improve the signal-to-noise ratio. Such procedures will use the correlation and covariance matrices of data. Sometimes it will be convenient to normalize the covariance and correlation coefficients by dividing the c_{ij} and r_{ij} by $\sigma_i \sigma_j$.

Example 4.24 | Consider the three-component random vector formed in the last quiz. Determine the covariance matrix. We follow [4.7.5]. The calculation is greatly simplified in this case because the components (random variables) of the random vector are mutually independent. The probability density function for one random variable is

$$p_X(x) = \frac{1}{2}[\delta(x) + \delta(x - 1)]$$

Consequently, the mean value for each component is $1/2$. Since the random variables are mutually independent, then we have

$$c_{ij} = E\left[\left(X_i - \frac{1}{2}\right)\left(X_j - \frac{1}{2}\right)\right]$$

$$= \int_{-\infty}^{\infty}\int_{-\infty}^{\infty} s\frac{1}{2}[\delta(s) + \delta(s - 1)]t\frac{1}{2}[\delta(t) + \delta(t - 1)]\,ds\,dt - \left(\frac{1}{2}\right)^2$$

$$= \int_{-\infty}^{\infty} s\frac{1}{2}[\delta(s) + \delta(s - 1)]\,ds\int_{-\infty}^{\infty} t\frac{1}{2}[\delta(t) + \delta(t - 1)]\,dt - \frac{1}{4}$$

$$= 0 \text{ for } i \neq j$$

and

$$c_{ii} = E[X_i^2] - \mu_x^2 = \sigma_i^2 = \frac{1}{2} - \frac{1}{4} = \frac{1}{4}$$

Then

$$C_{\vec{X}\vec{X}^T} = \begin{bmatrix} c_{11} & c_{12} & c_{13} \\ c_{21} & c_{22} & c_{23} \\ c_{31} & c_{32} & c_{33} \end{bmatrix}$$

$$= \begin{bmatrix} \frac{1}{4} & 0 & 0 \\ 0 & \frac{1}{4} & 0 \\ 0 & 0 & \frac{1}{4} \end{bmatrix}$$

Quiz 4.23   Determine the covariance matrix for Example 4.23.

Quiz 4.24   Determine the covariance matrix for Quiz 4.21.

In Chapter 3 and in this chapter we used the symbol ρ_{XY} to denote the correlation coefficient between two random variables, X and Y. We can see from the definition of the covariance matrix that if we consider only a (2 × 2) covariance matrix with $X_1 = X$ and $X_2 = Y$, then $(\rho_{XY}\, \sigma_X\, \sigma_Y) = \text{cov}(X, Y)$, which represents the off-diagonal terms in the covariance matrix. If the random vector has **mutually independent components,** then the off-diagonal terms are zero and the covariance matrix is diagonal, as we saw in Example 4.24. Furthermore, when this is the case for a Gaussian random vector, we see that the Gaussian joint probability density function may be written as follows:

$$p_{XY}(x, y) = \frac{1}{2\pi\, \sigma_X \sigma_Y} \exp\left\{ -\frac{1}{2}\left[\frac{(x - \mu_X)^2}{\sigma_X^2} + \frac{(y - \mu_Y)^2}{\sigma_Y^2} \right] \right\} \qquad \text{[4.7.7]}$$

$$= \frac{1}{\sqrt{2\pi}\, \sigma_X} \exp\left\{ -\frac{1}{2}\left[\frac{(x - \mu_X)^2}{\sigma_X^2} \right] \right\} \frac{1}{\sqrt{2\pi}\sigma_Y} \exp\left\{ -\frac{1}{2}\left[\frac{(y - \mu_y)^2}{\sigma_Y^2} \right] \right\}$$

which is the product of two one-dimensional Gaussian probability density functions. This result may be generalized to an n component Gaussian random vector with mutually independent components. Therefore, if an n component Gaussian random vector has mutually independent components, then the covariance matrix is diagonal, since the off-diagonal terms are zero. Thus, for this situation the joint Gaussian probability density function is the product of the individual one-dimensional (marginal) probability density functions.

In the general case, we may express the **probability density function for a Gaussian vector with dependent components** as

$$p_{\vec{X}}(\vec{x}) = \frac{1}{(2\pi)^{\frac{n}{2}} [\det(C_{\vec{X}\vec{X}^T})]^{\frac{1}{2}}} \exp\left[-\frac{1}{2}(\vec{x} - \vec{\mu}_{\vec{x}})^T C_{\vec{X}\vec{X}^T}^{-1}(\vec{x} - \vec{\mu}_{\vec{x}}) \right] \qquad \text{[4.7.8]}$$

where the determinant of the covariance matrix, $C_{\vec{X}\vec{X}^T}$, is denoted as $\det(C_{\vec{X}\vec{X}^T})$ and the inverse of $C_{\vec{X}\vec{X}^T}$ is $C_{\vec{X}\vec{X}^T}^{-1}$. Equation [4.7.8] is often referred to as the **multivariate Gaussian probability density function** or as the **multi-dimensional Gaussian probability density function**.

4.8   THE SUM OF MUTUALLY INDEPENDENT RANDOM VARIABLES

Let us consider two mutually **independent** random variables, X and Y, with corresponding probability density functions $p_X(x)$ and $p_Y(y)$ and joint probability density function $p_{XY}(x, y) = p_X(x)p_Y(y)$. Now consider a new random variable, Z, composed of the sum of X and Y; that is:

$$Z = X + Y \qquad \text{[4.8.1]}$$

What is the probability density function $p_Z(z)$ for Z? This density is most easily found by using the characteristic function; that is,

$$\phi_Z(u) = \int_{-\infty}^{\infty} e^{juz} p_Z(z)\, dz = \int_{-\infty}^{\infty}\int_{-\infty}^{\infty} e^{ju(x+y)} p_X(x)\, p_Y(y)\, dx\, dy \qquad [4.8.2]$$

$$= \int_{-\infty}^{\infty} e^{jux} p_X(x)\, dx \int_{-\infty}^{\infty} e^{juy} p_Y(y)\, dy$$

$$= E[e^{juZ}] = E[e^{ju(X+Y)}] = E[e^{juX}]\, E[e^{juY}]$$

Then we have the following

$$p_Z(z) = \frac{1}{2\pi}\int_{-\infty}^{\infty} e^{-juz}\phi_Z(u)\, du \qquad [4.8.3]$$

$$= \frac{1}{2\pi}\int_{-\infty}^{\infty} e^{-juz}\left\{\int_{-\infty}^{\infty} e^{jux} p_X(x)\, dx \int_{-\infty}^{\infty} e^{juy}\, p_Y(y)\, dy\right\} du$$

$$= \int_{-\infty}^{\infty}\int_{-\infty}^{\infty} p_X(x)\, p_Y(y)\, \frac{1}{2\pi}\int_{-\infty}^{\infty} e^{-ju(z-x-y)}\, du\, dy\, dx$$

From Appendix 1, recall that the **delta function** is defined as

$$\frac{1}{2\pi}\int_{-\infty}^{\infty} e^{-j\omega t}\, d\omega = \delta(t) \qquad [4.8.4]$$

where

$$\int_{-\infty}^{\infty} \delta(t)\, dt = 1 \qquad [4.8.5]$$

$$\int_{-\infty}^{\infty} f(t)\delta(t - t_0)\, dt = f(t_0) \qquad [4.8.6]$$

If [4.8.4] is substituted into [4.8.3], we obtain

$$p_Z(z) = \int_{-\infty}^{\infty}\int_{-\infty}^{\infty} p_X(x)\, p_Y(y)\, \delta(z - x - y)\, dy\, dx \qquad [4.8.7]$$

$$= \int_{-\infty}^{\infty} p_X(x)\, p_Y(z - x)\, dx = p_X(z) * p_Y(z)$$

where * denotes convolution.

Thus, to determine the probability density function of the sum of two independent random variables, we can either **convolve** the probability density functions of the two random variables or Fourier transform each probability density, multiply the two Fourier transforms, and then perform an inverse Fourier transform.

PROPERTIES

1. For the **sum of two independent random variables,** $Z = X + Y$, we can show that

$$E[Z] = E[X] + E[Y] \qquad [4.8.8]$$

$$\sigma_Z^2 = \sigma_X^2 + \sigma_Y^2 \qquad\qquad \textbf{[4.8.9]}$$

2. For the **sum of n mutually independent random variables,**

$$Z = \sum_{k=1}^{n} X_k$$

we can show that

$$E[Z] = \sum_{k=1}^{n} E[X_k] \qquad\qquad \textbf{[4.8.10]}$$

$$\sigma_Z^2 = \sum_{k=1}^{n} \sigma_{X_k}^2 \qquad\qquad \textbf{[4.8.11]}$$

4.9   THE CENTRAL LIMIT THEOREM

Next, suppose we have the sum of a large number of mutually independent random variables. The central limit theorem says that under very general conditions, the probability density function of the sum of a large number of mutually independent random variables is asymptotically normal, regardless of the probability density function of the individual random variables; that is, the random variables do not have to be identically distributed. The term *asymptotically normal* means that the sum will approach a normal probability density as the number of summed random variables becomes large. Thus, if

$$Z = X_1 + X_2 + X_3 + \cdots + X_n$$

where the X_i are mutually independent random variables with probability density functions $p_{X_i}(x)$. Then, as a generalization of the previous result for the sum of two random variables, the probability density function for the sum of X_i is

$$p_Z(z) = p_{X_1}(z) * p_{X_2}(z) * \cdots * p_{X_n}(z)$$

where * denotes convolution. In the limit as $n \to \infty$ the probability density function for Z becomes the normal, or Gaussian, probability density function, such that

$$\lim_{n \to \infty} p_Z(z) = \frac{1}{\sqrt{2\pi}\sigma_Z} e^{-(z-\mu_z)^2/2\sigma_z^2} \qquad\qquad \textbf{[4.9.1]}$$

where

$$\mu_Z = \mu_{X_1} + \mu_{X_2} + \cdots + \mu_{X_n} + \cdots$$

$$\sigma_Z^2 = \sigma_{X_1}^2 + \sigma_{X_2}^2 + \cdots + \sigma_{X_n}^2 + \cdots$$

Find the limiting probability density function for the sum of N mutually independent and identically distributed random variables, where each random variable has an exponential probability density function given by

$$p_{X_i}(x) = e^{-x}u(x) \text{ for } i = 1, 2, 3, \cdots, N.$$

We first find the mean and the second moment for each random variable as

Example 4.25

$$\mu_{X_i} = \int_{-\infty}^{\infty} x\, p_{X_i}(x)\, dx = 1$$

and

$$E[X_i^2] = \int_{-\infty}^{\infty} x^2 p_{X_i}(x)\, dx = \int_{-\infty}^{\infty} x^2 e^{-x}\, dx = \Gamma(3) = 2! = 2$$

Then $\sigma^2{}_{X_i} = E([X_i^2]) - (\mu_{X_i})^2 = 1 \qquad i = 1, 2, 3, \ldots, N$

Thus

$$\mu_Z = \mu_{X_1} + \mu_{X_2} + \cdots + \mu_{X_N} = N \quad \text{and} \quad \sigma^2{}_Z = \sigma^2{}_{X_1} + \sigma^2{}_{X_2} + \cdots + \sigma^2{}_{X_N} = N$$

Then by the central limit theorem the limiting probability density function is

$$p_Z(z) = \frac{1}{\sqrt{2\pi N}}\, e^{-(z-N)^2/2N}$$

4.10   TRANSFORMATION OF A RANDOM VARIABLE

Consider a random variable X with a probability density function and a cumulative probability distribution function given by $p_X(x)$ and $P_X(X \le x)$, respectively. Define a new random variable Y such that $Y = f(X)$ with an inverse $X = g(Y)$; that is, $Y = f(X) = g^{-1}(X)$. What is the probability density function $p_Y(y)$? This problem is often encountered in the study of systems where the probability density function for the input random variable X is known and the probability density function for the output random variable Y is to be determined. In such a case we say that the input random variable has undergone a transformation.

In order to solve this problem we must place some restrictions upon the function $f(X)$, so that the properties of the probability density function are maintained. For example, we require that $Y = f(X)$ be a continuous, one-to-one, monotonically increasing function. Then the inverse $X = g(Y)$ exists and is well behaved. Then we have

$$P_X(X \le x) = P_Y(Y \le y) \qquad \text{[4.10.1]}$$

where

$$X \le x$$

and

$$Y = f(X) \le f(x) = y$$

since

$$P_Y(Y \le y) = P_X(X \le x) = P_X(g(Y) \le x) \qquad \text{[4.10.2]}$$

Then the probability density for Y is found by taking the derivative with respect to y, giving

$$p_Y(y) = p_X(g(y)) \left[\frac{d}{dy} g(y) \right] \qquad \text{[4.10.3]}$$

We may generalize this result to include the case when $Y = f(X)$ is monotonically decreasing. Thus, the probability density function for a random variable that undergoes a monotonically increasing or a monotonically decreasing transformation is given as

$$p_Y(y) = p_X(g(y)) \left| \frac{d}{dy} g(y) \right|$$ [4.10.4]

where the vertical lines about the derivative denote absolute value. This result does not apply to functions that are multivalued, such as $y = x^2$ or $x = \pm\sqrt{y}$. However, if the transformation can be sectioned into regions that are either monotonically increasing or decreasing, then the result may be applied to each individual section one at a time. We illustrate these concepts in the following examples.

A random variable X has a probability density function $p_X(x)$. Find $p_Y(y)$ if $Y = 2X$. We may apply [4.10.4] with $g(y) = y/2$. Therefore,   **Example 4.26**

$$p_Y(y) = p_X\left(\frac{y}{2}\right)\left|\frac{d}{dy}\left(\frac{y}{2}\right)\right| = p_X\left(\frac{y}{2}\right)\left|\frac{1}{2}\right| = \frac{1}{2}p_X\left(\frac{y}{2}\right)$$

Let $p_X(x) = 2e^{-2x} u(x)$. Suppose the transformation to the random variable is   **Example 4.27**

$$Y = f(X) = X^3 \text{ then } X = Y^{\frac{1}{3}} = g(Y) = \sqrt[3]{Y}$$

Then

$$\frac{d}{dy} g(y) = \frac{1}{3} y^{-\frac{2}{3}}$$

which, when substituted into [4.10.4] gives

$$p_Y(y) = 2e^{-2\sqrt[3]{y}} \frac{1}{3} y^{-\frac{2}{3}} u(y)$$

$$= \frac{2}{3} y^{-\frac{2}{3}} e^{-2\sqrt[3]{y}} u(y)$$

Let   **Example 4.28**

$$p_\Theta(\theta) = \frac{1}{\pi}, \quad -\frac{\pi}{2} \leq \Theta \leq \frac{\pi}{2}$$

and consider the transformation

$$Y = a \sin \Theta \text{ or } \Theta = g(Y) = \sin^{-1}\frac{Y}{a}$$

In general, this transformation is not one-to-one as required for the application of [4.10.4]. However, if Θ is restricted to the interval $(-\pi/2, \pi/2)$, as it is in this problem, then the function is one-to-one. Thus:

$$\frac{dg(y)}{dy} = \frac{1}{a\sqrt{1 - \left(\frac{y}{a}\right)^2}}$$

and

$$p_Y(y) = \frac{1}{\pi a} \frac{1}{\sqrt{1 - \left(\frac{y}{a}\right)^2}}, \quad -a < y < a$$

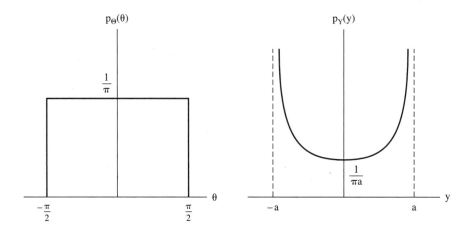

Figure 4.8   The probability density $p_Y(y)$ for the transformation $Y = a \sin \Theta$

Figure 4.8 shows the two probability density functions.

One interpretation of this result is that we may imagine the transformation $Y = a \sin \Theta$ to be the output of a sine phase angle generator. The random variable Y is a voltage that is dependent on the phase angle of the generator. The phase angle Θ is selected at random according to a uniform probability density; that is, it is equally likely that any phase angle Θ will occur. The transformation then maps the phase angle according to the sine function, which is also multiplied by the constant a. The probability density function for Y is the probability density function for obtaining a particular voltage level, according to the transformation. It is more likely that a voltage near $\pm a$ will occur when the generator is activated than a voltage near zero. Return to Example 3.5, which used MATLAB, and compare that result with the above theoretical result.

Quiz 4.25   Determine the mean and the variance for $p_Y(y)$ in the above example.

Example 4.29 | In this example consider the uniform probability density given by

$$p_X(x) = \frac{1}{2a}[u(x + a) - u(x - a)]$$

Let the transformation be $Y = X^2$, which is known as a square-law transformation. We know that [4.10.4] does not apply for this situation. However, we may consider two regions for X, namely $X < 0$ and $X > 0$. Dividing X into these two mutually exclusive intervals causes $g(Y) = \pm\sqrt{Y}$ to become a single-value function and we may apply [4.10.4] to each interval separately. Then because the intervals are mutually exclusive, we may add the results obtained from applying [4.10.4] to each interval to obtain the total $p_Y(y)$. This is done below. The partial contribution to the total probability density function from one interval for X is

$$p_Y(y) = \frac{1}{2a}\left|\frac{d}{dy}[g(y)]\right| = \frac{1}{2a}\frac{1}{2}y^{-\frac{1}{2}} = \frac{1}{4a\sqrt{y}}, \quad 0 < y \le a^2$$

But this result is the same if $X < 0$ or $X > 0$. Thus, the total probability density function is

$$p_Y(y) = \frac{1}{4a\sqrt{y}} + \frac{1}{4a\sqrt{y}} = \frac{1}{2a\sqrt{y}}, 0 < y \le a^2$$

Quiz 4.26   Verify that $p_Y(y)$, above, is a valid probability density function.

For this example suppose we have | **Example 4.30**

$$p_X(x) = 2x\,[u(x) - u(x - 1)]$$

and let the transformation be

$$Y = 2 - X \text{ or } g(Y) = 2 - Y$$

then

$$\frac{d}{dy}[g(y)] = -1$$

and

$$\left|\frac{d}{dy}[g(y)]\right| = |-1| = +1$$

Therefore,

$$p_Y(y) = 2(2 - y)[u(y - 1) - u(y - 2)]$$

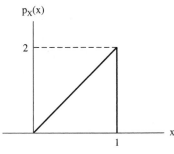
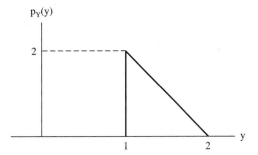

Quiz 4.27   Suppose X is a random variable with zero mean and a normal probability density function. If X is transformed such that $Y = X$ for $X \ge 0$ and $Y = 0$ for $X < 0$, then find the probability density function for Y.

4.11   MATLAB EXAMPLES

In Problem 3.4M we considered a sample of speech data, namely, data file P3_4M.d, which is a sample of a sustained vowel /i/, as pronounced in the word b*eet*. A plot of a segment of this data is shown | **Example 4.31**

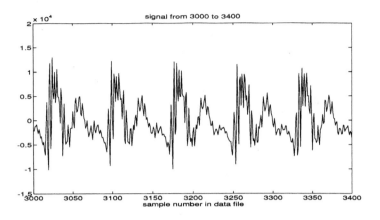

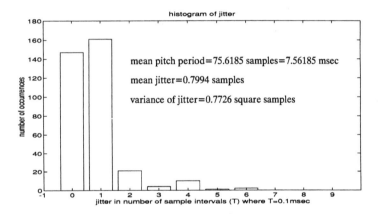

Figure 4.9   A segment of the vowel /i/ and the histogram of the jitter

in Figure 4.9. The signal was sampled at 10 kHz, so the interval between samples is 0.1 msec. The interval between the peaks is called the pitch period, and the reciprocal of this interval is the pitch or fundamental frequency of voicing. The random variation in the pitch period is called jitter. The histogram of the jitter is also shown in Figure 4.9, while the program for plotting these figures and for calculating the mean and variance for the jitter appear in Figure 4.10. The MATLAB program defines the jitter as the absolute value of the difference between the mean pitch period and the instantaneous pitch period. The execution of the m file shown in Figure 4.10 results in the following output

meanpitchperiod = 75.6185

meanjitter = 0.7994

varjitter = 0.7726

hit any key for next graph

```
%MATLAB Example 4.31 by jmw
load P3_4M.d                                        % load data from disk
s = P3_4M;                                          % s is now signal to be analyzed
maxsignal = max(s);                                 % find largest peak in signal
TH = 0.45* maxsignal;                               % set threshold at percentage of peak value
L = length(s);                                      % find length of signal
peakcount = 0;                                      % counter for number of peaks
mask = 0;                                           % mask to block false peaks from being counted
for i = 1:L,
          if (s(i) > TH & mask ==0)                 % signal exceeds threshold (new peak)
          peakcount = peakcount + 1;                % increase peak count
          peak(peakcount) = i;                      % record position of peak
          mask = 1;                                 % set mask
          maskcountdown = 55;                       % start mask down-counter
          elseif (mask == 1)
          maskcountdown = maskcountdown −1;          % decrease mask
          if (maskcountdown <= 0);                  % down counter
          mask = 0;                                 % reset mask if counter  = zero
          end;
          end;
end;
Lp = length(peak);                                  % find size of peak vector
pitchperiod = peak(2:Lp) − peak(1:Lp−1);            % find pitch periods
meanpitchperiod = mean(pitchperiod)                 % find mean pitch period in # samples & print
jitter = abs(pitchperiod − meanpitchperiod);        % find deviation from mean
meanjitter = mean(jitter)                           % mean of jitter & print
varjitter = std(jitter)*std(jitter)                 % variance of jitter & print
bins=[−1:1:10];                                     % bins for histogram
hist(jitter,bins);
a=axis;
axis([−1 10 a(3) a(4)]);
xlabel('jitter in number of sample intervals (T) where T=0.1msec');
ylabel('number of occurrences');
title('historgram of jitter');
disp('hit any key for next graph');
pause;
plot(s);                                            % plot a portion of the signal
a = axis;                                           % from 3000 to 3400
axis([3000 3400 a(3) a(4)]);
xlabel('sample number in data file');
title('signal from 3000 to 3400');
```

Figure 4.10   MATLAB program for Example 4.31

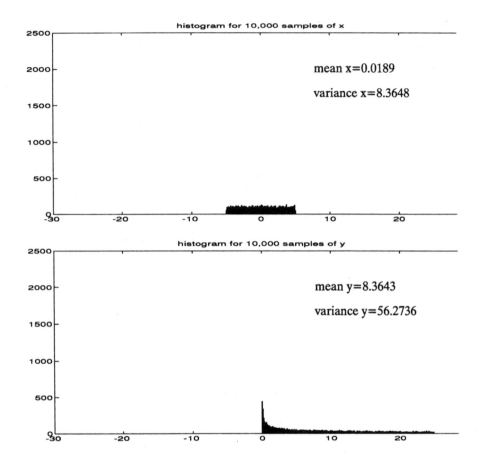

Figure 4.11   The histograms for example 4.32

Example 4.32 | In this example we use the function *rand* to generate a sequence of uniformly distributed random numbers which we transform as in Example 4.29. Then we calculate the histogram of the output of the transformation, as well as the mean and the variance. The histograms are shown in Figure 4.11, while the MATLAB program appears in Figure 4.12.

4.12 SUMMARY

Appendix 6 has two practice examinations that cover the material in Chapters 1 through 4. The purpose of these examinations is to provide the student with an opportunity to obtain some practice prior to taking an actual examination in class.

This chapter has covered numerous topics related to **expectation.** Perhaps the most useful concept is that of **moments.** This concept will be employed as a tool that

% MATLAB Example 4.32 by jmw

```
N = 10000;                      % number of random numbers
a = 5.0;                        % a can be any number
x = 2*a*rand(1,N);              % make x first
x = x 2 a;
bins = [2a*a:0.1:a*a];
g=hist(x,bins);
bar(bins,g);
a=axis;
axis(fa(1) a(2) a(3) 2500g);
title('histogram for 10,000 samples of x');
mean_x = mean(x)
variance_x = std(x)*std(x)
disp('hit any key for next graph');
pause;
y = x.*x;                       % make y
hist(y,bins);
axis([a(1) a(2) a(3) 2500]);
title('histogram for 10,000 samples of y');
mean_y = mean(y)               % calculate mean of y
variance_y = std(y)*std(y)     % calculate variance of y
```

Figure 4.12   MATLAB program for Example 4.32

we will use to measure parameters of **random processes** in later chapters. While it is desirable to be able to calculate the probability density function for a random variable, this is often not possible because we may lack sufficient information to do so. As a consequence we seek ways by which we may measure parameters of the random variable to provide us with insight to a problem. Examples of useful and frequently used parameters are the **mean,** the **variance,** the **covariance,** and the **correlation coefficient.** These parameters will be used extensively in the following chapters as descriptors or features of random processes. The **characteristic function,** the **central limit theorem,** and **functional transformations** are concepts that will prove useful in solving design and analysis problems involving random process, such as signals and noise in linear systems and devices. We also considered **random vectors** and introduced the **covariance** and **correlation matrices. Multidimensional Gaussian probability density functions** were introduced for random vectors with mutually independent components. There are occasions when there is a need to approximate probability density functions with polynomial expansions. This is discussed later.

PROBLEMS

4.1 A coin is flipped until a head appears. What is the expected (average) number of flips for a head to appear? Find the second moment and the variance.

4.2 Find $E[X]$ and $E[X^2]$ for a random variable with the following probability density function.

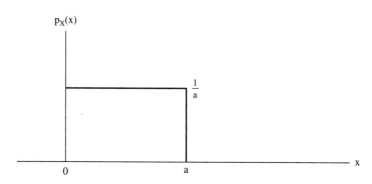

4.3 Show that *all* odd moments about the mean of a Gaussian probability density function are zero and derive the expression for all even moments about the mean in terms of σ_X. The answers are given in [4.5.24] and [4.5.25], respectively.

4.4 Find the variance for a geometric random variable.

4.5 Find the characteristic function for a Poisson random variable with the following probability density function:

$$p_X(x) = \sum_{r=0}^{\infty} \frac{\alpha^x e^{-\alpha}}{x!} \delta(x - r);$$

Show that the coefficients of the series of expansion of the characteristic function are related to the moments.

4.6 Given that $p_X(x) = c\, e^{-x}\, u(x)$, find

    a. c

    b. $\phi_X(u)$

    c. $E[X^k]$

       (1)Using $p_X(x)$

       (2)Using $\phi_X(u)$

    d. $(\sigma_X)^2$

       (1)Using $p_X(x)$

       (2)Using $\phi_X(u)$

    e. the coefficients of skewness and kurtosis.

4.7 Two points are chosen at random between 0 and 1. What is the probability that they are within ϵ of each other?

4.8 Given the transformation $Y = (X - 1)^2$ and that the probability for $X = x$ is $P(x)$ is given as follows:

Find $p_X(x)$ and $P_X(x)$. Find $p_Y(y)$ and $P_Y(y)$.

X	0	1	2
P(x)	$\dfrac{1}{4}$	$\dfrac{1}{2}$	$\dfrac{1}{4}$

4.9 Suppose $p_X(x) = \frac{1}{2}[u(x + 1) - u(x - 1)]$; and the transformation is $Y = X^2$. What is ρ_{XY}, the correlation coefficient? Are X and Y uncorrelated? Are X and Y independent?

4.10 If $Y_1 = X_1 + X_2$ and $Y_2 = X_1 + X_2 + X_3$, where each of the X_i are mutually independent and have identical uniform probability density functions given below; find $p_{Y1}(y)$ and $p_{Y2}(y)$. Sketch both probability density functions. Is it reasonable to conclude that the central limit theorem will be satisfied as the number terms being summed approaches infinity?

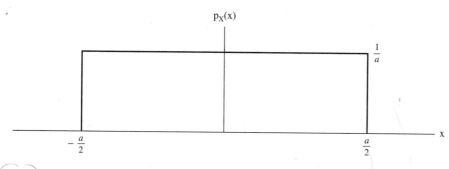

4.11 Given the transformation $Y = X^3$, and that $p_X(x)$ is Gaussian with $\mu_X = 0$, and σ_X^2 arbitrary. Find $p_Y(y)$.

4.12 Imagine that you are trapped in a circular room with three doors symmetrically placed around the perimeter. You are told by a mysterious voice that one door leads to the outside after a two-hour trip through a maze. However, the other two doors lead to mazes that terminate back in the room after a two-hour trip at which time you are unable to tell through which door you exited or entered. What is the average time for escape to the outside? Can you guess the answer ahead of time? If not, can you provide a physical explanation for the answer you calculate?

4.13 You are given a random variable with the probability density function $p_X(x) = 2\,e^{-2x}$ for $x > 0$ and the transformation $Y = 1 - X$. Find the range for X and Y. Find $p_Y(y)$.

4.14 Find and compare the coefficients of skewness and kurtosis for a random variable with the uniform probability density function given in Problem 4.10 and for a Gaussian random variable with zero mean and variance σ_X^2.

4.15 Prove equations [4.5.5] through [4.5.7].

4.16 A Gaussian random variable with zero mean and variance σ_X^2 is applied to a device that has only two possible outputs, zero or one. The output zero occurs when the input is negative, and the output one occurs when the input is zero or positive. What is the output probability density function? Rework the problem when $\mu_X = 0.5$ and $\sigma_X = 1$.

4.17 A football quarterback throws a football at a target marked out on the ground 40 yards from his position. Assume that the distribution for the football's hitting the target is Gaussian within the plane of the target. Let the coordinates of the plane of the target be denoted by the x and y axes. Thus, the probability density function is a two-dimensional Gaussian. The average location of the hits is at the origin of the target and the standard deviation in each direction is the same and is denoted as σ. Find the probability that the hits will be located within an annular ring of width dr located a distance r from the origin; that is, find the probability density function for hits as a function of the radius from the origin.

4.18 Use the characteristic function (or the moment generating function) to show that the Poisson probability density function is the limit of the binomial probability density function with n approaching infinity and p approaching zero in such a way that $np = \mu = $ constant.

4.19 Show that

$$\Gamma\left(\frac{1}{2}\right) = \int_0^\infty e^{-x} x^{-\frac{1}{2}}\, dx = \sqrt{\pi}$$

Hint: Convert $\Gamma(1/2)$ to a Gaussian form by a change of variable (e.g., $y^2 = x$). Then consider

$$I = \int_0^\infty e^{-x^2} dx \text{ and } I^2 = \int_0^\infty \int_0^\infty e^{-(x^2+y^2)}\, dx\, dy$$

Convert I^2 to polar coordinates and integrate.

4.20 Let X be a random variable with a Gaussian probability density function with zero mean and unity variance. Assume this random variable is transformed such that $Y = |X|$. Find the probability density function for Y.

4.21 Repeat Problem 4.20 if the transformation is $Y = X$ for $X > 0$ and $Y = 0$ for $X \le 0$.

4.22 A random variable is transformed by the following device. Suppose the random variable has a Gaussian probability density function with zero mean and variance σ_X^2. Find and sketch the probability density function of the transformed random variable.

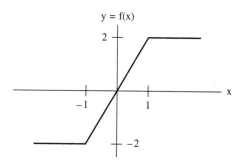

4.23 Show that the characteristic function of the geometric random variable is

$$\frac{pe^{ju}}{1 - qe^{ju}}$$

4.24 Mr. Hood is a good archer. He can regularly hit a target having a 3 ft. diameter, and often hits the bull's-eye, which is 0.5 ft. in diameter, from 50 ft. away. Suppose the miss is measured as the radial distance from the center of the target. Furthermore, suppose this radial miss distance is a Rayleigh random variable with the constant in the Rayleigh probability density function being $b = 4$ (ft)^2. Determine the probability of Mr. Hood's hitting the bull's-eye given that the arrow lands on the target.

4.25 Show that the coefficient of skewness is positive for a Rayleigh random variable.

4.26 Suppose two random variables are related such that $X = aY^2$. Assume that $p_Y(y)$ is even about the origin. Show that $\rho_{XY} = 0$. Interpret this result.

4.27 A real number between 0 and 100 is randomly selected and rounded off to the nearest integer. For example, 36.5001 is rounded off to 37, $(3)^{1/2}$ is rounded off to 2, and 69.49 is rounded off to 69. Define a random variable to be $X =$ (number selected) − (nearest integer). What is the range of this random variable? Determine the mean square value of the random variable. Hint: Determine the probability density function for X.

4.28 Find the characteristic function for the random variable with the following probability density function

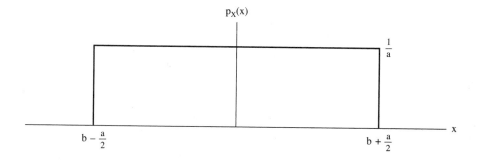

4.29 The joint probability density function for two random variables X and Y is

$$p_{XY}(x, y) = \left[\frac{3}{4} + xy\right][u(x) - u(x-1)][u(y) - u(y-1)]$$

Find the conditional probability density function $p_{Y|X}(y \mid x)$ and the probability that $Y > 1/2$ given that $X = 1/2$.

4.30 Find the geometric mean, sample mean, harmonic mean, and RMS of the numbers 3, 5, 6, 6, 7, 10, 12. Also determine the sample variance of the data.

4.31 Show that the RMS $\geq$ geometric mean (m_g) for two unequal positive numbers.

4.32 A random vector is generated as follows: A die is rolled and the outcome is observed. The components of the random vector are determined by successive rolls of the die. Roll the die two times. List the possible random vectors. Determine the probability of each vector. Determine the mean vector. Determine the covariance matrix.

4.33 Repeat Problem 4.32, except roll the die three times.

4.34 Show that [4.7.8] reduces to [4.7.7] when the random vector has only two mutually independent components.

4.35 When a Gaussian random vector has three mutually independent components, expand [4.7.8] to show that the three-dimensional probability density function is the product of 3 one-dimensional Gaussian probability density functions.

4.36 Consider a two-component random vector with dependent components. Show that [4.7.8] reduces to [4.6.11].

4.37 Each of the two independent random variables X and Y has a Gaussian probability density function given as $p_X(x)$ and $p_Y(y)$, respectively. Each random variable has a zero mean and the variances are equal; that is, $\sigma_X = \sigma_Y = \sigma$. Transform the random variables as follows: $X = R\cos(\Theta)$, $Y = R\sin(\Theta)$, then

$$R = \sqrt{X^2 + Y^2} \text{ and } \Theta = \tan^{-1}\left(\frac{Y}{X}\right)$$

so that the probability density for R and Θ is

$$p_{R\Theta}(r, \theta) = p_{XY}[r\cos(\theta), r\sin(\theta)]\,J$$

$$= p_{XY}[r\cos(\theta), r\sin(\theta)]\begin{vmatrix} \dfrac{\partial x}{\partial r} & \dfrac{\partial x}{\partial \theta} \\ \dfrac{\partial y}{\partial r} & \dfrac{\partial y}{\partial \theta} \end{vmatrix} = p_{XY}[r\cos(\theta), r\sin(\theta)]\,r$$

where J is the Jacobian of the transformation, which is

$$J = \begin{vmatrix} \cos(\theta) & -r\sin(\theta) \\ \sin(\theta) & r\cos(\theta) \end{vmatrix} = r$$

which in turn implies that dxdy = rdrdθ, which is the well-known area transformation from rectangular coordinates to polar coordinates.

Now complete the problem to find $p_{R\Theta}(r,\theta)$. Then find the marginal probability densities for R and Θ. What are names of the marginal probability densities? Are R and Θ independent?

MATLAB PROBLEMS

4.1M Plot the loci of points for the ellipses discussed in Example 4.21, equation [4.6.13]. Consider the following cases: $\sigma_X = \sigma_Y$ and $\rho_{XY} = 0$, $\sigma_X > \sigma_Y$ and $\rho_{XY} = 0$, $\sigma_X < \sigma_Y$ and $\rho_{XY} = 0$, and $\sigma_X = \sigma_Y$ and $\rho_{XY} \neq 0$. Let c^2 be the same value for each case. Indicate the alignment of the major and minor axes of each ellipse with the x and y axes for each of the cases. Discuss the effect σ_X, σ_Y, and ρ_{XY} have on the shape of the contour. Now select one of the cases and let c^2 increase and decrease. What is the significance of c^2? An alternative form of this problem is to let the two random variables be linearly related such that X = aY. Then describe the behavior of a contour of the probability density function as ρ_{XY} increases from 0 to unity.

4.2M Repeat Problem 4.27 using MATLAB with the following changes. Select a real number between 0 and 1,000 in a random manner and round the number off to the nearest integer. Define a random variable to be X = (number selected) − (nearest integer). Determine and plot the histogram for this problem. Determine the mean square value of the random variable using the histogram. Determine the sample variance of the data.

4.3M Use the data sequence of numbers in the data file P4_3M.d, to find the sample mean, the geometric mean, the harmonic mean, and the root mean square (quadratic mean). Assume the data in this file represents a sample sequence of a random variable. Determine and plot the histogram for the random variable. Determine the mean square value and the variance of the random variable using the histogram. Also determine the sample variance of the data.

4.4M Verify the entries for $p_X(x)$ and erf(x) in Table 4.4 for x = 1.00 and x = 2.70. Generalize your program so that you can calculate $p_X(x)$ and erf(x) for any value of x.

4.5M Repeat Problem 4.22 using MATLAB. Use the function *randn* as you did in Problem 3.2M to generate a sequence of 100,000 Gaussian random numbers. Transform this sequence using the transformation given in Problem 4.22. Calculate the histogram for the output of the transformation; that is, y = f(x). Does the histogram agree well with the probability density function you calculated for Problem 4.22? Estimate the mean and variance of the data at the output of the transformation.

4.6M Write a MATLAB program to implement a generalization of Problem 4.10, that is, for any $p_X(x)$. Also let there be N terms in the sum $Y = X_1 + X_2 + \ldots + X_N$. Test your program using the uniform probability density function given in Problem 4.10.

4.7M Write a program to simulate Problem 4.12.

4.8M Repeat Example 4.30 using MATLAB. Note that for this problem there is no function in MATLAB that provides a sequence of data samples that has the probability density function for $p_X(x)$ in Example 4.30. Thus, you must transform a uniform probability density function to give $p_X(x)$. Then you can proceed with the problem as in Example 4.32.

4.9M Implement Example 4.22 in MATLAB so that you can calculate the probability $P_{XY}(x_1 \leq X \leq x_2, y_1 \leq Y \leq y_2)$ for any x_i and y_i, $i = 1, 2$. You may have to consider several ranges of values for x_i and $y_{i,}$ $i = 1, 2$.

5

Random Processes

5.1 INTRODUCTION

This chapter introduces functions that depend both on the outcome of an experiment and on time. For example, the function $x(t) = a \sin(\omega t + \theta)$ depends on time as well as on the values of a, ω, and θ, which are constants for deterministic functions. However, a, ω, and θ may also be specific values of the random variables A, Ω, and Θ, respectively. Functions that depend on time as well as on one or more random variables serve as models of signals that convey information in various systems. A deterministic signal is not a good model for the transmission of data, even though such a signal may vary with time, because the future values of a deterministic signal are completely predictable from the known past values as we discussed in Chapter 2. If information is to be conveyed, then the signal must not be known. It must not be deterministic. The signal must be, in some sense, unpredictable. For example, the signal might depend on an experimental outcome over time. Such signals are random in some sense. Thus, one purpose of this chapter is to define a random process for which time is typically the independent variable, although distance is often another independent variable in some applications, such as the monitoring of seismic events. We will give numerous examples of random processes. In the chapters that follow we will develop procedures for analyzing the response of linear systems for signal plus noise inputs. In addition, we will study some system design procedures that include maximizing the signal-to-noise ratio, estimating the signal arrival time, determining the direction of arrival of a signal, recognizing the presence of a particular signal, making velocity measurements, and other applications.

5.2 RANDOM PROCESSES AND ENSEMBLES

For deterministic functions we often encounter four types or classes of signals:

Definition 5.1. A **continuous time and continuous amplitude** function, also known as an **analog** signal, is a function of the independent, continuous variable time. The range of the amplitude of the function is continuous.

Definition 5.2. A **continuous time and discrete amplitude** function is a function of the independent, continuous variable time, while the range of values for the amplitude is discrete. This type of signal may be generated by a digital-to-analog (D/A) converter prior to lowpass filtering.

Definition 5.3. A **discrete time and continuous amplitude** function, also known as a **sampled** signal, is a function of the independent, quantized variable time, while the range of the amplitude is continuous. It is common for the intervals between the quantized time samples to be uniformly spaced, but this is not necessary. The output of a sample-and-hold device, discussed in communications, is an example of this type of signal.

Definition 5.4. A **discrete time and discrete amplitude** function is a function for which both the independent variable time and the range of the amplitude of the function are quantized. Often the quantization in time is at uniform intervals. If the quantization in amplitude is also uniform, then the function is often called a **digital** signal because such signals typically are generated by an analog-to-digital (A/D) converter. The output of a codec, a coding device used in communications, is also a digital signal.

Figure 5.1 illustrates the above four definitions.
We shall also use discrete time sequences.

Definition 5.5. A **discrete time sequence** is a sequence of numbers defined for uniform intervals of an independent variable time, t; that is, $t = nT$, where T is the interval between successive values in the sequence and n is an integer greater than or equal to zero in this book. We denote the values of the numbers in the sequence by $x(nT)$ or more simply by $x(n)$ or by x_n.

Example 5.1 | A discrete time sequence can be generated by sampling a continuous time signal at uniformly spaced time intervals. In Figure 5.1 the two discrete time waveforms are examples of discrete time sequences.

We shall now define random processes that have properties with respect to both time and amplitude analogous to those defined above. However, we shall see that random processes have other distinguishing features as well.

Recall from Chapter 3 that a random variable, $X(s)$, is a function of the possible outcomes, s, of an experiment. Now we would like to extend this concept so that a continuous time function, $x(t, s)$, is assigned to every outcome, s, of an experiment, where t has a continuum of values. The function $x(t, s)$ may be real or complex and is a function of two variables: time, t, and experimental outcome, s. The function $x(t, s)$ may be the

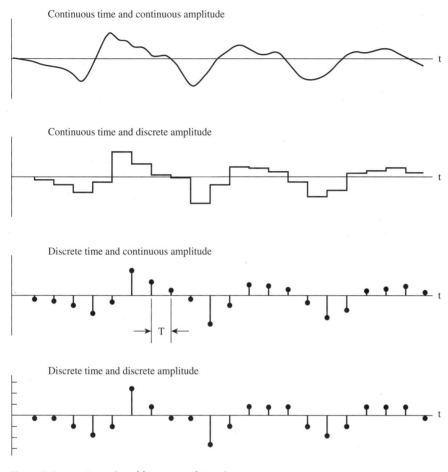

Figure 5.1   Examples of four types of signals

same function or a different function for every experimental outcome. For example, the function may be x(t, s) = a sin(ωt), where the value of the amplitude a is determined by the experimental outcome s. In general, the function x(t, s) is a member of an **ensemble** (family, set, collection) of functions with both t and s as variables. Just as we did for random variables, an **ensemble of member functions,** X(t, s), is denoted with an upper-case letter. Thus, X(t, s) denotes the **random process,** while x(t, s) is a particular member function of the random process, that is, is a particular member of the ensemble. The function x(t, s) is also sometimes called a **sample function** or a **member function** of the ensemble. To help illustrate these ideas, consider an experiment with only two possible outcomes, say the flip of a coin. Then s = H or s = T depending on whether the outcome of a flip of the coin is a head or a tail, respectively. Suppose a function from the random process X(t, s) = A(s) sin(ωt) is assigned to the two possible outcomes as follows. If s = H, then A(s) = A(H) = 1 and, thus, x(t, s) = sin(ωt), while if s = T, then A(s) = A(T) = 2 and, therefore, x(t, s) = 2 sin(ωt). Then the ensemble of member functions is X(t, s) = {sin(ωt), 2 sin(ωt)} and the two member functions are sin(ωt) and 2 sin(ωt).

   If the experimental outcome has occurred or is fixed at, say, s_1, then the time function, x(t, s_1) is said to be indexed with respect to time. The term *index* is used for both discrete and continuous values of t. Such a single time function may be considered a typical time function for that particular experimental outcome, s_1. Thus, for the coin flipping experiment we just considered, if s_1 = H, then x(t, s_1) = sin(ωt).

   If time is fixed say, at t_1, then we have an ensemble of random variables, X(t_1, s) indexed by the experimental outcome s, where again we use the term *index* for both discrete and continuous values of the experimental outcome. Thus, for the coin flipping experiment the ensemble of the two random variables would be X(t_1, s) = {sin(ωt_1), 2 sin(ωt_1)}. The value of the function x(t_1, s_1) is a single number (real or complex) when both t and s are fixed. We now define a random process using these ideas.

   Definition 5.6. A **continuous random process,** X(t,s), is a set of member (sample) functions of random variables that are a function of time, where t is a continuum of values and the range of values of the random variable (or variables if there are more than one) is continuous.

We may also think of a random process as an ensemble. According to the dictionary the term *ensemble* is all the parts of a thing taken together, so that each part is considered only in relation to the whole. Thus, a continuous random process may be considered to be defined by its ensemble of member functions of random variables, where their associated probability density functions are defined.

Example 5.2 | Suppose a random process is described by X(t, s) = A(s) sin(ωt + θ), where A(s) is a random variable with ω and θ real variables. Let the random variable A(s) have a uniform probability density function such that

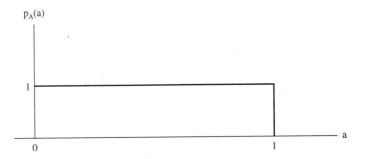

Then, we may depict the ensemble as in Figure 5.2. Here x(t, s_i) denotes the particular function of the random process for the s_i experimental outcome. Sometimes it may be more clear to replace the notation x(t, s_i) with x[t, A(s_i)] = x(t, a_i) to indicate more specifically the value of the random

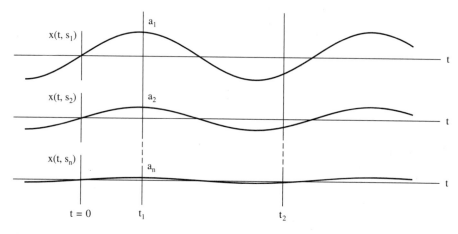

Figure 5.2   An ensemble example

variable for the particular experimental outcome s_i. Note that the largest value for A is 1, while the smallest value is zero. Furthermore, for this example, frequency, ω, and phase angle, θ, are not random variables and remain fixed for all member functions of the ensemble. In Figure 5.2, $\theta = 0$ and ω is set to an arbitrary but fixed value. If t is fixed, say, at t_1, then we have a random variable for the amplitude, which takes on various specific values $a_1, a_2, \ldots, a_n$, as shown in Figure 5.2. However, if the random variable is fixed, then we have an ordinary sine wave that is a function of time. This sine wave is just one member function of the ensemble and is said to be indexed by time, even though this index is a continuum. For convenience of illustration we have labeled the various values of $A(s_i)$ as a_i. However, this random process is a continuous random process, having an uncountable number of member functions.

If the observations of the ensemble are taken at time t_1 (i.e., the member functions of the ensemble are sampled at time t_1), then the probability density function for the amplitude random variable A(s) is that specified. Thus, for the example just considered, we would have $p_A(a, t_1)$, where the amplitude random variable is A(s). The probability density function becomes a joint probability density function if we make observations at t_1 and t_2, i.e., $p_A(a, t_1; a, t_2)$. And we would have a multivariate probability density function if we extend our number of observations. For Example 5.2 we see that the probability density function changes as t_i changes, since at $t = 0$, for example, the amplitude of all member functions is zero. When the probability density function for the random variable is a function of time, the random process is said to be **nonstationary.** In other situations, the probability density function for the random variable will not change with time and the random process is said to be **stationary.** We will discuss stationary and nonstationary random processes in the next chapter. In general, a random process, X(t, s), is said to be statistically determined if its nth order probability density function, $p_X(x, t_1;$

x, t_2, . . . , x, t_n), for any order n is known for the random variable X(s). We assume that the probability density function exists.

Example 5.3 | Let the random process X(t, s) be defined such that x(t, s) = x(t, H) = sin(2πt) if an unbiased coin is tossed once and the outcome is a head and x(t, s) = x(t, T) = sin(2πt + π/2) if the outcome is a tail. Thus, there are two member functions in the ensemble. Since the coin is unbiased, each member function is equally likely to occur. The experimental outcome s is either a head or a tail.

Quiz 5.1   Sketch an ensemble for the random process in Example 5.3. What is the random variable?

Example 5.4 | Example 5.3 may also be considered from an alternative view point. For example, we note that the amplitude of the random process may be considered a random variable at any time instant. Find the probability density function for the amplitude random variable X(s) for the random process X(t, s) when t = 0 in Example 5.3. We will also denote this random variable as X(t = 0, s). The amplitude can never be greater than unity at t = 0. In fact x(t = 0, H) = 0 and x(t = 0, T) = 1. Thus, $p_X(x, t = 0) = \{1/2\, \delta[x(t = 0, H)] + 1/2\, \delta[x(t = 0, T) - 1]\}$.

In the last example we note that the notation is becoming burdensome, particularly since we must denote the values for both t and s. Consequently, later in the chapter we will drop the experimental outcome notation for convenience, since the random variable will usually be apparent and the probability density function for the random variable will be known. Thus, in the example above we would use the following abbreviated expression for the probability density function: $p_X(x) = [1/2\, \delta(x) + 1/2\, \delta(x - 1)]$ for t = 0, where X is the amplitude random variable and x is the particular value of the amplitude random variable, which in this case is either zero or one.

Quiz 5.2   Find the probability density function for the amplitude random variable for Example 5.3 at t = 1/6.

Definition 5.7. Define a **sine wave random process** as

$$X(t, s) = A(s) \sin(\Omega(s)t + \Theta(s)) \qquad\qquad [5.2.1]$$

where A(s), Ω(s), and Θ(s) are random variables with defined probability density functions. For each experimental outcome s_i, the values of the random variables $A(s_i)$, $\Omega(s_i)$, and $\Theta(s_i)$ are determined by the experimental outcome s_i, which is determined by the respective probability density functions; for instance, if s = s_1, then we would have x(t, s_1) = $a_1 \sin(\omega_1 t + \theta_1)$. As noted previously, we will sometimes use the notation x(t, s_i) and x(t, a_i, ω_i, θ_i) interchangeably.

Example 5.5

The ensemble for a sine wave random process would look like that depicted in Figure 5.3, where we show only three member functions for three different values of $A(s)$, $\Omega(s)$, and $\Theta(s)$.

Example 5.6

Suppose we have the random process $X(t, s) = A(s) \sin(\omega t)$ for all t, where $A(s)$ is the random variable and the probability density for $A(s)$ is uniform from zero to unity. Then the random process is similar to that in Example 5.1, and the ensemble would also be similar.

So far, we have discussed only continuous random processes; that is, random processes for which the range of $X(t, s)$ is continuous and for which t is a continuum. We may, however, have a discrete range for $X(t, s)$ and t may also be discrete.

Definition 5.8. A continuous time, discrete amplitude random process is a random process whose range of values for $X(t, s)$ is discrete, while t is a continuum.

This definition is analogous to our Definition 5.2 for a continuous time and discrete amplitude deterministic signal.

Example 5.7

Let $X(t, s)$ be a random process whose value is either zero or one with equal probability determined by the toss of a coin with outcome s. Let the coin be tossed at uniform intervals, T. Thus, $X(t, s)$ can take on either the value zero or one for the interval T; then the experiment is repeated. We may depict the ensemble of member functions as in Figure 5.4.

Let us discuss this last example in more detail. The method by which we constructed the ensemble in Example 5.7 differs from that used for the previous ensembles in that the experiment is repeated at regular intervals, while the previous examples

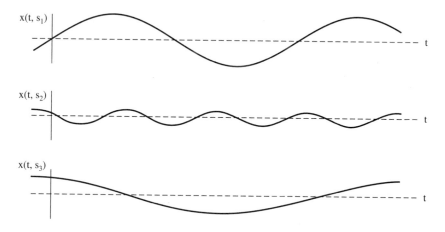

Figure 5.3   Three-member functions for the sine wave ensemble

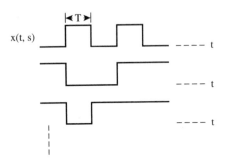

Figure 5.4   A continuous time, discrete
amplitude random process

performed the experiment only once. Example 5.7 can also be performed in this manner. To illustrate how this is done, first consider the simple experiment of tossing a coin. If a head occurs, then let $X(t, s)$ be the value one for an interval of T seconds following the flip, while if a tail occurs, then $X(t, s)$ is a zero for T seconds. In this manner we obtain a two-member ensemble for the random process. Now consider flipping a coin twice so that the possible outcomes are (Head Head), (Head Tail), (Tail Head), and (Tail Tail). Let $X(t, s)$ be one for T seconds followed by another one for T seconds if the outcome is (Head Head), and so on for the other possible outcomes. This generates a four-member ensemble random process with binary waveforms of (11), (10), (01), and (00), respectively, for each of the four possible outcomes. This process of waveform generation can be generalized to a finite (or countably infinite) number of intervals. For example, if the number of intervals is finite, say, N, then there are 2^N possible binary waveforms, where we designate each waveform by its digital number $1, \ldots, 2^N$. Each waveform is a member of the ensemble. The random process, $X(t, s)$, consists of the binary waveforms in this ensemble. We may now define a new experiment whereby a binary waveform is selected according to the experimental outcome. One such experiment would be to select a number from 1 to 2^N at random (according to a specified probability density function). The number selected would determine the waveform. In summary, the procedure illustrated in Example 5.7 represents one model for generating a random process, while the previous procedure illustrates another model. Sometimes it is more convenient to use one model than the other to solve a given problem.

We will find it convenient to use two types of notation for the two random-process models discussed above. For the first model we will continue to use the notation $X(t, s)$, since this tends to indicate that the experimental outcome does not change with time. We will use $X(s(t))$ for the second model, since this more clearly denotes a change in the experimental outcome with time. In this case we might think of the change in the random variable as due to a change in the "state" of the experimental outcome. Thus, in Example 5.7 we would denote $X(t, s)$ as $X(s(t))$, and the random variable changes value as the experimental outcome changes its state. If time is discrete, as we discuss below, then we will use the notation $X(nT, s)$ and $X(s(nT))$ for these two types of random processes.

Quiz 5.3 Create another example of a continuous-time, discrete-amplitude random process.

Quiz 5.4 Suppose we consider a sine wave random process with $\Theta(s)$ as the only random variable, which can be a continuous or a discrete random variable. If $\Theta(s)$ is continuous, then the random process is both continuous in time and continuous in amplitude. What type of random process occurs when $\Theta(s)$ is discrete? Sketch both of these random processes. How many member functions are in each random process? Hint: First let $\Theta(s)$ assume only two values depending on the outcome of the flip of a coin. Then generalize.

Rather than define discrete time random processes we shall define random sequences. A random sequence will be defined as a random process for which t has only discrete values.

> **Definition 5.9. A continuous (amplitude) random sequence** is a random process with discrete time. The range of the random variable is continuous. The range of values for t may be countably infinite, for example, the set of integers. The interval between the values of the random sequence is usually uniform.

This definition makes a continuous random sequence analogous to a discrete time function (or a time series) with a continuous range of values.

One example of a continuous random sequence can be obtained by reconsidering Example 5.2 with $X(t = nT, s) = A(s) \sin(\omega nT)$ for $-\infty < n < \infty$, where $A(s)$ is a random variable and ω and θ are real variables with $\theta = 0$. Let the random variable $A(s)$ have a uniform probability density function as previously. Then $X(nT, s)$ is a continuous random sequence. This is shown in Figure 5.5. | **Example 5.8**

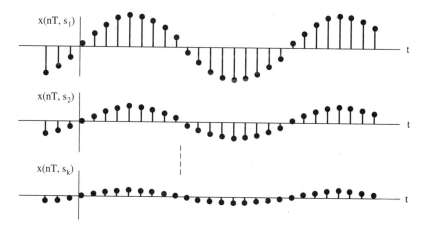

Figure 5.5 Three-member functions of an ensemble of a continuous (amplitude) random sequence

Definition 5.10. A discrete (amplitude) random sequence is a random process with a discrete range of values for the amplitude and time is discrete.

Thus, a discrete random sequence is analogous to a discrete-time, discrete-amplitude time function.

Example 5.9	Consider Example 5.7 again. However, let the outcome be a one or a zero for only an instant after each flip of the coin. The ensemble is shown in Figure 5.6 and is similar to that shown in Figure 5.4 except that the waveform is a discrete sequence.

Example 5.10	Flip a coin every T sec. Then the random process $X(s(nT))$ becomes a discrete random sequence of heads and tails spaced at intervals of T sec. If we assign the value 1 to the random variable when a head occurs and a 0 if a tail occurs, then the discrete random sequence becomes a sequence of 1s and 0s with the value changing every T sec.

Sometimes we need to determine if two random processes are equal and often we need to add, multiply, differentiate, and operate in other ways on random processes.

Definition 5.11. Two random processes are equal if and only if their respective member functions are equal for each and every experimental outcome, s.

Definition 5.12. The **sum of two random processes** (or sequences), $X(t,s) + Y(t, s)$, is obtained by operating on each and every member function of the random process. In a similar manner the **product** of two random processes, $X(t, s)Y(t, s)$, is obtained by operating on each and every member function of the random process. This definition can be applied in general to **any other operation,** such as differentiation or integration, involving one or more random processes. We may replace $X(t, s)$ and $Y(t, s)$ with $X(s(nT))$ and $Y(s(nT))$ provided the experimental outcomes occur synchronously.

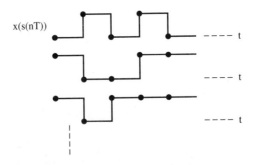

Figure 5.6   A discrete time, discrete amplitude random process

Let X(t, s) be the random process given in Example 5.3; that is, the member functions are | **Example 5.11**
$x(t, H) = \sin(2\pi t)$ and $x(t, T) = \sin(2\pi t + \pi/2) = \cos(2\pi t)$. Let Y(t, s) be another random
process such that a coin is flipped twice so that

$$y(t, HH) = 0$$

$$y(t, HT) = 1$$

$$y(t, TH) = \sin(\pi t + \pi/2)$$

$$y(t, TT) = 2$$

Then the sum of the two random processes $X(t, s) + Y(t, s)$ is given as follows:

$$x(t, H) + y(t, HH) = \sin(2\pi t) + 0$$

$$x(t, H) + y(t, HT) = \sin(2\pi t) + 1$$

$$x(t, H) + y(t, TH) = \sin(2\pi t) + \sin(\pi t + \pi/2)$$

$$x(t, H) + y(t, TT) = \sin(2\pi t) + 2$$

$$x(t, T) + y(t, HH) = \cos(2\pi t) + 0$$

$$x(t, T) + y(t, HT) = \cos(2\pi t) + 1$$

$$x(t, T) + y(t, TH) = \cos(2\pi t) + \sin(\pi t + \pi/2)$$

$$x(t, T) + y(t, TT) = \cos(2\pi t) + 2$$

Quiz 5.5   Find the product of the two random processes in Example 5.11.

Definition 5.13. A complex random process is

$$Z(t, s) = X(t, s) + jY(t, s)$$

where $j = \sqrt{-1}$ and Definition 5.12 applies. The ensemble consists of the set of
complex functions defined by the complex operator and is statistically described
by the two-dimensional random process $\{X(t, s), Y(t, s)\}$.

Quiz 5.6   Find the complex random process Z(t, s) where X(t, s) and Y(t, s) are defined
in Example 5.11.

Definition 5.14. Three of the most common methods of forming a finite dimensional **random vector** are now discussed. One method indexes the random variable in time. For example, suppose we have a random process, X(t, s) and we let t
assume discrete values $\{t_1, t_2, \ldots, t_n\}$ for a particular (fixed) experimental outcome s. Then for each t_i, $i = 1, 2, \ldots, n$ we have indexed the random variable of
the random process. We then form a finite dimensional random vector as

$$\vec{X}(t,s) = (X(t_1,s), X(t_2,s), \cdots, X(t_n,s))^\mathsf{T} \qquad \text{[5.2.2]}$$

where the vector is a column vector. This method is analogous to sampling a member function of a random process, where the random variable is a fixed value. One example would be to sample a member function of a sine wave random process. This method of forming a random vector is often used in sampling a data waveform.

Another method indexes the random variable, while time is fixed. For example, if the random process is $X(t, s)$ and t is fixed, then we index the random process by the experimental outcome s. In this case we form the random vector as

$$\vec{X}(t, s) = (X(t,s_1), X(t,s_2), \cdots, X(t,s_n))^\mathsf{T} \qquad \text{[5.2.3]}$$

This latter random vector is analogous to sampling across the member functions of a random process with time fixed at the value t.

The third method is analogous to Examples 5.7 and 5.10 in that we have a discrete random sequence whose values change according to an experimental outcome at each time sample. In this case we denote the random process as $X(s(t))$ and we form a random vector as

$$\vec{X}(s(t)) = (X(s(t_1)), X(s(t_2)), \cdots, X(s(t_n)))^\mathsf{T} \qquad \text{[5.2.4]}$$

Perhaps equations [5.2.3] and [5.2.4] represent the most common methods of forming a random vector when dealing with theoretical random processes, since each element of the random vector is determined by an experimental outcome. Note, however, that the method of generating a member function of the ensemble by [5.2.4] differs from that indicated by [5.2.3]. As we mentioned previously, it is sometimes useful to think of the random process denoted by $X(s(t))$ as one whose values change as the experimental outcome changes its "state." This notation will be useful later for Markov random processes. It will prove convenient on occasion to omit the comma between the elements of the random vector.

The indexed random variables have a defined joint probability density function (or a joint cumulative probability distribution function) and a joint sample space. This concept can be expanded to infinite dimensional spaces. The random vectors defined here differ slightly from the random vector we defined in Chapters 3 and 4 in that the above random vectors are also a function of time.

Definition 5.15. We form a **random matrix** with columns (or rows) of random vectors.

Example 5.12 | Consider a four-element random vector where each element can take on the value zero or one with equal probability. Select four possible vectors from this ensemble and form a random matrix. Then a random matrix for this example might contain the following four vectors:

$$\begin{bmatrix} 0 & 1 & 1 & 0 \\ 0 & 0 & 1 & 0 \\ 1 & 0 & 1 & 0 \\ 0 & 1 & 1 & 1 \end{bmatrix}$$

These concepts will be useful later when we deal with discrete random sequences in Markov chains and other random processes.

Definition 5.16. The **expected value of a random process** is calculated with respect to the random variable (or random variables if there are more than one) and is denoted as $E[X(t, s)]$ or as $E[X(s(t))]$ as the case may be.

Consider a sine wave random process such that $X(t, s) = A(s) \sin(\omega t)$ for all t, where ω is a constant, $\theta = 0$, and $A(s)$ is a random variable uniformly distributed between zero and a_0. Then | **Example 5.13**

$$E[X(t,s)] = \int_0^{a_0} x(t,s)\frac{1}{a_0}\, da = \int_0^{a_0} \frac{1}{a_0}\, a \sin(\omega t)\, da = \frac{a_0}{2} \sin(\omega t)$$

which is a function of t.

We will elaborate on Definition 5.16 and define other statistical averages, such as variances and correlation functions, for random processes in the following chapter. One definition we will discuss is a time average of a member function of a random process, whereby we select a member function and determine the time average of the member function, which is analogous to finding the dc level of a waveform.

Quiz 5.7   Suppose we have the sine wave random process $X(t, s) = \sin(\omega t + \Theta(s))$, where $\Theta(s)$ is the random variable, which is uniformly distributed between zero and 2π. Determine $E[X(t, s)]$.

Definition 5.17. If we have a random vector given as

$$\vec{X}(t,s) = (X(t,s_1), X(t,s_2), \cdots, X(t,s_n))^T$$

then the **expected value of the finite dimensional random vector** is defined as the vector of expected values of each component of the vector. Thus,

$$E[\vec{X}(t, s)] = E[(X(t, s_1), X(t, s_2), \cdots, X(t, s_n))^T] \qquad \text{[5.2.5a]}$$

$$= (E(X(t, s_1)), E(X(t, s_2)), \cdots, E(X(t, s_n)))^T$$

$$= \left(\int_{-\infty}^{\infty} x(t,s_1)\, p_X(x(t,s_1))\, d(x(t,s_1)), \cdots, \int_{-\infty}^{\infty} x(t,s_n)\, p_X(x(t,s_n))\, d(x(t,s_n))\right)^T$$

$$= \vec{\mu}_X(t) = (\mu_1(t), \mu_2(t), \cdots, \mu_n(t))^T$$

where $x(t, s_i)$ is the value of the ith element of the random vector, $\mu_i(t)$ represents the mean of the ith element in the random vector, and $\vec{\mu}_X(t)$ is the vector of mean values. Note that the elements of the mean vector and, thus, the vector of mean values can both be a function of time. We shall discuss this further in the next

chapter, where we will also define an average of a random vector with respect to time, that is, a time average of a vector of sample data values.
If we have a random vector

$$\vec{X}(s(t)) = (X(s(t_1)), X(s(t_2)), \cdots, X(s(t_n)))^T,$$

then the **expected value of the finite dimensional random vector** is defined in a manner analogous to that above. Thus,

$$E[\vec{X}(s(t))] = E[(X(s(t_1)), X(s(t_2)), \cdots, X(s(t_n)))^T] \qquad [5.2.5b]$$

$$= (E(X(s(t_1))), E(X(s(t_2))), \cdots, E(X(s(t_n))))^T$$

$$= \left(\int_{-\infty}^{\infty} x(s(t_1)) \, p_X(x(s(t_1))) \, d(x(s(t_1))), \cdots, \right.$$

$$\left. \int_{-\infty}^{\infty} x(s(t_n)) \, p_X(x(s(t_n))) \, d(x(s(t_n))) \right)^T$$

$$= \vec{\mu}_X(t) = (\mu(t_1), \mu(t_2), \cdots, \mu(t_n))^T$$

where, $x(s(t_i))$ is the value of the ith element of the random vector, $\mu(t_i)$ represents the mean of the ith element in the random vector, and $\vec{\mu}_X(t)$ is the vector of mean values. Again, note that the elements of the mean vector and, thus, the vector of mean values can both be a function of time.

Example 5.14 | We may define a random vector for the random process exemplified in Example 5.13. Then

$$\vec{X}(t, s) = (X(t, s_1), X(t, s_2), \cdots, X(t, s_n))^T$$

$$= (A(s_1) \sin(\omega t), A(s_2) \sin(\omega t), \cdots, A(s_n) \sin(\omega t))^T$$

and we apply [5.2.5a] with the probability density function being uniform as given in Example 5.13. Then the expected value of an element of the vector is $(a_0/2)\sin(\omega t)$ and the vector of the expected value for each element is

$$E[\vec{X}(t,s)] = \vec{\mu}_X(t) = \left(\frac{a_0}{2}\sin(\omega t), \frac{a_0}{2}\sin(\omega t), \cdots, \frac{a_0}{2}\sin(\omega t) \right)^T$$

This was expected since we had already obtained this answer for a single element in Example 5.13.
As a continuation of this example, suppose we have the following situation:

$$\vec{X}(s(t)) = (X(s(t_1)), X(s(t_2)))^T$$

where the random variable $X(s(t_1))$ assumes the value $+1$ or -1 with equal probability and the random variable $X(s(t_2))$ is independent of $X(s(t_1))$ and also assumes the value $+1$ or -1 with equal probability. Determine the mean of

$$\vec{X}(s(t))$$

We solve this example as follows:

$$E[\vec{X}(s(t))] = \left(\int_{-\infty}^{\infty} x_1 \left[\frac{1}{2}\delta(x_1 - 1) + \frac{1}{2}\delta(x_1 + 1) \right] dx_1, \right.$$

$$\left. \int_{-\infty}^{\infty} x_2 \left[\frac{1}{2}\delta(x_2 - 1) + \frac{1}{2}\delta(x_2 + 1) \right] dx_2 \right)^T$$

$$= (0,0)^T$$

where for convenience we have used the notation $x_i = x(s(t_i))$ to denote the specific value of the random variable $X(s(t_i))$. Since the outcome for $s_i = s(t_i)$, $i = 1, 2$, is either $+1$ or -1 with equal probability for both $X(s(t_1))$ and $X(s(t_2))$, the probability density function for the random variable is denoted with delta functions at these values.

Definition 5.18. A random process, $X(t, s)$ or $X(s(t))$, is said to be **Gaussian (normal)** if the random variables of the member functions of the random process are jointly Gaussian for any n, $s_1, s_2, \ldots, s_n$. For $X(t, s)$ or $X(s(t))$ to be Gaussian, the probability densities of all orders must be Gaussian.

In Chapter 4 we expressed the probability density function for a Gaussian random vector as follows:

$$p_{\vec{X}}(\vec{x}) = \frac{1}{(2\pi)^{\frac{n}{2}} [\det(C)]^{\frac{1}{2}}} \exp\left[-\frac{1}{2} (\vec{x} - \vec{\mu}_{\vec{X}})^T C^{-1} (\vec{x} - \vec{\mu}_{\vec{X}}) \right] \qquad [5.2.6]$$

The vector $\vec{x}$ is a vector of specific values of either $\vec{X}(t, s)$ or $\vec{X}(s(t))$, as discussed above. And the determinant of the covariance matrix C is denoted as det (C) and the inverse of C is C^{-1}. The same equation can be used for a continuous Gaussian random process, where t is continuous.

We can have a discrete-time random sequence, $X(nT)$, of independent Gaussian random variables with mean μ_X and variance σ^2_X. The covariance matrix for the sample times, $n = 1, \ldots, k$, is the identity matrix multiplied by σ^2_X. Thus, the joint probability density function becomes the product of the individual Gaussian probability density functions, which all have the same mean value and variance.

Consider the sine wave random process with A(s) as the only random variable, where $\Omega(s)$, and $\Theta(s)$ are fixed. Let the random process be given as | **Example 5.15**

$$X(t, s) = A(s) \sin\left(\frac{\pi}{2} t\right) = A \sin\left(\frac{\pi}{2} t\right)$$

where A(s) = A is a Gaussian random variable with zero mean and variance σ^2. If t = 0, then the probability density function for X(0, s) is $\delta(x)$, since X(0, s) = 0 for all values of A. However, if t = 1, then X(1, s) = A, and the probability density function for X(1, s) is a one-dimension Gaussian probability density function with zero mean and variance σ^2. Thus, the probability density function for the random process varies with time. As we mentioned previously, such random processes are said to be nonstationary. However, we postpone further discussion of this topic until the next chapter.

Quiz 5.8   Sketch several member functions for the random process in the above example.

We remind the reader that we shall often find it convenient to denote a random process expressed as either X(t, s) or X(s(t)) by the simpler notation X(t), thereby, suppressing the variable, s, that denotes the experimental outcome. This should not prove to be confusing, since the random variable in the random process is often easily identified and the probability density function for the random variable is usually known.

5.3   ADDITIONAL EXAMPLES OF RANDOM PROCESSES

In this section we will discuss several random processes, such as Poisson, Bernoulli, counting, random walk, and Markov, that might be encountered in the design of switching systems, computer systems, signal processing systems, speech recognition and synthesis systems, communications systems, network protocols, and other applications. Each random process will be illustrated with examples.

5.3.1   POISSON RANDOM PROCESS

The probability density function for the Poisson random process can be derived in several ways. We will discuss two approaches.

The first approach to the Poisson random process is to consider the possible number of arrivals of an event in a particular time interval [0, t]. The event may be a telephone call, an electron, or some similar occurrence. The number of arrivals is a random variable that depends on t. We will denote the random variable as X(t), or more simply as X. Let t and dt denote two contiguous time intervals. Let the various intervals be independent; that is, the occurrence of X in one interval is jointly independent of the occurrence of X in any other interval. The intervals are independent if the intervals do not overlap. The time of arrival is memoryless; that is, it does not matter when we select the time origin or the time at which we start our data collection. Define a parameter λ to be the rate of arrival of the events (say, telephone calls). (It turns out that λ is the mean rate of arrival of calls.) The probability of one call arriving in interval dt is λdt for sufficiently small dt, while the probability of zero calls arriving in dt is $(1 - \lambda dt)$. To find the probability of i calls arriving in the interval t + dt, we can have either i calls in t with probability $P_X(i, t)$ and zero calls in dt with probability $(1 - \lambda dt)$ or we may have i − 1 calls arrive in t with probability $P_X(i - 1, t)$ and one call arrive in dt with probability λdt. Then the discrete probability distribution function is

$$P_X(i, t + dt) = P_X(i, t)P_X(0, dt) + P_X(i - 1, t)P_X(1, dt)$$

$$= P_X(i, t)(1 - \lambda dt) + P_X(i - 1, t)\lambda dt$$

Note that for $i = 0$, then $P_X(-1, t) = 0$ since the probability of less than zero calls arriving is zero. If we assume that the probability is differentiable, then

$$\frac{P_X(i = 0, t + dt) - P_X(i = 0, t)}{dt} = \frac{dP_X(0, t)}{dt} = -\lambda P_X(0,t)$$

or

$$P_X(0, t) = ce^{-\lambda t}u(t)$$

Since the probability of having zero calls in zero time is unity, then $P_X(i, 0)$ is one for $i = 0$ and zero for $i > 0$. Then $c = 1$ and we have

$$P_X(0, t) = e^{-\lambda t}u(t)$$

which we note is exponential. In general the differential equation is

$$\frac{dP_X(i, t)}{dt} = -\lambda (P_X(i, t) - P_X(i - 1, t))$$

or

$$\frac{dP_X(i, t)}{dt} + \lambda P_X(i, t) = \lambda P_X(i - 1, t)$$

for $i \geq 1$. Then we may solve for $P_X(i, t)$ by integration. First, note that

$$\frac{d}{dt}[e^{\lambda t}P_X(i, t)] = e^{\lambda t}\frac{d}{dt}[P_X(i, t)] + \lambda e^{\lambda t}P_X(i, t) = \lambda e^{\lambda t}P_X(i - 1, t)$$

Then integrating both sides, we have

$$P_X(i, t) = C + \lambda e^{-\lambda t}\int_0^t P_X(i - 1, y)e^{\lambda y}\,dy$$

To determine C, the constant of integration, we note that

$$P_X(1, t) = C + \lambda e^{-\lambda t}\int_0^t P_X(0, y)e^{\lambda y}\,dy = C + \lambda t e^{-\lambda t}u(t)$$

Then at $t = 0$ we note that $P_X(i, 0) = 0$ for $i \geq 1$. Therefore, $C = 0$. By iteration we have

$$P_X(2, t) = \lambda e^{-\lambda t}\int_0^t \lambda y\,dy = \frac{(\lambda t)^2}{2!}e^{-\lambda t}u(t)$$

And by mathematical induction we conclude that

$$P_X(i, t) = \frac{(\lambda t)^i}{i!}e^{-\lambda t}u(t) \qquad\qquad [5.3.1]$$

The probability density function is Poisson and is given as

$$p_X(i, t) = \sum_{r=0}^{\infty} \frac{(\lambda t)^r}{r!} e^{-\lambda t} \delta(i - r)$$ [5.3.2]

Recall that the mean of the Poisson probability density function is λ. Thus, the mean arrival rate of calls is λ.

The above result may also be derived as the limit of the binomial distribution, where the number of intervals is $n = t/dt$, while $p = \lambda dt$, $q = (1 - \lambda dt)$. The probability of i calls in n intervals is given by the binomial distribution, where n is the number of trials, which becomes infinite. There are other ways in which [5.3.2] may also be derived.

Definition 5.19. In summary, we may define a **Poisson random process,** $X(t)$, as follows: Let $X(t)$ be the number of arrivals of an event, such as telephone calls, in the time interval $[0, t]$ for $t > 0$, where the number of calls in the interval $[0,t]$ is denoted as i with $X(0) = 0$. Then the number of calls in the interval $[0,t]$ is described by a Poisson probability density function. The family or ensemble of such functions is called a Poisson random process.

Example 5.16 (MATLAB)

A Poisson random process can be simulated with the MATLAB program shown in Figure 5.7, where a plot of a possible $X(t)$ for the process is also shown. The program calculates and plots an estimate of the probability density function $p_X(i, t)$ for the four time intervals specified at the beginning of the program. The plot of $X(t)$ is a result of selecting the most probable value for i for each estimate of the probability density function for each of the four time intervals. It is not necessary that the most probable value for i be selected. This is one possible outcome. The most probable values are i = 5 for the time interval $[0, 2.3]$, i = 9 for $[0, 4.0]$, i = 15 for $[0, 6.8]$, and i = 23 for $[0, 10.0]$, which can be verified by running the program. For very short intervals $[0, t]$, it is very likely that no events will occur. Thus, the graph of $X(t)$ simulates this fact by indicating that no events occur in the interval $[0, 1]$. As the interval $[0, t]$ becomes longer, it becomes more probable that i > 0 events will occur. Since for this example, five events occur in the interval $[0, 2.3]$ and none occur in the interval $[0, 1.0]$, then the five events must occur in the interval $[1, 2.3]$. The remainder of the graph is similarly interpreted.

```
%MATLAB Example 5.16 by jmw
clear                              % clear all variables from workspace (not required)
lambda = 2.3;                      % arbitrary value for lambda (constant)
ti(1,:) = [0.0 2.3];               % create four time intervals
ti(2,:) = [2.3 4.0];
ti(3,:) = [4.0 6.8];
ti(4,:) = [6.8 10.0];
for count = 1:4,                   % begin Main Loop here
        t = ti(count,2) - ti(1,1);   % t = [0 end of current time interval]
px = [];px_it = [];                % clear previous pdf results
i_max = ceil(1.5*ceil(2*lambda*t)); % arbitrary max number for i to help
                                   % plot graphs and constrain r < inf.
```

Figure 5.7a   MATLAB program for Example 5.16

```
%Continuation of MATLAB program for Example 5.16
for i = 0:i_max,
        r = i;                              %delta function ! = 0 only at at i = r
        lt = (lambda*t);                    % lambda times t raised to the r power
        if (r==0)                           % only for case r = 0
                px = exp(-1.0*lt);
        elseif(r==1)                        % only for case r = 1
                px = lt*exp(-1.0 *lt);
        else                                %for cases r > 1
                px = 1;
                for j=r:-1:1,               % this loop can be avoided but is illustrative
                        px = (lt/j)*px;
                end;
                px = px* exp(-1.0*lt);
        end;
        px_it(i + 1) = px;                  % store value in array
                                            % matlab does not allow zero as an index
                                            % so use px(i+1) instead of px(i)
end;
% Find max value of pdf for Poisson Process. This is one possible member function.
[sort_px_it, sort_index] = sort(px_it);
Process(count) = sort_index (i_max + 1) - 1;    % subtract 1 to account for
                                            % rearranged indexes from above
% graph pdf's at end of each time arrival
bar([0:1:i_max],px_it);
grid on;
xlabel('i');
ylabel('Poisson pdf for (i, t)');
s = sprintf('Poisson pdf for lambda = %4.2f and t = [0, %4.2f] ',lambda,t);
title(s);
axis([0 40 0 0.20]);
disp('hit any key to continue . . . ');
pause;
end;                                        % end Main Loop here
% graph member function of Poisson Process
ti(1,:) = [1.0 2.3];                        % shift start of plot to simulate the occurrence of
                                            % zero
                                            % events in interval from zero to 1
stairs([0;ti(:,1);10],[0 Process Process(4)]);
% (you have to add last value twice to get Matlab to graph it . . . )
xlabel('time');
ylabel('number of events');
s=sprintf('member function of Poisson R.P. with lambda = %4.2f', lambda);
title(s);
grid on;
axis([0 10 0 24]);
```

Figure 5.7a   (Concluded)

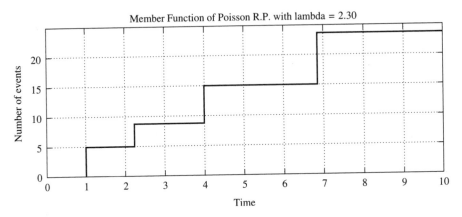

Figure 5.7b   One-member function of a Poisson random process for the program in Figure 5.7a for $\lambda = 2.30$

Example 5.17 This example is intended to be illustrative of the use of experimental data in determining certain characteristics of a data communications terminal, which might be a personal computer or a workstation. The data terminal may be connected to a network and/or a telephone line, as shown in Figure 5.8. The terminal must have word storage capability and other features. In one of the Problems we expand on this example to determine some of the design parameters and illustrate possible trade-offs between some of these parameters. For example, the problem considers memory storage size, number of input data channels, input data duty cycle, and probability of memory (word storage) saturation.

Assume the workstation has x input channels and y output channels. These channels may be telephone lines and/or computer networks. The data storage problem to be analyzed in one

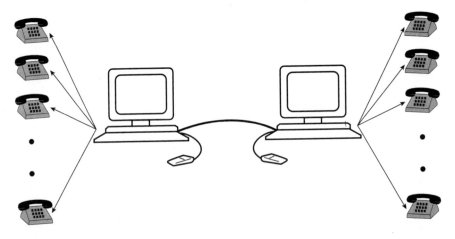

Figure 5.8   Data communications

of the Problems is one in which the data rate per channel undergoes a reduction from the input to the output of the terminal. This reduction in data rate per channel may be due to one or more factors, for instance, (1) translation from one language to another, (2) coding of data for increased security or for protection against interference, (3) or translation of symbols into code words (such as $).

Usually, extensive internal data storage is not needed when the information transfer is such that there is an increase in the data rate per channel from the input to output since resident memory storage can easily handle all requirements for this situation. Often a table of statistics on the length of calls (duration of an input data message) is provided. Such a table provides the cumulative probability distribution function of the length of calls.

For this example, we assume that it has been established experimentally that the calls can be expected to **arrive** in accordance with a Poisson distribution. The **length** of a call will satisfy an exponential probability distribution with parameter λ, where λ is the reciprocal of the mean length of a call, that is:

$$\lambda = \frac{1}{\mu_L}$$

where μ_L is the mean length of a call. We now show that μ_L can be determined from a cumulative probability distribution table.

The exponential probability density function for the length, L, of a call is

$$p_L(l) = \lambda\, e^{-\lambda l} = \frac{1}{\mu_L}\, e^{-\frac{l}{\mu_L}},\, l \geq 0$$

where L is a random variable and μ_L is the mean length of a call measured in an appropriate time unit, such as minutes, for each data channel.

The cumulative probability distribution function that the random variable L is less than or equal to l is

$$P_L(L \leq l) = \int_0^l p_L(x)\, dx = \int_0^l \frac{1}{\mu_L}\, e^{-\frac{x}{\mu_L}}\, dx = 1 - e^{-\frac{l}{\mu_L}}$$

or

$$P_L(L > l) = e^{-\frac{l}{\mu_L}}$$

where $P_L(L > l)$ may be determined from a cumulative probability distribution table, which we now illustrate.

Assume we are given some experimentally determined statistics concerning the length of data calls, as in Table 5.1.

Since the probability that the length of the call, L, is less than a specific value is denoted as $P_L(L \leq l)$, then Table 5.1 gives $P_L(L \leq 1)$ as the right-hand column with l as the left-hand column. These tabular data may be plotted if so desired.

If the data represent an exponential distribution with length L as the random variable and the calls occur in accordance with a Poisson distribution, then the mean length of a call, μ_L, can be determined as follows:

$$P_L(L \leq l) = 1 - e^{-\frac{l}{\mu_L}}$$

Table 5.1

Length of Call of l Minutes or Less	Percentages of Calls of l Minutes or Less
3	40.0%
4	53.3
5	63.4
6	70.8
7	76.0
10	86.1
15	93.4
20	96.1
30	98.9
∞	100.5

Note: The last entry in the right-hand column of the table should theoretically be 100.0. However, since the data were obtained experimentally, there is a slight departure from theory.

Let $l = \mu_L$. Then

$$P_L(L \le \mu_L) = 1 - e^{-1} = 0.64$$

By interpolating Table 5.1, we find that for $P_L(L \le \mu_L) = 0.64$ that μ_L is approximately five minutes.

Quiz 5.9 Plot Table 5.1

Quiz 5.10 What is the approximate probability that the length of a call is less than 10 minutes but greater than 7 minutes? What is the probability that the length of a call is greater than 10 minutes?

Example 5.18 | In modern communication systems, data are often transmitted in the form of packets, which are defined as a group of bits that may vary from a hundred or so to several thousand. A **packet** will typically have a header that contains the source and destination address as well as other information. Following the header will be the data that is to be sent, which in turn is followed by a trailer that may often contain error correction information. In a packet transmission system the packets may be routed through various transmission terminals called nodes. Suppose we examine a single node where the packets arrive at the node in successive times, $0 < T_1, T_2, \ldots$ Each packet is sent from the node on a first come, first served (or first in, first out) basis. Assume that the interarrival times of the packets are independent; that is, $T_1 - 0$, $T_2 - T_1$, . . . are independent. Then as we did previously we may show that i, the number of independently arriving packets in a time interval t, is Poisson and is

$$P_I(i, t) = \frac{(\lambda_a t)^i}{i!} e^{-\lambda_a t} u(t)$$

where I is the random variable representing the number of packets, and λ_a is the mean rate of arrival. The probability density function is Poisson and from [5.3.2] is

$$p_I(i, t) = \sum_{r=0}^{\infty} \frac{(\lambda_a t)^r}{r!} e^{-\lambda_a t} \delta(i - r)$$

Then, as we have seen, the average number of arrivals in an interval T is

$$E[I] = \int_0^T i \, p_I(i, t) \, dt = \lambda_a T$$

If T_i denotes the arrival time of a packet, then the interarrival times, $(T_i - T_{i-1})$, $i = 1, 2, \ldots$, are assumed to be independent and identically distributed random variables. It can be shown that the interarrival time T between packets has an exponential probability density function given as

$$p_T(t) = \lambda_a e^{-\lambda_a t} u(t)$$

As before, one may show that the average time between packet arrivals in seconds is $E[T] = 1/\lambda_a$.

Now suppose the packet lengths in bits are not all the same length, but have an exponential probability density function

$$p_L(l) = \mu_L e^{-\mu_L l} u(l)$$

where $(\mu_L)^{-1}$ is the average packet length in bits. If the packets are sent at a rate R bits/sec, then the arrival and transmission packet lengths in seconds are independent and exponentially distributed with an average length in sec given by $1/(R\mu_L)$.

This type of packet transmission system is called an **M/M/1 queue.** The first M denotes that the process is memoryless; that is, the process of arrival times is Poisson with an exponential distribution and the choice of the origin is arbitrary. The second M denotes that the service time is also exponentially distributed. The 1 denotes that the number of servers is unity.

After each packet is received at a node it is retransmitted; that is, it is serviced and sent on its way. Once a packet is received by a node it must wait in a queue before it is serviced. Thus, there are two time delays, the queue waiting time and the service time. For our example with exponentially distributed packet lengths and a fixed transmission rate of R bits/sec, it may be shown that the average service time has an exponential probability density function given as

$$p_S(s) = \mu_s e^{-\mu_s s} u(s)$$

where $(\mu_S)^{-1}$ is the average service time in seconds and $\mu_S = (R\mu_L)$. Note that the s here denotes the service time.

If we denote by N the number of packets that are either in the queue or being transmitted, then the probability density function for N is geometric in the steady state and is

$$p_N(n) = \sum_{r=0}^{\infty} \left\{ \frac{\lambda_a}{\mu_s} \right\}^r \left(1 - \frac{\lambda_a}{\mu_s} \right) \delta(r - n) \quad \text{for } n \ge 0 \text{ and } \frac{\lambda_a}{\mu_s} < 1$$

We shall return to the M/M/1 queue after we introduce Markov processes.

Quiz 5.11   Show that the average time between packet arrivals is $E[T] = 1/\lambda_a$.

Quiz 5.12   What is the average number of packets, μ_N, in the queue (or the average length of a queue) for the above example?

Quiz 5.13   What is the average delay per packet between arrival time and retransmission? Hint: Denote this delay time by T. Then $\lambda_a T = \mu_N$.

5.3.2   POISSON IMPULSES

Definition 5.20. Denote specific time instants as t_n for Poisson random process $X(t)$. Form a new random process, $D(t)$, that is the derivative of $X(t)$ (assuming it exists). Then a member function of $D(t)$ is

$$d(t) = \sum_n \delta(t - t_n) \tag{5.3.3}$$

This ensemble of functions is known as **Poisson impulses.** One-member function is shown in Figure 5.9 for a continuous process. When the process is discrete we will use unit pulses to represent discrete data as shown in Figure 5.10b.

5.3.3   SHOT NOISE

Definition 5.21. Shot noise is a physical phenomenon that occurs in electronic devices. It may be modeled as a filtered sequence of Poisson impulses. If h(t) is the impulse response of a filter, then a shot noise process, S(t), is

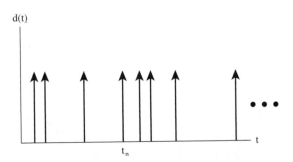

Figure 5.9   One-member function of Poisson impulses

$$S(t) = h(t)*D(t) \qquad\qquad [5.3.4]$$

$$= \sum_n h(t - t_n)$$

where the star denotes convolution.

```
%MATLAB Example 5.19 by cjw
 clear
clf
n=0:0.01:15;
a=0.3;                                  % Set exponential decay constant = 0.3
hn=exp(−a*n);                           % Exponential impulse response
h1=[zeros(1,200)hn zeros(1,2800)];      % Impulse response to 1st Poisson pulse at t=2
h2=[zeros(1,400)hn zeros(1,2600)];      % Impulse response to 2nd Poisson pulse at t=4
h3=[zeros(1,500)hn zeros(1,2500)];      % etc. at t=5
h4=[zeros(1,800)hn zeros(1,2200)];      % etc. at t=8
h5=[zeros(1,900)hn zeros(1,2100)];      % etc. at t=9
h6=[zeros(1,1000)hn zeros(1,2000)];     % etc. at t=10
h7=[zeros(1,1300)hn zeros(1,1700)];     % etc. at t=13
h8=[zeros(1,1500)hn zeros(1,1500)];     % etc. at t=15
h9=[zeros(1,2000)hn zeros(1,1000)];     % etc. at t=20
h=h1+h2+h3+h4+h5+h6+h7+h8+h9;           % Construct s(n)
x=0:length(h)−1;
subplot(2, 1, 2)
plot(x/100, h);                         % Plot Shot noise s(n)
axis ([0 30 0 3])                       % Rescale axis
x1=[0 0; 30 0];                         % Specify x1 for drawing the x-axis of s(n)
y1=[ 0 0; 0 3];                         % Specify y1 for drawing the y-axis of s(n)
hold on
plot(x1,y1,'−')                         % Draw x-axis & y-axis for s(n)
hold off
axis off;
x2=[0 0 2 4 5 8 9 10 13 15 20; 30 0 2 4 5 8 9 10 13 15 20];
y2=[0 0 0 0 0 0 0 0 0 0 0; 0 3 1.5 1.5 1.5 1.5 1.5 1.5 1.5 1.5 1.5];
x3=[2 4 5 8 9 10 13 15 20];
y3=[1.5 1.5 1.5 1.5 1.5 1.5 1.5 1.5 1.5];
subplot(2, 1, 1)
plot(x2, y2,'−')                        % Plot the vertical lines of Poisson
                                        % impulses d(n) and x&y axes
hold on
plot(x3, y3, '.')                       % plot the top dot on each vertical line of d(n).
axis off
hold off
```

Figure 5.10a   MATLAB program for Example 5.19

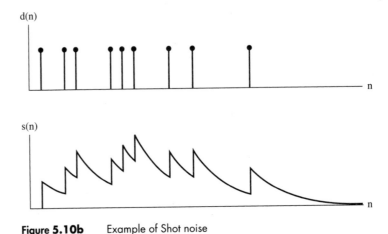

Figure 5.10b   Example of Shot noise

Example 5.19 (MATLAB)

Let a digital filter have an exponential impulse response; that is: $h(n) = e^{-an}u(n)$. If a sequence of Poisson unit pulses is applied to $h(n)$, then we obtain the filter output given by [5.3.4]. This is illustrated in Figure 5.10 using a MATLAB program.

5.3.4 POISSON INTERVALS

Definition 5.22. Poisson intervals are found from the random process in Section 5.3.1 as follows:

$$I(t) = \frac{X(t + \Delta) - X(t)}{\Delta}$$

[5.3.5]

where $\Delta > 0$ and is a given constant. Thus, a specific value for $I(t)$ is $i(t) = n/\Delta$, where n is the number of points in the interval $(t, t + \Delta)$, or n can be replaced by L, where L is the length of the interval. We can obtain $D(t)$ from $I(t)$ by letting $\Delta \to 0$.

Example 5.20

A member function of $I(t)$ is shown in Figure 5.11, where we have determined $i(t)$ from $x(t)$ in Figure 5.7. Figure 5.11 shows both $x(t)$ and $x(t + \Delta)$, where $x(t + \Delta)$ is offset from $x(t)$ for illustrative purposes so that the calculation of $i(t)$ may be seen more clearly.

Example 5.21

A **random telegraph signal** is a random process, $X(t)$, of Poisson intervals, $I(t)$, such that $I(t)$ assumes only the values +1 or −1. This is illustrated in Figure 5.12. The random telegraph signal is so named because it appears similar to a telegraph signal keyed by an operator sending a message using the Morse code of dots and dashes.

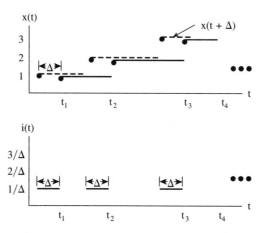

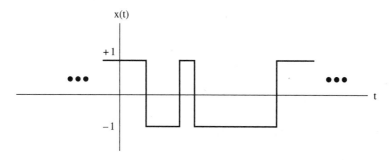

Figure 5.11   One-member function of a Poisson interval random process determined from a Poisson random process

Figure 5.12   One-member function of a random telegraph signal

5.3.5   BERNOULLI RANDOM PROCESS (MATLAB)

Definition 5.23. A **Bernoulli random process** is a discrete random sequence, $X(nT)$, of random variables that can assume only two values, typically $+1$ and -1 (or $+1$ and 0). The probability of $+1$ is p and -1 is $q = 1 - p$. When $p = q = 1/2$ the Bernoulli random process is called a **binary white noise process.** Such random processes are often used as models for certain types of data in telecommunications (e.g., PCM, where the transition between pulses occurs at discrete, uniformly spaced time intervals). A MATLAB program for a Bernoulli random process appears in Figure 5.13, while a typical member function for this process appears in Figure 5.14. A variation on this process is where the transition points remain uniformly spaced but the entire random process may be shifted by an amount Δ, where Δ is uniformly distributed over the interval $[0, T]$.

```
%MATLAB Example for a Bernoulli random process by jmw
clear                        % clear all variables from workspace (not required)
p=0.4;                       % arbitrary p probability of +1
q=1 − p;                     % resulting q probability of −1
N=20;                        % length of sequence
n=rand(1, N);                % start with uniformly distributed r.v. on [0 1.0]
x=zeros (size(n));           % allocate space to speed up following loop
for i=1; N,                  % this can be done more efficiently using matrix logicals
        if (n(i)  <=p)
                x(i)=1;
        else
                x(i)=−1;
        end;
end;
stairs(x);
a=axis;
axis([a(1) a(2) −1.5 1.5]);
xlabel('t/T');
ylabel('x(t)');
title('Bernoulli Random Process');
grid on;
```

Figure 5.13   MATLAB program for a Bernoulli random process

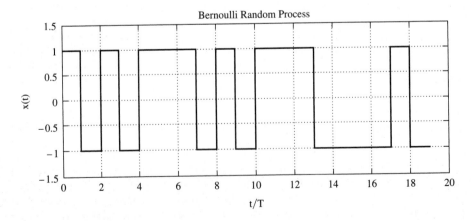

Figure 5.14   One-member function of a Bernoulli random process

Find the expected value of a Bernoulli random process. This is determined in the same manner as we did in Chapter 4. If we denote the random sequence by X(n), then | **Example 5.22**

$$E[X(n)] = [xp\delta(x - 1) + xq\delta(x + 1)] = p + (-1)q = 2p - 1$$

Thus, the mean value is the "dc" value of the random sequence.

5.3.6 BINARY COUNTING PROCESS

Definition 5.24. A **binary counting process** is a random process that counts the occurrence of pulses in a Bernoulli random process, where the pulses are $+1$ and 0. Thus, the discrete random variable, $X(i) = X_i$, is one if a pulse occurs at the ith instant and is zero if no pulse occurs. The counting random variable is

$$C(n) = C_n = \sum_{i=1}^{n} X_i \qquad [5.3.6]$$

which is also a discrete random variable that may be any value from zero to n. This random process may serve as a model for some communication detection problems.

The counting random variable has a binomial probability. If $C_n = k$, then we may think of the X_i's | **Example 5.23**
as a sequence of ones and zeros with k ones in the sequence and $n - k$ zeros. The number of such sequences is given by the binomial coefficient

$$\binom{n}{k} = \frac{n!}{k!(n-k)!}$$

Since a one occurs with probability p and a zero with probability q, then the probability that $C_n = k$ is

$$P(C_n = k) = \binom{n}{k}p^k q^{n-k} \qquad k = 0, 1, \dots, n$$

5.3.7 RANDOM WALK PROCESS

A **random walk process** is often used as a model for some communications coding schemes and for the movement of particles in environmental situations such as the flow of smoke. It also serves as a model for the movement of electrons and holes in electronic devices. Usually random walk processes are Bernoulli random processes with independent intervals. While we have previously discussed independent intervals, we define them again here.

Definition 5.25. A Bernoulli random process is said to have **independent intervals** or **independent increments** if the differences between successive values of the random sequence are mutually independent, that is, if $(x(1) - x(0))$, $(x(2) - x(1)), \dots (x(k) - x(k - 1)), \dots (x(n) - x(n - 1))$ are mutually independent. When a random process has this property, then the intervals are nonoverlapping and the events defined on these intervals are mutually independent.

Definition 5.26. The **random walk process** is described as follows. Consider a particle initially positioned at the origin on a line. The particle may move a single step to the right with probability p and to the left with probability q. The random walk process, expressed as $X(s(t))$, represents the particle's position t seconds after the initiation of movement, and s may be considered the experimental outcome that determines whether or not the particle moves to the right or left. This experimental outcome may be determined by the toss of a coin, for example. An alternative formulation assumes that the particle takes a step every T seconds. In this case we may denote the random walk process as $X(s(n))$, where n represents the number of steps and s is as before. We are usually interested in determining the probability that the particle is at position x after n steps.

Suppose the initial position of the particle is at the origin. The probability of the particle's moving to the right is p for each step and is independent of the previous step. Similarly, the probability is q for a step to the left. Thus, we have a set of Bernoulli trials. Therefore, the probability density function for movement is binomial for a finite number of steps. If out of n steps, r steps of length L are taken to the right (call these successes), then $n - r$ are taken to the left (failures) and hence the final position is a random variable, X, that may assume the value $x = [r - (n - r)]L = (2r - n)L$. For convenience we may normalize X so that it is an integer; that is, we consider X/L or equivalently we set $L = 1$. Then the probability distribution function of being at a specific x after n steps is

$$P_X(n, x) = \binom{n}{\frac{n + x}{2}} p^{\frac{n+x}{2}} q^{\frac{n-x}{2}} \qquad [5.3.7]$$

The probability density function is

$$p_X(n, x) = \sum_{i=-n}^{n} \binom{n}{\frac{n + i}{2}} p^{\frac{n+i}{2}} q^{\frac{n-i}{2}} \delta(x - i) \qquad [5.3.8]$$

where i is even if n is even and i is odd if n is odd. By replacing i by $2r - n$ we may rewrite [5.3.8] as follows:

$$p_X(n, x) = \sum_{r=0}^{n} \binom{n}{r} p^r q^{n-r} \delta(x - 2r + n) \qquad [5.3.9]$$

If the particle was initially positioned at n_0, instead of at the origin, then we replace n by $(n - n_0)$ in the above equations.

Example 5.24   The probability of the particle's being at x = 2 after 3 steps, if it starts at the origin, is $P_X(3, 2) = 0$. Why? The probability of $P_X(2, 2) = p^2$.

Quiz 5.14 Determine the probability density function $p_X(2, 2)$ and verify that $P_X(2, 2) = p^2$.

Let a random walk process be determined by the toss of a fair coin every T seconds. A particle takes a step of length L to the right if a head appears after each toss, while a step of length L is taken to the left if a tail appears. Assume the particle starts at the origin. Then X(nT) represents the position of the particle after nT seconds. We plot a possible member function of the random walk process in Figure 5.15, where we see that the member function represents a staircase type of waveform.

Example 5.25

Quiz 5.15   If the probability of a step to the right is p and a step to the left is q, then what is the probability that the individual particle taking the random walk in the previous example will be at the origin after two steps? after three steps?

5.3.8   WIENER RANDOM PROCESS (MATLAB)

Definition 5.27. A discrete Wiener random process is a random walk process with $p = q = 1/2$, which is a **binary white noise process.** A **Brownian motion process,** also known as a **continuous Wiener random process** or as a **Wiener–Levy process,** is a random walk process where the interval between consecutive values of the random sequence approaches zero. Brownian motion is used as a model for the motion of a particle in a gas or liquid, as well as for thermal electronic noise. Three typical waveforms for a Wiener process appear in Figure 5.16a. The MATLAB program for this discrete Wiener process is shown in Figure 5.16b. In Figure 5.16a we might imagine that each waveform is a measure of the motion of a particle, such as a chemically tagged red corpuscle in a blood stream or a tagged electron in a transistor. Each waveform represents a possible new measurement or another member function of the ensemble.

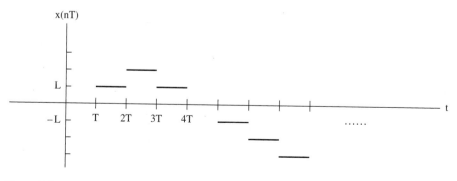

Figure 5.15   A member function for a random walk

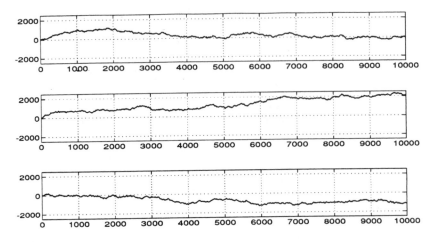

Figure 5.16a   Three-member functions of a discrete Weiner process

5.3.9   MARKOV RANDOM PROCESSES

We have seen that we can have a Bernoulli random process, that is, a discrete random sequence with mutually independent random variables. This means that each element or member in the sequence is mutually independent. Such independence of events is not true for all random processes. In general, one element of a discrete random sequence may depend on other elements in the sequence. One such process is a Markov process.

Definition 5.28. A **Markov process** is a random process where the occurrence of an event is dependent only upon the immediately preceding event. The terminology adopted for Markov processes differs from that used previously. A Markov process is said to be in one of a set of mutually exclusive, collectively exhaustive states $s_1, s_2, \ldots, s_k$, and is described by a set of probabilistic rules such that the process may change from one state to another (undergo state transitions) at certain discrete time instants. Such a process is called a discrete time, discrete state Markov process, which we will denote as $S(nT) = S(n)$. The values of $S(n)$ are the states of the process. The time at which the state transitions occur are numbered or indexed and are sometimes called trials or transition times. We denote by $s_i(n)$ that the Markov process is in state s_i immediately after the nth trial or transition has occurred. The probability of the occurrence of this event is denoted as $P_S(s_i(n))$, which we will sometimes denote more simply as $P(s_i(n))$; that is, we will drop the subscript on P. Each trail or transition of such a Markov process is described by conditional state transition probabilities, such as $P_S[s_j(n) \mid s_a(n-1), s_b(n-2), s_c(n-3), \ldots]$, where $k \geq j$, $a, b, c, \ldots \geq 1$ and $n = 1, 2, \ldots$ These transition probabilities are generally conditional on the previous states of the random process and specify the probability of making a transition

```
%MATLAB Example for Weiner process by jmw
%
clear                              % clear all variables from workspace (not required)
N = 10000;                         % length of sequence(s)
% main loop (do 3 times)
for PLT = 1:3,
% create binomial distribution w/p and q both = 0.5
p = 0.5;                           % p = 0.5 (probability of +1)
q = 1 - p;                         % q = 0.5 (probability of -1)
n = rand(1,N);                     % start with uniformly distributed r.v.on [0 1.0]
x = zeros(size(n));                % allocate space to speed up following loop
for i = 1:N,                       % this can be done faster using matrix logicals
    if (n(i) <=p)
    x(i) = 1;
    else
    x(i) = -1;
    end;
end;
dw = 10*randn(1,N);                % Gaussian distributed step sizes
wein = zeros(size(dw));            % allocate space to save time in loop
for i = 2:N,
    wein(i) = wein(i - 1) + (dw(i)*x(i));
end;
yl = -2500; yh = 2500;
if (PLT==1)
    clg;
    subplot(311);
    plot(wein);
    axis([0 N yl yh]);
    grid on;
elseif (PLT==2)
    subplot(312);
    plot (wein);
    axis ([0 N yl yh]);
    grid on;
else
    subplot (313);
    plot (wein);
    axis ([0 N yl yh]);
    grid on;
end;
end;                               % end main loop
```

Figure 5.16b   Discrete Weiner process MATLAB program

from one state to another. However, the Markov condition limits this conditional probability dependency to only the immediately preceding state. We may summarize the above as follows. A discrete state, discrete transition Markov process, $S(n)$, is said to satisfy the Markov condition if the transition probabilities for a sequence or series of trials is described by the following conditional probability relationship

$$P_S[s_j(n) \mid s_a(n-1), s_b(n-2), s_c(n-3), \ldots] = P_S[s_j(n) \mid s_a(n-1)] \quad \text{[5.3.10]}$$

Thus, the transition of a Markov process to one of the set of possible states at trial n is dependent only on the transition probability from the immediately preceding state at trial $n - 1$. We have adopted the above notation because the letter s conveniently denotes a state for a Markov random process. The reader should not confuse the use of S and s here as the symbol for the sample space or for an outcome in the sample space used previously.

For convenience we shall adopt the following more conventional notation for the conditional transition probabilities:

$$P_{ij} = P[s_j(n) \mid s_i(n-1)] \quad \text{for } 1 \le i, j \le k \text{ with } P_{ij} \text{ independent of } n \quad \text{[5.3.11]}$$

which is read as the probability of moving from state i to state j. We shall let $s_i(0)$ denote that the Markov process is in state i just prior to the first trial, and $P[s_i(0)]$ is the probability of this occurring.

Markov processes can be defined for discrete state and continuous time. However, we limit our discussion to discrete state, discrete time Markov processes, since this illustrates the major concepts of Markov processes.

Example 5.26 | Any independent increment process is a Markov process.
We note, however, that if a process is a Markov process, it is not necessarily an independent increment process.

Example 5.27 | A Wiener process is a Markov process with a continuous set of states or continuous amplitude.

Quiz 5.16 Is a Poisson impulse process a Markov process? Is a binary counting process a Markov process?

5.3.10 MARKOV CHAINS

Definition 5.29. A **Markov chain** process is a Markov random process that has an initial state, a finite or countable set of possible states, and associated transition probabilities. With this information we may calculate the probabilities of a sequence of states for a set of experiments. The Markov chain is defined to be the set of states (outcomes) for a particular sequence of experiments. A Markov chain is often defined such that the states (outcomes) are restricted to integer values. We follow that convention here.

The transition probabilities are often displayed in the form of a matrix, T; for instance, for a three-state process we would have

$$T = \begin{bmatrix} P_{11} & P_{12} & P_{13} \\ P_{21} & P_{22} & P_{23} \\ P_{31} & P_{32} & P_{33} \end{bmatrix}$$

We may also use a state transition diagram (also known as a trellis diagram), as in Figure 5.17.

Given the state transition diagram, we can determine the transition matrix as follows:

$$T = \begin{array}{c} \\ s_1 \\ s_2 \\ s_3 \end{array} \begin{array}{ccc} s_1 & s_2 & s_3 \\ \begin{bmatrix} P_{11} & P_{12} & P_{13} \\ P_{21} & P_{22} & P_{23} \\ P_{31} & P_{32} & P_{33} \end{bmatrix} \end{array}$$

where the s_i conditions in the column preceding the matrix indicate the initial states and the s_j conditions in the row above the matrix indicate the possible next states or the possible transition states. Thus, P_{11} is entered in the first row and first column of the transition matrix as the transition probability for moving from state 1 to state 1, and so on.

One property of the transition probabilities is that

$$\sum_j P_{ij} = 1 \quad \text{for } i = 1, 2, \ldots k \qquad \text{[5.3.12]}$$

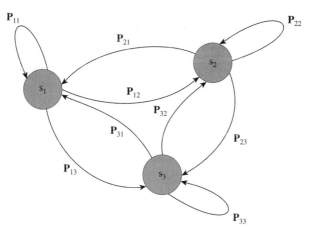

Figure 5.17   A state transition (trellis) diagram

Thus, the sum of the elements of each row of the transition probability matrix is unity. This is because the elements of the ith row represent the probabilities of all possibilities when the process is in state s_i.

Definition 5.30. A **transition probability matrix** is a square matrix with zero or positive elements less than or equal to one such that the sum of the elements in each row is unity. A row vector is called a **probability vector** whose element values are greater than or equal to zero and less than or equal to one and whose elements sum to one.

A problem often encountered in Markov chains is the following:

- The process starts in state i (s_i).
- Determine the probability that after m transitions the process (chain) will be in state j (s_j).
- Denote this probability as $P_{ij}(m)$, where

$$P_{ij}(m) = P[s_j(n + m) \,|\, s_i(n)] \qquad [5.3.13]$$

such that $P_{ij}(0) = 1$ if $i = j$ and $P_{ij}(0) = 0$ if $i \neq j$, and $P_{ij}(1) = P_{ij}$.

Note that this description defines a **random walk process**.
One can show that

$$P_{ij}(m) = \sum_{r=1}^{k} P_{ir}(m - l)P_{rj}(l) \qquad [5.3.14]$$

where $1 \leq l \leq m$, $1 \leq i, j \leq k$, k is the number of states and can be such that $k = 1, 2, \ldots$ When $l = 1$, [5.3.14] is particularly useful for calculating the m-step transition probabilities, which otherwise would have to be done by using a probability tree for m trials.

Example 5.28

Suppose we observe the state of the weather once a day each morning at 10:00 A.M. We specify three possible observation states:

- s_1 denotes sunny,
- s_2 denotes cloudy,
- s_3 denotes rainy.

We assume that the weather on day n is given by one and only one of these states. If the process is Markov, then the weather on day $n + 1$ depends only on the weather on the previous day, n. We are given the transition probabilities for any day as:

$$
T = \begin{array}{c}
 \\ \text{sunny} \\ \text{cloudy} \\ \text{rainy}
\end{array}
\begin{array}{ccc}
\text{sunny} & \text{cloudy} & \text{rainy} \\
\left[\begin{array}{ccc}
0.7 & 0.2 & 0.1 \\
0.3 & 0.2 & 0.5 \\
0.3 & 0.3 & 0.4
\end{array} \right]
\end{array}
$$

State

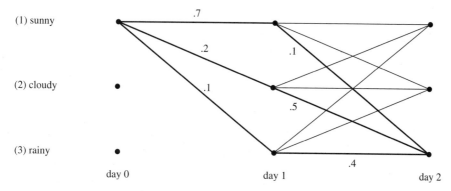

Figure 5.18   State transition (trellis) diagram or tree

Assume that our initial observation (say, day zero) is that the day is sunny. What is the probability that day 2 is rainy?

We might solve this problem by setting up a state transition diagram in the form of a tree, or a trellis diagram as in Figure 5.18.

The probability we seek is $P_{13}(2)$. The critical paths are shown darkened in Figure 5.18 along with the transition probabilities. The probability $P_{13}(2)$ is the sum of the probabilities assigned to the paths of the transition diagram for all paths that end at state 3 (s_3), which is a rainy day on day 2. Thus, $P_{13}(2) = (.7)(.1) + (.2)(.5) + (.1)(.4) = 0.21$. Now note that this is the same result using equation [5.3.14] as follows:

$$P_{ij}(m) = \sum_{r=1}^{k} P_{ir}(m - l)P_{rj}(l)$$

where for this example i = 1, j = 3, m = 2. We let l = 1 and we have

$$P_{13}(2) = \sum_{r=1}^{3} P_{1r}(2 - 1)P_{r3}(1) = P_{11}(1)\,P_{13}(1) + P_{12}(1)\,P_{23}(1) + P_{13}(1)\,P_{33}(1)$$

Quiz 5.17   In a similar manner show that $P_{12}(2) = 0.21$ and $P_{11}(2) = 0.58$.

Note that the answers obtained above may also be calculated as the appropriate elements of the product of the transition matrix with itself, that is, T^2, which is given as

$$T^2 = \begin{bmatrix} .7 & .2 & .1 \\ .3 & .2 & .5 \\ .3 & .3 & .4 \end{bmatrix} \begin{bmatrix} .7 & .2 & .1 \\ .3 & .2 & .5 \\ .3 & .3 & .4 \end{bmatrix} \qquad \textbf{[5.3.15]}$$

The probability $P_{13}(2)$ is the vector product of the first row of the first matrix with the third column of the second matrix. And similarly for $P_{12}(2)$ and $P_{11}(2)$. Each of these probabilities is an element in the square of the transition matrix, which can be readily calculated using MATLAB. This property may, of course, be generalized to matrices of other sizes. Equation [5.3.14] expresses the general result in equation form.

Quiz 5.18 Calculate T^2, above, and show that the same answers are obtained for $P_{11}(2)$, $P_{12}(2)$, $P_{13}(2)$. This problem is easily done by hand or by a calculator. However, it may also be implemented in MATLAB.

Example 5.29

A Markov chain has two states, say, $+1$ and -1, with transition probabilities given as

$$T = \begin{array}{c} +1 \\ -1 \end{array}\begin{matrix} +1 & -1 \\ \begin{bmatrix} 0.50 & 0.50 \\ 0.25 & 0.75 \end{bmatrix} \end{matrix} = \begin{bmatrix} P_{+1+1} & P_{+1-1} \\ P_{-1+1} & P_{-1-1} \end{bmatrix} \qquad [5.3.16]$$

We flip a coin to determine which state we start in. If the outcome of the flip is a head, we choose $+1$; if the outcome is a tail, we choose -1. Each outcome is equally probable. What is the probability that the random process is in state $+1$ after one step, no matter where we start? Denote this probability as $P_{+1}(1)$. Then

$$P_{+1}(1) = P(H)\,P_{+1+1} + P(T)\,P_{-1+1}$$

$$= (0.5)(0.5) + (0.5)(0.25) = 0.37$$

and

$$P_{-1}(1) = 1 - .37 = 0.63$$

Quiz 5.19 Suppose the coin above is biased and a head occurs with probability 0.33 and a tail with probability 0.67. What is $P_{+1}(1)$? (The answer is 0.33.)

The calculation made in Example 5.29 is the vector product of the initial-state vector with the transition matrix. If $\vec{P}(0)$ denotes the initial-state column vector, then

$$[\vec{P}(0)] = (P_{+1}(0)\ P_{-1}(0))^T \text{ or the row vector is } [\vec{P}(0)]^T = (P_{+1}(0)\ P_{-1}(0))$$

Then we may calculate the desired probabilities as follows:

$$(P_{+1}(1)\ P_{-1}(1)) = [\vec{P}(0)]^T T = (P_{+1}(0)\ P_{-1}(0))\begin{bmatrix} 1/2 & 1/2 \\ 1/4 & 3/4 \end{bmatrix} \qquad [5.3.17]$$

$$= (1/2\ 1/2)\begin{bmatrix} 1/2 & 1/2 \\ 1/4 & 3/4 \end{bmatrix} = (3/8\ 5/8)$$

Again, this property may be generalized to other sized matrices.

Suppose we denote the probability that a Markov chain will be in state s_j after n steps as $P_j(n)$. In general this probability will be a vector such that

$$[\vec{P}(n)]^T = (P_1(n)\ P_2(n)\ \ldots\ P_k(n)) \qquad [5.3.18]$$

where k denotes the highest state. From the above observations one can conclude that

$$[\vec{P}(n)]^T = [\vec{P}(n-1)]^T T \qquad [5.3.19]$$

which is a difference equation involving step n and probability. We also have that

$$[\vec{P}(n)]^T = [\vec{P}(0)]^T T^n \qquad [5.3.20]$$

where $\vec{P}(0)$ is the column vector of initial probabilities whose elements specify the probabilities of being in the initial states. We will return to difference equations shortly.

Example 5.30

Consider the last example. What is the probability that the random process is in state $+1$ after two steps? Using the above properties we have

$$[\vec{P}(2)]^T = (P_{+1}(2)\ P_{-1}(2)) = [\vec{P}(0)]^T T^2$$

$$= (1/2\ \ 1/2)\begin{bmatrix} 1/2 & 1/2 \\ 1/4 & 3/4 \end{bmatrix}\begin{bmatrix} 1/2 & 1/2 \\ 1/4 & 3/4 \end{bmatrix} = (11/32\ \ 21/32)$$

Definition 5.31. A state, s_i, is a **transient state** if there exists a state s_j and an integer l such that $P_{ij}(l) \neq 0$ and $P_{ji}(r) = 0$ for $r = 0, 1, 2, \ldots$ Thus, s_i is a transient state if there exists any other state to which the Markov process can move to from s_i, but from which the Markov process cannot return to s_i.

Example 5.31

In Figure 5.19, assuming that there are no nonzero transition probabilities, there are two transient states, s_1 and s_3. These are the only states that the Markov process can leave and not return to.

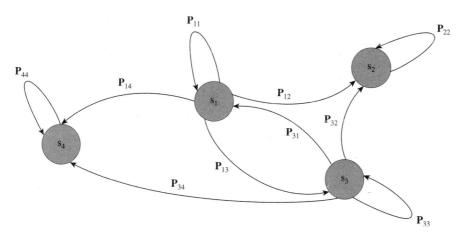

Figure 5.19   A state transition diagram with transient states s_1 and s_3

Definition 5.32. A state, s_i, is a **recurrent state** if for every state s_j, the existence of an integer r_j, such that $P_{ij}(r_j) > 0$, implies there exists an integer r_i, such that $P_{ji}(r_i) > 0$. This says that no matter what the history of the previous states, once the Markov process enters a recurrent state, the process will always be able to return to that state. Every state is either a transient state or a recurrent state.

Example 5.32 | Figure 5.20 illustrates a Markov process with three recurrent states.

Note that it is possible for recurrent states to exist such that the process may not be able to get from one recurrent state (or more) to other recurrent states. This is illustrated in Figure 5.19, where states 2 and 4 are recurrent states. Once the process reaches state 4 (or state 2), it can return to state 4 (or state 2), but it cannot get to state 2 (or state 4).

Definition 5.33. A recurrent state, s_i, is a **periodic state** if there exists an integer $c > 1$, such that $P_{ii}(r)$ is equal to zero for all values of r other than c, 2c, 3c, . . . We will not be concerned with the periodicity of transient states.

Quiz 5.20   For Figure 5.20, which states are periodic?

Definition 5.34. Some Markov chains may reach an **equilibrium,** or a steady state. Once this happens the probability of being in any particular state becomes a constant independent of the step and the initial condition. Markov processes for which this equilibrium or steady state exist satisfy

$$\lim_{m\to\infty} P[s_j(m)] = P_j \quad \text{for } j = 1, 2, \cdots, k \qquad [5.3.21]$$

In order to develop some properties of Markov chains in the steady state, we need to consider a certain type of Markov chain.

Definition 5.35. A Markov chain is called a **regular chain** if some power of the transition matrix has only positive (nonzero) elements. This implies that a regular chain has no periodic states.

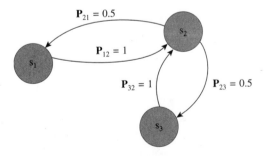

Figure 5.20   A state transition diagram with three recurrent states

Any transition matrix with no zero elements is a regular matrix. However, a transition matrix may contain zero elements and still be regular. For example, the following transition matrix is regular

$$T = \begin{bmatrix} 0 & 1 & 0 \\ 0 & 0 & 1 \\ 0.5 & 0.5 & 0 \end{bmatrix}$$

A check for the regularity of a transition matrix is to replace the nonzero elements with the variable x and then compute the successive powers of the transition matrix.

Check the regularity of the above transition matrix. Notice that we double the power each time to accelerate the testing process.

$$T = \begin{bmatrix} 0 & X & 0 \\ 0 & 0 & X \\ X & X & 0 \end{bmatrix}, T^2 = \begin{bmatrix} 0 & 0 & X \\ X & X & 0 \\ 0 & X & X \end{bmatrix}, T^4 = \begin{bmatrix} 0 & X & X \\ X & X & X \\ X & X & X \end{bmatrix}, T^8 = \begin{bmatrix} X & X & X \\ X & X & X \\ X & X & X \end{bmatrix}$$

Example 5.33

Definition 5.36. A Markov chain is called an **ergodic chain,** or **single chain,** if it is possible to go from every state to every other state.

Thus, a regular chain is also an ergodic chain. However, an ergodic chain may not be regular. For example, if from a given state we can go to certain states only in an even number of steps and to others only in an odd number of steps, then all powers of the transition matrix will have 0s. An example of this is given in Figure 5.20 for Example 5.32, where the transition matrix is

$$T = \begin{bmatrix} 0 & 1 & 0 \\ 0.5 & 0 & 0.5 \\ 0 & 1 & 0 \end{bmatrix}$$

We shall now examine regular Markov chains in a little more detail.

Definition 5.37. A **fixed point,** or **fixed probability, vector,** $\vec{F}$, of a regular chain with transition matrix T is a probability vector with all positive elements (no zeros) such that

$$\vec{F}^T = \vec{F}^T T \qquad\qquad\text{[5.3.22]}$$

If we are given

$$T = \begin{bmatrix} 1/2 & 1/2 \\ 1/3 & 2/3 \end{bmatrix} \quad \text{and} \quad \vec{F}^T = (2/5 \ \ 3/5)$$

then we have

$$\vec{F}^T T = (2/5 \ \ 3/5) \begin{bmatrix} 1/2 & 1/2 \\ 1/3 & 2/3 \end{bmatrix} = (2/5 \ \ 3/5)$$

Example 5.34

Thus, we see that for this transition matrix that if we had selected

$$\vec{F} = \vec{P}(0)$$

then we have

$$\vec{P}(0)^T = \vec{P}(0)^T T$$

Therefore

$$\vec{P}(0)^T T^n = \vec{P}(n)^T = \vec{P}(0)^T$$

Consequently, we would be in the initial state at any step n. We would be in equilibrium or steady state from step 0.

A transition matrix for a regular chain will approach steady state as n→ ∞ if

$$\lim_{n\to\infty} T^n = \begin{bmatrix} \leftarrow\vec{F}^T\rightarrow \\ \leftarrow\vec{F}^T\rightarrow \\ \vdots \\ \leftarrow\vec{F}^T\rightarrow \end{bmatrix}$$

[5.3.23]

It is sometimes useful to be able to determine $\vec{F}$. We have seen that if $\vec{F}$ is a fixed point of a transition matrix, then $\vec{F}^T T = \vec{F}^T$. Thus, $\vec{F}^T(T - I) = \vec{0}^T$. This equation plus the fact that the elements of $\vec{F}$ must sum to unity allow us to determine $\vec{F}$.

Example 5.35 | Consider the previous example.

$$\vec{F}^T(T - I) = (F_1\ F_2)\begin{bmatrix} (0.5 - 1) & 0.5 \\ 0.33 & (0.67 - 1) \end{bmatrix} = (0\ 0)$$

$$= (-0.5F_1 + 0.33F_2 \quad 0.5F_1 - 0.33F_2) = (0\ 0)$$

or

$$F_1 = 0.67\ F_2$$

which is not sufficient to determine F1 or F2. However, we know that $F_1 + F_2 = 1$. Thus, $F_2 = 3/5 = 0.6$ and $F_1 = 2/5 = 0.4$. Therefore, $\vec{F}^T = (2/5\ 3/5) = (0.4\ 0.6)$, which is the same as before. Note that if we use MATLAB to test the regularity of T, then we have

$$T^8 = \begin{bmatrix} 0.3976 & 0.6024 \\ 0.3976 & 0.6024 \end{bmatrix} \text{ which approaches } \begin{bmatrix} \vec{F}^T \\ \vec{F}^T \end{bmatrix} = \begin{bmatrix} 0.4 & 0.6 \\ 0.4 & 0.6 \end{bmatrix}$$

as n→ ∞.

Example 5.36 | A digital audio tape (DAT) deck uses a PCM format of +1 and 0 for recording and playing back data, which we will assume may be modeled as a Markov chain. Suppose a PCM data word is seven bits long. Let the transition matrix between bits be given as follows:

$$T = \begin{array}{c} \\ +1 \\ 0 \end{array} \begin{array}{c} +1 \qquad\ \ 0 \\ \begin{bmatrix} 0.50 & 0.50 \\ 0.25 & 0.75 \end{bmatrix} \end{array}$$

Determine the probability that after initiation of the playback of data we will observe a data word that is all $+1$s.

Since there are no periodic states and the first power of the transition matrix has nonzero elements, then the process is a regular chain. From the statement of the problem we assume that we have reached steady state, which is found to be

$$\vec{F}^T \, (T - I) = (F_1 \, F_2) \begin{bmatrix} -0.5 & 0.5 \\ 0.25 & -0.25 \end{bmatrix} = (0 \, 0)$$

Following the procedure shown above we find that

$$F_1 = 1/3 \text{ and } F_2 = 2/3$$

The probability that a PCM word will be all $+1$s is the probability that a $+1$ occurs (i.e., state 1 occurs) followed by the transition from state 1 to state 1 for six successive times. Therefore, the desired probability is $F_1(.5)^6 = 1/3(1/2)^6 = .00129$.

Quiz 5.21   Using MATLAB show for the last example that it is reasonable to conclude that

$$\lim_{n \to \infty} T^n = \begin{bmatrix} \vec{F}^T \\ \vec{F}^T \end{bmatrix}$$

Quiz 5.22   Find the probability that a PCM word in the above example is all 0s.

Quiz 5.23   Suppose the random process in the above example was not a Markov chain, but instead was a Bernoulli process with the same steady state probabilities. Determine the probability that a PCM word is all $+1$s. Compare the two answers and discuss the differences.

It may be shown that if T is a transition matrix of a regular chain that has an equilibrium or steady state, and if $\vec{P}$ is any probability vector, then $\vec{P}^T T^n$ will approach $\vec{F}$ as $n \to \infty$, where $\vec{F}$ is the unique fixed-point probability vector of T. Thus, we may conclude that a regular chain will reach a certain state after many trials, no matter what the initial conditions may have been. One interpretation of this is that a regular chain has a "limited memory." Therefore, no matter what the initial conditions, after a large number of steps a regular chain will reach a state that is not dependent on the number of steps or the initial state.

Some properties of Markov chains can be assessed from the eigenvalues of the transition matrix. The transition matrix for any Markov chain (regular or not) always has at least one eigenvalue equal to $+1$. Furthermore, the magnitude of the eigenvalues is less than or equal to unity. If a Markov chain has periodic states, then the transition matrix will have one and only one eigenvalue equal to -1, and conversely, if a transition matrix has one and only one eigenvalue equal to -1, then the Markov chain has at least one periodic state. If a transition matrix for a Markov chain (regular or not) has at most one eigenvalue equal to $+1$ and no eigenvalue equal to -1, then T^n will converge, and therefore, reach steady state, as $n \to \infty$. Although the matrix converges, this does not necessarily imply that the process is regular. Note that a regular chain has no periodic states; therefore, the transition matrix for a regular chain will not have an eigenvalue equal to -1. The test for checking the regularity of a Markov chain is given in Example 5.33, while Definition 5.29 in combination with [5.3.23] determines the steady state of the transition matrix for a regular chain.

Example 5.37 | Perhaps some of these ideas can be better understood by considering the following example. Let the transition matrix for a Markov process (not necessarily regular) be given as follows:

$$T = \begin{bmatrix} 0.33 & 0 & 0.67 \\ 0 & 1 & 0 \\ 0 & 0.2 & 0.8 \end{bmatrix}$$

Then using MATLAB, we determine that the eigenvalues are 0.33, 0.8, and 1.0. Then we can show using MATLAB that the matrix T will converge such that

$$\lim_{n \to \infty} T^n = \begin{bmatrix} 0 & 1 & 0 \\ 0 & 1 & 0 \\ 0 & 1 & 0 \end{bmatrix}.$$

While the row probability vector is the same for all three rows, the elements are not all greater than zero; that is, the transition matrix does not approach a matrix with all positive elements. Thus, this Markov process is not regular. It is interesting to note, however, that the row vector (0 1 0) times the matrix T is equal to the row vector (0 1 0). However, we stress that while this row vector is a probability vector, it is not a fixed-point or a fixed-probability vector.

Example 5.38 | This example considers the Markov process with periodic states from Figure 5.20 for Example 5.32, where the transition matrix is

$$T = \begin{bmatrix} 0 & 1 & 0 \\ 0.5 & 0 & 0.5 \\ 0 & 1 & 0 \end{bmatrix}$$

Then using MATLAB, we determine that the eigenvalues are -1.0, 0, and 1.0. Then we can show using MATLAB that the matrix T^n does not converge as $n \to \infty$. The process is such that the transition matrix alternates from one matrix to another depending upon whether the power of the matrix is even or odd; thus, for $n = 0, 1, \ldots$, we obtain

$$T^{2n} = \begin{bmatrix} 0.5 & 0 & 0.5 \\ 0 & 1 & 0 \\ 0.5 & 0 & 0.5 \end{bmatrix} \quad \text{and} \quad T^{2n+1} = \begin{bmatrix} 0 & 1 & 0 \\ 0.5 & 0 & 0.5 \\ 0 & 1 & 0 \end{bmatrix}$$

Therefore, we conclude that the process is not regular (which we already knew since the process has periodic states), it does not converge to a steady state, and it does not have a fixed-probability vector.

One interesting class of Markov chains contains an absorbing state.

Definition 5.38. An **absorbing state** in a Markov chain is defined as a state that is impossible to leave. For a **Markov chain to be absorbing** it must have at least one absorbing state and it must be possible to reach an absorbing state from any nonabsorbing state. When the process reaches an absorbing state, we sometimes say the process terminates.

Let the states be designated as 1, 2, 3 with the transition matrix given as

Example 5.39

$$T = \begin{array}{c} \\ 1 \\ 2 \\ 3 \end{array} \begin{array}{ccc} 1 & 2 & 3 \\ \left[\begin{array}{ccc} 1 & 0 & 0 \\ 0.33 & 0.33 & 0.33 \\ 0 & 0 & 1 \end{array} \right] \end{array}$$

Then states 1 and 3 are absorbing, while state 2 is nonabsorbing. Furthermore, we can reach either state 1 or 3 from state 2. Thus, this Markov chain is absorbing.

Quiz 5.24   Modify the above transition matrix so that the process is not an absorbing Markov chain.

Definition 5.39. A Markov chain that is absorbing is sometimes called a **random walk with an absorbing boundary** (or boundaries).

The transition matrix for an absorbing Markov chain can be rearranged into a standard form as follows:

$$T = \begin{array}{c} s \\ t \end{array} \left[\begin{array}{c|c} \begin{array}{c} s \\ I \end{array} & \begin{array}{c} t \\ O \end{array} \\ \hline L & M \end{array} \right]$$

[5.3.24]

where I is an sxs identity matrix (representing the absorbing states), O is an sxt zero matrix, L is a txs matrix, and M is a txt matrix. In equation [5.3.24] s stands for s states and similarly for t. The first s states are absorbing and the remaining t states are nonabsorbing. It can be shown that $M^n \rightarrow 0$ as $n \rightarrow \infty$ since for an absorbing Markov chain it is certain that the process will be eventually absorbed.

The matrix $[I-M]^{-1}$ is interesting in that the elements of this matrix are the mean number of times that the process spends in each nonabsorbing state for each possible nonabsorbing starting state.

Let

Example 5.40

$$T = \begin{array}{c} \\ 1 \\ 2 \\ 3 \\ 4 \end{array} \begin{array}{cccc} 1 & 2 & 3 & 4 \\ \left[\begin{array}{cccc} 1 & 0 & 0 & 0 \\ 1/4 & 1/4 & 1/4 & 1/4 \\ 0 & 1/2 & 0 & 1/2 \\ 0 & 0 & 0 & 1 \end{array} \right] \end{array}$$

which can be rearranged as

$$T = \begin{array}{c} \\ 1 \\ 4 \\ 2 \\ 3 \end{array} \begin{array}{cccc} 1 & 4 & 2 & 3 \\ \left[\begin{array}{cccc} 1 & 0 & 0 & 0 \\ 0 & 1 & 0 & 0 \\ 1/4 & 1/4 & 1/4 & 1/4 \\ 0 & 1/2 & 0 & 1/2 \end{array} \right] \end{array}$$

so that

$$M = \begin{array}{c} \\ 2 \\ 3 \end{array}\begin{array}{cc} 2 & 3 \\ \left[\begin{array}{cc} 1/4 & 1/4 \\ 0 & 1/2 \end{array}\right] \end{array} \qquad L = \begin{array}{c} \\ 2 \\ 3 \end{array}\begin{array}{cc} 1 & 4 \\ \left[\begin{array}{cc} 1/4 & 1/4 \\ 0 & 1/2 \end{array}\right] \end{array}$$

$$I - M = \left[\begin{array}{cc} 3/4 & -1/4 \\ 0 & 1/2 \end{array}\right]$$

$$\begin{bmatrix} a & b \\ c & d \end{bmatrix}^{-1} = \frac{1}{ad-bc}\begin{bmatrix} d & -b \\ -c & a \end{bmatrix}$$

$$[I - M]^{-1} = \begin{array}{c} \\ 2 \\ 3 \end{array}\begin{array}{cc} 2 & 3 \\ \left[\begin{array}{cc} 4/3 & 2/3 \\ 0 & 2 \end{array}\right] \end{array}$$

Thus, if you start in state 2, the mean number of steps in state 2 before absorption is 4/3, while in state 2, the mean number of steps in state 3 before absorption is 2/3. If the starting state is 3, the mean number of steps in state 2 before absorption is 0 (because the transition probability $P_{32} = 0$), while that in state 3 is 2.

Definition 5.40. If an absorbing Markov chain has t nonabsorbing states, then form a t element column vector, $\vec{B}$, with all unity entries. Then

$$\vec{A} = [I - M]^{-1}\vec{B} \qquad\qquad [5.3.25]$$

is the vector with elements representing the **mean number of steps before being absorbed** for each possible nonabsorbing starting state.

Example 5.41 | Consider the last example; then

$$\vec{A} = [I - M]^{-1}\vec{B} = \begin{array}{c} \\ 2 \\ 3 \end{array}\begin{array}{cc} 2 & 3 \\ \left[\begin{array}{cc} 4/3 & 2/3 \\ 0 & 2 \end{array}\right] \end{array}\left[\begin{array}{c} 1 \\ 1 \end{array}\right] = \begin{array}{c} 2 \\ 3 \end{array}\left[\begin{array}{c} 2 \\ 2 \end{array}\right]$$

This says the mean number of steps to absorption starting in state 2 or 3 is 2.

Quiz 5.25   Provide an interpretation for [5.3.25], i.e., why is it true?

Definition 5.41. The matrix

$$C = [I - M]^{-1}L \qquad\qquad [5.3.26]$$

contains elements c_{ij} that represent the **probability that an absorbing Markov chain will be absorbed in state s_j if it starts in state s_i.**

Example 5.42 | Consider Example 5.40 again. Then we have

$$C = \begin{array}{c} \\ 2 \\ 3 \end{array}\begin{array}{cc} 2 & 3 \\ \left[\begin{array}{cc} 4/3 & 2/3 \\ 0 & 2 \end{array}\right] \end{array}\begin{array}{c} \\ \end{array}\begin{array}{cc} 1 & 4 \\ \left[\begin{array}{cc} 1/4 & 1/4 \\ 0 & 1/2 \end{array}\right] \end{array} = \begin{array}{c} \\ 2 \\ 3 \end{array}\begin{array}{cc} 1 & 4 \\ \left[\begin{array}{cc} 1/3 & 2/3 \\ 0 & 1 \end{array}\right] \end{array}$$

We conclude that if we start from state 2, the probability is $1/3$ for absorption in state 1 and $2/3$ in state 4. If we start in state 3, then it is impossible to be absorbed in state 1 (because we cannot move to state 2) and it is certain that we will be absorbed in state 4.

Quiz 5.26 Provide an interpretation for [5.3.26].

Finally, we consider a special case of birth and death processes.

Definition 5.42. A **birth and death process** is a Markov process with the following transition probabilities:

$$P_{ij} = 0 \quad \text{if } j \neq i - 1, i, i + 1 \text{ or if } |j - i| > 2$$

And we will use the following birth (b) and death (d) notation to denote the transition probabilities

$$P_{i(i+1)} = b_i \quad \text{and} \quad P_{i(i-1)} = d_i$$

One example of a birth and death process is illustrated in Figure 5.21, where one can see that a movement to the right can be considered a birth, an increase in the population of one, or the receipt of a new telephone call, or the arrival of a new packet of information over a network, or the arrival of a new customer in a service line, while a movement to the left represents a death, the servicing of a telephone call or service order, the relaying of a packet of information, and so on. | **Example 5.43**
The transition matrix for this example is

$$T = \begin{array}{c} \\ 1 \\ 2 \\ 3 \\ 4 \end{array}\begin{array}{cccc} 1 & 2 & 3 & 4 \\ \left[\begin{array}{cccc} 1 - b_1 & b_1 & 0 & 0 \\ d_2 & 1 - b_2 - d_2 & b_2 & 0 \\ 0 & d_3 & 1 - b_3 - d_3 & b_3 \\ 0 & 0 & d_4 & 1 - d_4 \end{array}\right] \end{array}$$

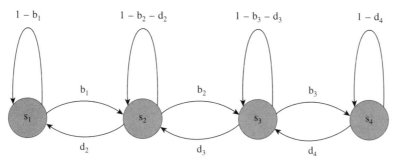

Figure 5.21 An example of a birth and death process

The movement of electrons and holes in a semiconductor can be modeled as a birth and death process, as is illustrated in one of the problems. Other examples include waiting line and servicing problems, network communications, as well as models of the birth and death of species and cells. Later in this chapter we will discuss a model for the M/M/1 queue that is a special case of a birth and death process.

5.3.11   RANDOM WALK AND DIFFERENCE EQUATIONS

We have seen that a one-dimensional random walk is a random process, $X(s(t))$, that represents the position along a line of a particle at time t after the initiation of the first experimental outcome. The experimental outcome, s, may be determined by the toss of a coin. If the outcome of the toss is a head, then the particle takes a step to the right. If the outcome is a tail, then a step is taken to the left. Let the probability of a head be p. (The coin may be biased.) Then the probability of a tail is $q = 1 - p$. Imagine the particle's initial position is at z. Let $P(z,n,x)$ denote the probability that the nth step takes the particle to position x, where, again, we have dropped the subscript X to simplify the notation. After step 1 the particle is either at $z + 1$ or $z - 1$. Then $P(z, n + 1, x)$ is the probability that the particle will reach x after n steps from $z + 1$ times the probability p of a step to the right plus the probability that it will reach x after n steps from $z - 1$ times the probability q of a step to the left. This process is illustrated in Figure 5.22.

Then we may form the following difference equation with z fixed.

$$P(z, n + 1, x) = q\,P(z, n, x + 1) + p\,P(z, n, x - 1) \qquad [5.3.27]$$

If x is fixed, then we would have

$$P(z, n + 1, x) = q\,P(z - 1, n, x) + p\,P(z + 1, n, x) \qquad [5.3.28]$$

Let the random walk start at position z, such that $0 < z < a$ along the x axis, where a is an upper bound. Determine the probability of the particle ending its random walk at $x = 0$. Then

$$P(z, n + 1, 0) = q\,P(z - 1, n, 0) + p\,P(z + 1, n, 0) \qquad [5.3.29]$$

As $n \to \infty$ we assume the random walk reaches an equilibrium or steady state, and the difference equation becomes independent of n. Then we have

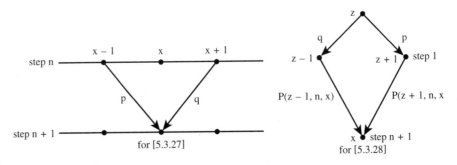

Figure 5.22   Illustration of possible movement for the particle

$$P(z, 0) = q\, P(z - 1, 0) + p\, P(z + 1, 0) \qquad \textbf{[5.3.30]}$$

This difference equation may be solved in a manner analogous to differential equations, which we illustrate in the next example.

A classical random walk problem is known as the gambler's ruin. A gambler has z dollars and the casino has $(a - z)$ dollars, $a > z$. Thus, the total number of dollars in the game is a. The gambler plays the game, making bets each time until either she or the casino wins all the money (i.e., a dollars). Determine the probability that the gambler is ruined. | **Example 5.44**

Suppose one game is played. Then the gambler has either $z + 1$ dollars or $z - 1$ dollars. She obtains $z + 1$ dollars with probability p and $z - 1$ dollars with probability q. Let $P(z, n + 1, x)$ be the probability that the gambler is ruined. We see that this is the random walk problem with one difference, which is that in this problem we have absorbing boundaries. The game ends when $z = 0$ or when $z = a$ in [5.3.28]. The difference equation is essentially the same as that derived previously. However, since we are interested in the gambler's ruin, we may suppress both x and n. Furthermore, we are given z. Thus, the difference equation becomes

$$P(\text{ruin} \mid z) = q\, P(\text{ruin} \mid z - 1) + p\, P(\text{ruin} \mid z + 1)$$

with boundary conditions of $P(\text{ruin} \mid 0) = 1$ and $P(\text{ruin} \mid a) = 0$. Suppose $p \neq q$. Then the solution to the difference equation is found in a manner analogous to that used for differential equations. We assume a solution of exponential form; that is, we let $P(\text{ruin} \mid z) = \lambda^z$. Then the characteristic equation is

$$\lambda^z = q\, \lambda^{z-1} + p\, \lambda^{z+1}$$

which becomes

$$\lambda^2 - \frac{1}{p}\lambda + \frac{q}{p} = 0$$

Thus

$$\lambda_1 = 1 \text{ and } \lambda_2 = \frac{q}{p}$$

This leads to

$$P(\text{ruin} \mid z) = A\, (\lambda_1)^z + B\, (\lambda_2)^z = A + B\left(\frac{q}{p}\right)^z$$

We now apply the boundary conditions to solve for A and B, obtaining the probability of the gambler's ruin given z as

$$P(\text{ruin} \mid z) = \frac{\left[\left(\frac{q}{p}\right)^a - \left(\frac{q}{p}\right)^z\right]}{\left[\left(\frac{q}{p}\right)^a - 1\right]} \qquad \textbf{[5.3.31]}$$

If $p = q = 1/2$, then $\lambda = 1$ and

$$P(\text{ruin} \mid z) = A + Bz = 1 - (z/a). \qquad \textbf{[5.3.32]}$$

Quiz 5.27   Derive [5.3.31] and [5.3.32].

Quiz 5.28   If the casino has $1,000 and the gambler has $1,000, what is the probability of the gambler's ruin if $p = 1/4$ and $q = 3/4$? What is the probability of the gambler's ruin if $p = q = 1/2$?

Example 5.45 | What is the expected duration, $D(z)$, of the game in the gambler's ruin problem if the starting point for the gambler is z dollars? The difference equation for $D(z)$ is

$$D(z) = q\, D(z - 1) + p\, D(Z + 1) + 1 \qquad [5.3.33]$$

since one step is required to get to either $z + 1$ or $z - 1$. The boundary conditions are $D(0) = D(a) = 0$. Assume $p \neq q$. The form of the solution is a multiple of z. Therefore, assume that cz is a particular solution. Then

$$cz = q\,(z - 1)c + p\,(z + 1)c + 1$$

which leads to $c = 1/(q - p)$.

The complete solution is the sum of the particular solution and the homogeneous solution; that is:

$$D(z) = \frac{z}{(q - p)} + A + B\left(\frac{q}{p}\right)^z$$

Using the boundary conditions, we have

$$D(z) = \frac{z}{q - p} - \frac{a}{q - p}\,\frac{1 - \left(\dfrac{q}{p}\right)^z}{1 - \left(\dfrac{q}{p}\right)^a} \qquad [5.3.34]$$

However, if $p = q = 1/2$, then the particular solution is $(-z^2)$, and the solution for $D(z)$ is

$$D(z) = -z^2 + A + Bz = z(a - z) \qquad [5.3.35]$$

Quiz 5.29   Find the expected duration of the gambler's ruin game when $p = 1/4$ and $q = 3/4$ and the casino and the gambler both start with $1,000. What is the expected duration if $p = q = 1/2$?

Example 5.46 | A certain noise voltage generator consists of a train of very narrow pulses where the pulse amplitudes are random and all pulses are independent of every other pulse. This noise source is applied to a threshold detector that counts the number of pulses that exceed the threshold. The threshold detector is followed by a storage counter. The probability that the ith pulse will exceed the threshold is P_i. Determine the difference equation and the boundary conditions that can be used to find the probability of x pulses being counted after n trials (pulses) have occurred.

We shall consider two solutions. First, we assume that all the P_is are equal; that is, $P_i = p$ for all i. This is a random walk problem for which the particle takes a step to the right for a success with probability p and the particle remains in that position for a failure with probability $q = 1 - p$. Here the counter records the occurrence of a pulse as a count for a success with probability p and fails to record a count with probability q. This is illustrated in Figure 5.23.

Consequently, the difference equation is

$$P(n, x) = q\,P(n - 1\ x) + p\,P(n - 1, x - 1)$$

where $P(n, x)$ is the probability of exactly x successes (pulses being counted) in n trials (pulses occurring). For this first case we have $P(0, x) = 0$ for $x > 0$ and $P(0, 0) = 1$. Furthermore, we have $P(n, 0) = q^n$ for $n \geq 0$ since if there are no successes in n trials, there are n failures in succession, and the probability for that is q^n. We may calculate the probabilities $P(n, x)$ by recursion, starting with $P(1, 1) = pP(0, 0) + qP(0, 1) = p$, and so on.

The second solution assumes that all the P_is are different. In this case the only change from the first case is that $P(n, x) = Q_1 Q_2 \ldots Q_n$ for $n > 0$ and $Q_i = 1 - P_i$ for all i.

Quiz 5.30   For the first solution in the previous example, calculate $P(2,1)$.

A radar antenna at a small local airport has a simple control system shown in Figure 5.24. | **Example 5.47**

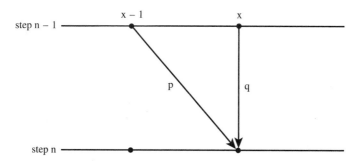

Figure 5.23   Illustration of possible movement for the particle

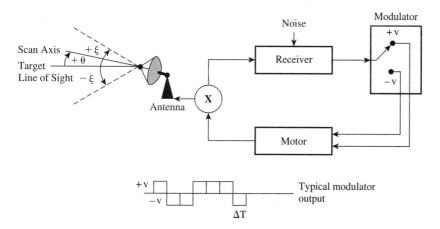

Figure 5.24   Simple radar antenna control system

If a target is present, the antenna control system tries to keep the scan axis along the line of sight (LOS, $\theta = 0$). For this example, θ is initially zero. However, if there is *no* target, then the scan axis moves off the LOS in a random fashion because of noise. As soon as $\theta \geq |\xi|$, the target is lost. Assume that once $|\xi|$ is exceeded, the scan axis never returns (i.e., θ is never again less than ξ). The receiver output consists of very narrow independent random noise pulses ("triggers") of repetition period ΔT, which drive a modulator. The modulator develops $+v$ for one repetition period if the trigger is positive and $-v$ if the trigger is negative. Because of receiver imbalance there are on the average twice as many positive pulses as negative pulses. The modulator output controls a motor that moves the antenna through an angle $+ \Delta\theta$ for every positive modulator pulse (height $+ v$, pulsewidth ΔT) and through $-\Delta\theta$ for every negative modulator pulse (height $-v$). The motor is very nearly a perfect integrator (i.e., a summer). At $t = 0$, $\theta = 0$ assume there is no target. Find the probability of loss, that is, the probability of $\theta = \pm \xi$. Let $|\xi| = 2^0$ and $\Delta\theta = 1^0$. (There are two answers.)

This is the gambler's ruin problem with absorbing boundaries at $\pm\xi$. We may illustrate this in Figure 5.25.

The number of steps from zero to ξ is $\xi/\Delta\theta$. Because of the imbalance, $p = 2/3$ and $q = 1/3$. Let the displacement, x, be measured from $\theta = -\xi$; then from the solution to the gambler's ruin problem, the probability of absorption at $-\xi$ is

$$P(\text{absorbed at } - \xi \,|\, z) = q\,P(\text{absorbed at } - \xi \,|\, z-1) + p\,P(\text{absorbed at } - \xi \,|\, z+1)$$

The boundary conditions are $P(0) = 1$ and $P(-\xi) = P(\xi) = 0$. Then

$$P(\text{absorbed at } -\xi \,|\, z) = \frac{\left[\left(\dfrac{q}{p}\right)^{\xi} - \left(\dfrac{q}{p}\right)^{z}\right]}{\left[\left(\dfrac{q}{p}\right)^{\xi} - 1\right]}$$

where $q/p = 1/2$, $\xi = 4$ and $z = \xi/\Delta\theta = 2$. Substituting these values, we have

$$P(\text{absorbed at } -\xi \,|\, z) = \frac{\left[\left(\dfrac{1}{2}\right)^{4} - \left(\dfrac{1}{2}\right)^{2}\right]}{\left[\left(\dfrac{1}{2}\right)^{4} - 1\right]} = \frac{1}{5}$$

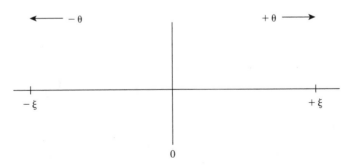

Figure 5.25   Antenna movement

while the probability of being absorbed at $+ \xi$ is

$$P(\text{absorbed at } +\xi \,|\, z) = 1 - P(\text{absorbed at } -\xi \,|\, z) = \frac{4}{5}$$

Example 5.48

We previously introduced the concept of an M/M/1 queue. Such a queue can also be represented as a Markov birth and death chain as in Figure 5.26, where this model of the birth and death Markov chain has a zero transition probability for P_{ii}. In Figure 5.26 λ_a is the average arrival rate of packets or messages and μ_s is the retransmission (or service) rate. This retransmission rate is also known as the service time in some applications. If we assume the process is in a steady state, and if the probability that we are in state i is denoted as P_i, then the rate of transmissions exiting from a given state is equal to the rate of arrivals to the same state. Thus, we have that $P_0\lambda_a = P_1\mu_s$, $P_1(\lambda_a + \mu_s) = P_0\lambda_a + P_2\mu_s$, and so on. It then follows that $P_{i-1}\lambda_a = P_i\mu_s$ or $P_i = P_{i-1}(\lambda_a/\mu_s) = P_0(\lambda_a/\mu_s)^i$. We have

$$\sum_{i=0}^{\infty} P_i = 1 = \sum_{i=0}^{\infty} \left(\frac{\lambda_a}{\mu_s}\right)^i P_0 = \frac{P_0}{1 - \left(\dfrac{\lambda_a}{\mu_s}\right)}$$

or

$$P_0 = 1 - \left(\frac{\lambda_a}{\mu_s}\right)$$

Then

$$P_i = \left[1 - \left(\frac{\lambda_a}{\mu_s}\right)\right]\left(\frac{\lambda_a}{\mu_s}\right)^i$$

Quiz 5.31   Determine the average number of packets in the queue.

5.3.12   DIFFUSION EQUATION*

*This subsection may be omitted.

The random walk problem may also be used to determine a **diffusion equation** that is useful for modeling the dispersion of fumes, smoke, and similar phenomena. Let P(n, x)

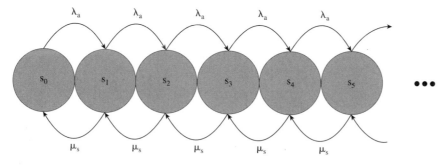

Figure 5.26   A state transition diagram for an M/M/1 queue

denote the probability of being at the position x after n steps, where for convenience for this example we drop the subscript X on P(n, x) so that our notation is simpler. Then if on the nth step the particle is at position x $-$ 1, there is a probability p that it will be at x on the (n + 1)st step; similarly, if the particle is at position x + 1 on the nth step, then there is a probability q that the particle will be at x on the (n + 1)st step; that is, we have the following **difference equation**:

$$P(n + 1, x) = p\,P(n, x - 1) + q\,P(n, x + 1) \qquad [5.3.36]$$

The boundary conditions are

$$P(0, 0) = 1 \text{ and } P(0, x) = 0 \text{ for } x \neq 0 \qquad [5.3.37]$$

Now, suppose that the length of each step is Δx and that this step is traversed in time Δt. Let $t = n\Delta t$. Then it can be shown that the mean and variance for a single step of length Δx are, respectively,

$$\mu_{\Delta x} = (p - q)\,|\Delta x| \text{ and } \sigma^2_{\Delta x} = 4\,p\,q\,(\Delta x)^2 \qquad [5.3.38]$$

Since each step is independent of, and has the same probability density function as, every other step, then we have

$$\mu_x = n\,\mu_{\Delta x} = t\,(p - q)\,\frac{|\Delta x|}{\Delta t} \qquad [5.3.39]$$

$$\sigma^2_x = n\,\sigma^2_{\Delta x} = 4\,p\,q\,t\,\frac{(\Delta x)^2}{\Delta t} \qquad [5.3.40]$$

In order that μ_x and $(\sigma_x)^2$ remain finite for all t, we set

$$\frac{(\Delta x)^2}{\Delta t} = 2\,D \qquad [5.3.41]$$

where D is called the diffusion coefficient and is usually a constant. With this specification we have

$$\mu_x = t\,(p - q)\,\frac{2\,D}{|\Delta x|} \qquad [5.3.42]$$

This implies that (p $-$ q) is of the order Δx. Next let

$$\frac{\mu_{\Delta x}}{2\Delta t} = c \qquad [5.3.43]$$

where c is a finite velocity. Since p = q when μ_x = 0, then set

$$p = \frac{1}{2} + \frac{c}{2D}\,|\Delta x| \qquad [5.3.44]$$

$$q = \frac{1}{2} - \frac{c}{2D}\,|\Delta x| \qquad [5.3.45]$$

This leads to

$$\mu_x = 2\,c\,t \qquad\qquad [5.3.46]$$

$$\sigma^2_x = 2\,D\,t \qquad\qquad [5.3.47]$$

Now we may rewrite [5.3.36] as follows:

$$P(t + \Delta t, x) = p\,P(t, x - |\Delta x|) + q\,P(t, x + |\Delta x|) \qquad [5.3.48]$$

The above equation also holds for the probability density function, which we shall use in the following equations.

Next expand [5.3.48] in a Taylor's series using the probability density function as follows:

$$\Delta t\,\frac{\partial p_X(t, x)}{\partial t} = (q - p)\,|\Delta x|\,\frac{\partial p_X(t, x)}{\partial x} + \frac{(\Delta x)^2}{2}\,\frac{\partial^2 p_X(t, x)}{\partial^2 x} + \cdots$$

If we take the limit as $\Delta t \to 0$ and use [5.3.46] and [5.3.47] and retain only the terms up to order $(\Delta x)^2$, we obtain

$$\frac{\partial p_X(t, x)}{\partial t} = -2\,c\,\frac{\partial p_X(t, x)}{\partial x} + D\,\frac{\partial^2 p_X(t, x)}{\partial^2 x} \qquad [5.3.49]$$

Equation [5.3.49] is a special case of the **Fokker–Planck diffusion equation** for the probability density function. In diffusion theory, D is known as the diffusion coefficient and c as the drift. This equation is used in models that involve the diffusion of smoke or other pollutants in the atmosphere, the diffusion of electrons in a conductive medium, the diffusion of liquid pollutants in water and soil, and the diffusion of plasmas. Equation [5.3.49] can be solved in several ways. Perhaps one of the easiest methods is to use Fourier transforms. This is explored further in the Problems, where you are asked to find $p_X(t,x)$, which is

$$p_X(t, x) = \frac{1}{\sqrt{4\pi D t}}\,\exp\left[-\frac{(x - 2ct)^2}{4Dt}\right] \qquad [5.3.50]$$

Note that this solution is a delta function at $x = t = 0$. The behavior of this function is explored in the following MATLAB example.

Quiz 5.32   Derive both terms in [5.3.38]. Hint: The probability density for one step of unity length is

$$p_X(x) = p\,\delta(x - 1) + q\delta(x + 1)$$

In this example we model the diffusion of smoke from a forest fire that starts in a National Park at time $t = 0$ and at location $x = 0$. The smoke from the fire drifts in the positive x direction due to wind blowing at 10 miles per hour and the diffusion coefficient is 1 square mile per hour. The probability density function, $p_X(t, x)$, is given in [5.3.50]. Here we plot this function for $t = 0$,

Example 5.49 (MATLAB)

0.25, 0.5, 1, and 2 hours. The first program determines the probability density function as a function of x and t (Figure 5.27a) and plots a 3-D rendition of this function in Figure 5.27b. In Figure 5.28b the changes in the probability density function (see Figure 5.28a) are shown at the various time instants. Note that the probability density function is initially a delta function at x = t = 0, and then it drifts and disperses with time.

```
%MATLAB solution for Example 5.49 by cjw
% Solution of Fokker-Planck diffusion equation with c = 10 miles/hour and D = 1 square mile per hour.
% One unit on x-axis equals 0.1 mile; one unit on t-axis equals 3 minutes.
clear
clg
c = 10;                                    % Drift equals 10 miles per hour.
D = 1;                                     % Diffusion coefficient is 1 square mile per hour
% Generate x and t array for the evaluation of function with two variables.
[x,t] = meshgrid(0.006:0.1:10, 0.006:0.05:1 );
% The probability density function p(t,x) given in [5.3-50] & to be solved in one of the problems.
p = (1./sqrt(4*pi*D.*t)).*exp(-(1./(4*D.*t)).*(x-2*c.*t).^2 );
p = p/3.6122;                              % Scale p to 1 at x = t = 0.006

axis([0 100 0 20 0 1.001]);                % Axis rescaling and appearance
hold on
mesh(p);                                   % 3-D mesh surface plot for p(t,x)
hold off
title('Solution of Fokker-Planck equation with c = 10 miles/hr, D = 1 sq. mile/hr ')
xlabel('x-axis(unit=0.1 mile)')
ylabel('t-axis(unit=3 minutes)')
zlabel('p (t, x)')
```

Figure 5.27a   MATLAB program for solution to Example 5.49

5.3.13   HIDDEN MARKOV PROCESSES

Deterministic signal models are not able to characterize most time-varying situations because the parameters of the signal model, such as amplitude, frequency, and phase, are fixed and therefore do not change with time. To overcome this fault, one approach to modeling time-varying signals and systems is to assume the signal does vary over time, but that for short time intervals the signal can be modeled reasonably well with certain types of random processes. The duration of the time interval for which this assumption is valid is usually determined empirically. Under these conditions the statistical properties of the time-varying signal or process appear to remain unchanged for an interval (this is a broad definition for stationarity, which we define in the next chapter), then the process will change its characteristics, either slowly or rapidly, to another or similar process with another set of statistical parameters. This change might be consid-

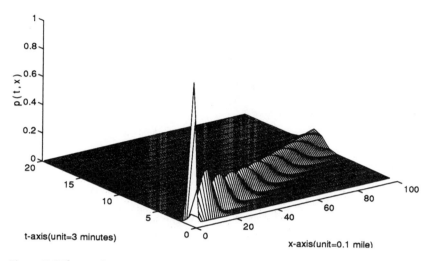

Figure **5.27b**   Three-dimensional plot of the solution to Example 5.49

ered something like the transitions that take place in a Markov chain transition matrix. Thus, there may be intervals where the characteristics of the signal or process appear to be unchanging and intervals where the process seems to be changing. We generally assume that the temporal variations that are observed in the process are governed by statistical laws. Thus, we may seek models that describe both the short-time variations in the process as well as the long-term and steady state features. We may be particularly concerned with describing the transitions from one interval to another. **Hidden Markov models** deal with these types of processes. In particular, these models address ways to identify the steady state intervals, methods to describe the sequential statistical changes from one interval to another, and the type of models that should be used to characterize each interval.

Definition 5.43. A **hidden Markov model** is a doubly random process that has an underlying random process that cannot be observed. Therefore, this process is hidden. However, some aspects of this hidden process may be observed through another random process or a set of random processes. The observed random process produces a sequence of symbols or characters or parameters that we may measure and for which we may determine statistical properties.

It turns out that hidden Markov models (HMMs) are an outgrowth of Markov processes and are used extensively in many of today's speech recognition systems. This topic is covered in other courses.

```
% MATLAB solution for Example 5.49 by cjw
% Observations at times t=0, 0.25, 0.5, 1, and 2 hours.
% Solution to the Fokker–Planck diffusion equation with c=10 miles/hour and D=1 square mile/hour.
clear;
clg;
c=10;                              % Drift is 10 miles per hour.
D=1;                               % Diffusion coefficient is 1 square mile per hour.
dt=[0.0001 0.25 0.5 1 2];          % Select five observation times.
for j=1:5                          % Compute & plot p(t,x) for each position.
    t=dt(j);
    i=1;
    for x=0:0.1:50                 % Compute p(t,x). This loop can be avoided but this way
                                   % is clearer.
        p(i)=(1/sqrt(4*pi*D*t))*exp(-(x − 2*c*t)^2/(4*D*t));
        i=i + 1;
    end;
    it=1:length(p);
    if j==1
        norm=max(p);
        t=0;
    end;
    p=p/norm;                      % Normalize p(t,x) for each case
    s=num2str(t);
    txt=['p('s',x)'];
    subplot(5,1,j);
    plot(it/10,p):                 % Plot p(t,x) for each case
    if j ~=1
        axis([0 60 0 0.03])        % Axis rescaling.
    end
    ylabel(txt)
    grid
end;                               % End of five loops
xlabel('miles');
subplot(5,1,1);
title('Observations of the probability density at times t=0, 0.25, 0.5, 1, and 2 hours.')
% orient tall and print
```

Figure 5.28a   MATLAB program for $p_x(t,x)$ for various values of t

5.4   SUMMARY

This chapter has introduced a number of new concepts. We reviewed **deterministic functions** such as **continuous time and continuous amplitude, continuous time and discrete amplitude, discrete time and continuous amplitude, discrete time and discrete amplitude,** and **discrete time sequences.** Then we defined a **continuous random**

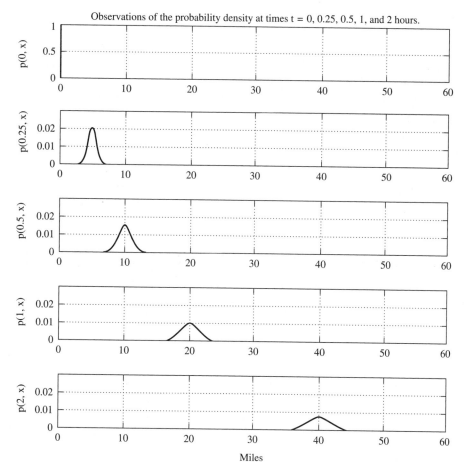

Observations of the probability density at times t = 0, 0.25, 0.5, 1, and 2 hours.

Figure 5.28b   Graph of the drift and dispersion of smoke for Example 5.49

process as an indexed **ensemble** of member functions of one or more random variables. Such random processes have continuous amplitude and continuous time. Various examples of such processes were given, including the sine wave random process. In a manner analogous to deterministic functions, we defined **random processes** with continuous time and discrete amplitude, a continuous amplitude random sequence, and a discrete amplitude random sequence. We defined **equal random processes** and **operations on random processes** such as the sum and product, as well as complex random processes. **Random vectors** were described along with **random matrices**. The **expected value of random processes** (and random vectors) was defined in a manner analogous to that for random variables. In Section 5.3 some important random processes were introduced along with numerous examples. These random processes included the **Poisson, Poisson impulses, shot noise, Poisson intervals, Bernoulli, binary white noise, binary counting, random walk, continuous and discrete Wiener, and Markov.** We showed that a random walk process is Markov, and we derived a diffusion equation from a random walk process.

We will study in the following chapters some additional properties, such as the classification of random processes as stationary, nonstationary, or ergodic. We will also define autocorrelation and cross-correlation functions. As we mentioned, each of the processes we examined may serve as models for signals, noise, diffusion, as well as other situations such as in the radar-tracking problem and the network terminal design problem. The following chapters will also examine the response of linear systems to random processes.

PROBLEMS

5.1   Figure 5.29 shows two-member functions of an ensemble of sine waves that all have the same maximum amplitude and the same frequency, but differ in their phase angles (or time displacement). Let the phase angle Θ be the random variable with respect to the time $t = 0$. If Θ has a uniform probability density from 0 to 2π, what is the amplitude probability density of the ensemble? With this probability density, show that the ensemble average of the square of the amplitude is equal to the mean square value of the sinusoid.

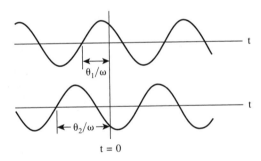

Figure 5.29

5.2   A random process $X(t)$ consists of three-member functions as follows:

$$x_1(t) = 1, x_2(t) = -3, x_3(t) = \sin 2\pi t$$

Each member function occurs with equal probability. Sketch the ensemble. Calculate $E[x(t)]$.

5.3   A random process $X(t)$ has the following member functions:

$$x_1(t) = -2\cos(t)$$
$$x_2(t) = -2\sin(t)$$
$$x_3(t) = 2[\cos(t) + \sin(t)]$$
$$x_4(t) = [\cos(t) - \sin(t)]$$
$$x_5(t) = [\sin(t) - \cos(t)]$$

and these occur with equal probability. Sketch the ensemble. Find $E[x(t)]$.

5.4 Find the sum of the two random processes in Problems 5.2 and 5.3.

5.5 A random process, X(t), consists of the following functions:

$$x_1(t) = \sin \pi t$$

$$x_2(t) = t/2$$

One of these functions is selected by the toss of a biased coin, where p is the probability of a head and q is the probability of a tail. If a head occurs, then x_1 is selected. If a tail occurs, then x_2 is selected. Find the cumulative probability distribution function $P_X(x)$ for $t = 1/4, t = 1/2, t = 1$.

5.6 The air temperature in your location is measured on the hour every hour each year. Describe the random process. Sketch an ensemble for the process.

5.7 You have a large number of pennies, which are tossed repeatedly by a machine. Assume that the tosses of the coins are independent. Denote the occurrence of a head by a 1 and the occurrence of tail by a 0. Sketch an ensemble for this random process. Determine the probability density function for each member function of the ensemble corresponding to each coin.

5.8 A random process is determined by tossing a fair die. Let the value of the random variable be equal to the value of the die that shows on each toss. Sketch an ensemble for this random process. Find the expected value for the process.

5.9 One type of packet transmission consists of dividing the transmission capacity of the transmitter or node into N channels. If R is the total bit rate, then R/N is the bit rate per channel. Each channel can be modeled as an M/M/1 queue with a packet arrival rate λ_a, while the packet transmission rate is μ_s. What is λ_a in packets per second and μ_s in bits per second? Express your answer in terms of R, N, and M_L. What is the average delay per packet?

5.10 Another type of packet transmission stores each packet as it arrives from each of N channels in memory. Then each packet is taken from memory and retransmitted. If each channel has a packet arrival rate of λ_a, then determine the total packet arrival rate. This type of multiplexing is Poisson and can be modeled as an M/M/1 queue with a total packet arrival rate. Determine the transmission rate in bits per second as well as the average delay. How does the average delay for this type of packet transmission compare to that for Problem 5.9.

5.11 A local copying business has an average arrival rate of customers as well as an average service rate. There are times when there are no customers. Determine the average interval between the times when there are no customers.

5.12 A multimedia communication system sends data and speech with a rate of R bits per second. There are M speech channels available and each speech channel has a fixed rate of R_s bits per second. The data consists of images and other information, which we assume can be modeled by a Poisson process with an arrival rate of λ_a. The data is sent in the form of packets that are independent and exponentially distributed with an average length of μ_L. What is the average transmission rate for speech and that for data? Assume that this is an M/M/1 queue model with an average packet delay of T seconds. How many speech channels can this system accommodate?

5.13 A communication system sends data in the form of packets of fixed length. Noise in the communication channel may cause a packet to be received incorrectly. If this happens, then the packet is retransmitted. Let the probability that a packet is received incorrectly be q. Determine the average number of transmissions that are necessary before a packet is received correctly. Draw a state diagram for this problem.

5.14 In Problem 5.13 let the the transmission time be T_t seconds for a packet. If the packet was received incorrectly, then a message is sent back to the transmitter that states that the message was received incorrectly. Let the time for sending such a message be T_i. Assume that if the packet is received correctly that we do not send an acknowledgement. What is the average time for a successful transmission? Draw a state diagram for this problem.

5.15 Alter Problem 5.14 as follows. Let there be three nodes. The packet is to be sent from node 1 to node 2 to node 3 without an error. The probability of the packets being received incorrectly at each node is the same and is q. The transmission time is T_t and the time to acknowledge that a packet was received incorrectly is T_i. Draw a state diagram for this problem. Determine the average time for the packet to reach node 3 correctly.

5.16 A workstation is used until it fails and then it is sent out for repair. The time between failures, or the length of time the workstation functions until it needs repair, is random variable T. Assume the times between failures, $T_1, T_2, \ldots$, of the workstations available are independent random variables that are identically distributed. For $t > 0$, let the number of workstations that have failed be N(t) in the interval $0 \le t$. If the time between failures of each workstation has an exponential probability density function, then what type of process is N(t)? Assume that you have just purchased 10 new workstations and that each has a 90-day warranty. If the mean time between failures (MTBF) is 250 days, what is the probability that at least one workstation will fail before the end of the warranty period?

5.17 Model lightning strikes to a power line during a thunderstorm as a Poisson impulse process. Suppose the number of lightning strikes in time interval t has a mean rate of arrival given by s, which is one per three minutes. What is the expected number of lightning strikes in 1 minute? in 10 minutes? What is the average time between lightning strikes? Suppose the power line has an impulse response that may be approximated by te^{-at}. What does the shot noise on the power line look like? Sketch a possible member function of the shot noise process for this problem if $a = 10$.

5.18 Model the gender of customers that arrive at a store as a Bernoulli process (e.g., the occurrence of a male customer is 0 and a female customer is $+1$). If a male customer has just arrived, what is the probability density function for the time before the next male customer arrives? If on the average there are 10 female customers to every male customer, what is the probability that after a male customer arrives there will be 5 female customers before the next male customer? Discuss whether or not this process has any memory. Does this process depend on the observation time? What assumptions did you make to answer the last question?

5.19 Let N(i) be a binary white noise process. The values of N(i) are determined by the toss of a coin, with a head generating a $+1$ and a tail generating a 0. Determine a sequence of 10 values of N(i) by flipping a coin. Set a threshold at 0.5 for this sequence and determine the corresponding member function for the counting process for this sequence.

5.20 Let N(i) be a binary white noise process. You measure the random process, S(i), where

$$S(i) = a\,S(i-1) + N(i) \quad \text{for } i = 0, 1, 2, \dots$$

where $S(-1) = 0$. The values of N(i) are determined by the toss of a coin. If a head appears, then a $+1$ is generated for N(i). If a tail appears, a -1 is generated. Repeat this procedure and use the recursion relation to determine S(i). Determine and plot a member function of this random process by flipping a coin 10 times if $a = 0.9$, if $a = 1$, if $a = -0.9$. Set a threshold at 0.5. For each value of a, determine the member function for a counting process that counts the number of values in each member function of S(i) that exceeds the threshold. Repeat your calculations with the threshold changed to (1) 1 and (2) 3.

5.21 A Poisson counting process is a random process with independent intervals that have a Poisson probability density function. Suppose the number of calls arriving at a switchboard has a Poisson probability density function with the rate of calls per minute being $\lambda_a = 0.1$. What is the probability that the number of calls counted is less than or equal to 10 in a 10-minute interval? Repeat the problem if $\lambda_a = 10$.

5.22 A random process is given as

$$X(t) = a\cos\left(2\pi f_c t + B(n)\frac{\pi}{2}\right) \quad \text{for } nT \le t < (n+1)T \quad \text{for all } n$$

where B(n) is a Bernoulli random process that has values of $+1$ or -1. Sketch several possible member functions of this random process. Determine the mean value for X(t). This is a model for phase shift keying in communication systems, where f_c is the carrier frequency.

5.23 A particle is positioned on a line at the origin. It can move initially only to $+1$. Once the particle is at $+1$ it can only move back to the origin. Then the process is repeated. Where will the particle be after n trials? Determine the probability density function for the position of the particle. This is a reflecting-boundary random walk problem.

5.24 A random waveform is generated as follows. The waveform starts at 0 voltage. It may move to $+1$ with probability p or it may move to -1 with probability q. However, once the waveform is at $+1$ (or -1), the probability of p (or q) becomes unity that the waveform will return to 0. Once at 0 the waveform must again move to $+1$ or -1; that is, it cannot stay at 0. What type of random process is this? (Hint: see the previous problem.) Determine the probability density function for the value of the waveform.

5.25 What is the expected time before the loss of the line of sight in Example 5.47?

5.26 Model the diffusion of electrons and holes across a potential barrier in an electronic device as follows. We have n black balls (electrons) in urn I, and n white balls (holes) in urn II. An experimental outcome selects randomly one ball from each urn. The ball from urn I is placed in urn II and that from urn II is placed in I. Let the state of the process be the number of black balls in urn I. By knowing the number of black balls in urn I, we know the composition of both urns. Let k denote the state of the process. Then explain why the transition probabilities are

$$P_{k\,(k-1)} = \left(\frac{k}{n}\right)^2 \quad k > 0$$

$$P_{kk} = \frac{2k(n-k)}{n^2}$$

$$P_{k\,(k+1)} = \left(\frac{n-k}{n}\right)^2 \quad k < n$$

$$P_{kj} = 0 \quad \text{otherwise}$$

Continue this problem using MATLAB. Write a computer program to show the "diffusion" of holes and electrons across the barrier. This is Problem 5.7M.

5.27 A PCM waveform has the two states +1 and 0. Suppose the transition matrix is

$$T = \begin{array}{cc} & \begin{array}{cc} +1 & 0 \end{array} \\ \begin{array}{c} +1 \\ 0 \end{array} & \left[\begin{array}{cc} 0.50 & 0.50 \\ 0.25 & 0.75 \end{array}\right] \end{array}$$

The initial value of the waveform is determined by the flip of a coin, with the outcome of a head corresponding to +1 and a tail to 0. What is the probability that the waveform will be at +1 after one step if the coin is a fair coin? Find the same probability if the coin is biased such that a head occurs with probability 1/3. Repeat the problem for two steps.

5.28 A PCM signal consisting of 1s and 0s is transmitted over a computer network. The signal goes through the network and is received by a repeater that then sends the signal onto the next repeater or computer. There is probability p that a 1 (or a 0) will be changed at each repeater. Sketch a state transition tree (trellis diagram) for a PCM 1 as it moves through a network with three successive repeaters. Find the probability that the output is correct (i.e., is a 1). What is the probability that the original 1 was changed in the network, but that the output was still a 1?

5.29 A student takes this course at period 1 on Monday, Wednesday, and Friday. Period 1 starts at 7:25 A.M. Consequently, the student sometimes misses class. However, she attends class depending only on whether or not she went to the last class. If she attended class on one day, then she will go to class the next time it meets with probability p. If she did not go to one class, then she will go to the next class with probability q. Find the transition matrix T. Find the probability that if she went to class on Wednesday that she will attend class (1) on Friday, (2) on the next Monday. Let $p = 1/2$ and $q = 3/4$ to find (1) and (2).

5.30 Two students play the following game. Two dice are tossed. If the sum of the numbers showing is less than 7, student A collects a dollar from student B. If the total is greater than 7, then student B collects a dollar from student A. If a 7 appears, then the student with the fewest dollars collects a dollar from the other. If the students have the same amount, then no dollars are exchanged. The game continues until one student runs out of dollars. Let student A's number of dollars represent the states. Let each student start with 3 dollars. What is the transition matrix, T? If student A reaches state 0 or 6, then he stays there with probability 1. What is the probability that student B loses in 3 tosses of the dice? What is the probability that student A loses in 5 or fewer tosses?

5.31 You play a driving game at the county fair. The driving time from one station to another is the same as is the distance. The time spent at each station is the same. At station 0 and at station 4 your car is disabled and you are out of the game. The object of the game is to keep driving as long as possible. The transition matrix for your moves is random and is given as

$$T = \begin{array}{c} \\ 0 \\ 1 \\ 2 \\ 3 \\ 4 \end{array} \begin{array}{c} \begin{array}{ccccc} 0 & 1 & 2 & 3 & 4 \end{array} \\ \left[\begin{array}{ccccc} 1 & 0 & 0 & 0 & 0 \\ .5 & 0 & .5 & 0 & 0 \\ 0 & .5 & 0 & .5 & 0 \\ 0 & 0 & .5 & 0 & .5 \\ 0 & 0 & 0 & 0 & 1 \end{array} \right] \end{array}$$

Is this a random walk with absorbing boundaries? Sketch a state transition diagram. If you start in a nonabsorbing state, how long will it take before you are disabled? How many times will you spend in each nonabsorbing state? Determine the probability that you will end up being disabled (1) at station 0, (2) at station 4.

5.32 On your summer vacation you go hiking. You may visit the beach (B), climb a mountain (M), walk to a lake (L), or hike to a river (R). On the first day you hike to one of these locations from your base camp according to your initial position. Once at a given site, it takes one day to walk to any other site. You prefer the water to the mountains. Assume you are initially positioned with probabilities

$$(B, M, L, R)^T = (0.3, 0.1, 0.3, 0.3)$$

Your trips are random and determined as follows:

$$
T = \begin{array}{c} \\ B \\ M \\ L \\ R \end{array}
\begin{array}{c} \overset{\text{B M L R}}{} \\ \begin{bmatrix} .5 & .1 & .2 & .2 \\ .7 & 0 & .2 & .1 \\ .4 & .1 & .2 & .3 \\ .6 & 0 & .2 & .2 \end{bmatrix} \end{array}
$$

What is the probability that at the end of the second day you are at the beach? What is the probability that at the end of the third day you are on the mountain?

5.33   A data bus on your computer sends binary data. A binary 1 is represented by a 5-volt level, while a binary 0 is represented by a 0-volt level. However, the power supply is weak and intermittent and causes the voltage level of both a 1 and a 0 to fluctuate. Consequently, data on the bus is sometimes received incorrectly. The transition matrix is

$$
T = \begin{array}{c} \\ 1 \\ 0 \end{array}
\begin{array}{c} \overset{1 \qquad 0}{} \\ \begin{bmatrix} 0.7 & 0.3 \\ 0.4 & 0.6 \end{bmatrix} \end{array}
$$

A data word of seven bits is sent over the bus. What is the probability that the data word is received correctly if the word is (1100101)? Are there any assumptions that you need to make?

5.34   A three-state Markov chain has the following transition matrix:

$$
T = \begin{array}{c} \\ 1 \\ 2 \\ 3 \end{array}
\begin{array}{c} \overset{1 \qquad 2 \qquad 3}{} \\ \begin{bmatrix} 0.25 & 0.50 & 0.25 \\ 0.40 & 0.60 & 0.00 \\ 1.00 & 0.00 & 0.00 \end{bmatrix} \end{array}
$$

Does this matrix have a unique fixed-point probability vector? If so, find it. What is the approximate value of P_{13} in T^{100}, where P_{ij} is the transition probability in T corresponding to the ith row and jth column. What interpretation do you give to this result? What is the probability that after the third step you are in state 3 if the initial state probability vector is (1/3 1/3 1/3)?

5.35   The three letters C, A, and T represent the states of a word-generating system. Let the initial state probability vector be (1/3 1/3 1/3) for the three letters, respectively. The transition matrix is given as

$$
T = \begin{array}{c} \\ C \\ A \\ T \end{array}
\begin{array}{c} \overset{C \qquad A \qquad T}{} \\ \begin{bmatrix} 0.1 & 0.7 & 0.2 \\ 0.6 & 0.1 & 0.3 \\ 0.1 & 0.8 & 0.1 \end{bmatrix} \end{array}
$$

What is the probability of generating a proper three-letter dictionary word after two transitions from the initial state?

5.36 Let a random process be defined as

$$X(t, s) = A(s) \sin\left(\frac{\pi}{2}t\right) = A \sin\left(\frac{\pi}{2}t\right)$$

where A is a Gaussian random variable with mean μ and variance σ^2. Define a two-dimensional random vector $(X(1/4, s), X(1, s))$. Determine the probability density function for the random vector. Calculate covariance matrix C and write out the complete probability density function.

5.37 Define a random process as

$$X(t) = A \sin(\omega t) + B \cos(\omega t)$$

where A and B are independent Gaussian random variables with means μ_A and μ_B, respectively and variances $(\sigma_A)^2$ and $(\sigma_B)^2$. Determine the one-dimensional probability density function for X(t).

5.38 For the random process in Problem 5.37 define a two-dimensional random vector $(X(t_1), X(t_2))$. Determine the probability density function for this random vector. Calculate covariance matrix C and write out the complete probability density function.

5.39 A farmer is planting two types of corn. His seeder contains twice as much seed for white corn as that for yellow corn. The seeder drops a seed every foot as it moves down a row that is 100 feet long. What type of random process is this? Sketch a possible member function for this random process. How does this process differ from most of those studied in this chapter?

5.40 A binary test image is generated on the screen of your personal computer as follows. Each raster scan contains 480 pixels (picture elements) that may become either black or white with equal probability as the raster is scanned. Assume each raster scan is independent of every other and that there are 500 rasters. What type of random process is this? What is the independent variable? Is there more than one independent variable? What is the probability that the binary test image is all white?

5.41 A Markov process has the following transition matrix. Determine whether or not the process is regular, and if it is regular, determine the fixed probability vector analytically.

$$T = \begin{bmatrix} 0.50 & 0.25 & 0.25 \\ 0.50 & 0.00 & 0.50 \\ 0.25 & 0.25 & 0.50 \end{bmatrix}$$

5.42 Solve the Fokker–Planck diffusion equation using Fourier transforms of the probability density function. Use boundary conditions of $p_X(0, 0) = 1$ and $p_X(0, x) = 0$ for $x \neq 0$.

5.43 This problem expands on Example 5.17 to illustrate how certain design parameters for the communications terminal can be determined and what trade-offs may exist between some of these parameters. For example, we will consider memory storage size, number of input data channels, input data duty cycle, and probability of memory (word storage) saturation. Assume the workstation has x input channels and y output channels. These channels may be telephone lines and/or computer networks. The data storage problem to be analyzed is one in which the data rate per channel undergoes a reduction from the input to the output of the terminal.

The following notation will be adopted:

Symbol	Definition
d	Duty cycle of an input data channel ($0 \leq d \leq 1$). The duty cycle may be considered to be the fraction of time the channel is active, that is, transmitting data.
N	Number of channels requiring data storage.
L	Length of a call (or message) (a random variable).
l	Specific value for L.
μ_L	Average (mean) length of a call per channel in minutes.
m_T	Total memory storage size in words (e.g., as might be needed for a facsimile message).
r	Input channel data rate in words per minute per channel for 100% duty cycle.
s	Output channel rate in words per minute per channel.
M	Memory storage required in words (a random variable).
m	Specific value for M.

From the above definitions it is easily deduced that:

$(rd-s)$ is the memory storage rate in words per minute per channel.

$(rd-s)\mu_L$ is the average storage requirement in words per channel.

$(rd-s)\mu_L N$ is the average storage requirement in words.

We have assumed that the output channel is continuously active; that is, it operates at 100 percent duty cycle. We have also assumed that a memory storage unit is the same for all words.

The probability that the memory storage required in words, M, is greater than the total memory storage capacity available in words, m_T, is assumed to be

$$P_M(M > m_T) = \exp\left[-\frac{m_T}{(rd - s)\mu_L N}\right]$$

By specifying the value of $P_M(M > m_T)$ that is tolerable, as well as the memory size available, the number of channels, N, requiring data storage can be determined as well as the duty cycle, d, for each channel.

There are other ways in which the trade-offs between parameters can be illustrated. However, one usually knows the items that are commercially available, as well as the size and price of these items. In this example the memory is the item that is available commercially. However, for some applications the memory may have to be specifically designed and some other parameter may need to be specified.

The customer or designer usually does not know the value of $P_M(M > m_T)$ that can be tolerated. However, the designer does have some idea of the amount of memory that can be afforded for each terminal. Therefore, one must usually use $P_M(M > m_T)$ as a parameter and observe the influence that variations in this probability have upon the other system parameters.

Assume we are given some experimentally determined statistics concerning the length of data calls, as in Table 5.1. We have already determined that μ_L is approximately five minutes.

We specify m_T, r, and s so that the duty cycle and the number of channels requiring storage can be determined for various memory saturation probabilities. Assume the system to be designed has 32 input and output channels with provisions to expand to at least 105 input/output channels.

For this example, let $m_T = 32{,}000$ words, $r = 110$, and $s = 67$. Then since

$$P_M(M > 32{,}000) = \exp\left[-\frac{32{,}000}{(110d - 67)(5)N}\right]$$

we can now design our system by selecting a value for the probability of memory saturation. Determine various values for N and d if the probability of memory saturation is 0.01. Plot d versus N for various saturation probabilities for a total memory saturation capacity of 32,000 words. This plot will contain a family of curves for which $P_M(M > m_T)$ is a constant. Check your results by assuming the memory size $M = 32{,}000$ and assume unity duty cycle for all N channels requiring storage. Discuss factors that may influence the selection of the probability of memory saturation.

MATLAB PROBLEMS

5.1M In Section 5.3.12 we derived a diffusion equation and illustrated the equation with Example 5.49. Repeat Example 5.49 assuming that $D = 5, 10, 20$ and that $c = 1, 10, 20$.

5.2M Suppose we have a communication system with the following transition matrix:

$$T = \begin{array}{c} r \\ w \\ s \end{array}\begin{bmatrix} 0.50 & 0.25 & 0.25 \\ 0.50 & 0.00 & 0.50 \\ 0.25 & 0.25 & 0.50 \end{bmatrix}$$

Let r denote the receipt of a packet, s denote sending, and w denote wait. (See Problem 5.41.) In this problem we want to simulate this Markov process by generating a sequence of states. Generate a sequence of 500 states, starting in state s. Estimate the fixed probability vector using the sequence you generate. Does this estimate agree with the theoretical answer?

5.3M You are given a member function of a random process as
y = 10sin(2πt + π/2), where the amplitude is in volts. Quantize the amplitude
of y into 21 levels with the intervals ranging from −10.5 to +10.5 in one-volt
steps. Consider 100 periods of y and let t take on discrete values given by nT,
where T = 0.005 s. Construct a histogram of y. Compare your result to Figure
4.8 of Example 4.28 in Chapter 4.

5.4M Let N(i) be a binary white noise process. The values of N(i) are determined by the
toss of a coin, with a head generating a +1 and a tail generating a 0. Model the tossing of a coin using MATLAB. Determine a sequence of 100 values of N(i) using
the coin flipping model. Set a threshold at 0.5 for this sequence and determine the
corresponding member function for the counting process for this sequence.

5.5M Determine which of the following transition matrices represent regular Markov
processes. Find the fixed probability vector for the regular matrices.

$$\begin{bmatrix} 0.33 & 0.67 \\ 0.83 & 0.17 \end{bmatrix}, \begin{bmatrix} 0.00 & 1.00 \\ 0.25 & 0.75 \end{bmatrix}, \begin{bmatrix} 0.2 & 0.8 \\ 1.0 & 0.0 \end{bmatrix}, \begin{bmatrix} 0 & 1 \\ 1 & 0 \end{bmatrix},$$

$$\begin{bmatrix} 0.50 & 0.50 & 0.00 \\ 0.00 & 0.50 & 0.50 \\ 0.33 & 0.33 & 0.33 \end{bmatrix}, \begin{bmatrix} 0.33 & 0.00 & 0.67 \\ 0.00 & 1.00 & 0.00 \\ 0.00 & 0.20 & 0.80 \end{bmatrix}, \begin{bmatrix} 0.50 & 0.25 & 0.25 \\ 0.33 & 0.67 & 0.00 \\ 0.00 & 0.25 & 0.75 \end{bmatrix}$$

5.6M This is Problem 5.20; however, we will model N(i), a binary white noise
process, using MATLAB. You measure random process s(i), where

$$S(i) = a\,S(i-1) + N(i) \quad \text{for } i = 0, 1, 2, \ldots$$

where S(−1) = 0. The values of N(i) are determined by the toss of a coin,
which you model using MATLAB. If a head appears, then a +1 is generated for
N(i). If a tail appears, a −1 is generated. Determine a member function of this
random process by flipping a coin 100 times if a = 0.9, if a = 1, if a = −0.9.
Set a threshold at 0.5. For each value of a, determine the member function for a
counting process that counts the number of values in each member function of
S(i) that exceeds the threshold. Repeat your calculations with the threshold
changed to (1) 1 and (2) 3.

5.7M Do Problem 5.26.

5.8M Simulate Problem 5.31 using MATLAB.

5.9M Let diffusion coefficient D be 0.1 square miles per hour and drift c be 10 miles per
hour. Solve the Fokker–Planck diffusion equation by discrete approximation
methods and sketch the solution for P(t,x). Assume zero initial conditions. Repeat
the problem with P(0,0) = 0.5. Experiment with several changes in D and c.

5.10M Simulate Problem 5.32 using MATLAB.

5.11M Simulate Problem 5.33 using MATLAB.

5.12M On the first day of the new year it is cloudy. What is the probability that it is sunny on July 4 if the following transition matrix applies?

$$T = \begin{array}{c} \\ \text{sunny} \\ \text{cloudy} \\ \text{rainy} \end{array} \begin{array}{ccc} \text{sunny} & \text{cloudy} & \text{rainy} \\ \left[\begin{array}{ccc} 0.7 & 0.2 & 0.1 \\ 0.3 & 0.2 & 0.5 \\ 0.3 & 0.3 & 0.4 \end{array} \right] \end{array}$$

5.13M Assume a model for photon noise in an optical amplifier is similar to shot noise with $h(t) = te^{-at}$. Simulate this noise process and plot a member function.

5.14M Develop a computer program to simulate a random telegraph signal.

5.15M Modify the program given in the text for a Bernoulli random process to simulate a binary counting process.

5.16M The position of a particle is governed by the probability density function [5.3.9]. Show a graph of the position of the particle as a function of the number of steps if $p = q = 1/2$. Then let $p = 1/4$ and $q = 3/4$ and repeat the problem.

chapter

6

Correlation and Power Spectral Density Functions by Ensemble Averaging

6.1   INTRODUCTION

The last chapter provided an introduction to random processes. In this chapter we study certain functions, properties, and classes of random processes, since a complete statistical description of a random process is usually not available for practical engineering problems. Three functions of primary importance are the autocorrelation function, the crosscorrelation function, and the power spectral density.

In Chapter 4 we introduced the correlation coefficient as a parameter that described the degree of linear relationship between two random variables. In a similar manner the autocorrelation function describes properties of a random process, while the crosscorrelation function describes the relationship between two random processes. We will also see that we can classify random processes using correlation functions and power spectral density functions. This chapter will focus on the theoretical properties of correlation and power spectral density functions, while the next chapter will introduce estimates for correlation and power spectral density functions that can be applied to data measured from one member function of an ensemble.

Frequency analysis, using Fourier series, the Fourier transform, and the Laplace transform, is a well-known procedure for analyzing certain characteristics of a function or of data. In this chapter we will define the power spectral density function as the Fourier transform of the autocorrelation function for wide sense stationary random processes. Thus, the power spectral density function will describe the distribution of the power of a random process in the frequency domain. This is useful in system design where, for example, one may want to design a system to maximize the signal-to-noise ratio.

6.2   AUTOCORRELATION FUNCTIONS BY ENSEMBLE AVERAGING

We recall that the definition for the expected value of a continuous time random process may be a function of time.

Definition 6.1. The **expected value of a continuous time random process** is the **expected function** or **mean function**, which is denoted as

$$\mu_X(t) = E[X(t)] \quad \text{for} \quad -\infty < t < \infty. \qquad \text{[6.2.1]}$$

$$= \int_{-\infty}^{\infty} x(t)\, p_X(x(t))\, d(x(t))$$

The expected function or mean function of a random process may be a function of time, as noted in [6.2.1]. However, in certain cases the mean function will be a constant. Note that in [6.2.1] we have suppressed the experimental outcome variable, s, which we used extensively in the previous chapters.

Example 6.1

Let us repeat Example 5.13, which calculated the mean function for the sine wave random process $X(t) = A \sin(\omega t)$ for all t, where ω is a constant and A is a random variable uniformly distributed between zero and a_0. Then

$$\mu_X(t) = E[X(t)] = \int_0^{a_0} \frac{1}{a_0} x(t)\, da = \int_0^{a_0} \frac{1}{a_0} a \sin(\omega t) da = \frac{a_0}{2} \sin(\omega t)$$

which is a function of t.

Example 6.2

Now suppose the random process is again the sine wave random process, but the random variable is phase Θ, which is uniformly distributed from zero to 2π. Thus, $X(t) = a \sin(\omega t + \Theta)$ for all t, where ω and a are constants. Then

$$\mu_X(t) = E[X(t)] = \int_0^{2\pi} \frac{1}{2\pi} x(t)\, d\theta = \int_0^{2\pi} \frac{1}{2\pi} a \sin(\omega t + \theta)\, d\theta = 0$$

which is a constant.

Quiz 6.1   Discuss the differences between the above two examples. Using sketches of member functions of the respective ensembles, describe why the mean function for the first example is a function of t and the mean function for Example 6.2 is not.

Definition 6.2. The **autocorrelation function,** $R_{XX}(t_1, t_2)$, of a random process, $X(t)$, is defined as the expected value of the product of $[X(t_1) X(t_2)]$; that is:

$$R_{XX}(t_1, t_2) = E[X(t_1) X(t_2)] = \int_{-\infty}^{\infty}\int_{-\infty}^{\infty} x(t_1) x(t_2)\, p_X(x(t_1), x(t_2))\, dx(t_1)\, dx(t_2) \quad \text{[6.2.2]}$$

If the process is complex, then

$$R_{XX*}(t_1, t_2) = E[X(t_1)\, X^*(t_2)]$$ [6.2.3]

where the * denotes complex conjugate. Generally, we will assume that the random process is real, unless stated otherwise. Assuming the autocorrelation function exists, it will generally be a function of both time, t_1, and time, t_2. Note for later reference, that t_2 may be replaced by $t_1 + \tau$, where $\tau = t_2 - t_1$ may be either a positive or a negative time shift. Using this notation, we may write [6.2.2] as follows:

$$R_{XX}(t, t + \tau) = E[X(t)\, X(t + \tau)]$$ [6.2.4]

where we have replaced t_1 with t to simplify the notation even further. Figure 6.1 presents a graphical interpretation of the calculation of the autocorrelation function.

Note that the above autocorrelation functions have been defined as statistical (ensemble) averages. Such averages require a knowledge of the probability density function of the random process. Usually such density functions are not known and must be assumed or determined experimentally. In the next chapter we will consider estimates that are often used when ensemble averaging is not possible.

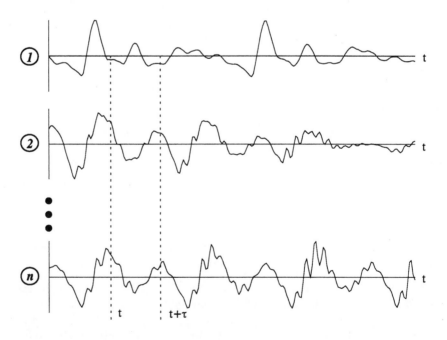

Figure 6.1   An ensemble. The autocorrelation function is calculated by ensemble averaging samples of the member functions of the ensemble taken at times t and t + τ.

Calculate the autocorrelation function for the sine wave random process $X(t) = A \sin(\omega t)$ for all t, where ω is a constant and A is a random variable uniformly distributed between zero and a_0. Then | **Example 6.3**

$$R_{XX}(t, t + \tau) = E[X(t) \, X(t + \tau)] = E[A^2] \sin(\omega t) \sin(\omega(t + \tau))$$

$$= \frac{1}{3} a_0^2 \sin(\omega t) \sin(\omega(t + \tau))$$

In this example, note that the autocorrelation function is a function of both t and τ (or t_1 and t_2). We saw in Example 6.1 that the mean function for this random process was also a function of time.

We now determine the autocorrelation function for the following sine wave random process $X(t) = Y(t) \sin(\omega t)$ for all t, where ω is a constant and $Y(t)$ is a random process. This is done as follows: | **Example 6.4**

$$R_{XX}(t, t + \tau) = E[X(t) \, X(t + \tau)] = E[Y(t) \, Y(t + \tau)] \sin(\omega t) \sin(\omega(t + \tau))$$

$$= R_{YY}(t, t + \tau) \sin(\omega t) \sin(\omega(t + \tau))$$

Definition 6.3. The **autocovariance** is defined as

$$\text{Cov}_{XX}(t, t + \tau) = E[(X(t) - \mu_X(t)) \, (X(t + \tau) - \mu_X(t + \tau))] \qquad \text{[6.2.5]}$$

$$= R_{XX}(t, t + \tau) - \mu_X(t)\mu_X(t + \tau)$$

$$= \sigma_{XX}^2(t, t + \tau)$$

This function is the autocorrelation function with the product of the two mean functions at t and $t + \tau$ subtracted.

Definition 6.4. The **autocorrelation coefficient** of a random process is defined in a similar manner to that for a random variable, namely:

$$\rho_{XX}(t, t + \tau) = \frac{\text{Cov}_{XX}(t, t + \tau)}{[\text{Cov}_{XX}(t, t) \, \text{Cov}_{XX}(t + \tau, t + \tau)]^{\frac{1}{2}}} \qquad \text{[6.2.6]}$$

The autocovariance for the sine wave random process described in Examples 6.1 and 6.3 is | **Example 6.5**

$$\text{Cov}_{XX}(t, t + \tau) = R_{XX}(t, t + \tau) - \mu_X(t) \, \mu_X(t + \tau)$$

$$= \frac{a_0^2}{3} \sin(\omega t) \sin(\omega(t + \tau)) - \frac{a_0^2}{4} \sin(\omega t) \sin(\omega(t + \tau))$$

$$= \frac{a_0^2}{12} \sin(\omega t) \sin(\omega(t + \tau))$$

The autocorrelation coefficient is

$$\rho_{XX}(t, t + \tau) = \frac{\text{Cov}_{XX}(t, t + \tau)}{[\text{Cov}_{XX}(t, t)\,\text{Cov}_{XX}(t + \tau, t + \tau)]^{\frac{1}{2}}}$$

$$= \frac{\left[\dfrac{a_0^2}{12}\sin(\omega t)\,\sin(\omega(t + \tau))\right]}{\left[\dfrac{a_0^2}{12}\sin(\omega t)\,\sin(\omega(t + \tau))\right]} = 1$$

This last result is for all t and τ, and tells us that the random process at time $t + \tau$ is linearly predictable from the random process at time t. This is because all member functions have identically the same frequency and phase. They differ only in amplitude.

6.3   STATIONARY RANDOM PROCESSES

From the few simple examples given above, we conclude that the mean function and the autocorrelation function can provide information about the temporal structure of a random process. We now examine this topic more fully for two special classes of continuous time stationary random processes.

Definition 6.5. A continuous time random process, X(t), is **stationary** in the **strict,** or **narrow, sense** if for all positive n, the nth order probability density function does not depend on the time shift parameter, τ; that is, for all $n \geq 1$

$$p_X[x(t_1), x(t_2), \ldots, x(t_n)] = p_X[x(t_1 + \tau), x(t_2 + \tau), \ldots, x(t_n + \tau)] \qquad \text{[6.3.1]}$$

This implies that all moments are independent of time. One way of interpreting a strict sense stationary random process is that a time translation of a member of the ensemble is still a member of the ensemble. If this is true, then the process is stationary in the strict (narrow) sense. Such processes are independent of the choice of the time origin and their statistics depend only upon time differences. This is because the joint probability density function is the same for all time instants, thereby implying that all moments are independent of time. Thus, the statistics do not depend upon the time origin, but only upon the time difference between observations.

Example 6.6 | An independent, identically distributed random process is stationary in the strict sense, since we have

$$p_X[x(t_1), x(t_2), \ldots, x(t_n)] = p_X[x(t_1)]\,p_X[x(t_2)] \ldots p_X[x(t_n)]$$

which is true for all $n \geq 1$, for all $t_1, \ldots, t_n$. Since $p_X[x(t_i)]$ are all the same for all t_i, then $p_X[x(t_i)] = p_X[x(t_i + \tau)]$ for all t_i. Thus, [6.3.1] is satisfied and therefore, an independent, identically distributed random process is strict sense stationary.

Example 6.7 | Consider the sine wave random process $X(t) = a\sin(\omega t + \Theta)$ for all t, where ω and a are constants, while Θ is a random phase angle, uniformly distributed between 0 and 2π. It is easily shown that the mean function is zero and, thus, independent of time. In fact, this process is stationary in the strict sense, which is shown by noting that a time translation of a member function is also a member function of the ensemble; that is, the statistics of the ensemble are independent of the time origin. This can be seen if the reader will make sketches of the waveforms of the member functions of the ensemble. Next we calculate the autocorrelation function as follows:

$$R_{XX}(t, t + \tau) = E[a \sin(\omega t + \Theta) \, a \sin(\omega(t + \tau) + \Theta)]$$

$$= a^2 \int_0^{2\pi} \sin(\omega t + \theta) \sin(\omega(t + \tau) + \theta) p_\Theta(\theta) d\theta$$

$$= \frac{a^2}{2} \int_0^{2\pi} [\cos(\omega\tau) - \cos(\omega(2t + \tau) + 2\theta)] \frac{1}{2\pi} d\theta$$

$$= \frac{a^2}{2} \cos(\omega\tau) = R_{XX}(\tau)$$

since

$$\sin(A) \sin(B) = \frac{1}{2} [\cos(A - B) - \cos(A + B)]$$

Thus, this random process has an autocorrelation function that is not a function of t, but is a function of τ only. Furthermore, as we noted above, the mean function is a constant, namely, zero. Random processes with these two properties form a special class, which we now define.

Definition 6.6. Random processes that are **stationary in the wide sense,** or **wide sense stationary,** have a non-time-varying mean and an autocorrelation function that depends only on the time difference between t_1 and t_2; that is, it depends only on $\tau = t_2 - t_1$. Thus, wide sense stationary random processes satisfy the following relationships, provided they exist:

$$\mu_X(t) = \mu_X, \text{ where } \mu_X \text{ is a constant.} \qquad \textbf{[6.3.2]}$$

$$R_{XX}(t, t + \tau) = R_{XX}(\tau) \qquad \textbf{[6.3.3]}$$

for all t and τ.

All strict sense stationary random processes are also stationary in the wide sense, provided the mean function and autocorrelation function exist. Is the converse true? We say that if a random process is not stationary in the wide sense, then it is **nonstationary.**

Figure 6.2 presents illustrative member functions for two random processes, X(t) and Y(t), where X(t) is strict sense stationary and Y(t) is nonstationary.

Another example of a nonstationary random process is the following: | **Example 6.8**

$$X(t) = Rt, \quad T_1 \leq t \leq T_2$$

where R is the random variable. A shift of this function to some other time, τ, introduces a new function that is not a member of the original ensemble, as seen in Figure 6.3, where one member function of the shifted ensemble is shown.

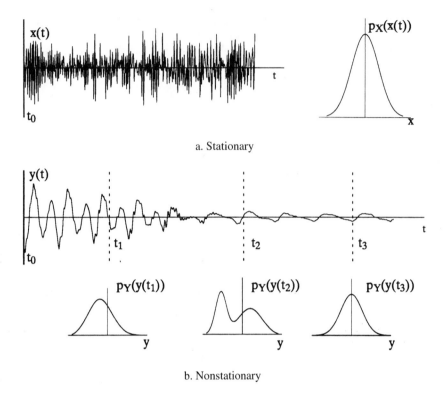

a. Stationary

b. Nonstationary

Figure 6.2   A member function for each of two random processes: (a) stationary in the strict sense and (b) nonstationary. The probability density function for the amplitude of the stationary process is the same at any time instant. The probability density varies at different time instants for the nonstationary process.

Quiz 6.2   Modify the sine wave random process given in Example 6.7 so that it is a nonstationary random process. Hint: Consider windowing the process, that is, multiplying the random process by a function such as $[u(t) - u(t - \tau)]$, where $u(t)$ is the unit step function.

Note that from $[6.3.3]$ that for $\tau = 0$ we have

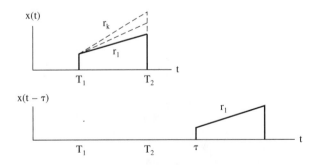

Figure 6.3   Example of a nonstationary random process

$$R_{XX}(0) = E[X^2(t)], \quad \text{for all t.} \qquad \text{[6.3.4]}$$

Thus, the autocorrelation function for a wide sense stationary random process evaluated at $\tau = 0$ gives the average power (the second moment) of the random process.

Definition 6.7. The **autocovariance function** for a wide sense stationary random process is

$$\text{Cov}_{XX}(\tau) = R_{XX}(\tau) - \mu_X^2 = \sigma^2_{XX}(\tau) \qquad \text{[6.3.5]}$$

Definition 6.8. The **autocorrelation coefficient** for a wide sense stationary random process is given as

$$\rho_{XX}(\tau) = \frac{\sigma^2_{XX}(\tau)}{\sigma_{XX}(0)\,\sigma_{XX}(0)} = \frac{\sigma^2_{XX}(\tau)}{\sigma^2_{XX}(0)} \qquad \text{[6.3.6]}$$

since

$$\text{Cov}_{XX}(t, t) = \text{Cov}_{XX}(t + \tau, t + \tau) = \text{Cov}_{XX}(0, 0) = \sigma^2_{XX}(0)$$

for a wide sense stationary random process.

Consider the sine wave random process $X(t) = a\sin(\Omega t + \Theta)$ for all t, where a is a constant, and Ω and Θ are independent random variables, both uniformly distributed as follows:

Example 6.9

$$p_\Theta(\theta) = \frac{1}{2\pi}, \quad 0 \le \theta \le 2\pi$$

$$p_\Omega(\omega) = \frac{1}{\omega_0}, \quad 0 \le \omega \le \omega_0$$

Is this process wide sense stationary? First, we calculate the mean function as follows:

$$E[X(t)] = \int_0^{2\pi} \int_0^{\omega_0} \frac{a}{2\pi\omega_0} \sin(\omega t + \theta)\, d\theta\, d\omega$$

$$= \int_0^{2\pi} \int_0^{\omega_0} \frac{a}{2\pi\omega_0} \{\sin \omega t \cos \theta + \cos \omega t \sin \theta\}\, d\theta\, d\omega = 0$$

Next we compute $R_{XX}(t, t + \tau)$. We do this because we are uncertain if the autocorrelation function is a function of t only. Thus, we have

$$R_{XX}(t, t + \tau) = E\left[a\sin(\Omega t + \Theta)\, a\sin(\Omega(t + \tau) + \Theta)\right]$$

$$= a^2 \int_0^{2\pi} \int_0^{\omega_0} \frac{1}{2\pi}\frac{1}{\omega_0} \sin(\omega t + \theta)\sin(\omega(t + \tau) + \theta)\, d\theta\, d\omega$$

$$= \frac{a^2}{2\pi\omega_0}\frac{1}{2}\left\{\int_0^{2\pi}\int_0^{\omega_0} \cos\omega(\tau)\, d\theta\, d\omega - \int_0^{2\pi}\int_0^{\omega_0} \cos(\omega(2t + \tau) + 2\theta)\, d\theta\, d\omega\right\}$$

$$= \frac{a^2}{4\pi\omega_0}\left\{2\pi\frac{\sin\omega_0(\tau)}{\tau} - \int_0^{2\pi}\int_0^{\omega_0}(\cos\omega(2t + \tau)\cos 2\theta - \sin\omega(2t + \tau)\sin 2\theta)\, d\theta\, d\omega\right\}$$

$$= \frac{a^2}{2}\frac{\sin\omega_0\tau}{\omega_0\tau} = R_{XX}(\tau)$$

Thus, this process is stationary in the wide sense, since the mean is a constant and the autocorrelation is a function of τ only.

The random process in the last example is stationary in the strict sense. This can be established by imagining first that there is only one sine wave with frequency ω_0. Such a random process is strict sense stationary, as argued previously. Now imagine that the random process consists of two frequencies. Is such a process strict sense stationary? Now extend the argument to multiple frequencies.

Quiz 6.3   Determine the autocovariance and the autocorrelation coefficient for Example 6.9 using [6.3.5] and [6.3.6], respectively. Compare your result with that obtained for Example 6.5. Discuss the differences.

Example 6.10 | **A** random process, $X(t)$, consists of two member functions, namely, $x_1(t) = 1$ and $x_2(t) = \sin(t)$. Each member function can occur with equal probability. Calculate $E[X(t)]$ and the autocorrelation function, $E[X(t)X(t + \tau)]$, for this random process. Is the random process stationary in the wide sense?

The mean function of the random process is determined by taking the expectation with respect to the selection of the member function. Thus, the mean function is

$$E[X(t)] = \frac{1}{2} x_1(t) + \frac{1}{2} x_2(t) = \frac{1}{2}[1 + \sin(t)]$$

In a similar manner, the expectation for the autocorrelation function, $R_{XX}(t, t + \tau)$, is with respect to the selection of the member function. We then perform the product $x_i(t)x_i(t + \tau)$, for $i = 1, 2$. Thus, the autocorrelation function is

$$E[X(t) \, X(t + \tau)] = \frac{1}{2}[x_1(t) \, x_1(t + \tau) + x_2(t) \, x_2(t + \tau)] = \frac{1}{2}[1 + \sin(t) \sin(t + \tau)]$$

The random process in this example is not wide sense stationary since both the mean function and the autocorrelation function are functions of t. Thus, the process is nonstationary.

Quiz 6.4   Find the mean function and the autocorrelation function for random process $X(t)$ that consists of the following two member functions: $x_1(t) = 2$, $x_2(t) = 5$. The member function $x_1(t)$ occurs with a probability of 1/3, while $x_2(t)$ occurs with a probability of 2/3.

In summary, we represent the three **classes of random processes,** namely, nonstationary, wide sense stationary, and strict sense stationary, in the form of a set structure, as depicted in Figure 6.4. Imbedded within the universe of random processes is the subset of nonstationary random processes, along with the subset of wide sense stationary random processes, which in turn contains the subset of strict sense stationary random processes.

6.4   PROPERTIES OF THE AUTOCORRELATION FUNCTION

We now consider some of the properties of the autocorrelation function for wide sense stationary random processes, since, as mentioned above, the autocorrelation function, along with the mean function, is considered to be a principal statistical descriptor of a wide sense stationary random process.

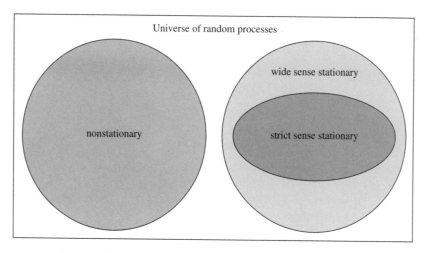

Figure 6.4   A set structure for three classes of random processes

We will assume that the autocorrelation function exists for every value of the argument, τ, and is the same for all member functions of the ensemble.

Property 6.4.1   We have already seen that the autocorrelation function at $\tau = 0$ is the average power of the random process.

Property 6.4.2   The autocorrelation function of a wide sense stationary real random process is an even function; that is:

$$R_{XX}(\tau) = R_{XX}(-\tau). \qquad \text{[6.4.1]}$$

This latter property is established using the ensemble average definition for a wide sense stationary real random process, as follows:

$$R_{XX}(\tau) = E[X(t)X(t + \tau)] = E[X(t - \tau)X(t)] = R_{XX}(-\tau) \qquad \text{[6.4.2]}$$

Property 6.4.3   The autocorrelation function for a wide sense stationary real random process is maximum at the origin.

This property is established using the fact that for any two random variables, X and Y, we have

$$(E[XY])^2 \leq E[X^2]E[Y^2] \qquad \text{[6.4.3]}$$

Then

$$R_{XX}^2(\tau) = \{E[X(t)X(t + \tau)]\}^2 \leq E[X^2(t)]E[X^2(t + \tau)] = R_{XX}^2(0) \qquad \text{[6.4.4]}$$

Thus

$$|R_{XX}(\tau)| \leq R_{XX}(0) \qquad \text{[6.4.5]}$$

Property 6.4.4   If $R_{XX}(0) = R_{XX}(T)$, then the autocorrelation function is periodic with period T, and the random process, X(t), is said to be mean square periodic; that is, $E[(X(t + T) - X(t))^2] = 0$. The proof of this property is left as an exercise.

Property 6.4.5 If a wide sense stationary random process is such that $X(t) = \mu_X + Y(t)$, where μ_X is a constant and $Y(t)$ is a zero mean, and wide sense stationary random process for which $R_Y(\tau)$ goes to zero as τ goes to infinity, then

$$R_{XX}(\tau) = E[X(t)X(t + \tau)] = E[(\mu_X + Y(t))(\mu_X + Y(t + \tau))] \quad \text{[6.4.6]}$$

$$= \mu^2_X + 2\,\mu_X\,E[Y(t)] + R_{YY}(\tau)$$

$$= \mu^2_X + R_{YY}(\tau) \to \mu^2_X, \text{ as } \tau \to \infty$$

Thus, for this case $R_{XX}(\tau)$ approaches the square of the mean value of the random process, $X(t)$, as τ approaches infinity.

One final property deals with the "connectivity" of the random process, or the rate of change of the random process.

Property 6.4.6 If the difference $R_{XX}(0) - R_{XX}(\tau)$ is small, such that $R_{XX}(\tau)$ decreases slowly, then the probability of a large change in $X(t)$ in τ seconds is small. This is established as follows. Using Chebyshev's inequality from Chapter 4, we have

$$P[\,|X(t + \tau) - X(t)\,| > \epsilon] = P[(X(t + \tau) - X(t))^2 > \epsilon^2] \quad \text{[6.4.7]}$$

$$\leq \frac{E[(X(t + \tau) - X(t))^2]}{\epsilon^2}$$

$$= \frac{2[R_{XX}(0) - R_{XX}(\tau)]}{\epsilon^2}$$

Note that the autocorrelation function can have a periodic component, can decay slowly or rapidly, and can have a nonzero mean component. Some of the properties discussed above are shown in Figure 6.5, where some typical autocorrelation functions are presented.

If the random process for which the autocorrelation function is being calculated has units of volts, then the autocorrelation function has units of (volts)^2.

For a certain type of wide sense stationary random process, the autocorrelation function is a delta function; that is, $R_{XX}(\tau) = \delta(\tau)$. We will see later in this chapter that this type of random process is called a white noise random process, since the process is infinite bandwidth and therefore contains all frequencies, thereby being an optically white process. We will discuss this more fully later.

6.5   RANDOM SEQUENCES

In Chapter 5 we defined a random sequence as a random process with discrete time. We also defined the expected value of random sequences. Here we build on those concepts to define the autocorrelation function for a random sequence. First, we introduce some simplifying notation. We will assume that a random process with discrete time is sampled at a fixed time interval that satisfies the sampling theorem. Thus, the random sequence is denoted as $X(nT)$, where we have again suppressed the experimental outcome

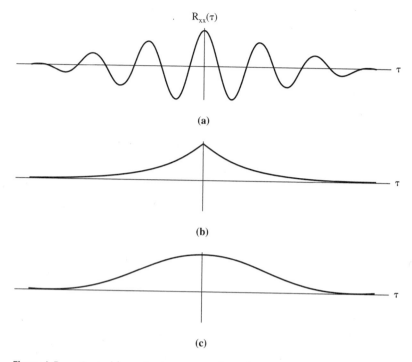

Figure 6.5   Typical forms for the autocorrelation function for random processes

variable, s. Furthermore, since T is presumed known for the random sequence, we may represent the random sequence as X(n). Note that some authors use the square-bracket notation for random sequences; that is, a random sequence may be denoted as X[n]. This seems unnecessary since the context of a problem usually makes it clear whether we are dealing with a continuous random process or a random sequence. We now define the mean function.

Definition 6.9. The **mean function** of a random sequence is denoted as

$$\mu_X(n) = E[X(n)] \quad \text{for} \quad -\infty < n < \infty. \qquad \text{[6.5.1]}$$

$$= \int_{-\infty}^{\infty} x(n) \, p_X(x(n)) \, d(x(n))$$

Definition 6.10. The **autocorrelation function**, $R_{XX}(n, n + k)$ of a random sequence is

$$R_{XX}(n, n + k) = E[X(n) X(n + k)] \qquad \text{[6.5.2]}$$

$$= \int_{-\infty}^{\infty}\int_{-\infty}^{\infty} x(n) \, x(n + k) \, p_X(x(n), x(n + k)) \, dx(n) \, dx(n + k)$$

In an analogous manner we define the autocovariance function and the autocorrelation coefficient.

Definition 6.11. The **autocovariance** of a random sequence is

$$\text{Cov}_{XX}(n, n+k) = E[(X(n) - \mu_X(n))(X(n+k) - \mu_X(n+k))] \quad \text{[6.5.3]}$$

$$= R_{XX}(n, n+k) - \mu_X(n)\mu_X(n+k)$$

$$= \sigma_{XX}^2(n, n+k)$$

Definition 6.12. The **autocorrelation coefficient** for a random sequence is defined as

$$\rho_{XX}(n, n+k) = \frac{\text{Cov}_{XX}(n, n+k)}{[\text{Cov}_{XX}(n, n) \, \text{Cov}_{XX}(n+k, n+k)]^{\frac{1}{2}}} \quad \text{[6.5.4]}$$

The definitions for strict and wide sense stationary random sequences are analogous to those for continuous time random processes.

Definition 6.13. A **random sequence**, $X(n)$, is **stationary in the strict sense** if for all positive m, the mth order probability density function does not depend on the time shift parameter, k; that is, for all $m \geq 1$ the joint probability density function is such that

$$p_X[x(n_1), x(n_2), \ldots, x(n_m)] = p_X[x(n_1 + k), x(n_2 + k), \ldots, x(n_m + k)] \quad \text{[6.5.5]}$$

Definition 6.14. A **random sequence is stationary in the wide sense** if the mean function is not time varying and the autocorrelation function depends only on the time difference between n and n + k; that is, it depends only on k. Thus, wide sense stationary random sequences satisfy the following relationships, provided they exist:

$$\mu_X(n) = \mu_X, \text{ where } \mu_X \text{ is a constant} \quad \text{[6.5.6]}$$

$$R_{XX}(n, n+k) = R_{XX}(k) \quad \text{[6.5.7]}$$

for all n and k.

Similarly, we have

Definition 6.15. The **autocovariance function** for a wide sense stationary random sequence is

$$\text{Cov}_{XX}(k) = R_{XX}(k) - \mu_X^2 = \sigma^2_{XX}(k) \quad \text{[6.5.8]}$$

Definition 6.16. The **autocorrelation coefficient** for a wide sense stationary random sequence is given as

$$\rho_{XX}(k) = \frac{\sigma_{XX}^2(k)}{\sigma_{XX}^2(0)} \quad \text{[6.5.9]}$$

The properties for a random sequence are analogous to those for a continuous random process.

Example 6.11   A discrete time random process, or random sequence, is created by the successive tosses of a biased coin. The member functions of the ensemble are generated by repeating the process using a large number of identically biased coins that are independently and repeatedly tossed. Let the oc-

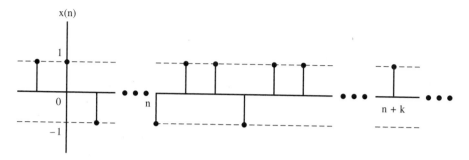

Figure 6.6   One-member function for Example 6.11

currence of a head be denoted by 1, which occurs with probability p, and that of a tail by -1, which occurs with probability $q = 1 - p$. To make the random sequence a function of time, let us assume that each flip of the coin occurs every T seconds, where for convenience we will let $T = 1$. Figure 6.6 shows one-member function of this random process. Determine the mean function, the autocorrelation function, the autocovariance, and the autocorrelation coefficient for this random sequence.

The mean function is

$$\mu_X(n) = E[X(n)] = \int_{-\infty}^{\infty} x(n)\{p\,\delta(x - 1) + q\,\delta(x + 1)\}\,dx$$

$$= (-1)\,q + (1)\,p = p - q = 2p - 1 = \mu_X$$

which is independent of n, but a function of p. If $p = q = 1/2$, then $\mu_X = 0$, which is reasonable, since in this case 1 and -1 occur equally likely. If $p > q$, then $\mu_X > 0$, and if $p < q$, then $\mu_X < 0$.

The autocorrelation function is determined in several steps. First, we note that

$$R_{XX}(0, 0) = E[X(0)\,X(0)] = (1)(1)\,p + (-1)(-1)\,q = p + q = 1$$

This is the same result we would obtain if $k = 0$ for any n. Now the more general case is

$$R_{XX}(n, n + k) = E[X(n)\,X(n + k)]$$

We may calculate this function by considering the four possible products, $X(n)X(n + k)$, that can occur for a member function of the random process, namely, $(1)(1) = 1$, $(1)(-1) = -1$, $(-1)(1) = -1$, $(-1)(-1) = 1$. These products occur with probability $(p)(p) = p^2$, pq, qp, and $(q)(q) = q^2$, respectively. Then

$$R_{XX}(n, n + 1) = E[X(n)\,X(n + 1)]$$

$$= (1)(1)\,p^2 + (1)(-1)\,pq + (-1)(1)qp + (-1)(-1)q^2$$

$$= (2p - 1)^2 = (p - q)^2$$

Since the successive coin flips are statistically independent, we have

$$R_{XX}(n, n + 1) = R_{XX}(n, n + 2) = R_{XX}(n, n + 3) = \cdots = (p - q)^2 = (2p - 1)^2$$

Thus, the autocorrelation function for $k = 0$ and any n is

$$R_{XX}(0) = 1$$

and for $k \neq 0$ and any n is

$$R_{XX}(k) = (p - q)^2 = (2p - 1)^2$$

Thus, this random sequence is stationary in the wide sense. Sketch the autocorrelation function versus k.

The autocovariance function is

$$Cov_{XX}(k) = R_{XX}(k) - \mu_X{}^2$$
$$= 1 - (p - q)^2 \quad \text{for } k = 0.$$
$$= (p - q)^2 - (p - q)^2 = 0 \quad \text{for } k \neq 0.$$

When $p = q = 1/2$, then the autocovariance is 1 for $k = 0$, while $p > 1/2$ or $p < 1/2$ causes the autocovariance to decrease below unity.

Quiz 6.5   In Example 6.11 show that the autocorrelation coefficient is unity for $k = 0$ and zero for $k \neq 0$, which implies that the random sequence is not linearly predictable for any time shift $k \neq 0$.

Quiz 6.6   Is the random sequence in Example 6.11 stationary in the strict sense? Hint: Is a time shift of a member function also a member function? Is the probability density function a function of time or of the time origin?

6.6   CROSSCORRELATION FUNCTIONS BY ENSEMBLE AVERAGING

So far we have considered a relationship between member functions of the same random process. We now address a similar relationship between two random processes.

Definition 6.17. The expected value of two continuous time random processes, $X(t)$ and $Y(t)$, is the **crosscorrelation function** between the two random processes, provided it exists. This is written as

$$R_{XY}(t, t + \tau) = E[X(t) \, Y(t + \tau)] \qquad \text{[6.6.1]}$$

We may also have

$$R_{YX}(t, t + \tau) = E[Y(t) \, X(t + \tau)] \qquad \text{[6.6.2]}$$

The two crosscorrelation functions in [6.6.1] and [6.6.2] are generally not equal.

Thus, the **crosscorrelation function,** $R_{XY}(t, t + \tau)$, is given as

$$R_{XY}(t, t + \tau) = E[X(t) \, Y(t + \tau)]$$

$$= \int_{-\infty}^{\infty} \int_{-\infty}^{\infty} x(t)\, y(t+\tau)\, p_{XY}(x(t), y(t+\tau))\, dx(t)\, dy(t+\tau) \qquad \text{[6.6.3]}$$

while a similar definition applies to $R_{YX}(t, t+\tau)$. If the process is complex, then

$$R_{XY*}(t, t+\tau) = E[X(t)\, Y^*(t+\tau)] \qquad \text{[6.6.4]}$$

where the * denotes complex conjugate. Generally, we will assume that the random processes are real, unless stated otherwise.

Definition 6.18. The **crosscovariance** is defined as

$$\mathrm{Cov}_{XY}(t, t+\tau) = E[(X(t) - \mu_X(t))(Y(t+\tau) - \mu_Y(t+\tau))] \qquad \text{[6.6.5]}$$

$$= R_{XY}(t, t+\tau) - \mu_X(t)\mu_Y(t+\tau)$$

$$= \sigma_{XY}^2(t, t+\tau)$$

Definition 6.19. The **crosscorrelation coefficient** for a continuous time random process is defined in a similar manner to that for the autocorrelation coefficient, namely:

$$\rho_{XY}(t, t+\tau) = \frac{\mathrm{Cov}_{XY}(t, t+\tau)}{[\mathrm{Cov}_{XY}(t, t)\, \mathrm{Cov}_{XY}(t+\tau, t+\tau)]^{\frac{1}{2}}} \qquad \text{[6.6.6]}$$

Definition 6.20. Two random processes, $X(t)$ and $Y(t)$, are **jointly stationary in the strict sense** if for all positive n, the nth order probability density function does not depend on the time shift parameter, τ.

One can show that if two random processes are jointly stationary in the strict sense, then each is individually stationary in the strict sense.

Definition 6.21. Two random processes, $X(t)$ and $Y(t)$, are **jointly stationary in the wide sense** if they satisfy the following relationships, provided they exist:

1. Both $X(t)$ and $Y(t)$ are individually stationary in the wide sense.   [6.6.7]
2. $R_{XY}(t, t+\tau) = R_{XY}(\tau)$.   [6.6.8]

One can establish that if two random processes are jointly stationary in the strict sense, then they are jointly stationary in the wide sense. However, the converse is not true. Also by definition, if the two random processes are jointly stationary in the wide sense, then they are individually stationary in the wide sense. However, the converse is not generally true. The terms *jointly* and *independently* are often omitted, since the meaning is usually clear within the context of the discussion.

Consider two random processes as follows: | **Example 6.12**

$$X(t) = \sin(\omega t + \Theta) \text{ and } Y(t) = \cos(\omega t + \Theta)$$

where Θ is a random variable uniformly distributed between $-\pi$ and π. Find the crosscorrelation function between $X(t)$ and $Y(t)$. Are $X(t)$ and $Y(t)$ individually stationary in the wide sense?

Since we do not know if the two random processes are jointly stationary in the strict sense or wide sense, then we use [6.6.1].

$$R_{XY}(t, t + \tau) = E\left[\sin(\omega t + \Theta) \cos(\omega(t + \tau) + \Theta)\right]$$

$$= \frac{1}{2} E[\sin(\omega(2t + \tau) + 2\Theta) + \sin(\omega(-\tau))]$$

$$= -\frac{1}{2} \sin(\omega \tau) = R_{XY}(\tau)$$

Note that the maximum value of $R_{XY}(\tau)$ does not occur at the origin.

Quiz 6.7   Are the two random processes jointly stationary in the wide sense?

Quiz 6.8   Determine the crosscovariance and the crosscorrelation coefficient for the two random processes in Example 6.12.

Example 6.13 | Suppose the autocorrelation function for wide sense stationary random process X(t) is $R_{XX}(\tau)$. Determine $R_{XY}(\tau)$, if $Y(t) = X(t - T)$.

$$R_{XY}(\tau) = E[X(t) Y(t + \tau)] = E[X(t) X(t + \tau - T)] = R_{XX}(\tau - T)$$

Quiz 6.9   Determine the crosscovariance and the crosscorrelation coefficient for the two random processes in the last example.

In two of the problems it is shown that the random process $Z(t) = X(t) + Y(t)$ may be a wide sense stationary process even though the random processes X(t) and Y(t) are not.

The definitions given for continuous time random processes can be modified to apply to random sequences in a manner similar to that done in Section 6.5.

6.7   PROPERTIES OF THE CROSSCORRELATION FUNCTION

As for the autocorrelation function we will assume that the crosscorrelation function for two jointly wide sense stationary random processes exists for every value of the argument, τ.

Property 6.7.1

$$R_{XY}(\tau) = R_{YX}(-\tau) \qquad\qquad \text{[6.7.1]}$$

This property, which is easily established using the appropriate definitions, says that $R_{XY}(\tau)$ and $R_{YX}(\tau)$ are antisymmetric.

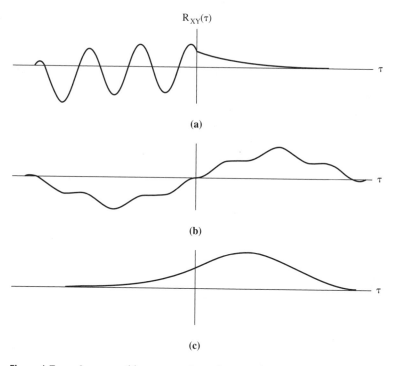

$R_{XY}(\tau)$

(a)

(b)

(c)

Figure 6.7   Some possible crosscorrelation functions for random processes

Property 6.7.2

$$|R_{XY}(\tau)| \leq 1/2 [R_{XX}(0) + R_{YY}(0)] \qquad [6.7.2]$$

To establish this property take the expectation of $[X(t) \pm Y(t + \tau)]^2 \geq 0$.

Property 6.7.3

$$|R_{XY}(\tau)|^2 \leq R_{XX}(0) R_{YY}(0) \qquad [6.7.3]$$

To establish this property use [6.4.3].

Another characteristic of the crosscorrelation function is that the maximum value of the function may not occur at $\tau = 0$.

Figure 6.7 illustrates some of the possible forms that the crosscorrelation function may assume. Note that since the autocorrelation function can be considered as a special case of a crosscorrelation function, it is clear that the crosscorrelation function could also assume any of the forms shown in Figure 6.5.

The units of the crosscorrelation function are the product of the units of the two random processes. If the units of both random processes are volts, then the crosscorrelation function has units of $(volts)^2$.

6.8   VECTOR RANDOM PROCESSES

Vector random processes can be considered as a generalization or extension of random processes in general. In Chapter 5 we discussed three methods of forming a finite dimensional random vector along with defining the expectation of a random vector.

Definition 6.22. A finite dimensional **random vector** is formed by indexing a random process in time as

$$\vec{X}(t) = (X(t_1), X(t_2), \cdots, X(t_n))^T \qquad [6.8.1]$$

where the vector $\vec{X}(t)$ is a column vector and $\vec{X}^T(t)$ is a row vector. Note that in MATLAB it is common to use square brackets, [ ], to delimit the elements of a vector. We have suppressed the outcome variable, s. For convenience we will also use the following notation:

$$\vec{X}(t + \tau) = (X(t_1 + \tau), X(t_2 + \tau), \cdots, X(t_n + \tau))^T \qquad [6.8.2]$$

Note that as in the earlier chapters we will sometimes omit the use of commas between the elements of the random vector.

As mentioned in Chapter 5, the indexed random variables that form the elements of the random vector have a defined joint probability density function (or a joint cumulative probability distribution function) and a joint sample space. This concept can be expanded to infinite dimensional spaces.

In a manner similar to that used in Chapter 4 we define the correlation matrix next, where we use the term *correlation* instead of *autocorrelation* since the matrix will contain elements that are both autocorrelation and crosscorrelation functions.

Definition 6.23. The **correlation matrix**, $R_{\vec{X}\vec{X}^T}$ of a real random vector, $\vec{X}(t)$, is defined as the expected value of the outer vector product $[\vec{X}(t)\vec{X}^T(t + \tau)]$; that is:

$$R_{\vec{X}\vec{X}^T} = E[\vec{X}(t)\vec{X}^T(t + \tau)] \qquad [6.8.3]$$

$$= E[(X(t_1), X(t_2), \cdots, X(t_n))^T (X(t_1 + \tau), X(t_2 + \tau), \cdots, X(t_n + \tau))]$$

$$= E\left\{ \begin{bmatrix} X(t_1) \\ X(t_2) \\ \vdots \\ X(t_n) \end{bmatrix} [X(t_1 + \tau), X(t_2 + \tau), \cdots, X(t_n + \tau)] \right\}$$

$$= \begin{bmatrix} r_{11} & r_{12} & \cdots & r_{1n} \\ r_{21} & r_{22} & \cdots & r_{2n} \\ & \vdots & & \\ r_{n1} & r_{n2} & \cdots & r_{nn} \end{bmatrix}$$

where for convenience we have let $r_{ij} = E[X(t_i) X(t_j + \tau)]$. The subscript $\vec{X} \vec{X}^T$ is sometimes denoted as $\vec{X} \vec{X}$ for convenience; that is, the T denoting transpose on the second random vector is dropped. The r_{ij} are called the crosscorrelation functions for the individual components of the random vector for i ≠ j. Since we are assuming that the random vector, $\vec{X}$, is real, then the r_{ij} are real. Furthermore, for strict and wide sense stationary random processes the correlation matrix, $R_{\vec{X}\vec{X}^T}$, is antisymmetric; that is, $r_{ij}(\tau) = r_{ji}(-\tau)$ for i ≠ j. When i = j, then the correlations become the autocorrelation functions for the elements of the random vector. The elements of the random vector may be samples of the same random process taken at different times or the elements of the random vector may be composed of samples from different random processes taken at the same (or different) times. In either case we assume that the proper probability density functions are defined and that the appropriate expected values exist.

Note that the definition of the autocorrelation (crosscorrelation) function is just a one-dimensional autocorrelation (crosscorrelation) matrix, that is, the expected value of the outer vector product of one element vectors.

Example 6.14

Form a two-element random vector by taking samples at times t and t + τ of the sine wave random process X(t) = a sin (ωt + Θ), where Θ is the only random variable, and it is uniformly distributed between 0 and 2π. Then determine the correlation matrix. The random vector is expressed as

$$\vec{X}(t)^T = (a \sin(\omega t_1 + \Theta) \quad a \sin(\omega t_2 + \Theta))$$

$$\vec{X}(t + \tau)^T = (a \sin(\omega(t_1 + \tau) + \Theta) \quad a \sin(\omega(t_2 + \tau) + \Theta))$$

Then the correlation matrix is determined with the help of Example 6.7, as follows:

$$R_{\vec{X}\vec{X}^T} = E[\vec{X}(t)\vec{X}^T(t + \tau)]$$

$$= a^2 E \begin{bmatrix} \sin(\omega t_1 + \Theta)\sin(\omega(t_1 + \tau) + \Theta) & \sin(\omega t_1 + \Theta)\sin(\omega(t_2 + \tau) + \Theta) \\ \sin(\omega t_2 + \Theta)\sin(\omega(t_1 + \tau) + \Theta) & \sin(\omega t_2 + \Theta)\sin(\omega(t_2 + \tau) + \Theta) \end{bmatrix}$$

$$= \frac{a^2}{2} \begin{bmatrix} \cos(\omega\tau) & \cos(\omega(t_1 - t_2 - \tau)) \\ \cos(\omega(t_2 - t_1 - \tau)) & \cos(\omega\tau) \end{bmatrix}$$

Quiz 6.10   Verify the results in the last example using Example 6.7.

Quiz 6.11   Discuss the two cases when $t_2 = t_1$ and $t_2 - t_1 = \tau$ in the last example.

Definition 6.24. In a similar manner the **covariance matrix,** $C_{\vec{X}\vec{X}^T}$, of a real random vector, $\vec{X}$, is the expected value of the matrix formed by the outer vecto product, $(\vec{X} - \vec{\mu}_{\vec{X}})(\vec{X} - \vec{\mu}_{\vec{X}})^T$.

$$C_{\vec{X}\vec{X}^T} = \begin{bmatrix} c_{11} & c_{12} & \cdots & c_{1n} \\ c_{21} & c_{22} & \cdots & c_{2n} \\ & & \vdots & \\ c_{n1} & c_{n2} & \cdots & c_{nn} \end{bmatrix} \qquad [6.8.4]$$

where $c_{ij} = E[(X(t_i) - \mu_X(t_i))(X(t_j + \tau) - \mu_X(t_j + \tau))]$. The c_{ij} are called the covariances for the individual components of the random vector. Since we are assuming that the random vector, $\vec{X}$, is real, then the c_{ij} are real. When $i = j$, then the covariances become the variances of the individual components of the random vector.

Quiz 6.12   Determine the covariance matrix for the last example.

One can also define a correlation coefficient matrix similarly to what was done previously.

Random vectors and correlation matrices have numerous applications in various fields, such as radar, image processing, spectral analysis, pattern recognition, and speech recognition. These applications are covered in other courses and books. Here we have only introduced the subject since it is closely connected to the other topics previously covered.

6.9   ADDITIONAL CLASSIFICATIONS OF RANDOM PROCESSES

We have previously defined three classes of random processes, namely, nonstationary, strict sense stationary, and wide sense stationary. Now we may use the definitions of autocorrelation and crosscorrelation functions to define several additional classes of random processes.

Definition 6.25. Two random processes, denoted as $X(t)$ and $Y(t)$, are said to be **independent** if the joint probability density function for $X(t)$ and $Y(t)$ is the product of the individual probability density functions of $X(t)$ and $Y(t)$. This definition can be extended to the case of finite dimensional random vectors.

Definition 6.26. Two random processes, $X(t)$ and $Y(t)$, are said to be **orthogonal** if the crosscorrelation function $R_{XY}(\tau, t + \tau) = 0$ for all t and τ.

The rationale for this definition is easily seen if we consider the two random processes to be one-dimensional vector random processes, in which case the orthogonality, defined as the expectation of the product of the two vectors, is analogous to the dot (or inner) product of two geometrical vectors. When the dot product of two vectors is zero, then they are perpendicular. Thus, if two vectors $\vec{X}(t)$ and $\vec{Y}(t + \tau)$ are orthogonal, then their expected (dot) product is

$$E[\vec{X}^T(t)\,\vec{Y}(t + \tau)] = \sum_{i=1}^{n} E[X(t_i)\,Y(t_i + \tau)] = 0 \qquad [6.9.1]$$

Example 6.15 | One case that illustrates the above situation is when we have the expectation of the product of two random processes, such as $E[X(t)Y(t)]$ but with the condition that the two random processes are independent, then we have $E[X(t)Y(t)] = E[(X(t)]E[Y(t)]$. Furthermore, if one of the random processes has a zero mean function, then the crosscorrelation function is zero for all t and τ. This situation occurs frequently in communications problems where one often calculates the expectation of the square of a signal plus noise.

Definition 6.27. Two random processes, X(t) and Y(t), are said to be **uncorrelated** if the crosscovariance function $\text{Cov}_{XY}(t, t + \tau) = 0$ for all t and τ. This implies that $R_{XY}(t, t + \tau) = \mu_X(t)\mu_Y(t + \tau)$ for all t and τ.

As we saw above, this definition tells us that the two random processes are orthogonal if they are uncorrelated and at least one of the mean values is zero.

For the case of two real finite dimensional random vectors, $\vec{X}(t)$ and $\vec{Y}(t + \tau)$, if

$$E[\vec{X}(t)\,\vec{Y}^T(t + \tau)] = E[\vec{X}(t)]\,E[\vec{Y}^T(t + \tau)] \qquad [6.9.2]$$

then the two vectors are said to be uncorrelated.

An illustration of this case occurs when the two random processes are independent. | **Example 6.16**

A random process, X(t), may be orthogonal, uncorrelated, or independent of itself at earlier and/or later times.

The next example is an illustration of another class of random processes, which we will discuss more thoroughly in the next chapter. However, we show this example here because it demonstrates several of the theoretical concepts that have been used in Chapters 4, 5, and 6.

Consider the random process generated by turning on a set of identical sawtooth waveform generators at different times. Examine the amplitude of each member of the ensemble of waveforms at a particular time instant, which is taken to be the origin for convenience, as shown in Figure 6.8. | **Example 6.17**

Each member of the ensemble is identical to every other member function except for a time displacement, Δ. We wish to show that the ensemble average with respect to the amplitude of the waveforms of the member functions is equal to the time average of a member function of the ensemble for this particular example.

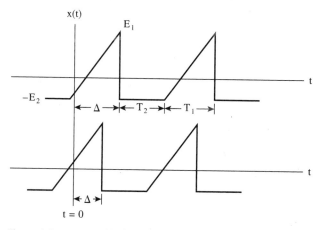

Figure 6.8   Ensemble for Example 6.17

The ensemble average is computed first. Let D have a uniform probability density as shown here, where D denotes the time displacement random variable, and Δ is a particular value of D.

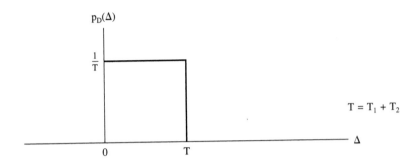

$$T = T_1 + T_2$$

The time function for the one period, T, of the sawtooth waveform that starts at the origin is given by

$$x_T(t) = \frac{E_1 + E_2}{T_1} t - E_2 \quad 0 < t < T_1$$

$$= -E_2 \quad T_1 \leq t < T_1 + T_2 = T$$

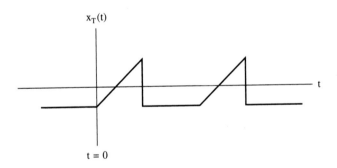

The equation for a member of the ensemble shown in Figure 6.8 is

$$x(t) = \cdots + \left\{ \frac{E_1 + E_2}{T_1}[t + (T_1 - \Delta)] - E_2 \right\} [u(t + (T_1 - \Delta)) - u(t - \Delta)]$$

$$-E_2[u(t - \Delta) - u(t - \Delta - T_2)] + \cdots$$

This equation is a function of Δ and can be written functionally as $x = g(\Delta)$. Then

$$\left| \frac{dx}{d\Delta} \right| = \frac{E_1 + E_2}{T_1}, \quad -(T_1 - \Delta) < t < \Delta$$

$$= 0, \quad \Delta \leq t \leq \Delta + T_2$$

From Chapter 4 we have

$$p_X(x)dx = p_D(\Delta)d\Delta \quad \text{or} \quad p_X(x) = \frac{p_D(\Delta)}{\left|\dfrac{dx}{d\Delta}\right|}$$

$$= \frac{T_2}{T_1 + T_2}, \quad x = -E_2$$

$$= \frac{T_1}{T_1 + T_2} \cdot \frac{1}{E_1 + E_2}, \quad -E_2 < x \le E_1$$

This is shown below:

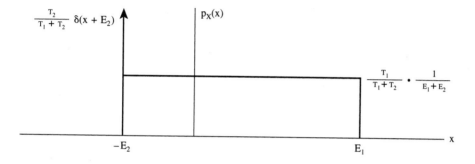

The ensemble average is

$$E[X] = \int_{-\infty}^{\infty} x p_X(x)\,dx = \int_{-E_2}^{E_1} \frac{T_1}{T_1 + T_2}\frac{1}{E_1 + E_2} x\,dx + \int_{-E_2-\epsilon}^{-E_2+\epsilon} \frac{T_2}{T_1 + T_2} x\delta(x + E_2)\,dx$$

$$= \frac{T_1}{T_1 + T_2}\left(\frac{E_1 - E_2}{2}\right) + \frac{T_2}{T_1 + T_2}(-E_2)$$

The time average of a member function is defined below and calculated for this example as follows:

$$<x(t)> = \lim_{T\to\infty} \frac{1}{2T}\int_{-T}^{T} x(t)\,dt$$

$$= \frac{1}{T_1 + T_2}\int_{-(T_1-\Delta)}^{\Delta}\left\{\frac{E_1 + E_2}{T_1}[t + (T_1 - \Delta)] - E_2\right\}dt + \frac{1}{T_1 + T_2}\int_{\Delta}^{\Delta+T_2}(-E_2)\,dt$$

$$= \frac{T_1}{T_1 + T_2}\left(\frac{E_1 - E_2}{2}\right) + \frac{T_2}{T_1 + T_2}(-E_2)$$

Thus, for this case we have shown that the ensemble average of a member function of this particular random process is equal to the time average of a member function of the ensemble. We shall see in the next chapter that random processes with this property are a special class of random processes. Not all random processes have this property, as we have seen.

6.10   ADDITIONAL EXAMPLES

The examples presented in this section are intended to be illustrative of the type of applications that can occur. Since the examples are not discussed thoroughly, some details are omitted.

Example 6.18 Let a random process be $X(t) = y(t) + N(t)$, where $N(t)$ is a zero mean, Gaussian noise random process that is wide sense stationary with an autocorrelation function $R_{NN}(\tau)$, and where $y(t) = a \sin \omega t$ is a deterministic signal, not a random process. A member function of $X(t)$ is shown in Figure 6.9. The autocorrelation function for $X(t)$ is

$$R_{XX}(t, \tau) = E[X(t)X(t + \tau)]$$

$$= a^2 \sin \omega t \sin(\omega(t + \tau)) + R_{NN}(\tau)$$

Thus, $X(t)$ is not wide sense stationary due to the deterministic signal. In a similar manner we can show that the mean function is also time varying.

Quiz 6.13   Show that the mean function for the last example is time varying.

Example 6.19 Another application of correlation is the measurement of the time delay of a signal due to a propagation delay. One such application is measuring the speed of the flow of water through a pipe. A sensor picks up a signal from a transmitting device floating in the water inside the pipe. A similar sensor is placed downstream from the first sensor by a known distance, d. The time for the transmitting device to move from the position of the first sensor to the second sensor is measured by crosscorrelation, as shown in Figure 6.10, where we find that the crosscorrelation function will peak at the time shift corresponding to the time delay between the two waveforms. We may measure the instant at which the peak occurs in the crosscorrelation function to determine the time delay. The speed of the water is then d/T.

Example 6.20 A simulated radar pulse appears in Figure 6.11a. This pulse is transmitted, reflected from an object, and returned to the receiver. The returned signal is noisy, as shown in Figure 6.11b. To measure the time delay between the transmitted signal and the returned signal, we calculate the crosscorrelation function for an approximate signal-to-noise ratio, S/N, of 10 dB, as shown in Figure 6.11c. The S/N may be defined as the ratio of the variance of the signal to the variance of the noise. If the signal propagates at velocity c and if the time to the target is T/2 (total travel time is T), then the distance to the target is $d = Tc/2$. The crosscorrelation builds up slowly to its maximum value at T and then decays. The envelope of the crosscorrelation function is a triangle with its peak at T. This is more easily imagined if we replace the simulated radar signal with its envelope, namely, a rectangular pulse. We shall see in the next chapter that one estimate of the correlation function is obtained by time averaging. Radar mappings of the Moon, Sun, Mars, and Venus have been done using such techniques.

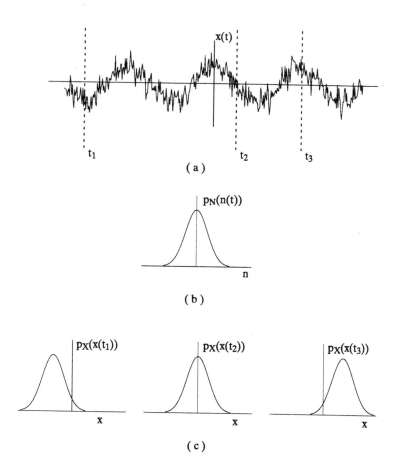

Figure 6.9   Sine wave plus Gaussian noise

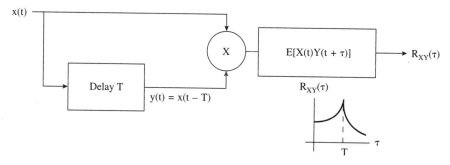

Figure 6.10   Measurement of time delay by crosscorrelation

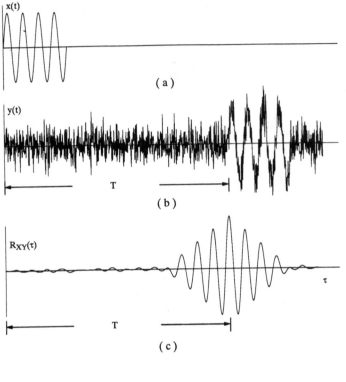

(a)

(b)

(c)

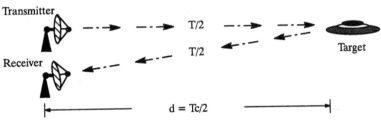

Figure 6.11   A radar example

Example 6.21 | System identification is another useful application. Suppose it is desired to measure the impulse response, or equivalently the system transfer function, of a linear system. We may use crosscorrelation techniques to accomplish this task as follows. Let the input to the system be random process $X(t)$ and the output be the random process $Y(t)$, with the impulse response denoted as $h(t)$. Then the crosscorrelation function between the input and the output is

$$R_{XY}(\tau) = E[X(t - \tau)\, Y(t)] = E\left\{X(t - \tau)\int_{-\infty}^{\infty} X(\sigma)\, h(t - \sigma)\, d\sigma\right\}$$

$$= \int_{-\infty}^{\infty} E[X(t - \tau)\, X(\sigma)]\, h(t - \sigma)\, d\sigma$$

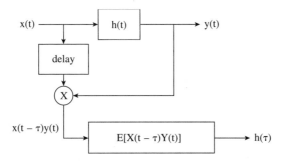

Figure 6.12   Measuring the impulse response of a
linear system

$$= \int_{-\infty}^{\infty} R_{XX}(\sigma - t + \tau)\, h(t - \sigma)\, d\sigma$$

Let the input be white noise so that

$$R_{XX}(\sigma - t + \tau) = \delta(\sigma - t + \tau)$$

then

$$R_{XY}(\tau) = h(\tau)$$

We illustrate the above steps in Figure 6.12, where τ is a time delay, and x(t) is a white noise process.

Example 6.22

If a source is located far from a pair of receivers, then the direction of propagation of the source signal can be determined by crosscorrelation, as Figure 6.13 shows. The time T for the signal to propagate from receiver 1 to receiver 2 in the direction of propagation is measured in a manner similar to the method used in Example 6.18. Then the angle θ is calculated knowing d, T, and c, that is, $\theta = \cos^{-1}(\mathrm{Tc}/\mathrm{d})$.

Example 6.23

An antenna array can be adjusted to enhance its response to a signal and reduce its response to another signal. This is done by adjusting the sidelobes of the antenna in the direction of the desired signal and adjusting the nulls in the direction of the undesired signal. This is called directivity adjustment and is accomplished by adjusting system parameters to maximize or minimize the appropriate crosscorrelation function.

The procedures illustrated in the above examples are also used for the detection of weak signals in noise, the measurement of time delays in production plants, acoustic absorption measurements, velocity measurements, pattern and speech recognition, and other applications.

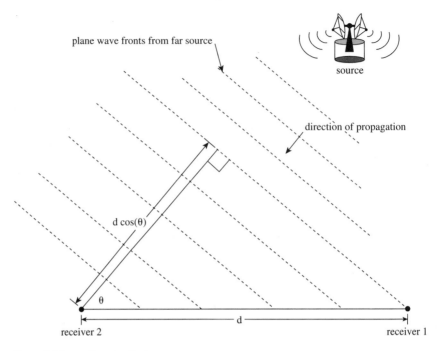

plane wave fronts from far source

source

direction of propagation

d cos(θ)

θ

d

receiver 2

receiver 1

Figure 6.13   Direction finding

6.11   THE POWER SPECTRAL DENSITY FUNCTION

In the following sections we will use Fourier and z transforms. In this section we define the power spectral density function.

Definition 6.28. The **power spectral density function** for a continuous time, real, wide sense stationary random process, $X(t)$, is defined as the Fourier transform of the autocorrelation function of the random process; that is:

$$S_{XX}(\omega) = S_{XX}(2\pi f) = \int_{-\infty}^{\infty} R_{XX}(\tau)\, e^{-j\omega\tau}\, d\tau \qquad [6.11.1]$$

where

$$R_{XX}(\tau) = \int_{-\infty}^{\infty} S_{XX}(f)\, e^{j\omega\tau}\, df = \frac{1}{2\pi}\int_{-\infty}^{\infty} S_{XX}(\omega)\, e^{j\omega\tau} d\omega \qquad [6.11.2]$$

Definition 6.28 is known as the **Wiener–Khintchine theorem** or the Einstein–Wiener–Khintchine theorem. We shall refer to this method of calculating the power spectral density function as the **correlation method.** It should be noted that often the notation $S_{XX}(f)$ is used to denote $S_{XX}(\omega)$ for convenience.

Some properties of the power spectral density are:

Property 6.11.1   The power spectral density function is an even, real, and positive function of radian frequency, ω, provided the random process is real.

For a real valued random process, the autocorrelation function is even, thus

$$S_{XX}(\omega) = \int_{-\infty}^{\infty} R_{XX}(\tau)\,\cos\omega\tau\,d\tau \qquad [6.11.3]$$

which implies that $S_{XX}(\omega)$ is a real and even function of ω. The fact that $S_{XX}(\omega) \geq 0$ is established later. The power spectral density yields no phase information.

Property 6.11.2   The average power of the random process $X(t)$ is

$$R_{XX}(0) = \int_{-\infty}^{\infty} S_{XX}(f)\,df = \frac{1}{2\pi}\int_{-\infty}^{\infty} S_{XX}(\omega)\,d\omega \geq 0 \qquad [6.11.4]$$

which says that the average power of the random process is the integral of the power spectral density function over all frequencies. Thus, the units of $S_{XX}(\omega)$ are power per hertz, which is power spectral density.

The units for the Fourier transform of a voltage signal are volts/Hz, which is also volts-sec. The units of the power spectral density are determined by the Fourier transform of the autocorrelation function, which are $(volts)^2$-sec or $(volts)^2$/Hz. It is often assumed that the power of a random process is the power dissipated in a one-ohm-resistive load. In this case the units of the power spectral density become $(volts)^2$-sec or $(volts)^2$/Hz across a one-ohm resistor, giving units of $(volts)^2$-sec per ohm or watts-sec or watts/Hz, which is energy or joules.

The power spectral density function is known by several names, including energy spectrum, spectral density, spectrum, and perhaps most commonly as simply the power spectrum, even though this latter term is incorrect in terms of units.

As mentioned earlier in this chapter, there is a random process known as **white noise.** The term *white* comes from optics and means all frequencies are present with equal power density. For this case the spectrum appears as shown in Figure 6.14.   **Example 6.24**

Here

$$S_{XX}(f) = N_0$$

Thus

$$R_{XX}(\tau) = \int_{-\infty}^{\infty} S_{XX}(f)\,e^{j\omega\tau}\,df = \int_{-\infty}^{\infty} N_0\,e^{j\omega\tau}\,df = N_0\delta(\tau)$$

That is, the autocorrelation function for white noise is a delta function at the origin.

Note that in the above example that N_0 was used to denote the level of the "two-sided" power spectral density. Often $N_0/2$ is used instead.

Consider the sine wave random process with Θ as the random variable, which is uniformly distributed between zero and 2π; that is: **Example 6.25**

$$X(t) = a\sin(\omega_0 t + \Theta)$$

Find the power spectral density. The autocorrelation function is known to be

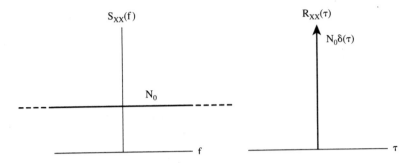

Figure 6.14   White noise

$$R_{XX}(\tau) = \frac{a^2}{2}\cos\omega_0\tau$$

Then, the power spectral density is

$$S_{XX}(f) = \frac{a^2}{4}[\delta(f - f_0) + \delta(f + f_0)] = \frac{a^2}{4}2\pi[\delta(\omega - \omega_0) + \delta(\omega + \omega_0)]$$

This is shown in Figure 6.15. Note that the power is

$$\int_{-\infty}^{\infty} S_{XX}(f)\ df = \frac{a^2}{2} = R_{XX}(0)$$

Quiz 6.14   Does the power calculated above agree with the square of the rms value of the sine wave?

Example 6.26   In one of the problems it is shown that the autocorrelation function for the random telegraph process is an exponential function; that is:

$$R_{XX}(\tau) = e^{-2\alpha|\tau|}$$

The power spectral density is

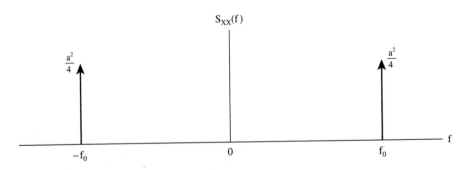

Figure 6.15   Example 6.25

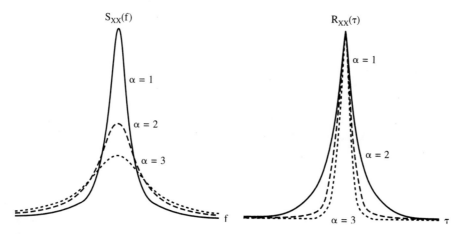

Figure 6.16   Power spectral density and autocorrelation function for the random telegraph process

$$S_{XX}(f) = \int_{-\infty}^{\infty} R_{XX}(\tau)\, e^{-j\omega\tau}\, d\tau = \int_{-\infty}^{\infty} e^{-2\alpha\,|\tau|}\, e^{-j\omega\tau}\, d\tau$$

$$= \int_{-\infty}^{0} e^{2\alpha\tau}\, e^{-j\omega\tau}\, d\tau + \int_{0}^{\infty} e^{-2\alpha\tau}\, e^{-j\omega\tau}\, d\tau$$

$$= \frac{1}{2\alpha - j\omega} + \frac{1}{2\alpha + j\omega} = \frac{4\alpha}{(2\alpha)^2 + (\omega)^2}$$

The autocorrelation function and the power spectral density function for this example are shown in Figure 6.16 for several values of α using MATLAB.

A common model for noise in communication systems is low pass, bandlimited white noise, as Figure 6.17 shows. The autocorrelation function for this model is | **Example 6.27**

$$R_{XX}(\tau) = \int_{-\infty}^{\infty} S_{XX}(f) e^{j\omega\tau}\, df = \int_{-f_0}^{f_0} N_0\, e^{j\omega\tau}\, df = \frac{N_0 \omega_0}{\pi} \frac{\sin(\omega_0\tau)}{(\omega_0\tau)}$$

As f_0 goes to infinity, then

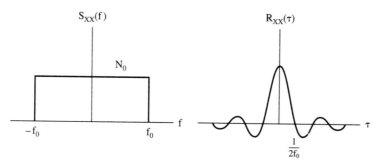

Figure 6.17   Low pass, bandlimited white noise

$$R_{XX}(\tau) = N_0 \lim_{\omega_0 \to \infty} \left[\frac{\omega_0}{\pi} \frac{\sin(\omega_0 \tau)}{(\omega_0 \tau)} \right] = N_0 \, \delta(\tau)$$

which is the same result obtained for the white noise example.

Quiz 6.15   By the duality properties of the Fourier transform, if the autocorrelation function is rectangular with finite duration, then the power spectral density would be of the form sin(f)/f. Is this a valid autocorrelation function and a power spectral density?

Quiz 6.16   In the last example show that the power calculated using the autocorrelation function is the same as that calculated using the power spectral density.

Definition 6.29. The **equivalent (or effective) noise bandwidth, B_N,** of a random process is defined as

$$B_N = \frac{\displaystyle\int_{-\infty}^{\infty} S_{NN}(f) \, df}{[S_{NN}(f)]_{max}} \qquad \qquad \textbf{[6.11.5]}$$

where $[S_{NN}(f)]_{max}$ is the maximum value of the power spectral density of the random process. This is illustrated in Figure 6.18. The **equivalent noise power spectral density** is a low pass, bandlimited white noise with amplitude $[S_{NN}(f)]_{max}$. The definition states that the areas under both power spectral densities are equal.

An alternative definition for the power spectral density function is arrived at by noting the following. Assuming that the Fourier transform of a member function of a random process, X(t), exists over a range from $-T$ to T, then we have the random variable

$$F_T[X(t)] = \int_{-T}^{T} X(t) \, e^{-j\omega t} \, dt \qquad \qquad \textbf{[6.11.6]}$$

where F_T denotes the Fourier transform over the range $-T$ to T. The magnitude squared of this random variable is

$$|F_T[X(t)]|^2 = \int_{-T}^{T}\int_{-T}^{T} X(t_1) \, X^*(t_2) \, e^{-j\omega(t_1-t_2)} \, dt_1 \, dt_2$$

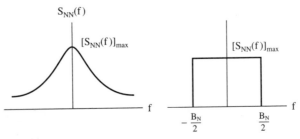

Spectrum of random process   Equivalent noise spectrum

Figure 6.18   Equivalent noise bandwidth and noise spectrum

If we take the expectation and divide by 2T, we have

$$\frac{1}{2T} E[\,|F_T[X(t)]|^2] = \frac{1}{2T}\int_{-T}^{T}\int_{-T}^{T} R_{XX}(t_1 - t_2)\,e^{-j\omega(t_1-t_2)}dt_1\,dt_2$$

which can be shown using the procedure used in Example 6.28, below, to be

$$\frac{1}{2T} E[\,|F_T[X(t)]|^2] = \int_{-2T}^{2T}\left[1 - \frac{|\tau|}{2T}\right]R_{XX}(\tau)\,e^{-j\omega\tau}\,d\tau$$

If we take the limit as T goes to infinity, then we are led to the alternative definition for the power spectral density function, namely:

Definition 6.30. The **power spectral density function** can be defined as

$$S_{XX}(f) = \lim_{T\to\infty}\frac{1}{2T} E[\,|F_T[X(t)]|^2] = \int_{-\infty}^{\infty} R_{XX}(\tau)e^{-j\omega\tau}\,d\tau \geq 0 \quad [6.11.7]$$

which shows that the power spectral density is positive. This method of calculating the power spectral density function is called the **direct method** and is equivalent to the correlation method.

In this example we will calculate the power spectral density function using Definition 6.30. Let the random process be the one considered in Example 6.25, namely, the sine wave random process with Θ as the random variable, which is uniformly distributed between zero and 2π; that is: | **Example 6.28**

$$X(t) = a\sin(\omega_0 t + \Theta)$$

We have already determined the autocorrelation function and the power spectral density by the correlation method. Here we use the direct method.

$$F_T[X(t)] = \int_{-T}^{T} X(t)\,e^{-j\omega t}\,dt = \int_{-T}^{T} a\sin(\omega_0 t + \Theta)e^{-j\omega t}\,dt$$

Express the sine using Euler's formula

$$F_T[X(t)] = a\int_{-T}^{T}\frac{1}{2j}\{e^{j\Theta}[e^{(j\omega_0 t)}] - e^{-j\Theta}[e^{(-j\omega_0 t)}]\}e^{-j\omega t}\,dt$$

Consider the first integral

$$I = \int_{-T}^{T} e^{-j(\omega-\omega_0)t}\,dt$$

Then

$$|I|^2 = \int_{-T}^{T}\int_{-T}^{T} e^{-j(\omega-\omega_0)t_1}e^{j(\omega-\omega_0)t_2}\,dt_1\,dt_2 = \int_{-T}^{T}\int_{-T}^{T} e^{-j(\omega-\omega_0)(t_1-t_2)}\,dt_1\,dt_2$$

If we let $u = t_1 + t_2$ and $v = t_1 - t_2$, then $dt_1dt_2 = |J|^{-1}dudv$, where the $|J|$ is the Jacobian, which is

$$\text{Jacobian} = |J| = \left|\begin{vmatrix}\frac{\partial u}{\partial t_1} & \frac{\partial u}{\partial t_2}\\ \frac{\partial v}{\partial t_1} & \frac{\partial v}{\partial t_2}\end{vmatrix}\right| = \left|\begin{vmatrix}1 & 1\\ 1 & -1\end{vmatrix}\right| = |-2| = 2$$

Then we have

$$|I|^2 = \int_{-2T}^{2T}\left[\int_{-(2T-|v|)}^{2T-|v|} e^{-j(\omega-\omega_0)(v)}\frac{1}{2}\,du\right]dv$$

$$|I|^2 = \int_{-2T}^{2T} (2T - |v|)\, e^{-j(\omega - \omega_0)(v)}\, dv$$

Then

$$\lim_{T \to \infty} \frac{1}{2T} |I|^2 = \lim_{T \to \infty} \int_{-2T}^{2T} \left(1 - \frac{|v|}{2T}\right) e^{-j(\omega - \omega_0)(v)}\, dv = \delta(f - f_0)$$

The expectation with respect to Θ is unity, since the term $\exp(j\Theta)$ is canceled with its conjugate. Therefore, we finally have

$$\lim_{T \to \infty} \frac{1}{2T} |E[F_T(X(t))]|^2 = \frac{a^2}{4}[\delta(f - f_0) + \delta(f + f_0)]$$

which is the same result we obtained in Example 6.25.

Quiz 6.17 Fill in the missing steps in the above example.

6.12   CROSS-SPECTRAL DENSITY FUNCTIONS

Occasionally we consider a random process that is the sum of two other random processes; that is, $Z(t) = X(t) + Y(t)$. In this case the autocorrelation function of $Z(t)$ is

$$R_{ZZ}(t, t + \tau) = E[(X(t) + Y(t))(X(t + \tau) + Y(t + \tau))]$$

$$= R_{XX}(t, t + \tau) + R_{YY}(t, t + \tau) + R_{XY}(t, t + \tau) + R_{YX}(t, t + \tau) \quad \textbf{[6.12.1]}$$

If the random processes, $X(t)$ and $Y(t)$, are jointly stationary in the wide sense, then $Z(t)$ is stationary in the wide sense and

$$R_{ZZ}(\tau) = R_{XX}(\tau) + R_{YY}(\tau) + R_{XY}(\tau) + R_{YX}(\tau) \qquad \textbf{[6.12.2]}$$

The power spectral density for the autocorrelation has been defined. In a similar manner we define the cross-spectral density.

Definition 6.31. If $X(t)$ and $Y(t)$ are jointly wide sense stationary random processes with autocorrelations $R_{XX}(\tau)$ and $R_{YY}(\tau)$ and crosscorrelations $R_{XY}(\tau)$ and $R_{YX}(\tau)$, then the Fourier transforms of the crosscorrelations are defined as the **power cross-spectral density functions;** that is:

$$S_{XY}(f) = S_{XY}(\omega) = \int_{-\infty}^{\infty} R_{XY}(\tau)e^{-j\omega\tau}\, d\tau \qquad \textbf{[6.12.3]}$$

and

$$R_{XY}(\tau) = \int_{-\infty}^{\infty} S_{XY}(f)e^{j\omega\tau}\, df = \frac{1}{2\pi}\int_{-\infty}^{\infty} S_{XY}(\omega)e^{j\omega\tau}\, d\omega \qquad \textbf{[6.12.4]}$$

and similarly for $S_{YX}(\tau)$. The term power cross-spectral density is often abbreviated to cross-spectral density.

Some properties of the cross-spectral density are:

Property 6.12.1   The cross-spectral density, $S_{XY}(f)$, is not necessarily real. This property is established by noting that $R_{XY}(\tau)$ is not necessarily even.

Property 6.12.2

$$S_{XY}(f) = S_{YX}(-f) \qquad\qquad \text{[6.12.5]}$$

This can be established by noting that

$$S_{XY}(f) = \int_{-\infty}^{\infty} R_{XY}(\tau) e^{-j\omega\tau}\, d\tau$$

but

$$R_{XY}(\tau) = R_{YX}(-\tau)$$

Then

$$S_{XY}(f) = \int_{-\infty}^{\infty} R_{YX}(-\tau) e^{-j\omega\tau}\, d\tau$$

Let $s = -\tau$; then

$$S_{XY}(f) = \int_{-\infty}^{\infty} R_{YX}(s)\, e^{j\omega s}\, ds = S_{YX}(-f) \qquad\qquad \text{[6.12.6]}$$

It is also true that

$$S_{XY}^{*}(f) = S_{XY}(-f) \quad \text{or} \quad S_{XY}(f) = S_{XY}^{*}(-f) \qquad\qquad \text{[6.12.7]}$$

which is known as **Hermitian symmetry.**

Property 6.12.3   If two random processes are uncorrelated, then their cross-spectral densities are zero. This property is established by definition.

In Example 6.12 the crosscorrelation function for a frequency f_0 was

$$R_{XY}(\tau) = -\frac{1}{2}\sin(\omega_0\tau)$$

The cross-spectral density is

$$S_{XY}(f) = -\frac{1}{4j}[\delta(f - f_0) - \delta(f + f_0)]$$

which is zero if $f_0 = 0$, as it should be since $R_{XY}(\tau) = 0$. Furthermore, note that in general the cross-spectral density is complex.

Example 6.29

Consider the random process formed by the sum of a signal plus noise; that is:

$$X(t) = a\cos(\omega_0 t + \Theta) + N(t)$$

where Θ is the random variable uniformly distributed between zero and 2π. The noise is independent of Θ, is not zero mean, but is wide sense stationary with autocorrelation function $R_{NN}(\tau)$. Then the autocorrelation function for $X(t)$ is

$$R_{XX}(t, t + \tau) = E[(a\cos(\omega_0 t + \Theta) + N(t))(a\cos(\omega_0(t + \tau) + \Theta) + N(t + \tau))]$$

Let $s_1 = a\cos(\omega_0 t + \Theta)$, $N_1 = N(t)$, $s_2 = a\cos(\omega_0(t + \tau) + \Theta)$, and $N_2 = N(t + \tau)$. Then with this shorthand notation, we have

Example 6.30

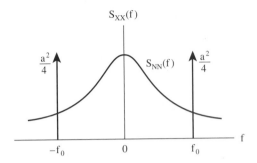

Figure 6.19   Power spectral density for Example 6.30

$$R_{XX}(t, t + \tau) = E[s_1 s_2] + E[s_1 N_2] + E[s_2 N_1] + E[N_1 N_2]$$

Since the signal and noise are independent, then

$$R_{XX}(t, t + \tau) = E[s_1 s_2] + E[s_1] E[N_2] + E[s_2] E[N_1] + E[N_1 N_2]$$

which becomes

$$R_{XX}(t, t + \tau) = R_{XX}(\tau) = \frac{a^2}{2} \cos\omega_0\tau + R_{NN}(\tau)$$

The power spectral density is the Fourier transform of the above, which is

$$S_{XX}(f) = \int_{-\infty}^{\infty} R_{XX}(\tau)\, e^{-j\omega\tau}\, d\tau$$

$$= \frac{a^2}{4}[\delta(f - f_0) + \delta(f + f_0)] + S_{NN}(f)$$

where $S_{NN}(f)$ is the power spectral density of the noise. This is illustrated in Figure 6.19 for a low-pass noise random process.

6.13   POWER SPECTRAL DENSITY FOR RANDOM SEQUENCES

The definition for the power spectral density for a random sequence follows directly from that for continuous time random processes.

Definition 6.32. The **power spectral density function** for a real, wide sense stationary random sequence, $X(n)$, is defined as the Fourier transform of the autocorrelation function of the random sequence; that is:

$$S_{XX}(\omega) = S_{XX}(2\pi f) = S_{XX}(f) = \sum_{-\infty}^{\infty} R_{XX}(k)\, e^{-j\omega k} \qquad [6.13.1]$$

where

$$R_{XX}(k) = \int_{-\infty}^{\infty} S_{XX}(f)\, e^{j\omega k}\, df = \frac{1}{2\pi} \int_{-\infty}^{\infty} S_{XX}(\omega)\, e^{j\omega k}\, d\omega \qquad [6.13.2]$$

Note that we could also use the z transform of the autocorrelation function evaluated on the unit circle to calculate the power spectral density.

Similarly we have for the cross-spectral density:

Definition 6.33. If $X(n)$ and $Y(n)$ are jointly wide sense stationary random sequences with autocorrelations $R_{XX}(k)$ and $R_{YY}(k)$ and crosscorrelations $R_{XY}(k)$ and $R_{YX}(k)$, then the Fourier transforms of the crosscorrelations are defined as the **power cross-spectral density functions**; that is:

$$S_{XY}(f) = S_{XY}(\omega) = \sum_{-\infty}^{\infty} R_{XY}(k)e^{-j\omega k} \qquad [6.13.3]$$

and

$$R_{XY}(k) = \int_{-\infty}^{\infty} S_{XY}(f)e^{j\omega k}\, df = \frac{1}{2\pi} \int_{-\infty}^{\infty} S_{XY}(\omega)e^{j\omega k}d\omega \qquad [6.13.4]$$

and similarly for $S_{YX}(f)$. The power cross-spectral density is often abbreviated to cross-spectral density.

The properties for the power spectral density and the cross-spectral density for random sequences are similar to those for continuous time random processes. Similarly the units are the same. Since the power spectral density for a random sequence is periodic in f with period 1, then we need only consider frequencies in the range $-1/2 < f \le 1/2$.

Example 6.31

Let the random sequence $X(n)$ be samples from a white noise process. Then

$$R_{XX}(k) = E[X(n)X(n + k)] = \sigma^2_{XX} \quad \text{for } k = 0$$

$$= 0 \quad \text{for } k \ne 0$$

where the random sequence is one with uncorrelated random variables with zero mean and variance $(\sigma_{XX})^2$. Then the power spectral density is

$$S_{XX}(f) = \sigma^2_{XX}$$

Thus, as for a continuous time white noise random process, the power spectral density for the white noise random sequence is also a constant for all frequencies.

Three types of data models are used in statistics and signal processing. These are known as moving average (MA), autoregression (AR) (also called linear prediction, or LP), and a combination of the two, called autoregressive-moving average (ARMA) process. We shall examine some of the features of these data models in the following examples and the problems.

Example 6.32

Perhaps the simplest data model is the moving average, which is given as

$$X(n) = b_0 Y(n) + b_1 Y(n-1) + \cdots + b_q Y(n-q) = \sum_{i=0}^{q} b_i Y(n-i)$$

where $X(n)$ and $Y(n)$ are random sequences. The sequence $X(n)$ is a "moving" average of the present and past values of the random sequence, $Y(n)$. Let us simplify this moving average to the following:

$$X(n) = Y(n) + b_1 Y(n - 1)$$

where we let $b_0 = 1$ and assume that the random sequence, $Y(n)$, is a zero mean, white noise process with variance $(\sigma_{YY})^2$. Then the autocorrelation is

$$R_{XX}(k) = E[X(n)X(n + k)] = (1 + b_1^2)\,\sigma_{YY}^2 \qquad \text{for } k = 0$$
$$= b_1\,\sigma_{YY}^2 \qquad \text{for } k = \pm 1$$
$$= 0 \qquad \text{otherwise}$$

The power spectral density is

$$S_{XX}(f) = [(1 + b_1^2) + 2b_1 \cos(\omega)]\,\sigma_{YY}^2$$

which is simply a raised cosine, which is, of course, periodic in frequency.

Quiz 6.18   Fill in the missing steps in the calculation of the autocorrelation in the last example.

Example 6.33   Next we examine the data model for linear prediction, which is

$$X(n) = -a_1 X(n - 1) - a_2 X(n - 2) - \cdots - a_p X(n - p) + E(n)$$

$$= -\sum_{i=1}^{p} a_i X(n - i) + E(n)$$

This data model predicts the next data sample of the sequence using a linear weighting of the past sample values of the same sequence, where $E(n)$ is a zero mean, white noise error process. The choice of the minus sign in front of the a_i coefficients is to make the model compatible with MATLAB's solution of these equations. While we will discuss this data model more extensively later, we point out one way to consider this model as follows:

$$X(n) = -\sum_{i=1}^{p} a_i X(n - i) + E(n) = \hat{X}(n) + E(N)$$

where

$$\hat{X}(n) = -\sum_{i=1}^{p} a_i X(n - i)$$

is often called an estimate for $X(n)$, which, as we stated above, is a linear weighting of past values of the process. Another way to view the estimate is that it is a linear prediction of $X(n)$ based on a linear weighting of past values of the process. Thus, $E(n)$ can be considered an error process since

$$E(n) = X(n) - \hat{X}(n) = X(n) + \sum_{i=1}^{p} a_i X(n - i)$$

Later we will see that this model can be viewed as a filter. For now we simplify the model to be the following, where $|a| < 1$,

$$X(n) = -aX(n - 1) + E(n)$$

Then the autocorrelation for k = 0 is

$$R_{XX}(0) = E[X(n)X(n)] = E[X(n)\{-aX(n-1) + E(n)\}] = -aR_{XX}(-1) + R_{XE}(0)$$

while for k ≠ 0, the autocorrelation function is

$$R_{XX}(k) = E[X(n)X(n+k)] = E[X(n)\{-aX(n+k-1) + E(n+k)\}]$$

$$= -aR_{XX}(k-1)$$

In order to arrive at the above results, we note the following for k = 0:

$$R_{XE}(0) = E[X(n)E(n)] = E[\{-aX(n-1) + E(n)\}E(n)]$$

$$= -aE[X(n-1)E(n)] + R_{EE}(0) = R_{EE}(0)$$

and for k ≠ 0, we have

$$R_{XE}(k) = E[X(n)E(n+k)] = E[\{-aX(n-1) + E(n)\}E(n+k)] = 0$$

Thus, past values of the prediction random process (or the data) are orthogonal to the error random process; that is, in general, $E[X(n-k)E(n)] = 0$ for all $k \geq 1$. This is an extremely important concept that will be dealt with more thoroughly later. By recursion we have

$$R_{XX}(k) = \frac{[-a]^{|k|} \sigma^2_{EE}}{1 - a^2}$$

where $R_{EE}(0) = (\sigma_{EE})^2$. The envelope of the autocorrelation function is a decaying exponential. So the power spectral density will have a form that is similar to a periodic extension of the random telegraph random process; that is:

$$S_{XX}(f) = \sum_{-\infty}^{\infty} R_{XX}(k) e^{-j\omega k} = \frac{\sigma^2_{EE}}{1 - a^2} \sum_{-\infty}^{\infty} [-a]^{|k|} e^{-j\omega k}$$

$$= \frac{\sigma^2_{EE}}{1 - a^2} \left[\frac{1}{1 + ae^{-j\omega}} + \frac{1}{1 + ae^{j\omega}} - 1 \right] = \frac{\sigma^2_{EE}}{(1 + a^2 + 2a\cos(\omega))}$$

which is periodic. Both the autocorrelation function and the power spectral density are plotted in Figure 6.20.

Quiz 6.19   Derive the autocorrelation function in the last example using the recursion relations.

6.14   ADDITIONAL EXAMPLES

In this example we will determine the correlation function and the power spectral density for a pulse amplitude modulated (PAM) wave train. We will show how the results apply to a pulse code modulated (PCM).   **Example 6.34**

Let us represent the PAM wave train as shown in Figure 6.21. Each pulse is of the same duration, t_0, and the interval between pulses is T_0. The **duty cycle** is defined as the ratio $\frac{t_0}{T_0} \leq 1$.

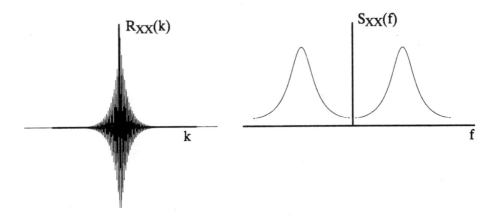

Figure 6.20   The autocorrelation and power spectral density functions for a first order linear prediction model

The amplitude of each pulse is random and independent from pulse to pulse. A member function of the ensemble is shown in Figure 6.21. The various pulse trains of the ensemble are unsynchronized. We will solve the example using the correlation method for power spectral analysis.

Let the PAM wave train be represented as

$$X(t) = \sum_{-\infty}^{\infty} A_n g(t + \epsilon - nT_0)$$

where

$$g(t) = u\left(t + \frac{t_0}{2}\right) - u\left(t - \frac{t_0}{2}\right)$$

and A_n is the amplitude of the nth pulse and ε is a random variable that represents the arbitrary starting time for each member of the ensemble. Note that ε is fixed within each member of the ensemble but varies randomly from ensemble member to ensemble member. Let ε be uniformly distributed over the range $\frac{-T_0}{2} \le \epsilon \le \frac{T_0}{2}$. The autocorrelation function for $X(t)$ is

$$R_{XX}(\tau) = E[X(t)X(t + \tau)]$$

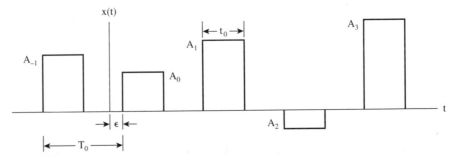

Figure 6.21   A member function of the PAM random process

$$= E\left[\sum_n \sum_m A_n A_m g(t + \epsilon - nT_0)\, g(t + \epsilon + \tau - mT_0)\right]$$

Since we have assumed the PAM pulses to be independent of one another and independent of ϵ, then

$$R_{XX}(\tau) = \sum_n \sum_m E[A_n A_m]\, E[g(t + \epsilon - nT_0)\, g(t + \epsilon + \tau - mT_0)]$$

$$= \sum_n E[A_n^2]\, E[g(t + \epsilon - nT_0)g(t + \epsilon + \tau - nT_0)]$$

$$+ (E[A])^2 \sum_{n \ne m} \sum_{n \ne m} E[g(t + \epsilon - nT_0)g(t + \epsilon + \tau - mT_0)]$$

Observe that

$$E[g(t + \epsilon - nT_0)\, g(t + \epsilon + \tau - mT_0)] = \int_{-T_0/2}^{T_0/2} \frac{1}{T_0}\, g(t + \epsilon - nT_0)g(t + \epsilon + \tau - mT_0)d\epsilon$$

Changing variables in the expression for $R_{XX}(\tau)$ such that $n - m = k$ and $k \ne 0$; then

$$R_{XX}(\tau) = E[A^2]\, E[g(t + \varepsilon)g(t + \epsilon + \tau)] + (E[A])^2 \sum_{k \ne 0} E[g(t + \epsilon)\, g(t + \varepsilon + \tau - kT_0)]$$

where only the $k = 0$ term contributes to the sum over k, since only the zero[th] term of $g(t + \varepsilon - kT_0)$ lies in the interval

$$\frac{-T_0}{2} \le \epsilon \le \frac{T_0}{2}$$

We have also assumed that the ensemble mean square value for the pulse train is denoted as $E[A^2]$, and that the ensemble mean value is denoted as $E[A]$.

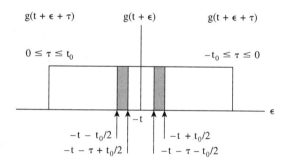

Note that

$$\int_{-T_0/2}^{T_0/2} g(t + \epsilon)\, g(t + \epsilon + \tau)\, d\epsilon$$

$$= \int_{-T_0/2}^{T_0/2}\left[u\left(t + \epsilon + \frac{t_0}{2}\right) - u\left(t + \epsilon - \frac{t_0}{2}\right)\right]\left[u\left(t + \epsilon + \tau + \frac{t_0}{2}\right) - u\left(t + \epsilon + \tau - \frac{t_0}{2}\right)\right]d\epsilon$$

$$= \int_{-t-(t_0)/2}^{-t-\tau+(t_0)/2} d\epsilon + \int_{-t-\tau-(t_0)/2}^{-t+(t_0)/2} d\epsilon$$

$$= \begin{cases} (t_0 - \tau), & 0 \leq \tau \leq t_0 \\ (t_0 + \tau), & -t_0 \leq \tau \leq 0 \end{cases}$$

$$= t_0 \left\{ 1 - \frac{|\tau|}{t_0} \right\}, \qquad |\tau| < t_0$$

$$= t_0 \left\{ 1 - \frac{|\tau|}{t_0} \right\} \{ u(\tau + t_0) - u(\tau - t_0) \}$$

Applying the above to both parts of the autocorrelation function we finally have

$$R_{XX}(\tau) = \frac{t_0}{T_0} \left\{ 1 - \frac{|\tau|}{t_0} \right\} \{ \sigma^2 [u(\tau + t_0) - u(\tau - t_0)]$$

$$+ (E[A])^2 \sum_{-\infty}^{\infty} [u(\tau + t_0 - nT_0) - u(\tau - t_0 - nT_0)] \}$$

where $\sigma^2 = E[A^2] - (E[A])^2$; one of the problems asks you to graph this equation.

This result can be applied to PCM where only two voltage levels for the pulse are allowed (e.g., zero and one, or one and minus one). In this case $t_0 = T_0$ and we can compute the appropriate σ^2 and $E[A]$ provided we know the proper assignment of probabilities for a zero and one. In fact, Problem 6.3 is such an exercise.

We now find the power spectral density of the PAM wave train by transforming $R_{XX}(\tau)$. This is given by

$$S_{XX}(f) = \frac{1}{T_0} \left\{ t_0 \frac{\sin 2\pi f \frac{t_0}{2}}{2\pi f \frac{t_0}{2}} \right\}^2 \left\{ \sigma^2 + \frac{(E[A])^2}{T_0} \sum_{-\infty}^{\infty} \delta \left(f - \frac{n}{T_0} \right) \right\}$$

$$= \frac{|G(j\omega)|^2}{T_0} \left\{ \sigma^2 + \frac{(E[A])^2}{T_0} \sum_{-\infty}^{\infty} \delta \left(f - \frac{n}{T_0} \right) \right\}$$

where $G(j\omega)$ is the Fourier transform of a PAM pulse of unit height, which is

$$|G(j\omega)|^2 = \left(t_0 \frac{\sin 2\pi f \frac{t_0}{2}}{2\pi f \frac{t_0}{2}} \right)^2$$

The plotting of this equation is left as an exercise.

Example 6.35

In this example we repeat the solution of the PAM example using the direct method. As before let the PAM wave train be represented as

$$X(t) = \sum_{-\infty}^{\infty} A_n g(t + \epsilon - nT_0)$$

where

$$g(t) = u \left(t + \frac{t_0}{2} \right) - u \left(t - \frac{t_0}{2} \right)$$

and A_n is the amplitude of the nth pulse and ε is a random variable that represents the arbitrary starting time for each member of the ensemble. Note that ε is fixed within each member of the ensemble but varies randomly from ensemble member to ensemble member. Let ε be uniformly distributed over the range

$$\frac{-T_0}{2} \le \epsilon \le \frac{T_0}{2}$$

The Fourier transform of X(t) is

$$F_T[X(t)] = \int_{-T}^{T} \sum_n A_n g(t + \epsilon - nT_0) \, e^{-j\omega t} \, dt$$

$$= \sum_n A_n e^{-j\omega nT_0} e^{j\omega \epsilon} \int_{-T+\epsilon-nT_0}^{T+\epsilon-nT_0} g(x) e^{-j\omega x} dx$$

Let

$$G_T(j\omega) = \int_{-T}^{T} g(x) e^{-j\omega x} dx = t_0 \frac{\sin 2\pi f \frac{t_0}{2}}{2\pi f \frac{t_0}{2}}$$

where g(x) is a single pulse of unit height centered about the origin. Then

$$G_{T+\epsilon-nT_0}(j\omega) = \int_{-T+\epsilon-nT_0}^{T+\epsilon-nT_0} g(x) e^{-j\omega x} dx = G_T(j\omega) \, e^{j\lambda}$$

where the λ in the term $e^{j\lambda}$ represents a phase term. Next

$$S_{XX}(f) = \lim_{T \to \infty} \frac{1}{2T} E[\, |F_T(j\omega)|^2 \,]$$

$$= \lim_{T \to \infty} \frac{1}{2T} \sum_n \sum_m E[A_n A_m] \, e^{-j\omega T_0(n-m)} \, |G_T(j\omega)|^2$$

where the expected value with respect to the random variable ε becomes unity because of the absolute magnitude operation; that is, the $e^{j\omega \varepsilon}$ and the $e^{j\lambda}$ terms become unity when multiplied by their complex conjugates.

Next note that in the interval $[-T, T]$ there are $[2N + 1] T_0$ periods; that is:

$$2T = (2N + 1) T_0$$

Therefore

$$S_{XX}(f) = |G(j\omega)|^2 \lim_{N \to \infty} \frac{1}{(2N+1)T_0} \left\{ \sum_{-N}^{N} E[A_n^2] + \sum_{n \ne m} \sum_{n \ne m} E[A_n] E[A_m] \, e^{-j\omega T_0(n-m)} \right\}$$

$$= \frac{|G(j\omega)|^2}{T_0} \lim_{N \to \infty} \frac{1}{(2N+1)} \left\{ (2N+1)E[A^2] + \left| \sum_n E[A_n] e^{-j\omega nT_0} \right|^2 - \sum_n (E[A_n])^2 \right\}$$

$$= \frac{|G(j\omega)|^2}{T_0} \lim_{N \to \infty} \frac{1}{(2n+1)} \left\{ (2N+1)[E[A^2] - (E[A])^2] + (E[A])^2 \left| \sum_n e^{-j\omega nT_0} \right|^2 \right\}$$

$$= \frac{|G(j\omega)|^2}{T_0} \left\{ \sigma^2 + \lim_{N \to \infty} \frac{(E[A])^2}{(2N+1)} \left| \sum_n e^{-j\omega nT_0} \right|^2 \right\}$$

In Problem 6.42 it is shown that

$$\sum_{n=-\infty}^{\infty} e^{-j\omega nT_0} = \frac{1}{T_0} \sum_{n=-\infty}^{\infty} \delta\left(f - \frac{n}{T_0} \right)$$

Then

$$\left| \sum_n e^{-j\omega n T_0} \right|^2 = \sum_n \sum_m e^{-j\omega T_0(n-m)}$$

$$= \frac{1}{T_0} \sum_n \delta\left(f - \frac{n}{T_0}\right) \sum_{m=-N}^{N} e^{j2\pi n m}, \text{ since } \omega = \frac{2\pi n}{T_0}$$

$$= \frac{2N+1}{T_0} \sum_n \delta\left\{f - \frac{n}{T_0}\right\}$$

Therefore

$$S_{XX}(f) = \frac{|G(j\omega)|^2}{T_0}\left\{\sigma^2 + \frac{(E[A])^2}{T_0} \sum_{-\infty}^{\infty} \delta\left(f - \frac{n}{T_0}\right)\right\}$$

where

$$|G(j\omega)|^2 = \left(t_0 \frac{\sin 2\pi f \frac{t_0}{2}}{2\pi f \frac{t_0}{2}}\right)^2$$

This result is the same as what was obtained using the correlation method.

6.15   NOISE MODELS*

*This subsection may be omitted.

Perhaps two of the most important electrical noise sources are thermal and shot noise. Thermal noise arises as a consequence of the random motion of electrons in a resistor. It can be shown that the power spectral density for thermal noise may be expressed as

$$S_{NN}(f) = 2RkT \tag{6.15.1}$$

where R is the value of the resistor in ohms, T is the absolute temperature of the resistor in degrees Kelvin (K), k is Boltzman's constant (1.38×10^{-23} joules/K), and $S_{NN}(f)$ is the noise power spectral density expressed in units of joules-ohms or (volts)^2-sec or (volts)^2/Hz. The mean-squared value of the noise is

$$E[N^2(t)] = \int_{-B/2}^{B/2} S_{NN}(f)\, df = 4RkTB \tag{6.15.2}$$

where B is the noise bandwidth.

The available noise power is the maximum power that can be drawn from a source. For a resistive network this occurs when the resistor of the load (R_L) matches the resistor of the source (R_S); that is, $R_S = R_L = R$. If we express the available noise power in terms of the noise power spectral density, then for thermal noise we have

$$S_{AA}(f) = \frac{S_{NN}(f)\, R_L}{(R_S + R_L)^2} = \frac{1}{4}\frac{S_{NN}(f)}{R} = \frac{1}{2}kT \tag{6.15.3}$$

The available power from the thermal source for a bandwidth B in Hz is

$$P_A = \int_{-B/2}^{B/2} S_{AA}(f)\, df = \frac{1}{2}kT \int_{-B/2}^{B/2} df = kTB/2 \tag{6.15.4}$$

which does not depend on the value of the resistor.

The noise temperature for the thermal noise source is found by solving the above equation for T; that is:

$$T = \frac{P_A}{kB/2} \qquad \text{[6.15.5]}$$

Shot noise arises from the random arrival of electrons at the cathode of a tube or as the diffusion of carriers across a barrier. Shot noise has a power spectral density that is expressed as

$$S_{NN}(f) = eI \qquad \text{[6.15.6]}$$

where e represents the charge of the carrier or electron, I is the average current, and $S_{NN}(f)$ is the power spectral density in units of $(amps)^2$-sec or $(amps)^2$/Hz.

Both thermal and shot noise are characterized by a wide, flat spectrum. A stationary random process having a constant power spectral density is called a purely random process. Such a process is not actually found in nature since the average power

$$P_{ave} = \int_{-\infty}^{\infty} S_{NN}(f)\,df \qquad \text{[6.15.7]}$$

would be infinite. The bandwidth of physical systems with internal noise is normally much less than the bandwidth of the noise spectrum. Consequently, the noise power spectral density is a convenient mathematical idealization; for instance, the thermal and shot noise spectra are constant over a wide band of frequencies. Noise characterized by this type of spectrum is called white noise because it contains all the frequencies of the spectrum. Usually white noise has a zero mean value as well. Thus, the mean value of the noise, N(t), is

$$E[N(t)] = 0$$

and the power spectral density may be expressed as

$$S_{NN}(f) = N_0 \qquad \text{[6.15.8]}$$

The autocorrelation function $R_{NN}(\tau)$ is the inverse Fourier transform of the power spectral density; that is:

$$R_{NN}(\tau) = \int_{-\infty}^{\infty} S_{NN}(f)\,e^{j\omega\tau}\,df = N_0\delta(\tau) \qquad \text{[6.15.9]}$$

We will further assume that white noise is a Gaussian random process. This proves to be the case in nature since the noise is made up of the sum of many small random voltages, which by the central limit theorem are Gaussian at any time instant.

There are three common mathematical models for random noise. One is established by considering a stationary purely random process, X(t), over a long time interval, T. Assume X(t) is periodic with period T. Then X(t) can be represented using the following Fourier series:

$$X(t) = \sum_{k=1}^{\infty} (A_k \cos(\omega_k t) + B_k \sin(\omega_k t)) \qquad \text{[6.15.10]}$$

where $\omega_k = 2\pi f_k = 2\pi k/T$. Note that the dc term is zero. The Fourier coefficients are defined as

$$A_k = \frac{2}{T}\int_0^T X(t)\,\cos(\omega_k t)\,dt \qquad \text{[6.15.11]}$$

$$B_k = \frac{2}{T} \int_0^T X(t) \, \sin(\omega_k t) \, dt \qquad\qquad [6.15.12]$$

The mean square value is

$$E[A_k^2] = \frac{4}{T^2} \int_0^T \int_0^T E[X(t_1)_X(t_2)] \cos(\omega_k t_1) \, \cos(\omega_k t_2) \, dt_1 dt_2 \qquad [6.15.13]$$

$$= \frac{4N_0}{T^2} \int_0^T \int_0^T \delta(t_1 - t_2) \cos(\omega_k t_1) \cos(\omega_k t_2) \, dt_1 dt_2$$

$$= \frac{4N_0}{T^2} \int_0^T (\cos(\omega_k t_1))^2 dt_1 = \frac{2N_0}{T}$$

From the results of Chapter 4 for Gaussian moments, we have the result that the odd moments are zero, while the even moments are given by

$$E[A_k^{2n}] = 1 \cdot 3 \cdot 5 \cdots (2n - 1)(E[A_k^2])^n = \frac{(2n)!}{2^n n!} (E[A_k^2])^n \qquad [6.15.14]$$

Assuming A_k and B_k to be Gaussian, $X(t)$ is the result of a linear operation on Gaussian variables and hence is itself Gaussian. The actual distribution of A_k and B_k can be found as follows:

$$\phi_A(u) = E[e^{ju a_k}] = \sum_{n=0}^{\infty} \frac{(ju)^n}{n!} E[A_k^n] = \sum_{m=0}^{\infty} \frac{(ju)^{2m}}{(2m)!} E[A_k^{2m}] = \sum_{m=0}^{\infty} \frac{(ju)^{2m}}{(2m)!} \frac{(2m)!}{(2^m m!)} (E[A_k^2])^m$$

$$= \sum_{m=0}^{\infty} \frac{(-1)^m}{m!} \left(\frac{2N_0 u^2}{2T}\right)^m \qquad\qquad [6.15.15]$$

$$= \exp\left(-\frac{N_0}{T} u^2\right)$$

which is the characteristic function of the Gaussian probability density function; that is:

$$p_A(a_k) = \sqrt{\frac{T}{2\pi \, 2N_0}} \exp\left(-\frac{1}{2}\left(\frac{a_k^2 T}{2 \, N_0}\right)\right) \qquad [6.15.16]$$

while $p_B(b_k)$ is the same but with a_k replaced by b_k. Note that using [6.15.13] we have

$$E[A_k B_j] = \frac{4}{T^2} \int_0^T \int_0^T E[X_1 X_2] \cos(\omega_k t_1) \sin(\omega_j t_2) \, dt_1 dt_2 \qquad [6.15.17]$$

$$= \frac{4N_0}{T^2} \int_0^T \cos(\omega_k t_1) \sin(\omega_j t_1) dt_1 = 0$$

and

$$E[A_k A_j] = \frac{4N_0}{T^2} \int_0^T \cos(\omega_k t_1) \cos(\omega_j t_1) dt_1 = \frac{2N_0}{T} \delta_{kj} \qquad [6.15.18]$$

where δ_{kj} is zero for $k \neq j$ and is one for $k = j$. Similarly, we have

$$E[B_k B_j] = \frac{2N_0}{T} \delta_{kj} \qquad \text{[6.15.19]}$$

and by assumption we have

$$E[A_k] = E[B_k] = 0 \qquad \text{[6.15.20]}$$

If we set

$$E[A_k^2] = E[B_k^2] = \sigma_{kk}^2 \qquad \text{[6.15.21]}$$

then

$$E[X^2(t)] = \sum_{k=1}^{\infty} \left(E[A_k^2] \cos^2(\omega_k t) + E[B_k^2] \sin^2(\omega_k t) \right) = \sum_{k=1}^{\infty} \sigma_{kk}^2 \qquad \text{[6.15.22]}$$

Also

$$\sigma_{kk}^2 = \frac{2N_0}{T} = \frac{S_{XX}(f_k)}{T} = S_{XX}(f_k) \Delta f \qquad \text{[6.15.23]}$$

where

$$\Delta f = f_{k+1} - f_k = \frac{k+1}{T} - \frac{k}{T} = \frac{1}{T} \qquad \text{[6.15.24]}$$

where k may be either positive or negative. Then

$$E[X^2(t)] = \sum_{k=-\infty}^{\infty} S_{XX}(f_k) \Delta f \qquad \text{[6.15.25]}$$

which in the limit becomes

$$E[X^2(t)] = \int_{-\infty}^{\infty} S_{XX}(f) df = \sigma^2_{XX} \qquad \text{[6.15.26]}$$

where $(\sigma_{XX})^2$ is the variance of the noise.

A second model for noise is

$$X(t) = \sum_{k=1}^{\infty} c_k \cos(\omega_k t - \Theta_k) \qquad \text{[6.15.27]}$$

where

$$c_k^2 = 2S_{XX}(f_k) \Delta f \qquad \text{[6.15.28]}$$

The c_ks are constants and the Θ_ks are random phase angles uniformly distributed between 0 and 2π.

A third representation for noise is

$$X(t) = \sum_{k} A_k \Delta t_k \delta(t - t_k) \qquad \text{[6.15.29]}$$

where the A_k are normally distributed with a mean value of zero and a variance $\sigma_{kk}^2 = E[(A_k)^2] = S_{XX}(f_k)/T$.

Each of the above models is a valid model for white, Gaussian noise, which is often called white noise, since $X(t)$ can be shown to be Gaussian and the power spectral density of $X(t)$ is constant.

6.16   MATLAB SOFTWARE

An interactive software package has been prepared for your use, and can be found in the subdirectory ch6. This software has been written for use in this chapter and Chapter 7. The software is written in MATLAB for version 4.2c or higher and can be executed in Windows 3.11 or Windows 95. It makes use of the menu options provided by this version of MATLAB. After you install the software in a subdirectory of your choice, start MAT-LAB, and then be sure you change your directory to the directory in which you installed the software. Next type *main* in the MATLAB *command* window, and the first menu, called main, will appear on your screen. The software is generally self-explanatory. However, to facilitate its use, examine Figure 6.22. Here we see most of the various menu options available. For this chapter we will use menus ("called") main, file, analysis, and spectra. The wave generator and edit menus offer the user a means by which new data can be generated and edited. These two menus are described below. The main menu allows the user to select one of four options, including file selection, editing, analysis, and quit. Generally, the file menu should be selected first, after which the *load* option in the file menu should be selected. Two data format options are available, ASCII and MATLAB. Included with this software package are some example data files, which are stored in the subdirectory data.

An example of the use of the software appears in Figure 6.23. Here we started the software as described above. Then the *file* option was selected, followed by the *load Matlab* option. (The user must use the left *mouse* button, holding it down as it is moved to the option desired.) Once a data format option is selected, a window opens, displaying the subdirectory folders for this software. (This window is not shown in either Figure 6.22 or Figure 6.23.) In the right panel of this window the user is to select the data subdirectory, using a double click of the left *mouse* button. The left panel of this window will display the data files in the data subdirectory. The MATLAB data format files are:

a.mat	A segment of the vowel /a/, as in Bach.
ee.mat	A segment of the vowel /i/, as in see.
noise.mat	A segment of noise data.
sin1.mat	A sinewave.
sine.mat	A sinewave.
tri.mat	A triangle waveform.
tri1.mat	A triangle waveform.
tric.mat	A triangle waveform.
we.mat	The sentence "We were away a year ago."

The speech files in MATLAB format are sampled at 10 kHz. The variables for these files are SPEECH. (See the last paragraph of this section for an additional discussion of variables.)

The ASCII data format files are:

dg_bye.d	The word *bye*
dg_hello.d	The word *hello*

257

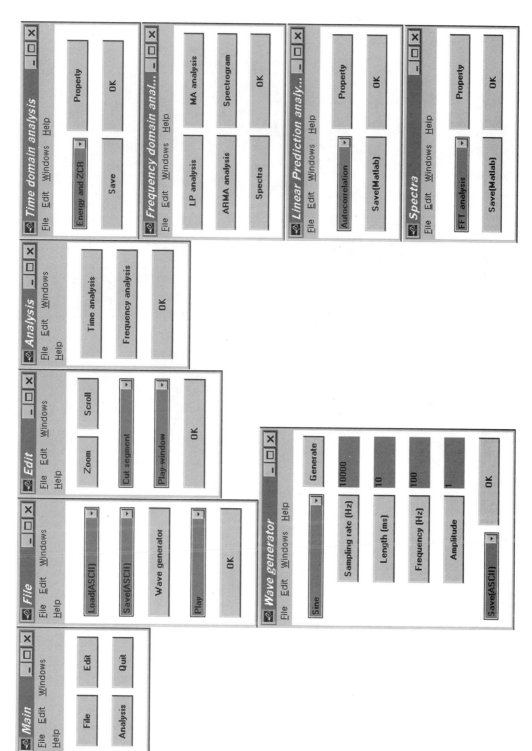

Figure 6.22 Window options for the software provided

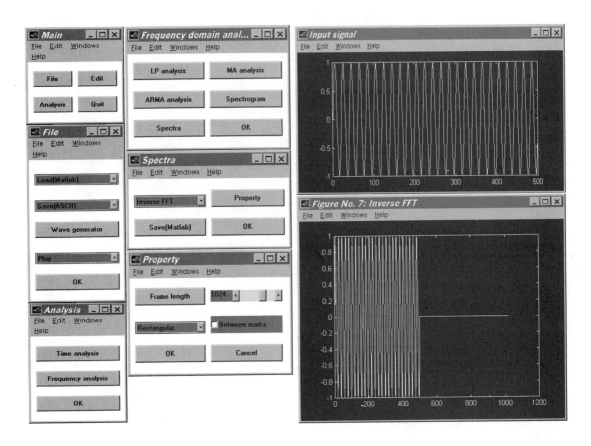

Figure 6.23   Menu options for an example

| dg_no.d | The word *no* |
| dg_yes.d | The word *yes* |

These speech files are sampled at 16 kHz. The variables for these files are the name of the file preceding the .d extension. (See the last paragraph of this section for an additional discussion of the variables.)

Note that if the MATLAB *load* option is selected, then only the MATLAB data files are displayed in the left panel. If the ASCII *load* option is selected, then all files are displayed; however, only ASCII data files will be loaded properly. An example of an ASCII file is dg_yes.d. Often files with the extension x.dat are ASCII files as well. The file selection can be made by either double-clicking the left *mouse* button on the file name or by a single click on the file name followed by a click on the *ok* button. In Figure 6.23 after selecting the MATLAB load option, we selected the file sine.mat, which is displayed in the input signal window. Do not close the input signal window until you are finished with the software. You may select other data files as desired. These files will be displayed in the input signal window.

After performing the above steps, we made the following sequence of button presses, as Figure 6.23 shows: *analysis* (in the main menu), *frequency analysis,* and *spectra*. After the spectra menu came up, we pressed the *property* button. The properties available include the frame length (i.e., the length of the data record to be analyzed). The number for the frame length can be changed from the default by moving the sliding bar with the mouse, by pressing the arrows, or by placing the cursor in the number area and typing in the desired number. If the user sets the frame length to be greater than the selected data file displayed in the input signal window, then the software automatically appends zeros to the data when the FFT (fast Fourier transform) or periodogram is calculated. The number of zeros appended is printed in the MATLAB *command* window. Note that the FFT and periodogram are calculated using a frame length that is equal to 2^k, where k is a positive integer. Thus, the frame length is 16, 32, 64, 128, and so on. If the frame length is set to 100, for example, then the FFT and the periodogram are calculated using 128 data points; that is, the frame length is rounded upward to the next power of 2. The property below the frame length is a data window, which we discuss in Chapter 7. For this chapter use the default window, which is rectangular. The *between marks* option is discussed below. The *ok* button is pressed once the user has selected the desired properties. The *cancel* button offers the usual option. The default for the upper left button in the spectra menu is FFT analysis, as can be seen in Figure 6.22. The four options for this button are FFT analysis, inverse FFT, periodogram, and autocorrelation. The FFT and inverse FFT are the usual pair of functions. Chapter 7 explains the periodogram but for the purposes of this chapter, the periodogram can be thought of as the power spectral density. This option is paired with the autocorrelation option. In Figure 6.23 we see the inverse FFT, which is the original sinewave data file of 512 data points with 512 zeros appended to the data because we changed the property of the data from 512 to 1024. Figure 6.24 shows the FFT (spectrum), inverse FFT, periodogram (power spectral density), and the autocorrelation function for this data file. In MATLAB the autocorrelation function is calculated by first calculating the periodogram (power spectral density) and then taking the inverse transform of the periodogram. This is the manner by which this software works as well. Thus, to calculate the autocorrelation function, you must first calculate the periodogram and then calculate the autocorrelation function.

Return to Figure 6.22 and examine the wave generator menu. If the user clicks on the sine button in the wave generator menu, then other waveform options will appear, including random waveforms. This option allows the user to generate some simple waveforms for experimentation. The other options available are self-explanatory. The files created by the user can be saved in one of the two formats discussed above.

The edit menu allows the user to edit the data file displayed in the input signal window. This menu works as follows. Press the *zoom* button with the left *mouse* button. The cursor changes form. Move the cursor to the desired starting point of the section of data that is to be zoomed in on. Click the left *mouse* button once. Move the cursor to the desired end point. Click the left *mouse* button once. The section of data selected by this

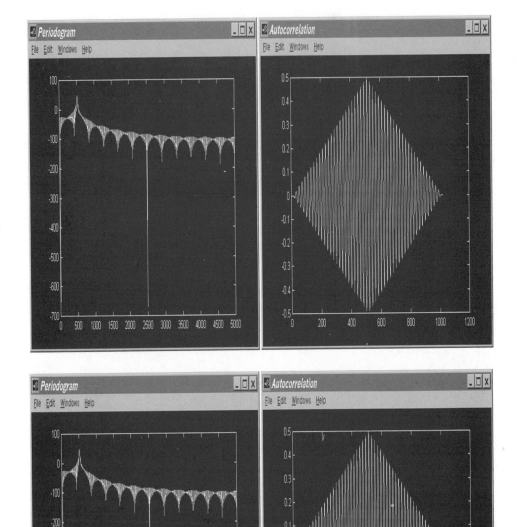

Figure 6.24   Data displays for the example in the text

process is displayed in the window. To zoom out double click the right *mouse* button while the cursor is on the data. To exit zoom, double click the left and right *mouse* buttons together. The cursor will change back to its original form and the MATLAB command window prints the message "exit zooming function." The double click can be achieved most easily by placing one finger over the seam between the two *mouse* buttons and pressing the seam twice with one finger. The user will probably not need the zoom option because MATLAB automatically scales the display window to accommodate the length and amplitude of the data. Furthermore, most of the data files are short and are easily examined in one display.

The scroll option in the edit menu is to be used when the data has been zoomed in. It works as follows. Select the *scroll* button. The cursor changes form. Move the cursor to the data. Single click the left *mouse* button to move the data to the left. Single click the right *mouse* button to move the data to the right. Single click both *mouse* buttons simultaneously to exit the scroll option. When the scroll option has been successfully exited the cursor changes back to its original form and the MATLAB command window prints the message "exit moving function." The scroll option will only scroll a short way before the data display reverts back to its original form.

Now return to the property menu under spectra in Figure 6.23. Select *property*. Select the *between marks* button. A check mark will appear in the space indicated. Select the *ok* button. Next any of the options under the FFT button may be selected; say that we select FFT. Move the cursor to the data. It will change form. Now move the cursor to the desired starting point for calculating the FFT. Press the left *mouse* button. Now the FFT for the selected data will be calculated. There is no need to select the end point of the data, since the frame length selected in the *property* window is used to automatically determine the end point. Note that this option does not automatically append zeros to the data. So if the data length beyond the selected starting point in the *input signal* window is not the same length as that specified for the frame length, then an error message is printed in the MATLAB *command* window and the FFT will not be calculated. Note that this option remains functional until the right mouse button is clicked. Thus, the user can repeatedly change the position of the cursor to calculate the FFT at various positions in the data file. To exit this option the user clicks the right *mouse* button once. However, the *between marks* button remains checked until the user removes the check by clicking on this button.

The *play* button in the file menu (or the *play-window* button in the edit menu) is functional provided your PC has the proper hardware installed along with the proper drivers. If this is so, then you can listen to the speech files. The vowel segments are so short that they sound unnatural. However, the sentence in MATLAB format may be played. The software calls the MATLAB function *sound*, which works as follows. Assume that you are not using the above software. However, assume you have opened MATLAB and that you are in the data directory. Then do the following:

>> load we (no extension because this is a MATLAB file)

>> sound(SPEECH, 10000)

The sentence "We were away a year ago" will be played. Recall that SPEECH is the variable name and 10,000 is the sampling frequency for the MATLAB data format.

The software package provided with this chapter calls the function *sound* with the sampling frequency set to 10,000. Consequently, if you load an ASCII format speech file, such as dg_yes.d, then the play option will work, but the word *yes* will sound distorted, as if spoken in slow motion. This is because these ASCII speech files have a sampling frequency of 16 kHz. So to hear these files properly, go to the MATLAB command window, change directory to the data directory, load an ASCII speech file as follows:

>> load dg_yes.d (use the extension for non-MATLAB data files)

>> who

Your variables are dg_yes

>> sound(dg_yes,16000)

The speech file *yes* will be played properly. One final note concerning the playing of speech or audio files is that you may have to set the amplification for the speakers to the auto mode by the following function, *saxis('auto')*. This should be inserted before calling sound.

A brief summary of the major steps to follow for the software package for this chapter is:

- Start the program.
- Select the *file* button.
- Select the *load* button: ASCII or MATLAB.
- Select the desired data file. (The data file will be plotted in the input signal window. Do not close this window.)
- Select the *analysis* button.
- Select the *frequency analysis* button.
- Select the *spectra* button.
- Select the *property* button. (Be sure the desired frame length is specified. Click ok.)
- Click on the FFT option. The following menu is displayed:

    FFT

    Inverse FFT

    Periodogram (power spectral density)

    Autocorrelation

- Select the desired option, say, periodogram.
- The periodogram is displayed in a window labeled *periodogram*.
- To calculate the autocorrelation, click on the periodogram analysis button and select autocorrelation. The autocorrelation function will be displayed in a window labeled *autocorrelation*. Remember that the frame length is still the same as that used for calculating the periodogram.
- To exit any menu, press the *ok* or *cancel* button.
- To exit the software, press the *quit* button in the main menu.

Some additional examples appear in Appendix 2. The MATLAB files for generating these examples can be found in subdirectory ap2. If these files are executed in MATLAB, then the waveforms shown in Appendix 2 will appear. These same files generate an autocorrelation function and the power spectral density, which can be saved and used as an input to the above software package.

Sometimes you may want to convert a data file from one format to another. All of the MATLAB data files in the ch 6 software have the variable SPEECH (all upper case letters). Thus, if the user wishes to create an ASCII data file from a MATLAB data file, then do the following:

>> load x (where x is the name of the MATLAB data file)

>> who (a command to list the variables)

>> your variables are: SPEECH

>> save y.d SPEECH−ascii

The file y.d will now contain the data in ASCII format. In a similar manner a MATLAB data format file can be created from an ASCII file.

6.17　SUMMARY

The emphasis of this chapter has been autocorrelation, crosscorrelation, and power spectral density functions. We addressed autocorrelation and crosscorrelation functions for strict sense stationary, wide sense stationary, and nonstationary process.

It should be emphasized that the power spectrum (or its corresponding autocorrelation function) is not a unique representation for a random process; that is, more than one random process may have the same autocorrelation function and power spectral density. These functions are a characteristic common to the ensemble of the random process. The power spectrum provides no phase information about the random process. If phase is not an important consideration in the analysis or design of a system with random inputs, then the power spectrum can be quite useful. The ear is an example of one receiving device that is sensitive to variations in the power spectrum, but relatively insensitive to changes in phase. There are, however, receivers that are very sensitive to the shape of the time domain signal and thus to phase (e.g., a TV set).

The two methods for computing the power spectral density for a wide sense stationary random process are summarized below.

Correlation Method

1. Determine $R_{XX}(\tau) = E[X(t)X(t + \tau)]$.

2. The power spectral density is

$$S_{XX}(f) = \int_{-\infty}^{\infty} R_{XX}(\tau) \, e^{-j\omega\tau} \, d\tau$$

Direct Method

1. Determine $|F_T(X(t))|^2$ for a member function of the ensemble of the random process for the interval $-T$ to T. This function may involve one or more random variables.

2. Determine the power spectrum as

$$S_{XX}(f) = \lim_{T \to \infty} \frac{1}{2T} E \,|\, F_T(X(t)) \,|^2$$

Two sets of software for use in MATLAB are provided in subdirectories ch6 and ap2, respectively.

PROBLEMS

6.1   Rework Example 6.2 with $p_\Theta(\theta) = \frac{1}{\pi}$ for $-\frac{\pi}{2} \le \theta \le \frac{\pi}{2}$. This process is non-stationary because the mean is a function of time. However, the autocorrelation function remains the same. Thus, this problem is an example of a nonstationary process, but one that has an autocorrelation function that depends only on τ. Rework the problem again for

$$p_\Theta(\theta) = \frac{1}{\theta_0}, \quad 0 \le \theta \le \theta_0$$

Is there any value of θ_0 (other than 2π) that makes the process wide sense stationary?

6.2   Rework Example 6.9 with $p_\Theta(\theta) = \frac{1}{\pi}$ for $-\frac{\pi}{2} \le \theta \le \frac{\pi}{2}$. Keep the probability density for ω the same. Is the mean value the same? Is the autocorrelation function the same? Rework the problem for

$$p_\Theta(\theta) = \frac{1}{\theta_0} \quad 0 \le \theta \le \theta_0$$

6.3   Let a random process consist of a sequence of pulses with the following properties:

   a. The pulses are of equal duration, Δ.

   b. The pulses are equally likely to be ± 1.

   c. All pulses are statistically independent.

   d. The various members of the ensemble are not synchronized.

   Find the autocorrelation function.

6.4   Prove Property 6.4.4.

6.5   Let $X(t) = A\cos(\omega t) + B\sin(\omega t)$ where A and B are independent, zero mean, identically distributed random variables. Show that $X(t)$ is wide sense stationary, but not strict sense stationary. For the latter case consider $E[X^3(t)]$.
   If

$$X(t) = \sum_{n=1}^{\infty} [A_n \cos n\omega t + B_n \sin n\omega t]$$

   is a random process, where A_n and B_n are random variables such that $E[A_n] = E[B_n] = 0$, $E[A_n B_m] = 0$, $E[A_n A_m] = \delta_{mn} E[A^2{}_n]$, and $E[B_n B_m] = \delta_{mn} E[B^2{}_n]$ for all m and n. δ_{mn} is the Kronecker delta function. Find the time-varying autocorrelation function $R_{XX}(t, \tau)$. If $E[B^2{}_n] = E[A^2{}_n]$, is this process wide sense stationary? This process is sometimes used as a model for random noise. See Section 6.15 on noise models.

6.6 A random process $X(t) = \{x_i(t)\}$ consists of three member functions as follows:

$$x_1(t) = 1, x_2(t) = -3, x_3(t) = \sin 2\pi t$$

Each member function occurs with equal probability. Calculate $E[X(t)]$ and $E[X(t)X(t + \tau)]$ for the random process. Is this process stationary in the wide sense? Show every step in your calculations. Is the process stationary in the strict sense?

6.7 A random process $X(t) = \{x_i(t)\}$ has the following member functions:

$$x_1(t) = -2\cos(t)$$

$$x_2(t) = -2\sin(t)$$

$$x_3(t) = 2[\cos(t) + \sin(t)]$$

$$x_4(t) = [\cos(t) - \sin(t)]$$

$$x_5(t) = [\sin(t) - \cos(t)]$$

which occur with equal probability. Find $E[X(t)]$ and $E[X(t)x(t + \tau)]$. Is this process stationary in the wide sense? Show every step in your calculations. Is the process stationary in the strict sense?

6.8 Prove Properties 6.7.2 and 6.7.3.

6.9 Suppose we construct a random process of dc voltage waveforms, where the probability density function for the dc voltage is given by a uniform probability density as

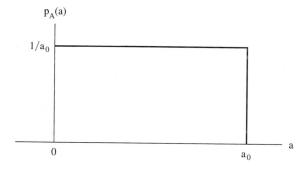

The ensemble of member functions for this example is depicted in Figure 6.25.

In this example the amplitude of each member function of the ensemble varies, but the statistics of the ensemble remain the same regardless of the time instant at which we make an observation. Is this a strict sense stationary process? Does your answer change if the probability density function becomes symmetric about the origin? Does the probability density function affect your answer at all?

6.10 Figure 6.26 shows two member functions of an ensemble of sine waves that all have the same maximum amplitude and the same frequency, but differ in their phase angles (or time displacement). Let the phase angle, Θ, be the random variable. If Θ has a uniform probability density from 0 to 2π, what is the amplitude probability density of the ensemble? With this probability density show that the ensemble average of the square of the amplitude is equal to the mean square value of a member function of the random process, that is, the mean square value of a sinusoid. (This is Problem 5.1. Skip this problem if you have already worked it in Chapter 5.)

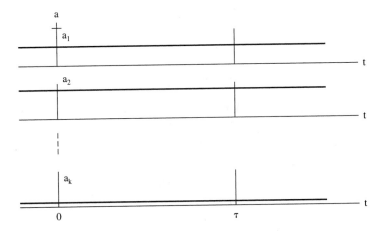

Figure 6.25   An ensemble of dc voltages

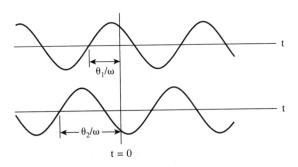

Figure 6.26

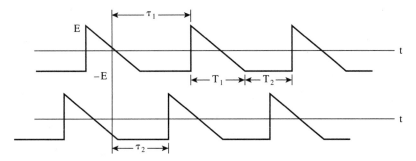

Figure 6.27

6.11   Figure 6.27 shows two member functions of an ensemble of periodic functions that are the same except for a displacement in time. Let the time from t = 0 to the first positive transition of each member function of the ensemble be τ. If τ has a uniform probability density function, what is the amplitude probability density of the ensemble? Then show that the ensemble average with respect to the amplitude is equal to the time average of the amplitude of a particular member of the ensemble.

6.12   The random telegraph signal discussed in Chapter 5 is a random process, X(t), where the alternate amplitude values are a and −a with probability 1/2. Let X(t) change signs with the occurrence of an event in a Poisson process with a rate α, that is, let the probability that i changes in sign occur in a time interval of length t be given as

$$P_I(i, t) = \frac{(\alpha t)^i}{i!} e^{-(\alpha t)} u(t)$$

Show that the autocorrelation function of X(t) is

$$R_{XX}(\tau) = a^2 e^{-2\alpha |\tau|}$$

Find the power spectral density and equivalent noise bandwidth using analytic techniques. Next, using the MATLAB software provided, calculate the power spectral density.

6.13   Determine the autocorrelation function of X(t), where

$$X(t) = \sum_{i=1}^{N} a_i \cos(\omega_i t + \Theta_i)$$

where all of the ω_i are nonzero constants, the a_i are constants, and the Θ_i are the random variables, each uniformly distributed from 0 to 2π. Determine the power spectral density.

6.14   Determine the autocorrelation function for a real function, X(t), where

$$X(t) = \sum_{n=-\infty}^{\infty} A_n e^{-j2\pi nf_0t}$$

where the A_n are real random variables, each statistically independent from the other, with identical distributions with mean $E[A]$ and mean square value $E[A^2]$.

6.15 A random process is given as

$$X(t) = Y(t) \sin(\omega_0 t + \Theta)$$

where $Y(t)$ and Θ are statistically independent, with $E[Y(t)] = 0$ and Θ uniformly distributed over the interval 0 to 2π, and ω_0 is a constant. Find $R_{XX}(\tau)$ in terms of $R_{YY}(\tau)$.

6.16 Let $R_{YY}(\tau) = a^2 e^{-2\alpha|\tau|}$ in Problem 6.15. Calculate the power spectral density function both analytically and using the software provided for MATLAB for both $X(t)$ and $Y(t)$. Using MATLAB, plot the autocorrelation function and the power spectral density for both $X(t)$ and $Y(t)$.

6.17 If $X(t)$ and $Y(t)$ are two jointly wide sense stationary Gaussian random processes with zero means, and with autocorrelation and crosscorrelation functions denoted as $R_{XX}(\tau)$, $R_{YY}(\tau)$, $R_{XY}(\tau)$, then determine the crosscorrelation function between $X^2(t)$ and $Y^2(t)$.

6.18 If $X(t)$ is a wide sense stationary Gaussian random process, find the crosscorrelation between $X(t)$ and $X^3(t)$ in terms of the autocorrelation function $R_{XX}(\tau)$.

6.19 A wide sense stationary, zero mean, discrete random process, $X(n)$, has an autocorrelation function $R_{XX}(k)$. Show that the crosscorrelation function of $X(n)$ and $Y(n) = aX(n) + b$, where a and b are constants, is

$$R_{XY}(k) = a R_{XX}(k)$$

Determine the autocorrelation for $Y(n)$.

6.20 Two zero mean discrete random processes, $X(n)$ and $Y(n)$, are statistically independent. Let a new random process be $Z(n) = X(n) + Y(n)$. Let the autocorrelation functions for $X(n)$ and $Y(n)$ be

$$R_{XX}(k) = \left(\frac{1}{2}\right)^{|k|}, \quad R_{YY}(k) = \left(\frac{1}{3}\right)^{|k|}$$

Find $R_{ZZ}(k)$. Using MATLAB, plot all three autocorrelation functions. Determine all three power spectral density functions analytically and, using the software provided for MATLAB, plot the power spectral densities.

6.21 Let a discrete random process be generated by repeated tosses of a fair die. Let the value of the random variable be equal to the result of each toss. Determine the mean function and the autocorrelation function of the random process.

6.22 Two discrete independent random processes are generated by repeated tosses of two fair dice, as in Problem 6.21. Find the crosscorrelation function of the two processes.

6.23 A discrete random process, X(n), is generated by repeated tosses of a coin. Let the occurrence of a head be denoted by 1 and that of a tail by -1. A new discrete random process is generated by $Y(2n) = X(n)$ for $n = 0, \pm1, \pm2 \ldots$ and $Y(n) = X(n + 1)$ for $\pm$ n even. Find the autocorrelation function for $Y(n)$.

6.24 Let a discrete random process be given as $X(n) = (-1)^{n+m}$ where m is an arbitrary integer. Determine the autocorrelation function for $X(n)$. Then determine the power spectral density analytically and using the software provided for MATLAB.

6.25 Show that the autocorrelation function for the sum of two zero mean, independent, wide sense stationary discrete random processes is equal to the sum of the autocorrelation functions of the individual random processes.

6.26 Find the autocorrelation function for the discrete random process $Y(n) = X(n) + c$, where $X(n)$ is a wide sense stationary, discrete random process with autocorrelation function $R_{XX}(k)$, and c is a constant. Are $X(n)$ and $Y(n)$ independent? uncorrelated? orthogonal?

6.27 A wide sense stationary, discrete random process, $X(n)$, has an autocorrelation function of $R_{XX}(k)$. Find the expected value of $[X(n + m) - X(n - m)]^2$, where m is an arbitrary integer.

6.28 Let $X(n)$ be a random sequence. Define another random sequence as $Y(n) = X^2(n)$. Show that $X(n)$ and $Y(n)$ are uncorrelated. Is $Y(n)$ wide sense stationary? Assume that $p_X(x)$ is an even function and that $X(n)$ is a zero mean, wide sense stationary random process.

6.29 In Chapter 5, Problem 5.22, a model for phase shift keying was given as

$$X(t) = a \cos\left(2\pi f_c t + B(n)\frac{\pi}{2}\right)$$

where $nT \le t \le (n + 1)T$ for all n, and $B(n)$ is a Bernoulli random process that has values of $+1$ or -1. Determine the autocorrelation function for the random process $X(t)$.

6.30 In Example 6.10 a random process, $X(t)$, consists of two member functions, $x_1(t) = 1$ and $x_2(t) = \sin(t)$, which can occur with equal probability. Form a random vector

$$\vec{X}(t) = [X(t_1)\ X(t_2)]^T$$

Determine $E[\vec{X}(t)]$ and the correlation matrix for $\vec{X}(t)$.

6.31 Repeat Problem 6.30 if $X(t)$ consists of two member functions $x_1(t) = 1$ and $x_2(t) = 5$, which occur with probability 1/3 and 2/3, respectively.

6.32 In Example 6.12 there are two random processes

$$X(t) = \sin(\omega t + \Theta) \text{ and } Y(t) = \cos(\omega t + \Theta)$$

where Θ is a random variable uniformly distributed between $-\pi$ and π. Form the random vector

$$\vec{X}(t) = [X(t_1) \ Y(t_2)]^T$$

Determine $E[\vec{X}(t)]$ and the correlation matrix for $\vec{X}(t)$.

6.33 Form a random vector

$$\vec{X}(n) = [X(n_1) \ Y(n_2)]^T$$

where $X(n)$ is a wide sense stationary, zero mean discrete random process with the autocorrelation function $R_{XX}(k)$, and $Y(n) = aX(n) + b$, where a and b are constants. Determine $E[\vec{X}(n)]$ and the correlation matrix for $\vec{X}(n)$.

6.34 Find the equivalent noise bandwidth for the power spectral density in Example 6.26.

6.35 Using the procedure applied in Example 6.28, show that the double integral, below, can be expressed as the following single integral; that is:

$$\lim_{T\to\infty} \frac{1}{2T} E[\,|F_T[X(t)]|^2] = \lim_{T\to\infty} \frac{1}{2T} \int_{-T}^{T} \int_{-T}^{T} R_{XX}(t_1 - t_2) \, e^{-j\omega(t_1-t_2)} \, dt_1 \, dt_2$$

$$= \lim_{T\to\infty} \int_{-2T}^{2T} \left[1 - \frac{|\tau|}{2T} \right] R_{XX}(\tau) \, e^{-j\omega(\tau)} \, d\tau = S_{XX}(f)$$

6.36 Show by example that the random process $Z(t) = X(t) + Y(t)$ may be a wide sense stationary process even though the random processes $X(t)$ and $Y(t)$ are not. Hint: let $A(t)$ and $B(t)$ be independent, wide sense stationary random processes with zero means and identical autocorrelation functions. Then let $X(t) = A(t) \sin(t)$ and $Y(t) = B(t) \cos(t)$. Show that $X(t)$ and $Y(t)$ are not wide sense stationary. Then show that $Z(t)$ is wide sense stationary.

6.37 If $X(t) = A(t)\cos(\omega_0 t + \Theta)$, where $A(t)$ is a wide sense stationary random process independent of Θ and Θ is a random variable distributed uniformly from 0 to 2π and $Y(t) = A(t) \cos[(\omega_0 + \omega_1)t + \Theta]$, then show that $X(t)$ and $Y(t)$ are stationary in the wide sense but that the crosscorrelation $R_{XY}(t, t + \tau)$, between $X(t)$ and $Y(t)$, is not a function of τ only and that $Z(t) = X(t) + Y(t)$ is not stationary in the wide sense.

6.38 Find the power spectral density for a process for which $R_{XX}(\tau) = 1$ for all τ.

6.39 Let $X(t) = \cos(\omega_0 t + \Theta) + N(t)$ such that Θ is a random variable uniformly distributed from 0 to 2π and is independent of $N(t)$, which is a zero mean, wide sense stationary, white noise random process. Find the autocorrelation function and the power spectral density of $X(t)$.

6.40 A train of pulses of fixed height a and pulse width t_0 has a randomly varying repetition interval, as shown in Figure 6.28. Let T be the average repetition period

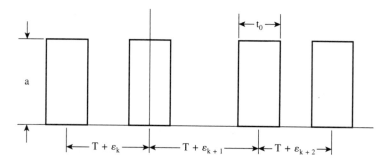

Figure 6.28

with $t_0 \ll T$ and let ε_k be the deviation of the kth spacing from T, so that $E[\varepsilon_k] = 0$. Assume that $T - \varepsilon_k > t_0$.

Show that the power spectral density is

$$S_{XX}(f) = \frac{a^2 t_0^2}{T}\left(\frac{\sin \pi ft_0}{\pi ft_0}\right)^2\left\{[1 - |\phi_E(f)|^2] + \frac{|\phi_E(f)|^2}{T}\sum_{-\infty}^{\infty}\delta\left(f - \frac{n}{T}\right)\right\}$$

where $\phi_E(f)$ is the characteristic function of the random variable ε.

6.41 A train of pulses of width t_0 and repetition period T has a random amplitude that is Gaussianly distributed with mean μ_X and variance $(\sigma_{XX})^2$. The pulses are independent and orthogonal and with zero mean. Find the power spectral density of the train.

6.42 Consider a train of pulses with height $1/t_0$ and width t_0 and period T_0. Find the Fourier series representation for this train of pulses. Then take the limit as $t_0 \to 0$ and show that

$$\frac{1}{T_0}\sum_{n=-\infty}^{\infty}\delta\left(f - \frac{n}{T_0}\right) = \sum_{n=-\infty}^{\infty}e^{-j\omega nT_0}$$

where $n = fT_0$ is an integer.

6.43 Determine the autocorrelation function for band limited white noise, namely, a random process whose power spectral density is $S(f) = N_0$ for $f_1 < |f| < f_2$ and zero elsewhere. Plot the power spectral density and the autocorrelation function using MATLAB. Also use the software provided for MATLAB to calculate the autocorrelation function using the given power spectral density.

6.44 Determine the autocorrelation function for a narrow band, band limited white noise random process. Hint: In Problem 6.43 let $f_0 = (f_2 - f_1)/2 = \Delta f/2$, where $\Delta f \ll f_0$. Plot the results using MATLAB. Also use the software provided for MATLAB to calculate the autocorrelation function using the given power spectral density.

6.45 Determine the autocorrelation function for a random process with a lowpass Gaussian power spectral density; that is:

$$S_{XX}(f) = N_0 \exp\left[\frac{-\omega^2}{2\omega_0^2}\right]$$

Plot the autocorrelation function and the power spectral density using MAT-LAB. Also use the software provided for MATLAB to calculate the autocorrelation function using the given power spectral density.

6.46 Determine the autocorrelation function for a random process with a band pass Gaussian power spectral density, namely:

$$S_{XX}(f) = N_0\left[\exp\left[\frac{-(\omega - \omega_c)^2}{2\omega_0^2}\right] + \exp\left[\frac{-(\omega + \omega_c)^2}{2\omega_0^2}\right]\right]$$

Plot the autocorrelation function and the power spectral density using MAT-LAB. Also use the software provided for MATLAB to calculate the autocorrelation function using the given power spectral density.

6.47 The sample mean of a random sequence, $X(n)$, is one estimator for the mean and is given as

$$\hat{\mu}_X = \frac{1}{N}\sum_{i=1}^{N} X(i)$$

Assume that the $X(n)$ are independent, identically distributed random variables. Determine the mean, variance, and covariance of $\hat{\mu}_X$.

6.48 Consider the special case of a moving average where $X(n) = 1/2[Y(n) + Y(n-1)]$ with $Y(0) = 0$. Let the random variables $Y(n)$ be independent, identically distributed Gaussian random variables. Determine the probability density function for $X(n)$.

6.49 Suppose we have the linear prediction random process $X(n) = 1/2 X(n-1) + E(n)$, where $E(0) = 0$ and $E(n)$ is a zero mean, independent, identically distributed random process. Find the autocorrelation function for $X(n)$. Is $X(n)$ wide sense stationary?

MATLAB PROBLEMS

6.1M Write a MATLAB program to simulate Problem 6.21.

6.2M Write a MATLAB program to simulate Problem 6.22.

6.3M Write a MATLAB program to simulate Problem 6.23.

6.4M Write a MATLAB program to simulate Problem 6.24.

6.5M Write a MATLAB program to simulate Problem 6.29.

6.6M Consider Example 6.7. Write a MATLAB program to simulate the ensemble. Then estimate the mean of the ensemble and the autocorrelation function. Describe your procedure.

6.7M   Consider Example 6.12. Write a MATLAB program to simulate the ensemble. Then estimate the mean of the ensemble and the autocorrelation function. Describe your procedure.

6.8M   Plot the autocorrelation function and the power spectral density for the PAM example, which is Example 6.34.

chapter
7

Ergodicity, Statistics, Estimation, and Simulation

7.1   INTRODUCTION

As the title suggests, this chapter will discuss several topics that are important for various applications of random processes. Most applications require the measurement of one or more parameters of a random process. For example, we may wish to estimate the mean or the autocorrelation function or the power spectral density function. Certainly one procedure for doing this is to repeat an experiment a number of times. However, it is difficult to measure the ensemble properties of a random variable. So we usually rely on measurements obtained from one member function of the ensemble. For example, consider the sample mean of random sequence X(n) introduced in Problem 6.47, as one estimator for the mean. The estimator is usually expressed as

$$\hat{\mu}_X = \frac{1}{N} \sum_{i=0}^{N-1} X(i) \quad \text{or} \quad \hat{\mu}_X = \frac{1}{N} \sum_{i=1}^{N} X(i) \qquad [7.1.1]$$

The X(n) are assumed to be independent, identically distributed random variables. Thus, the question arises as to how time averages of a member function of an ensemble are related to ensemble averages. Such questions are answered by ergodic theorems that provide the conditions for which time averages for long intervals converge to the ensemble average. This topic will be discussed first. Next we will cover two topics from statistics: estimators and confidence intervals. Then we will take up some estimation and simulation methods. One important simulation technique to be covered is a method for generating random numbers, a procedure similar to *rand* and *randn,* which we have already used in MATLAB.

There are several conventions for denoting time averages. One convention uses the one-sided average, which is expressed for continuous random processes as

$$< X(t) > \ = \lim_{T \to \infty} \frac{1}{T} \int_0^T X(t) \, dt \qquad [7.1.2]$$

while the respective convention for discrete random processes is either

274

$$< X(n) > = \lim_{N \to \infty} \frac{1}{N + 1} \sum_{i=0}^{N} X(n) \qquad \textbf{[7.1.3]}$$

or

$$< X(n) > = \lim_{N \to \infty} \frac{1}{N} \sum_{i=0}^{N-1} X(n) \qquad \textbf{[7.1.4]}$$

Another convention is called the two-sided average, which is denoted as

$$< X(t) > = \lim_{T \to \infty} \frac{1}{2T} \int_{-T}^{T} X(t) \, dt \qquad \textbf{[7.1.5]}$$

while the respective convention for discrete random processes is either

$$< X(n) > = \lim_{N \to \infty} \frac{1}{2N + 1} \sum_{i=-N}^{N} X(n) \qquad \textbf{[7.1.6]}$$

or

$$< X(n) > = \lim_{N \to \infty} \frac{1}{2N - 1} \sum_{i=-(N-1)}^{(N-1)} X(n) \qquad \textbf{[7.1.7]}$$

Perhaps the two-sided convention is more common, especially for theoretical definitions. Consequently, we will use this convention in the next section. As we develop estimators for parameters for discrete random sequences, we will adopt a notation similar to the form in [7.1.4] without the limit operation, since we will be dealing with equations for estimators that will depend on the use of finite length data sequences. This will become more apparent later.

7.2   ERGODIC RANDOM PROCESSES

In the previous chapters we have assumed that the statistical properties of a random process were given. However, in practice such knowledge is often not available. Consequently, we need to develop procedures for acquiring or estimating the statistical parameters of interest by using measurements taken from a member function of a random process. It turns out that for many stationary random processes, we can use time averages of a member function in place of ensemble averages of the random process. For example, under certain circumstances, we can use the sample mean, discussed above, in place of the mean value calculated by ensemble averaging. When we can use time averages in place of ensemble averages, we have what is referred to loosely as an ergodic random process. It turns out that there are a number of ergodic theorems that mathematically define ergodicity. We will discuss a few of these theorems.

One ergodic theorem comes from the strong law of large numbers and says that if $X(n)$ is a wide sense stationary, discrete random sequence with independent, identically distributed random variables with finite mean μ_X, then the time average of the sequence of a member function will converge to the ensemble average with probability one.

Definition 7.1. A wide sense stationary independent, identically distributed random sequence is said to be **ergodic in the mean** if it satisfies

$$\text{Probability}\left[\lim_{N\to\infty}\frac{1}{2N+1}\sum_{i=-N}^{N}X(i)=\mu_X\right]=1 \qquad [7.2.1a]$$

While for a continuous random process we have

$$\text{Probability}\left[\lim_{T\to\infty}\frac{1}{2T}\int_{-T}^{T}X(t)\,dt=\mu_X\right]=1 \qquad [7.2.1b]$$

Example 7.1

In Chapter 6, Example 6.11, we considered a discrete time random process, or random sequence created by the successive tosses of a biased coin. The member functions of the ensemble are generated by repeating the process using a large number of identically biased coins that are independently and repeatedly tossed. Let the occurrence of a head be denoted by 1, which occurs with probability p, and that of a tail by –1, which occurs with probability q=1−p. To make the random sequence a function of time, let us assume that each flip of the coin occurs every T seconds, where for convenience we will let T=1. One member function of this random process is shown in Figure 7.1. In Chapter 6, Quiz 6.6, it was established that this random process was stationary in the strict sense. This process is also ergodic in the mean because the mean of the process is the same whether it is calculated by ensemble or time averaging.

The ensemble mean is

$$\mu_X(n)=E[X(n)]=\int_{-\infty}^{\infty}x(n)\left\{p\,\delta(x-1)+q\,\delta(x+1)\right\}dx$$

$$=(-1)\,q+(1)\,p=p-q=2p-1=\mu_X$$

which is independent of n, but a function of p. If p=q=1/2, then μ_X=0, which is reasonable, since in this case 1 and –1 occur equally likely. If p > q, then $\mu_X > 0$, and if p < q, then $\mu_X < 0$.

The mean estimated by time averaging must be calculated using a particular member function of the ensemble. Each member function is considered to be representative of the process. Consequently, the time average of a member function is the same as the ensemble average with probability one.

We now show by example that time averages do not in general converge to ensemble averages.

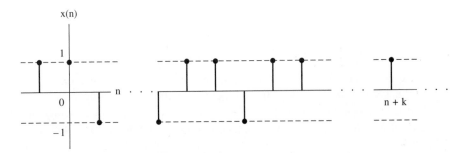

Figure 7.1   One member function for Example 7.1

In Chapter 6, Problem 6.9, we defined a random process of dc voltage waveforms, where the probability density function for the dc voltage was a uniform probability density from zero to a, so that the mean was a/2. The ensemble of member functions is shown in Figure 6.25. This process is strict sense stationary. The mean estimated by time averaging a member function depends on the member function. For example, the mean estimated by time averaging might be a_l or a_k, which may not be a/2. In other words, the statistics for a member function are not the same as those for the ensemble. Thus, the mean estimated by time averaging will not always converge to the ensemble average mean. Although this random process is strict sense stationary, it is not ergodic in the mean. | **Example 7.2**

An alternative definition for ergodic in the mean is given next.

Definition 7.2. A wide sense stationary random process X(t) is **ergodic in the mean** if and only if

$$\lim_{T \to \infty} \frac{1}{2T} \int_{-2T}^{2T} \left(1 - \frac{|\tau|}{2T} \right) Cov_{XX}(\tau) \, d\tau = 0 \qquad \textbf{[7.2.2]}$$

Recall from Example 6.28 that the reason for the limits arises from the product of two integrals. This definition is the same as saying that the estimate for the mean converges to the true mean in the mean square sense, namely:

$$\lim_{T \to \infty} \frac{1}{2T} E[\, |\hat{\mu}_X - \mu_X|^2 \,] = 0 \qquad \textbf{[7.2.3]}$$

Definition 7.2 can be stated as a theorem and proven from [7.2.3] in a manner similar to that shown in Chapter 6, Example 6.28 and Problem 6.35.

From Definition 7.2 one can define other definitions of ergodicity.

Definition 7.3. A wide sense stationary random process X(t) is **ergodic in the autocorrelation** if and only if for all τ

$$< X(t)X(t + \tau) > \; = \hat{R}_{XX}(\tau) = \lim_{T \to \infty} \frac{1}{2T} \int_{-T}^{T} X(t)X(t + \tau) \, dt = R_{XX}(\tau) \quad \textbf{[7.2.4]}$$

where $< X(t)X(t+\tau) >$ denotes the estimate of the autocorrelation function by time averaging.

The hat over the $R_{XX}(\tau)$ is used to emphasize that this is an estimate of the autocorrelation function, which in this case, is calculated by time averaging as distinguished from ensemble averaging. Various symbols are used to denote an estimate of the autocorrelation function, including R, **R,** and, $\mathfrak{R}$. Note that the above definitions can be easily modified to accommodate random sequences. For example, the definition for ergodic in the mean would be as follows.

Definition 7.4. A wide sense stationary random sequence X(n) is **ergodic in the mean** if and only if

$$\lim_{N \to \infty} \frac{1}{2N+1} \sum_{k=-2N}^{2N} \left(1 - \frac{|k|}{2N+1}\right) \text{Cov}_{XX}(k) = 0 \qquad \textbf{[7.2.5]}$$

And similarly we have the following definition for a random sequence.

Definition 7.5. A wide sense stationary random sequence X(n) is **ergodic in the autocorrelation** if and only if for all k

$$< X(n)X(n+k) > = \hat{R}_{XX}(k) = \lim_{N \to \infty} \frac{1}{2N+1} \sum_{n=-N}^{N} X(n)X(n+k) = R_{XX}(k) \qquad \textbf{[7.2.6]}$$

Example 7.3

The autocorrelation function for Example 7.1 for k=0 and any n is

$$R_{XX}(0) = 1$$

and for $k \neq 0$ and any n is

$$R_{XX}(k) = (p - q)^2 = (2p - 1)^2$$

Thus, this random sequence is stationary in the wide sense. Since the statistics for a member function are the same as those for the ensemble, the autocorrelation function calculated by time averaging a member function as per [7.2.5] is the same as that calculated by ensemble averaging.

Quiz 7.1   Is the random process in Example 7.1 ergodic in the autocorrelation?

Example 7.4

Show that the random telegraph random process is ergodic in the mean. From Chapter 6, Problem 6.12, we have that the mean is zero and

$$R_{XX}(\tau) = e^{-2\alpha|\tau|}$$

Then by [7.2.2] we have

$$\lim_{T \to \infty} \frac{1}{2T} \int_{-2T}^{2T} \left(1 - \frac{|\tau|}{2T}\right) e^{-2\alpha|\tau|} \, d\tau = \lim_{T \to \infty} \frac{2}{2T} \int_{0}^{2T} e^{-2\alpha\tau} \, d\tau = 0$$

Thus, the random telegraph process is ergodic in the mean.

Example 7.5

Example 6.17 consisted of an ensemble of sawtooth waveforms with displacement as the random variable. The ensemble is illustrated again in Figure 7.2. In Example 6.17 we showed that the ensemble mean was equal to the mean estimated by time averaging a member function of the ensemble. Thus, this random process is ergodic in the mean.

As we mentioned in the Introduction, it is usually difficult to measure the statistics of an ensemble. Typically, it is desirable to measure selected parameters using a member function. The measurement is usually based on time averaging a function of a signal, such as the mean or the autocorrelation function. If two random processes are involved, then we might also estimate the crosscorrelation function by time averaging as follows.

$$< X(t)Y(t + \tau) > \; = \hat{R}_{XY}(\tau) = \lim_{T \to \infty} \frac{1}{2T} \int_{-T}^{T} X(t)Y(t + \tau)dt \qquad \text{[7.2.7]}$$

It is generally not possible to test whether or not a random process is ergodic in the mean or the autocorrelation, since in practice the statistics of a random process may not be known. Consequently, it is often assumed that a process is ergodic in the mean or autocorrelation or both. Such an assumption provides a method for obtaining an estimate for the random process from one member function of the ensemble. The assumption that a random process is ergodic (in the mean or autocorrelation or both) is sometimes referred to as the **ergodic hypothesis**.

The properties of the autocorrelation and crosscorrelation functions estimated by time averaging are the same as those for the same functions calculated by ensemble averaging.

Consider the sine wave random process with phase as the random variable, which is uniformly distributed from zero to 2π. We have already calculated by ensemble averaging the mean and the autocorrelation function, which are zero and $(a^2/2)\cos(\omega_0\tau)$, respectively. The autocorrelation function estimated by time averaging is

Example 7.6

$$\hat{R}_{XX}(\tau) = \lim_{T \to \infty} \frac{1}{2T} \int_{-T}^{T} a^2 \sin(\omega_0 t + \theta)\sin(\omega_0 t + \omega_0\tau + \theta)dt$$

$$= \frac{a^2}{2} \cos\omega_0\tau$$

The mean estimated by time averaging is zero. Thus, this random process is ergodic in the mean and in the autocorrelation.

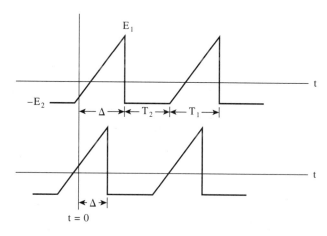

Figure 7.2   Two member functions of an ensemble of sawtooth waveforms

7.3   SOME EXAMPLES USING CORRELATIONS ESTIMATED BY TIME AVERAGING

Example 7.7 | **A** method for estimating the autocorrelation function by time averaging is outlined in Figure 7.3.

In Example 7.7 we use lower-case notation for the functions because we are treating the functions as though they are observed data records. However, as before, if the discussion refers to a random process in general, then we will continue to use upper-case notation to denote the random process. If we refer to a particular member function of the random process, then we will use lower-case notation, as we have previously.

Example 7.8 | In this example we apply the procedure outlined in the last example to a discrete sequence, or data record, $x(nT)$, as illustrated in Figure 7.4a. This data record is of finite length, that is, NT data samples. For convenience let the samples cover the time interval from $n = 0$ to $n = (N - 1)T$ seconds, with $T = 1$. Assume that the function is zero outside this range. To calculate one point of the autocorrelation function, we shift $x(n)$ by an amount k to form $x(n + k)$. Suppose $k = 2T = 2$; then $x(n + 2)$ appears as in Figure 7.4b. Next, we multiply the two functions $x(n)$ and $x(n + 2)$ at their corresponding time samples and sum the products; then we average by the total number of points, N, namely, we calculate

$$\hat{R}_{XX}(2) = \frac{1}{N} \sum_{n=-2}^{N-1-2} x(n)x(n + 2)$$

We plot for $\hat{R}_{XX}(k)$ for $k = 2$ in Figure 7.4c. We repeat this calculation for the other possible values of $k = n$ for $n = 0, 1, 2, \ldots, N - 1$. $\hat{R}_{XX}(k)$ might appear as in Figure 7.4d. The autocorrelation function is always symmetric about the origin, so we have also plotted the function for negative values of k.

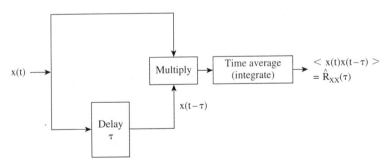

Figure 7.3   Procedure for estimating autocorrelation function by time averaging

Autocorrelations are calculated routinely in applications involving radar, geophysics, sonar, adaptive systems, communications, and the like. The similarity between two waveforms may be measured using correlation methods by multiplying the two waveforms, ordinate by ordinate, and then adding the products over the duration of the waveforms, as we did in the last example. The similarity between the two waveforms is assessed by the size of the sum of the products. If the waveforms are identical (or nearly so), then nearly every product contributes a positive term to the sum. The sum will therefore be large. If, however, the waveforms are dissimilar, then some positive products may be canceled by negative products in the sum, and the final result will be small.

Another application of correlation is the measurement of the time delay of a signal, as we considered in Example 6.19. Imagine we have two identical waveforms, but one is shifted in time relative to the other, as in Figure 7.5, except that the shift is a delay, that is, shifted to the right rather than to the left. If we calculate the crosscorrelation function for these two waveforms, we will find that the crosscorrelation function will peak at the time shift corresponding to the time delay between the two waveforms. We may measure the instant at which the peak occurs in the crosscorrelation function to determine the time delay.

Example 7.9

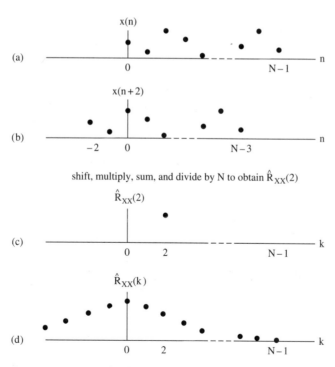

Figure 7.4   Example of estimating an autocorrelation function from data

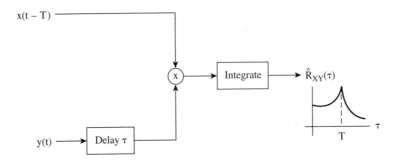

Figure 7.5   Measurement of time delay by crosscorrelation

Example 7.10 | System identification is another useful application. Suppose it is desired to measure the impulse response, or the system transfer function, of a linear system, as Figure 7.6 shows. In Chapter 6, Example 6.21, we did this example using ensemble averaging. We may use time averaging techniques to estimate the crosscorrelation function. Let the input to the system be a random process $X(t)$ and the output be $Y(t)$, with the impulse response denoted as $h(t)$. Then the crosscorrelation function between the input and output is estimated by time averaging as follows:

$$\hat{R}_{XY}(\tau) = \lim_{T\to\infty} \frac{1}{2T} \int_{-T}^{T} X(t-\tau)\, Y(t)\, dt = \lim_{T\to\infty} \frac{1}{2T} \int_{-T}^{T} X(t-\tau) \int_{-\infty}^{\infty} X(t-\sigma)\, h(\sigma)\, d\sigma\, dt$$

$$= \int_{-\infty}^{\infty} \left\{ \lim_{T\to\infty} \frac{1}{2T} \int_{-T}^{T} X(t-\tau)\, X(t-\sigma)\, dt \right\} h(\sigma)\, d\sigma$$

$$= \int_{-\infty}^{\infty} \hat{R}_{XX}(\tau-\sigma)\, h(\sigma)\, d\sigma = \int_{-\infty}^{\infty} \hat{R}_{XX}(\sigma)\, h(\tau-\sigma)\, d\sigma$$

Let the input be an ergodic white noise random process such that

$$\hat{R}_{XX}(\tau-\sigma) = \delta(\tau-\sigma)$$

Then $\hat{R}_{XY}(\tau) = h(\tau)$.

Quiz 7.2   Suppose a random process $X(t)$ has an autocorrelation function estimated by time averaging that is $\hat{R}_{XX}(\tau)$. Determine $\hat{R}_{XY}(\tau)$ if $Y(t) = X(t-T)$.

Example 7.11 | Another example is a simple speech recognition scheme. Suppose we have a speech signal that represents the sound /i/, which is pronounced as "e," as in *see*. We wish to determine if one or more of four other sounds are the same as the sound /i/. The five waveforms are shown in Figure 7.7. The waveforms have been aligned for convenience only. We calculate the cross-

correlation functions between /i/ and the four other sounds. These are shown in the same figure. Note that the /i/ sound from *see* and *me* give the best match in that the peak of the crosscorrelation function is greater for these two signals than for the others. Speech recognition for
continuous speech is very complicated and requires more sophisticated techniques than those
presented here. However, for simple, isolated sounds these principles can work.

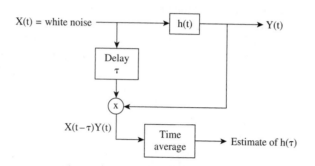

Figure 7.6   Measuring the impulse response of a linear
system

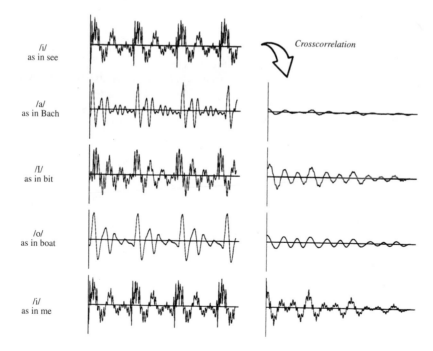

Figure 7.7   A simple speech recognition example

The radar example in Chapter 6 (Example 6.20) will typically use correlations estimated by time averaging, as will direction finding applications (Example 6.22).

7.4   STATISTICAL INFERENCE

One objective of statistics is to make inferences, such as decision making and prediction about a population of data, including random processes and using information gathered from a sample of data taken from the population. As we have seen, the population, or random process, is represented by parameters. Consequently, statistical inference is concerned with making inferences about the parameters of the random process, such as the mean, the variance, and the autocorrelation function.

Statistical inference can be considered as consisting of two parts: estimation and tests of significance, such as hypothesis testing. A test of significance attempts to determine if the data are consistent with a specified hypothesis. Estimation uses the data to estimate parameters of a population, often to determine the accuracy of a specific estimate. We will deal only with estimation here.

Probability theory attempts to predict apriori the probability of an outcome of an experiment. Statistical inference can be considered the converse; that is, it examines how to use the data after the experiment has been performed to make inferences about the properties of the random process, such as to estimate parameters.

7.4.1   TYPES OF ESTIMATION

There are basically two types of estimates: point and interval. A point estimate is a single number, such as the mean value. An interval estimate defines an interval with two end points, typically on the real line. Thus, we might estimate that the mean of a random process would fall in an interval $[x_1, x_2]$. A good interval estimator would enclose the true value of the parameter being estimated a large fraction of the time, that is, with a high probability. The interval estimator is often called the confidence interval. We shall deal with interval estimators shortly.

> **Definition 7.6.** An **estimator** is typically a function or rule that calculates the estimate of a parameter based on data measured from the population or random process. We shall denote an estimator as $\hat{\Theta}$, since it is a random variable, while the estimate of the parameter will be denoted as $\hat{\theta}$. The true value of the parameter will be denoted as θ. For convenience, the subscript X for this general class of estimators will not be used.

Example 7.12 The sample mean $\hat{\mu}_X$ of a discrete sequence X(n) is a point estimator $\hat{\Theta}$ of the true mean μ_X where

$$\hat{\mu}_X = \frac{1}{N}\sum_{i=0}^{N-1} X(i)$$

An interval estimator of the mean would use the available data to calculate two points that are intended to enclose the true mean.

An estimator $\hat{\Theta}$ is a random variable and as such has a probability density function, which we illustrate in Figure 7.8. Here θ represents the true value of the parameter. For example, $\hat{\Theta}$ might be the sample mean $\hat{M}_X$, with the particular estimate being $\hat{\mu}_X$ given in [7.1.1] and θ would be the true value of the mean μ_X. Note in Figure 7.8 that the largest probability for $\hat{\theta}$ corresponds to the peak in the probability density function. So we would like the probability density function to be "peaky" near the true value of θ. This implies that the standard deviation should be small as well. This leads us to consider more carefully some features of estimators.

One desirable feature of an estimator is that it be unbiased.

Definition 7.7. If $E[\hat{\Theta}] = \theta$, then the estimator is said to be **unbiased**. Otherwise, it is said to be **biased**.

Definition 7.8. The **bias** of an estimator $\hat{\Theta}$ is

$$B = E[\hat{\Theta}] - \theta \qquad\qquad [7.4.1.1]$$

An unbiased estimator would appear as shown in Figure 7.8, while a biased estimator would appear as shown in Figure 7.9.

The sample mean μ_X is unbiased for a sequence of independent, identically distributed random variables, each with true mean μ_X that is: | **Example 7.13**

$$E[\hat{\mu}_X] = E\left[\frac{1}{N}\sum_{i=0}^{N-1} X(i)\right] = \frac{1}{N}\sum_{i=0}^{N-1} E[X(i)] = \frac{1}{N}\sum_{i=0}^{N-1} \mu_X = \mu_X \qquad [7.4.1.2]$$

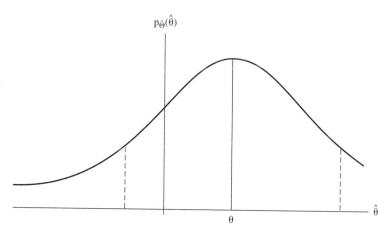

$$p_{\hat{\Theta}}(\hat{\theta})$$

$$\theta$$

$$\hat{\theta}$$

Figure 7.8   An example of a probability density function for an estimator

Quiz 7.3   Suppose we take one sample, X(i), from a random process with true mean μ_X. Let this sample be an estimator for the mean. Call this estimator a single point estimator. Is this estimator biased?

Another desirable feature of an estimator is that its variance be a minimum or at least small. Thus, the probability density function shown in Figure 7.10a is preferable to that shown in Figure 7.10b.

7.4.2   POINT ESTIMATORS

Here we examine point estimators in more detail.

Definiton 7.9. The **variance** of an estimator $\hat{\Theta}$ is

$$VAR[\hat{\Theta}] = \sigma^2_{\hat{\Theta}} = E[(\hat{\Theta} - E[\hat{\Theta}])^2] \qquad\qquad [7.4.2.1]$$

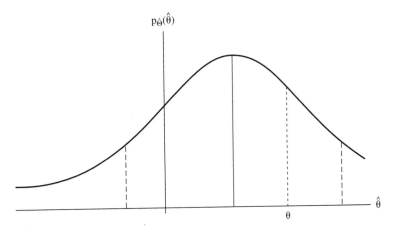

Figure 7.9   An example of a biased estimator

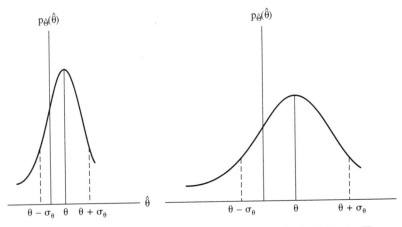

(a) Probability density for Estimator I   (b) Probability density for Estimator II

Figure 7.10   An example of two estimators with different variances

The variance of the sample mean for independent, identically distributed random variables is

Example 7.14

$$E[(\hat{M}_X - E(\hat{M}_X))^2] = E[(\hat{M}_X - \mu_X)^2] \qquad [7.4.2.2]$$

$$= E\left[\frac{1}{N^2}\sum_{i=0}^{N-1}\sum_{j=0}^{N-1}X(i)X(j) - 2\mu_X\frac{1}{N}\sum_{i=0}^{N-1}X(i) + \mu_X^2\right]$$

$$= \frac{1}{N^2}\sum_{i=0}^{N-1}\sum_{j=0}^{N-1}E[X(i)X(j)] - 2\mu_X\frac{1}{N}\sum_{i=0}^{N-1}E[X(i)] + \mu_X^2$$

$$= \frac{1}{N^2}[(N^2 - N)\mu_X^2 + NE(X^2)] - 2\mu_X^2 + \mu_X^2$$

$$= \frac{1}{N^2}[(N^2\mu_X^2 + N\sigma_X^2] - \mu_X^2$$

$$= \frac{\sigma_X^2}{N}$$

Thus, the variance of the sample mean approaches zero as the number of samples increases.

The variance of the estimator is a measure of the spread of the probability density function of $\hat{\Theta}$ with respect to its expected value, as Figure 7.10 shows.

Quiz 7.4   Consider the single point estimator of Quiz 7.3. What is the variance of this estimator of the mean? Let the true variance of the random process be σ^2_X.

Quiz 7.5   Is the single point estimator of the mean in Quiz 7.4 a better estimator than the sample mean? Discuss.

By using the Chebyshev inequality we can show that the probability that the sample mean approaches the true mean will approach one as N approaches infinity. This is done as follows:

$$P[|\hat{\mu}_X - E[\hat{\mu}_X]| \geq \epsilon] \leq \frac{Var[\hat{\mu}_X]}{\epsilon^2} \qquad [7.4.2.3]$$

which becomes

$$P[|\hat{\mu}_X - \mu_X| \geq \epsilon] \leq \frac{\dfrac{\sigma_X^2}{N}}{\epsilon^2} \qquad [7.4.2.4]$$

This last result can be written in its compliment form as

$$P[|\hat{\mu}_X - \mu_X| < \epsilon] \geq 1 - \frac{\sigma_X^2}{N\epsilon^2} \qquad [7.4.2.5]$$

This says that the probability of the difference between the sample mean and the true mean is less than some error, ϵ, and that the probability of this inequality will approach one as N approaches infinity.

Definition 7.10. If $\hat{\Theta}_N$ is an estimator computed using N samples, $N \geq 1$, then $\hat{\Theta}_N$ is said to be a **consistent estimator** if

$$\lim_{N\to\infty} P[\,|\hat{\Theta}_N - \theta| > \epsilon\,] = 0 \qquad [7.4.2.6]$$

for every $\epsilon > 0$. If the above probability tends to zero as the number of samples, N, approaches infinity for every $\epsilon > 0$, then we say the estimator is asymptotically consistent or more simply consistent. Equation [7.4.2.6] is often called **convergence in probability**.

Example 7.15 | The sample mean is a consistent estimator.

Quiz 7.6   Is the single point estimator of the mean consistent?

Example 7.16 | We can use [7.4.2.5] to determine the number of samples N such that $\hat{\mu}_X$ is within a specified error, ϵ, of μ_X with probability

$$1 - \frac{\sigma_X^2}{N\epsilon^2}$$

as follows. Suppose we make measurements of a random variable that has a variance of 2. How many measurements must we make if we want the probability to be 0.9 and the sample mean to be within $\epsilon = 1/2$ of the true mean? This requires that

$$1 - \frac{\sigma_X^2}{N\epsilon^2} = 0.9$$

which becomes

$$1 - \frac{2}{N(1/2)^2} = 0.9$$

so that N=80 measurements are required.

It often turns out that when we attempt to reduce the bias of an estimator its variance will increase or the opposite may occur. As a consequence it has been found useful to minimize the mean square error.

Definition 7.11. An estimator $\hat{\Theta}$ is said to be a **minimum mean square error estimator** if

$$E[(\hat{\Theta} - \theta)^2] \leq E[(\hat{\Theta}_1 - \theta)^2] \qquad [7.4.2.7]$$

where $\hat{\Theta}_1$ is any other estimator.

It can be shown that the mean square error is

$$E[(\hat{\Theta} - \theta)^2] = VAR[\hat{\Theta}] + B^2 \qquad [7.4.2.8]$$

Quiz 7.7   What is the mean square error for the single point estimator?

Definition 7.12. If the mean square error of an estimator $\hat{\Theta}$ is minimized and its bias is zero, then the estimator is said to be a **minimum variance, unbiased estimator**.

One estimator for the variance of a random variable is **Example 7.17**

$$s_k^2 = \frac{1}{k} \sum_{i=0}^{N-1} [X(i) - \hat{\mu}_X]^2 \qquad [7.4.2.9]$$

where

$$\hat{\mu}_X = \frac{1}{N} \sum_{i=0}^{N-1} X(i)$$

One of the Problems asks you to verify the following results, namely:

$$E[s_k^2] = \frac{N-1}{k} \sigma_X^2 \qquad [7.4.2.10]$$

and the bias of this estimator is

$$B_k = \left(\frac{N-1-k}{k}\right) \sigma_X^2 \qquad [7.4.2.11]$$

while the variance is

$$VAR[s_k^2] = 2\left(\frac{N-1}{k^2}\right) \sigma_X^4 \qquad [7.4.2.12]$$

Thus, when $k = N - 1$ the estimator is unbiased and the variance is $[2/(N-1)]\sigma_X^4$. However, note that the variance decreases as k increases but the bias increases (away from zero). Thus, minimize the mean square error; that is, minimize

$$E[(\hat{\Theta} - \theta)^2] = 2\left(\frac{N-1}{k^2}\right)\sigma_X^4 + \left(\frac{N-1-k}{k}\right)^2 \sigma_X^4 \qquad [7.4.2.13]$$

with respect to k. This yields $k = N+1$ with the minimum mean square error being $[2/(N+1)]\sigma_X^4$, which is slightly less than the variance, but it is also slightly biased.

A random variable X is sampled only once. This sample is used as an estimate $\hat{\mu}_X$ for the mean. **Example 7.18**
Find the expected value of $\hat{\mu}_X$ and $E[(\hat{\mu}_X)^2]$ if the probability density function for X is $p_X(x)=e^{-x}$ for $x \geq 0$ and is zero for $x < 0$. This is done as follows.

$$E[\hat{\mu}_X] = \mu_X = \int_0^\infty x\,e^{-x}\,dx = \Gamma(2) = 1$$

Next, by [7.4.2.2] we have

$$E[(\hat{\mu}_X)^2] = \frac{\sigma_X^2}{N} + [E[\hat{\mu}_X]]^2$$

For this problem N=1 and $E[(\hat{\mu}_X)^2] = 1$. So

$$E[(\hat{\mu}_X)^2] = \sigma_X^2 + [E[\hat{\mu}_X]]^2 = [E[\hat{\mu}_X]]^2 + \left(\int_0^\infty x^2 e^{-x}\,dx - [E[\hat{\mu}_X]]^2\right)$$

Then

$$E[(\hat{\mu}_X)^2] = \int_0^\infty x^2 e^{-x}\, dx = \Gamma(3) = 2$$

7.4.3   INTERVAL ESTIMATORS

In the previous section we considered point estimators, where a single value was considered a best estimate of a population or a random process parameter in some sense. Interval estimators consider the error between the estimator and the true value of the parameter being estimated. This error is expressed as an interval.

> **Definition 7.13.** An **interval estimator** is two numbers between which the random process parameter can be expected to fall with a certain level of confidence. The two numbers are called the **confidence limits** and are the end points of the **confidence interval**. A $(1 - \alpha)100$ percent confidence interval is an interval that has a $(1 - \alpha)100$ percent probability of containing the random process parameter. The **confidence level** is the quantity $(1 - \alpha)$ and the **level of significance** is the quantity α. Both the confidence level and the **level of significance** can be expressed in percent terms. The confidence level is sometimes called the confidence coefficient.

The standardized mean is expressed as

$$Z = \frac{\hat{\mu}_X - \mu_X}{\sigma_X / \sqrt{N}} \tag{7.4.3.1}$$

If the sample size N is large, then most statisticians assume that the standardized mean is normally distributed. This assumption of normality is made even if the standard deviation is unknown and the unbiased sample standard deviation

$$S = \sqrt{\frac{1}{N-1} \sum_{i=0}^{N-1} (X(i) - \hat{\mu}_X)^2} \tag{7.4.3.2}$$

is substituted for σ_X. If N is small (less than 30), the assumption is usually made that the sample mean comes from a normal population. In this case we have

$$T_\nu = \frac{\hat{\mu}_X - \mu_X}{S / \sqrt{N}} \tag{7.4.3.3}$$

where $\nu = N-1$ and S is given in [7.4.3.2]. The distribution of T_ν is called the Student's t distribution, which is a function of the parameter $\nu = N-1$ used in calculating the sample standard deviation. The parameter ν is called the degrees of freedom and represents the number of independent samples. The Student's t distribution is symmetrical about its mean of zero and is similar to the normal distribution curve. The variance of the Student's t distribution depends on ν, which is greater than one but approaches one as N approaches infinity. The Student's t distribution is tabulated in most books on statistics.

The purpose of the above discussion is to establish that the random variables Z and T_ν have known probability density functions, namely, Z is normal with zero mean and unit variance and T_ν is Student's t. Thus, we can compute the probability of events of the type $[a \leq Z \leq b]$ and $[a \leq T_\nu \leq b]$, such as

$$P[a \leq Z \leq b] = 0.95 \qquad \textbf{[7.4.3.4]}$$

A common situation occurs when $a = -b$. Denote for the 0.95 probability case the value of a as $a_{0.95}$; then we have

$$P[-a_{0.95} \leq Z \leq a_{0.95}] = 0.95 \qquad \textbf{[7.4.3.5]}$$

For the normal probability distribution case, we have from Chapter 4 that $a_{0.95} = 1.96$. Also since Z is given by [7.4.3.1], we have that

$$P\left[(-a_{0.95})\left(\frac{\sigma_X}{\sqrt{N}}\right) \leq \hat{\mu}_X - \mu_X \leq (a_{0.95})\left(\frac{\sigma_X}{\sqrt{N}}\right)\right] = 0.95 \qquad \textbf{[7.4.3.6]}$$

or

$$P\left[\hat{\mu}_X - a_{0.95}\left(\frac{\sigma_X}{\sqrt{N}}\right) \leq \mu_X \leq \hat{\mu}_X + a_{0.95}\left(\frac{\sigma_X}{\sqrt{N}}\right)\right] = 0.95 \qquad \textbf{[7.4.3.7]}$$

This says that the true mean lies within the interval

$$\left[\hat{\mu}_X - a_{0.95}\left(\frac{\sigma_X}{\sqrt{N}}\right), \ \hat{\mu}_X + a_{0.95}\left(\frac{\sigma_X}{\sqrt{N}}\right)\right] \qquad \textbf{[7.4.3.8]}$$

$$= [\hat{\mu}_X - a_{0.95}(\sigma_{\hat{\mu}_X}), \ \hat{\mu}_X + a_{0.95}(\sigma_{\hat{\mu}_X})]$$

$$= [\hat{\mu}_X - 1.96 \, \sigma_{\hat{\mu}_X}, \ \hat{\mu}_X + 1.96 \, \sigma_{\hat{\mu}_X}]$$

with a probability of 0.95, or a 95 pecent probability. This interval is called the 95 percent confidence interval for the mean. This tells us that although for every sample value of $\hat{\mu}_X$ we may have a different interval, the interval will 95 out of 100 times include the true mean.

As shown in Figure 7.11, the confidence level $(1 - \alpha)$ is the area under the normal curve from $(\hat{\mu}_X - 1.96 \, \sigma_{\hat{\mu}_X})$ to $(\hat{\mu}_X + 1.96 \, \sigma_{\hat{\mu}_X})$ for the 95 percent confidence interval. The level of significance is $100 - 95 = 5$ percent. This says that there is a 5 percent

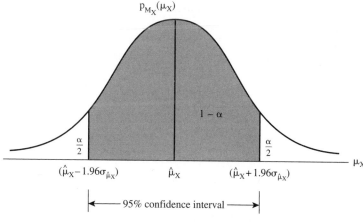

Figure 7.11   The confidence level $(1-\alpha)$ for a 95% confidence interval

chance that the true mean will lie outside the confidence interval, namely, in one of the two tails beyond the two confidence limits. Since the normal distribution is symmetric, then there is a 2.5 percent probability that the true mean will lie within the right tail and a 2.5 percent probability that it will lie within the left tail.

Note that we may also have a confidence interval for the sample mean if we know the true mean; that is, the interval is

$$\left[\mu_X - 1.96\left(\frac{\sigma_X}{\sqrt{N}}\right), \quad \mu_X + 1.96\left(\frac{\sigma_X}{\sqrt{N}}\right)\right] \qquad [7.4.3.9]$$

$$= [\mu_X - 1.96(\sigma_{\hat{\mu}_X}), \quad \mu_X + 1.96(\sigma_{\hat{\mu}_X})]$$

We are generally not interested in this case, since usually we are estimating the mean and we want to know the confidence interval for the mean, not for the estimate.

Example 7.19   Suppose we have a normally distributed random variable with $\sigma_X^2 = 4$. A sample of 100 values is taken and the sample mean is found to be 10.2. Determine the 95 percent confidence interval for the true mean μ_X.

From [7.4.3.8] the 95 percent confidence interval is

$$\left[\hat{\mu}_X - 1.96\left(\frac{\sigma_X}{\sqrt{N}}\right), \quad \hat{\mu}_X + 1.96\left(\frac{\sigma_X}{\sqrt{N}}\right)\right]$$

Substituting the values given we find that the 95 percent interval is [9.808, 10.592]. The probability that the true mean lies within this interval is 0.95, or 95 percent.

As noted in Chapter 4, we can determine other constants for the confidence level using the normal distribution. This is summarized in Table 7.1, where we let $c = a_{1-\alpha}$. Thus, for $\alpha = 0.05$, $1 - \alpha = 0.95$, we have $c = a_{0.95} = 1.96$.

Quiz 7.8   Determine the 99 percent confidence interval for Example 7.19.

Table 7.1

Confidence level $(1-\alpha)100\%$	Level of Significance $\alpha 100\%$	c
90	10	1.64
95	5	1.96
99	1	2.58
99.9	0.1	3.29
99.99	0.01	3.89

If the variance of each sample of a random process is 25, what is the number of samples that we need to insure that at the 99 percent confidence level the true mean is within the following	**Example 7.20**

$$[\hat{\mu}_X - 0.5 \le \mu_X \le \hat{\mu}_X + 0.5]$$

Thus, we have that $2.58(5/N^{0.5}) = 0.5$, giving $N = (25.8)^2 = 665.64$ or since N must be an integer, we have N = 666.

Quiz 7.9   What is N in Example 7.20 for a 95 percent confidence interval?

For the previous material we assumed that the sample mean is estimated and that the mean is unknown and that the variance of the sample mean is known. If we know the variance of the sample mean, then we also know the true variance. However, if the true variance is unknown, but can be estimated, say, by S in [7.4.3.2], then the confidence interval can be found using the Student's t distribution using the appropriate tables. We do not consider this topic here. It is also possible to develop confidence intervals for the variance, a topic discussed in statistics books.

If we have a random sequence X(n) with a true mean of 1 and a standard deviation of 1.2, then we can plot the 90 percent confidence interval, which is	**Example 7.21**

$$\hat{\mu}_X \pm 1.64 \left(\frac{\sigma_X}{\sqrt{N}} \right)$$

This means that the interval is approximately ± 0.2 about the individual sample values, as Figure 7.12 shows using the bar about the data point. Generally we want the true mean to fall within the confidence interval of the data as in Figure 7.12.

7.5   MAXIMUM LIKELIHOOD ESTIMATION

So far we have covered several types of estimators, including the minimum mean square error estimator. In this section we briefly discuss the maximum likelihood estimation (MLE) method, which is perhaps the most theoretically powerful estimation procedure.

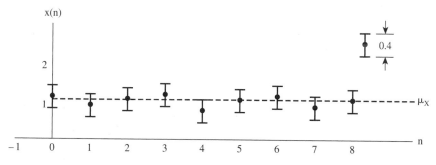

Figure 7.12   Illustration of a confidence interval about data points for a random sequence

The method estimates an unknown, but fixed, parameter θ of $p_X(x|\theta)$ by determining the value of $\hat{\theta}$ that maximizes $p_X(x|\theta)$, where the observed value of x is substituted into $p_X(x|\theta)$. The parameter θ is unknown and is to be estimated. The objective of the MLE method is to determine the most probable value of $\hat{\theta}$ after the data have been measured. Since after estimation the probability density function is also a function of $\hat{\theta}$, it is referred to as a likelihood function. The idea is that since the observed data x are assumed to be equally likely for each measurement, then the value of $\hat{\theta}$ is the one that will give the largest probability for the observed data. And this value of $\hat{\theta}$ has a high probability of being close to the true value of θ.

A maximum likelihood estimate will be unbiased as the number of samples, denoted as, N, increases. It is also consistent and will become Gaussian as N increases. The estimate has other properties as well, which are discussed in more advanced texts. Several disadvantages of the MLE are that the probability density function must be known (or assumed) and that the estimate may be difficult to compute analytically.

Definition 7.14. The **maximum likelihood estimate** (MLE) $\hat{\Theta}_{ML}$ of the fixed, but unknown parameter θ is the value of $\hat{\Theta}_{ML}$ that maximizes the probability density function $p_X(x|\hat{\theta}_{ML})$. The particular value of $\hat{\Theta}_{ML}$ that does this for the given data is the most likely value of $\hat{\Theta}_{ML}$, which is $\hat{\theta}_{ML}$.

We typically have more than one value of data that is observed, for instance, a sequence of values $x(0), x(1), \ldots x(N-1)$, which we assume are independent and identically distributed. In this case the probability density function (likelihood function L) becomes

$$L = L(x(0)x(1)\ldots x(N-1)|\theta)$$

$$= p_{X(0)\ldots X(N-1)}(x(0), x(1), \ldots, x(N-1)|\theta)$$

$$= p_{X(0)}(x(0)|\theta)p_{X(1)}(x(1)|\theta)\ldots p_{X(N-1)}(x(N-1)|\theta)$$

or

$$L = \prod_{i=0}^{N-1} p_{X(i)}(x(i)|\theta) \tag{7.5.1}$$

The log likelihood function is

$$\log[L] = \sum_{i=0}^{N-1} \log[p_{X(i)}(x(i)|\theta)] \tag{7.5.2}$$

The MLE is computed by differentiating L or log[L] with respect to θ and setting the derivative equal to zero, namely:

$$\partial L/\partial\theta = 0 \quad \text{or} \quad \partial\log[L]/\partial\theta = 0 \tag{7.5.3}$$

Example 7.22 | Suppose we measure a signal plus noise, such that $X(i)=s+V(i)$, $i=0, 1, \ldots, N-1$, where the $V(i)$ are independent, identically distributed Gaussian white noise samples with zero mean and variance σ^2. Since the measured data is $X(i)$ and $V(i)=X(i)-s$, the MLE for s as a function of the data is found as follows:

$$L = p_{V(0)}(v(0) \mid s) \, p_{V(1)}(v(1) \mid s) \dots p_{V(N-1)}(v(N-1)|s) = \prod_{i=0}^{N-1} p_{V(i)}(v(i) \mid s)$$

$$= \frac{1}{(2\pi\sigma^2)^{N/2}} \exp\left[-\frac{1}{2\sigma^2} \sum_{i=0}^{N-1} (x(i) - s)^2 \right]$$

The log[L] is

$$\log[L] = -\frac{N}{2}\log(2\pi\sigma^2) - \frac{1}{2\sigma^2}\sum_{i=0}^{N-1}(x(i) - s)^2$$

Then

$$\partial \log[L]/\partial s = 0 = \frac{1}{\sigma^2}\sum_{i=0}^{N-1}(x(i) - s)$$

Thus, we have

$$\hat{s}_{ML} = \frac{1}{N}\sum_{i=0}^{N-1} x(i) = \hat{\mu}_X$$

which is the sample mean estimate of the true mean. By previous results we know that this maximum likelihood estimate is unbiased and consistent.

7.6   ESTIMATES OF THE AUTOCORRELATION FUNCTION

Two major estimators for the autocorrelation function are used on a regular basis. The applications that call for autocorrelation estimates include data modeling, such as linear prediction, and power spectral estimation. We shall deal with both of these applications.

Definition 7.15. The first estimate is called the **unbiased autocorrelation estimate** and is expressed as

$$\hat{R}_{XX}(k) = \frac{1}{N - |k|}\sum_{i=0}^{N-1-|k|} X(i + |k|)\, X(i) \quad \text{for } |k| < N \qquad \textbf{[7.6.1]}$$

The summation is sometimes expressed as from 1 to $N - |k|$, but the total number of terms is the same, namely, N. The choice depends solely on the manner by which the data is indexed, that is, whether the initial value of the data starts at $i = 0$ or $i = 1$. Note that when we calculate [7.6.1], we use an observed data record.

This estimate is unbiased, since

$$E[\hat{R}_{XX}(k)] = \frac{1}{N - |k|}\sum_{i=0}^{N-1-|k|} E[X(i + |k|)\, X(i)] \qquad \textbf{[7.6.2]}$$

$$= \frac{1}{N - |k|}\sum_{i=0}^{N-1-|k|} R_{XX}(k) = R_{XX}(k)$$

When the random variables are zero mean Gaussian, the variance of this estimate is approximately

$$\text{VAR}\,[\hat{R}_{XX}(k)] = \frac{1}{N - |k|} \sum_{i=-(N-1-|k|)}^{N-1-|k|} \left\{ \left(1 - \frac{|i|}{N - |k|} \right) \right. \qquad \text{[7.6.3]}$$

$$\left. (R_{XX}^2(i) + R_{XX}(i + |k|)\, R_{XX}(i - |k|)) \right\}$$

Provided k is fixed, this estimate of the autocorrelation function approaches zero as N approaches infinity, making this estimate consistent. We will presently discuss this more fully. One problem with this estimate is that its largest value does not always occur at the origin. This is illustrated in the following example. For correlation matrices, this means that the estimate is not always positive definite.

Example 7.23 | Consider the data sequence x(n), shown in Figure 7.13. The autocorrelation estimate is calculated as follows:

$$\hat{R}_{XX}(0) = \frac{1}{3}[2^2 + 1^2 + 2^2] = 3$$

$$\hat{R}_{XX}(1) = \frac{1}{2}[(2)(1) + (1)(2)] = 2$$

$$\hat{R}_{XX}(2) = \frac{1}{1}[(2)(2)] = 4$$

The last example shows that this autocorrelation estimate does not have its largest value at the origin.

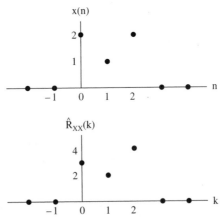

Figure 7.13   An example of an auto correlation estimate that is not positive semidefinite

Definition 7.16. Another estimate is called the **biased autocorrelation estimate** and is given as

$$\hat{R}_{XX}(k) = \frac{1}{N} \sum_{i=0}^{N-1-|k|} X(i + |k|) \, X(i) \quad \text{for } |k| < N \qquad \text{[7.6.4]}$$

where $X(i)$ is a zero mean Gaussian random sequence. Although this estimate is biased, it is asymptotically unbiased as N increases for k fixed. And the variance is approximately

$$VAR[\hat{R}_{XX}(k)] = \frac{1}{N^2} \sum_{i=-(N-1-|k|)}^{N-1-|k|} \Bigg\{ (N - |i| - |k|)$$

$$(R_{XX}^2(i) + R_{XX}(i + |k|) \, R_{XX}(i - |k|)) \Bigg\} \qquad \text{[7.6.5]}$$

This estimate is also consistent as N increases, provided k is fixed. It can also be shown that this estimate does have its largest value at the origin, which in correlation matrix terms means that this estimate is positive definite.

Quiz 7.10   Show that the above autocorrelation estimate is biased. Hint: How is the biased estimate related to the unbiased estimate?

Given the above two possible autocorrelation estimates, which is the best? Suppose $|k|$ approaches N; then the variance of the unbiased estimate becomes large, because k, the shift in the data, is large. This shift k is often called the number of lags. When this shift, or number of lags, is large, then the estimate of the autocorrelation function is unreliable since there is very little overlap of the data sequence with its shifted version. Consequently, this has led to the rule of thumb that the number of lags should not be greater than 10 percent of the length of the data sequence, namely, N/10. On the other hand, the variance of the biased estimate does not become large as k becomes large. In addition, the expected value of this estimate goes to zero, not to the true autocorrelation function. Since the bias is as large as the autocorrelation function we are estimating, we do not obtain a good estimate.

Now let k be fixed and let N increase. Then the variance of the biased estimate decreases as does the bias. The variance of the unbiased estimate also decreases. So we remain perplexed about which estimate is the best. It is conjectured that the mean square error of the biased estimate is less than that for the unbiased estimate. Thus, it is recommended that the biased autocorrelation estimate be used when possible.

Calculating the autocorrelation estimate involves several practical matters. First, is the data sequence. This is usually of finite length and can be thought of as being observed through a window, where a typical window is rectangular. This process sets the data outside the window to zero. Thus, as we calculate the autocorrelation estimate for increasing k, we have less and less data contributing to the estimate and more and more zeros. This is one reason why the estimate becomes unreliable as the number of lags increases. Figure 7.14 illustrates this point using a sliding rectangular window to represent the data. Note that the total number of data points is N, where the range is zero to $N - 1$.

Sometimes the data may be periodically extended outside the observation window. Here the idea is that this periodic extension is better in some sense than using zeros outside

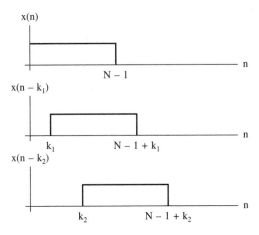

Figure 7.14   Illustration of shifting the data when calculating the autocorrelation estimate

the window. In either case, the experimenter must decide where such assumptions are justified. The problems offer several cases to explore the effects of both of these assumptions.

A rectangular window may be replaced by a window with less sharp leading and trailing edges in many applications. The reason for this is that the fast rise and fall time of the leading and trailing edges of the rectangular window introduce large spectral sidelobes in the spectral estimate, as well as high frequencies due to the window alone, thereby, distorting the spectral estimate obtained by transforming the autocorrelation estimate. We shall discuss this more later.

Both of the autocorrelation estimates can be calculated using the function *xcorr* in the MATLAB Signal Processing Toolbox. However, they can also be calculated using vector notation as follows. Let the data sequence be represented in vector form as

$$\vec{x}(t)^T\big|_0 = [x(0)\ x(1)\ x(2) \cdots x(N-1)\ \underbrace{0\ 0\ 0 \cdots 0}_{K-1 \text{ zeros}}] \qquad \textbf{[7.6.6]}$$

$$\vec{x}(t)^T\big|_1 = [0\ x(0)\ x(1)\ x(2) \cdots x(N-1)\ \underbrace{0\ 0\ 0 \cdots 0}_{K-2 \text{ zeros}}]$$

$$\vec{x}(t)^T\big|_2 = [0\ 0\ x(0)\ x(1)\ x(2) \cdots x(N-1)\ \underbrace{0\ 0\ 0 \cdots 0}_{K-3 \text{ zeros}}]$$

$$\vec{x}(t)^T\big|_{K-1} = [\underbrace{0\ 0 \cdots 0}_{K-1 \text{ zeros}}\ x(0)\ x(1)\ x(2) \cdots x(N-1)]$$

Note that [7.6.6] could use either upper- or lower-case notation for the vectors and their elements. Since the discussion is primarily directed toward formulating data vectors, we adopted the lower-case notation. Thus, we have K data vectors, numbered from zero to $K - 1$, where $K < N$. The $K - 1$ zeros appended to the end of the first data sequence and to the beginning of the last data sequence represents the largest value of the lag to be calculated in the autocorrelation estimate, namely, the number of lags ranges from 0 to $K - 1$. The subscript K on the vector represents the number of lags in the data sequence. To calculate the biased estimate of the autocorrelation function, we do the following:

$$\hat{R}_{XX}(0) = \vec{x}(t)^T |_0 \vec{x}(t)|_0 = [x(0)\ x(1)\ x(2)\cdots x(N-1)\ 0\ 0\ 0\cdots 0] \begin{bmatrix} x(0) \\ x(1) \\ x(2) \\ \vdots \\ x(N-1) \\ 0 \\ 0 \\ 0 \\ \vdots \\ 0 \end{bmatrix}$$

In general, therefore we calculate the autocorrelation estimate in the following manner. Note that N is the length of the data, not the length of the data plus the number of appended zeros. This agrees with [7.6.4].

$$\hat{R}_{XX}(0) = \frac{1}{N}\vec{x}(t)^T |_0 \vec{x}(t)|_0 \qquad\qquad \text{[7.6.7]}$$

$$\hat{R}_{XX}(1) = \frac{1}{N}\vec{x}(t)^T |_1 \vec{x}(t)|_0$$

$$\hat{R}_{XX}(k) = \frac{1}{N}\vec{x}(t)^T |_k \vec{x}(t)|_0$$

One can also create a data matrix [X] of the data vectors. The matrix has $(N+K - 1)$ rows and (K) columns. The autocorrelation matrix $[\hat{R}_{XX}(k)]$ is calculated by multiplying the transpose of the data matrix by the data matrix, as follows:

$$[X] = \begin{bmatrix} x(0) & 0 & 0 & & 0 \\ x(1) & x(0) & 0 & & 0 \\ x(2) & x(1) & x(0) & & 0 \\ \vdots & x(2) & x(1) & & \vdots \\ x(N-1) & \vdots & x(2) & & 0 \\ 0 & x(N-1) & \vdots & \cdots & x(0) \\ 0 & 0 & x(N-1) & & x(1) \\ 0 & 0 & 0 & & x(2) \\ \vdots & \vdots & \vdots & & \vdots \\ 0 & 0 & 0 & & x(N-1) \end{bmatrix} \qquad\qquad \text{[7.6.8]}$$

$$[\hat{R}_{XX}(k)] = \frac{1}{N}[X]^T[X] \tag{7.6.9}$$

This matrix calculation yields a KxK Toeplitz matrix, namely, a matrix that is symmetric about the main diagonal and one that has equal elements on the principal diagonal. This autocorrelation matrix is also positive definite (see the Problems). However, note that the matrix multiplication requires more computations than are necessary since the autocorrelation estimate is symmetric about the origin. In a similar manner we can calculate the unbiased autocorrelation estimate. However, if we do this by matrix multiplication, then the resulting autocorrelation matrix is not Toeplitz and, furthermore, the matrix may not be positive definite. This is another reason why the unbiased estimate is not usually used.

Example 7.24 Consider the data shown in Example 7.23. The biased autocorrelation matrix for K = 3 (K − 1 = 2) is

$$[X] = \begin{bmatrix} 2 & 0 & 0 \\ 1 & 2 & 0 \\ 2 & 1 & 2 \\ 0 & 2 & 1 \\ 0 & 0 & 2 \end{bmatrix} \quad [X]^T = \begin{bmatrix} 2 & 1 & 2 & 0 & 0 \\ 0 & 2 & 1 & 2 & 0 \\ 0 & 0 & 2 & 1 & 2 \end{bmatrix}$$

$$[\hat{R}_{XX}(k)] = \frac{1}{3}\begin{bmatrix} 2 & 1 & 2 & 0 & 0 \\ 0 & 2 & 1 & 2 & 0 \\ 0 & 0 & 2 & 1 & 2 \end{bmatrix}\begin{bmatrix} 2 & 0 & 0 \\ 1 & 2 & 0 \\ 2 & 1 & 2 \\ 0 & 2 & 1 \\ 0 & 0 & 2 \end{bmatrix} = \frac{1}{3}\begin{bmatrix} 9 & 4 & 4 \\ 4 & 9 & 4 \\ 4 & 4 & 9 \end{bmatrix}$$

Thus, the number of lags k ranges from 0 to 2 with values of 3, 4/3, and 4/3, respectively. If we had let K=4, then the value of the autocorrelation estimate for lag 3 would be zero.

7.7   ESTIMATES OF THE POWER SPECTRUM

7.7.1   CLASSICAL ESTIMATION

Many problems in electrical engineering require a knowledge of the distribution of the power of a random process in the frequency domain, for example, the design of filters to remove noise, to cancel signal echoes, or to represent features of a signal for pattern recognition. If the data records are long, then reliable power spectrum estimates can be obtained using standard fast Fourier transform (FFT) techniques. However, if the data records are short, as they usually are, then the task of obtaining reliable (i.e., small bias and small variance) power spectrum estimates becomes difficult. Spectral estimators are usually classified as parametric and nonparametric. The latter generally make no assumptions about the statistics of the data other than that it is wide sense stationary or, perhaps, ergodic. The parametric spectral estimators typically use models of the data. In this case the data may be modeled as a moving average process or as an autoregressive (linear prediction) process. The parametric approach to spectral estimation typically results in estimates with a smaller bias and variance for a given data record length than nonparametric methods. There is no one best spectral estimator at this time. One reason for this is that the spectral estimate is data dependent. Therefore, one estimator is good for one type of data, but not for another type of data. If we knew a priori the type of data we are to analyze, then the choice of the type of spectral estimator to be used could be narrowed. However, we usually do not have such knowledge. Consequently, we often use a "bouquet" of spectral estimators and use our experience to make a judgment as to which estimator is the most accurate for the given data.

In Chapter 6 the power spectrum was defined using expectation. We saw that either we could take the expected value of the magnitude squared of the Fourier transform of the data or we could Fourier transform the autocorrelation function determined by expectation. In practical situations we usually have limited knowledge of the data, as well as limited data records. So we need estimates of the autocorrelation function, as defined in the last section.

Perhaps the oldest and most commonly used spectral estimator is the periodogram, which is one of the classical spectral estimators.

Definition 7.17. The **periodogram** is defined as

$$\hat{S}_{XX}(f) = \frac{1}{N} |X_N(f)|^2 = \frac{1}{N} \left| \sum_{n=0}^{N-1} X(n) \, e^{-j2\pi f n} \right|^2 \qquad [7.7.1.1]$$

where $X(n)$ is a random process.

The periodogram is related to the transform of the biased estimate of the autocorrelation function as follows. Suppose we window the data sequence so that

$$X_N(n) = w(n)X(n)$$

where $w(n)$ is the window sequence and is zero for $n < 0$ and $n \geq N$. Then

$$X_N(z) = \sum_{n=-\infty}^{\infty} X_N(n)z^{-n} = \sum_{n=0}^{N-1} w(n) X(n) z^{-n}$$

However, we have

$$\hat{R}_{XX}(k) = \frac{1}{N} \sum_{n=0}^{N-1-|k|} X_N(n + |k|) X_N(n) = \frac{1}{N} [X_N(k) * X_N(-k)]$$

This estimate is zero for $|n| \geq N$ due to the window. The spectral estimate is

$$\hat{S}_{XX}(f) = \sum_{k=-(N-1)}^{N-1} \hat{R}_{XX}(k) z^{-k}|_{z=e^{-j2\pi f}} = \sum_{k=-(N-1)}^{N-1} \left[\frac{1}{N}[X_N(k) * X_N(-k)] \right] z^{-k}|_{z=e^{-j2\pi f}}$$

$$= \frac{1}{N} X_N(z) X_N(z^{-1})|_{z=e^{-j2\pi f}} = \frac{1}{N} |X_N(f)|^2$$

While the periodogram seems to be a reasonable spectral estimator, it has some faults. First, the estimator is biased. If we denote the ensemble average autocorrelation function of the window as $R_{WW}(k)$ and the spectrum of the window as the Fourier transform of this autocorrelation function as $S_{WW}(f)$, then the expected value of the periodogram turns out to be the true spectrum of the data convolved with the power spectrum of the window. Thus, if the window is short, then the bias of the periodogram is large. As the window length in the time domain increases, the bias decreases and approaches the true power spectrum of the data. (See the Problems.) Furthermore, the variance of the periodogram does not decrease as N increases. This is because no averaging of the estimate is done either by using the expectation operator or by time averaging. So the periodogram is not a good spectral estimator, even for long data records. Nevertheless, it is commonly used.

Several proposals have been made to improve the power spectral estimate of the periodogram. One such proposal suggests that the data record be segmented into M independent data records each with L points, as Figure 7.15 shows. These data records can overlap if desired, as shown. The periodogram is then calculated for each segmented data record, and the periodogram for the entire data record is the average of the periodograms for each segment. However, the bias of this spectral estimate is larger than the periodogram for the original data record, although the variance of the estimate is reduced by the factor M over that of the periodogram of a single L point segment. Note that this approach has fewer points in the spectral estimate due to the segmentation of the data. Consequently, the spacing between spectral line components is increased, thereby, decreasing the spectral resolution of the estimate.

Since the variance of the spectral estimate of the segmental averaging approach is reduced, this implies that smoothing the periodogram of the original (unsegmented) data record may give an improved spectral estimate. Thus, another approach is to segment the autocorrelation estimate and average the segmented autocorrelation estimates, as shown in Figure 7.16. This approach yields a smoothed spectral estimate of the peri-

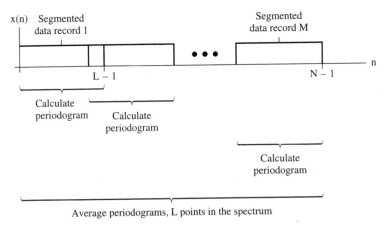

Figure 7.15   Illustration of segmenting the data record to improve the statistical stability of the power spectral estimate

odogram in that the periodogram is convolved with the power spectrum of a triangular window. However, since K is 10 percent of N, and L is less than K, we have even fewer points in the spectral estimate than averaging the periodograms. But we again achieve improved statistical stability (a reduction in the variance of the estimate), but at the cost of reduced spectral resolution.

Appending M zeros to extend the data record from length N to N+M does not result in increased resolution in the spectral estimate. The spectral lines in the transform are closer, thus assisting the interpretation of the spectral envelope. But no new information has been added by appending zeros. This process is basically one of interpolation.

Windowing the data record will reduce the sidelobes of the periodogram. However, this increases the bandwidth of the main lobe, which reduces the spectral resolution of the estimate. A number of data windows are available in the MATLAB Signal Processing Toolbox. Several of the Problems ask you to explore the effects of these windows on power spectral estimation. If the autocorrelation function estimate is windowed before transforming, then the spectral estimate may have negative values. Thus, the transform of the window should be nonnegative.

Another classical spectral estimator is the Blackman–Tukey estimate.

Definition 7.18. The **Blackman–Tukey spectral estimate** is

$$\hat{S}_{XX}(f) = \sum_{k=-M}^{M} w(k)\,\hat{R}_{XX}(k)e^{-j2\pi fk} \qquad [7.7.1.2]$$

where $M \leq N - 1$, and $w(k)$ is a window applied to the autocorrelation estimate, which is zero for $|k| > M$. The value of M is usually restricted so that $M \leq N/10$. The window is usually normalized such that $w(0)=1$ and $0 \leq w(k) \leq 1$ for $k \neq 0$. The windows in MATLAB, as well as others, can be used. Typically the biased autocorrelation estimate is used. The Blackman–Tukey spectral estimate is biased, and for certain conditions is asymptotically consistent, since the variance of the estimate does decrease as N increases.

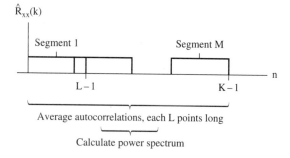

Figure 7.16 Illustration of segmenting the autocorrelation function to improve the statstical stability of the power spectral estimate

Example 7.25

In this example we compare the periodogram and the Blackman–Tukey spectral estimates for a speech data record of the sustained vowel /i/ as in see. The data record is shown in Figure 7.17 along with the spectral estimates. All spectra are plotted on the same dB scale. The frequency axis is scaled such that 0.5 is 5000 Hz. The windowed data contain approximately three pitch periods of data, representing about 25 ms of data sampled at 10 kHz. For the periodogram we calculate the spectrum using a rectangular window and a hamming window applied to the data record. For the Blackman–Tukey spectral estimate we first calculate the biased autocorrelation estimate and then apply the rectangular and hamming windows to the autocorrelation function prior to calculating the power spectrum. The hamming window tends to enhance the peaks and the nulls of the periodogram over that for the rectangular window. The power spectrum of the rectangular-windowed autocorrelation function is similar to that for the corresponding periodogram, as one might expect. The Blackman–Tukey power spectrum with the hamming window is the smoothest of all four, with perhaps the best-defined peaks. We shall return to this example again after we discuss the parametric spectrum methods, at which point you will see that the methods shown here do not provide good estimates of the spectral peaks (formants) around 300, 2200, and 3000 Hz. This example can be done using MATLAB (software in Appendix 7.1 at the end of this chapter), or using the software supplied with this chapter, which is discussed later.

Appendix 3 provides a review of Fourier transforms, Z-transforms, windowing, appending zeros, and related topics.

7.7.2 Parametric Spectral Estimation

The parametric spectral estimation procedures are relatively new, having appeared within the last 30 years. Their attraction is that they obtain good spectral estimates for short data records. The methods tend to be data adaptive in that they adjust themselves to be least disturbed by power at frequencies other than the one being estimated.

One parametric spectral estimator is called the maximum entropy estimator. The idea for this estimator is that instead of appending zeros to increase the length of the estimated autocorrelation function estimate, the estimated autocorrelation function is to be extrapolated (predicted) beyond the data-limited range. The principle used for this extrapolation process is that the spectral estimate must be the most random or have the maximum entropy of any power spectrum that is consistent with the sample values of the calculated autocorrelation function. The objective is to add no information as a result of the prediction process, but yet make an improvement over that obtained by just appending zeros. This spectral estimate is equivalent to linear prediction or autoregression and is the same as the maximum likelihood method for Gaussian data.

Perhaps the simplest way to introduce the parametric spectral estimation procedure is with data models. One way to generate a data model is to excite a filter and measure the filter output. For example, Figure 7.18 shows a filter with both poles and zeros (an autoregressive-moving average, ARMA, model) such that the output is given as

$$X(n) = -\sum_{i=1}^{p} a_i X(n-i) + \sum_{i=0}^{q} b_i E(n-i) \qquad [7.7.2.1]$$

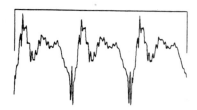

(a) Speech signal with rectangular window.

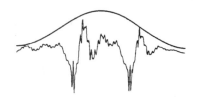

(b) Speech signal with hamming window.

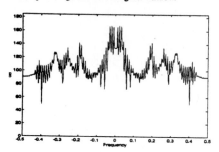

(c) Periodogram of speech signal with rectangular window.

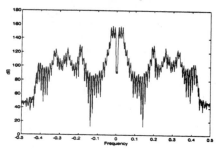

(d) Periodogram of speech signal with hamming window.

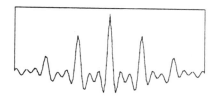

(e) Autocorrelation function with rectangular window.

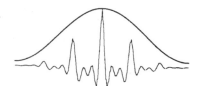

(f) Autocorrelation function with hamming window.

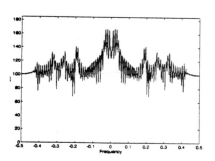

(g) Blackman–Tukey spectrum with rectangular window

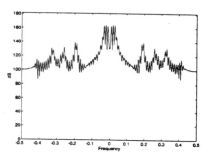

(h) Blackman–Tukey spectrum with hamming window.

Figure 7.17   An example of power spectra for the vowel /i/

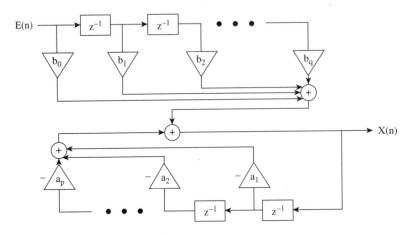

Figure 7.18   An ARMA filter model

which we can also write as

$$X(z) = -\sum_{i=1}^{p} a_i z^{-i} X(z) + \sum_{i=0}^{q} b_i z^{-i} E(z) \qquad [7.7.2.2]$$

Note that we still denote a random process with upper-case notation and a particular member function of the random process with lower-case notation. Thus, [7.7.2.1] denotes the difference equation for an ARMA random process data model.

The minus sign in front of the a_i coefficients in [7.7.2.1] is one convention that is also used in MATLAB. The input $E(n)$ to the filter is the driving function, which is typically white noise, while the output $X(n)$ is the random process to be modeled. This model is called an ARMA(p, q) process. The transfer function for the ARMA filter is

$$H(z) = \frac{X(z)}{E(z)} = \frac{\displaystyle\sum_{i=0}^{q} b_i z^{-i}}{1 + \displaystyle\sum_{i=1}^{p} a_i z^{-i}} = \frac{B(z)}{A(z)} \qquad [7.7.2.3]$$

where $B(z)$ represents the moving average (MA) branch of the filter, while $A(z)$ represents the autoregressive (AR) branch, which is also called the linear prediction (LP) branch. Note that there are q zeros in the MA branch of the filter, and p poles in the AR branch.

Since

$$X(z) = H(z) E(z) \qquad [7.7.2.4]$$

The power spectrum is expressed as

$$S_{XX}(f) = S_{EE}(f) |H(f)|^2 \qquad [7.7.2.5]$$

This is not an estimate, since this last step can be done using ensemble averaging. However, we will soon address the estimation problem.

If all of the $a_i = 0$, except for the unity coefficient in $A(z)$, which is usually called $a_0 = 1$, then we have an all-zero MA model of order q, namely:

$$X(n) = \sum_{i=0}^{q} b_i E(n - i)$$ [7.7.2.6]

which is shown in Figure 7.19.

The MA(q) power spectrum for a white noise excitation with variance $(\sigma_E)^2$ is

$$S_{MA}(f) = S_{XX}(f) = \sigma_E^2 |B(f)|^2$$ [7.7.2.7]

If all the $b_i = 0$ except for $b_0 = 1$, then

$$X(n) = -\sum_{i=1}^{p} a_i X(n - i) + E(n)$$ [7.7.2.8]

which is an all-pole AR(p) process, also called an LP(p) process, shown in Figure 7.20, and the power spectrum is

$$S_{AR}(f) = S_{XX}(f) = \frac{\sigma_E^2}{|A(f)|^2}$$ [7.7.2.9]

The estimation process requires a procedure for estimating the a_i and b_i coefficients, given a data record. Several theorems tell us more about these data models. One theorem is called the Wold decomposition theorem, which says that a wide sense stationary random

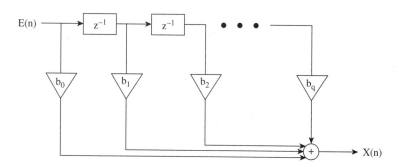

Figure 7.19   An MA(q) filter model

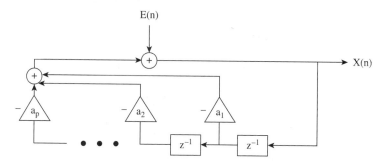

Figure 7.20   An AR(p) filter model

process can be decomposed into a component that is random and one that is deterministic. Another theorem says that any ARMA or AR process can be represented by a unique MA process of infinite order, namely, MA(∞). The third theorem says that any ARMA or MA process can be represented by an AR(∞) process. These theorems tell us that if we should select the wrong model to represent the data, we can still obtain an adequate approximation, although not an optimum approximation, if we use a high enough model order. In practical terms this is unsatisfactory since if we have to improve the model by increasing its order toward infinity, then we also have to consider a larger data set from which to estimate reliably the parameters of the model. And one purpose of data modeling for spectral analysis is to obtain a good spectral estimate with as few model parameters as possible. From a practical viewpoint, therefore, it is not a good idea to think that if the result from a low order model is unsatisfactory in some sense, that the model order can be increased until a good result is obtained. A better idea is to try another data model.

Example 7.26 Consider a first order AR model, such that

$$X(n) = -a_1 X(n-1) + E(n)$$

Then

$$X(z) = -a_1 z^{-1} X(z) + E(z)$$

which can be expressed as

$$X(z) = \frac{E(z)}{1 + a_1 z^{-1}} = z \frac{E(z)}{z + a_1}$$

where $|a_1| < 1$. This process has a simple pole at $z = -a_1$, and depending on the value of a_1, the process will be lowpass or highpass, as shown in Figure 7.21. The process cannot be bandpass unless the process has more than one pole. The power spectrum for a white noise input with variance σ_E^2 is given below and is sketched in Figure 7.21.

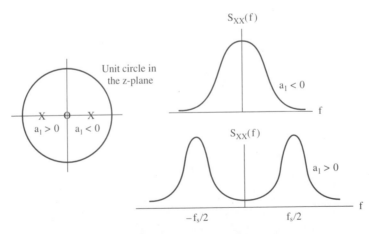

Figure 7.21   The power spectral density of an AR (1) model

$$S_{XX}(f) = \frac{\sigma_E^2}{|1 + a_1 \, e^{-j2\pi f}|^2}$$

7.7.3   LEAST SQUARES ESTIMATION

In this chapter we will use the method of least squares for estimating the AR parameters. We will focus on AR estimation only. In the next chapter we will minimize the mean square error. The method of least squares estimation may be introduced with the following simple situation. We conduct an experiment by measuring specific data values of a function x(n). We wish to design a filter that will estimate the data at time n using one previous data sample at time n − 1, namely:

$$\hat{x}(n) = -\hat{a} \, x(n-1) \qquad \text{[7.7.3.1]}$$

where $\hat{x}(n)$ and x(n) are real discrete sequences, and $\hat{a}$ is a parameter to be estimated. The term $\hat{x}(n)$ is an estimate of the true value x(n). Consequently, we have an error, defined as

$$e(n) = x(n) - \hat{x}(n) = x(n) + \hat{a} \, x(n-1) \qquad \text{[7.7.3.2]}$$

Note that this model is predicting the true value of the data at time n using a weighted value of the data at time n − 1. This model is called linear prediction (LP) or autoregression (AR). The method of least squares says that the constant $\hat{a}$ can be chosen so that we can minimize the sum of the errors over some interval from n = 0 to n = N − 1 (or 1 to N); that is, we minimize the total squared error:

$$\mathscr{E} = \sum_{n=0}^{N-1} e^2(n) = \sum_{n=0}^{N-1} (x(n) - \hat{x}(n))^2 = \sum_{n=0}^{N-1} (x(n) + \hat{a} \, x(n-1))^2 \qquad \text{[7.7.3.3]}$$

The total squared error is sometimes normalized by the number of data points expressed as N. However, this has no effect on the solution, as we show below. The total squared error is often called the prediction error or the prediction error power.

A word about notation is appropriate here. The method of least squares assumes that we are dealing with data and does not use statistics. Consequently, the lowercase notation is used for functions. In Chapter 8 we will consider X(n) to be a random process and solve for the parameter $\hat{a}$, using expectation. The procedure will minimize the mean square error and give the true value (not an estimate) for the parameter $\hat{a}$.

A necessary condition for a relative minimum is that the partial derivative with respect to $\hat{a}$ is zero. Then

$$\frac{\partial \mathscr{E}}{\partial \hat{a}} = 0 = 2 \sum_{n=0}^{N-1} (x(n) + \hat{a} \, x(n-1)) \, x(n-1) \qquad \text{[7.7.3.4]}$$

which gives

$$\hat{a} \sum_{n=0}^{N-1} x(n-1) \, x(n-1) = - \sum_{n=0}^{N-1} x(n) \, x(n-1) \qquad \text{[7.7.3.5]}$$

Note that if there had been a multiplicative factor of $1/N$ in [7.7.3.3], then this would have no effect on the solution to [7.7.3.4]. Equation [7.7.3.5] can be arranged in terms of autocorrelation estimates as follows:

$$\hat{a} = \cfrac{-\cfrac{1}{N}\sum_{n=0}^{N-1} x(n)\,x(n-1)}{\cfrac{1}{N}\sum_{n=0}^{N-1} x(n-1)\,x(n-1)} = -\frac{\hat{R}_{XX}(1)}{\hat{R}_{XX}(0)} \qquad [7.7.3.6]$$

where we will continue to use $\hat{R}_{XX}(k)$ to denote an estimate of the autocorrelation function. Equation [7.7.3.6] gives the least squares estimate for the parameter $\hat{a}$. This estimate gives the best linear prediction of $x(n)$ using only one weighted past data sample. The solution is best in the sense that the total error, namely, the sum of the squared error terms, is minimized.

We shall soon generalize the above results for p $\hat{a}_i$ coefficients. However, first we can observe that [7.7.3.4] provides us with the result that the error is orthogonal to the data in a least squares sense; that is:

$$\sum_{n=0}^{N-1} (x(n) + \hat{a}\,x(n-1))\,x(n-1) = \sum_{n=0}^{N-1} e(n)\,x(n-1) = 0 \qquad [7.7.3.7]$$

This **principle of orthogonality** is illustrated in Figure 7.22.

Next we note that [7.7.3.5] is called the normal equation, which becomes multiple equations when we consider p $\hat{a}_i$ coefficients. The method of least squares makes no assumption about the statistics of the random sequence. However, Gauss proved a theorem, named after him years ago, that says if the errors are uncorrelated with zero mean and the same variance, then the optimum estimate for the coefficient $\hat{a}$ is the value that minimizes the square of the error between the observed data and the true value. The estimate is optimum in the sense that any linear function can be estimated with the minimum mean square error using the estimator.

We now form a more general linear prediction model using p $\hat{a}_i$ coefficients and p past values of the data to predict the value of the data at time n. The data are given and

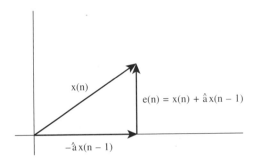

Figure 7.22   The principle of orthogonality. The data is orthogonal to the error.

may or may not be from an AR process. This knowledge is often unknown. Nevertheless, we are modeling the data as if it were an AR data model. Therefore:

$$\hat{x}(n) = -\sum_{k=1}^{p} \hat{a}_k x(n-k)$$

[7.7.3.8]

Then, we have

$$x(n) = -\sum_{k=1}^{p} \hat{a}_k x(n-k) + e(n) = \hat{x}(n) + e(n)$$

[7.7.3.9]

which we illustrate in Figure 7.23.

The z-transform of [7.7.3.9] is

$$X(z) = -\left[\sum_{k=1}^{p} \hat{a}_k z^{-k}\right] X(z) + E(z) = \hat{X}(z) + E(z)$$

[7.7.3.10]

which can be expressed as

$$X(z) = \frac{E(z)}{1 + \left[\sum_{k=1}^{p} \hat{a}_k z^{-k}\right]} = \frac{E(z)}{A(z)}$$

[7.7.3.11]

where

$$A(z) = 1 + \left[\sum_{k=1}^{p} \hat{a}_k z^{-k}\right]$$

[7.7.3.12]

Equation [7.7.3.11] is implemented as a filter in Figure 7.24. This form is often called the forward filter model, since E(z), the input excitation, is filtered by $1/A(z)$ to produce X(z), the LP data.

We can also write [7.7.3.10] in the following form:

$$E(z) = \left[1 + \sum_{k=1}^{p} \hat{a}_k z^{-k}\right] X(z) = A(z) X(z)$$

[7.7.3.13]

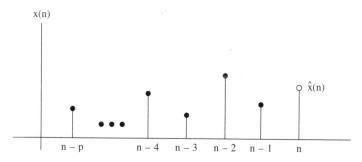

Figure 7.23   Linear prediction model

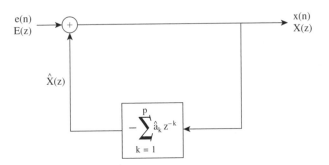

Figure 7.24   The forward filter model

This is the form used in Figure 7.25, where the data $X(z)$ is "inverse" filtered by $A(z)$ to yield the excitation $E(z)$. Consequently, this form is called the inverse filter model.

The method of least squares determines the coefficients $\hat{a}_i$ such that the sum of the errors over some interval is minimized. The interval over which we observe the data is what distinguishes the two methods that are used to solve for the $\hat{a}_i$ coefficients. For the **autocorrelation method** it is assumed that the data are windowed such that the data are zero outside the window. Note that the error is likely to be large at both the beginning and ending of the estimation interval since we are trying to predict the true data using zeros because we have windowed the data. This is why the data window is typically tapered at both ends. This causes the data to gradually increase at the beginning of the data record and similarly gradually decrease at the end, thereby reducing the error for these segments. The total squared error (total prediction error, or total prediction power) over this interval is

$$\mathscr{E} = \sum_{n=0}^{N-1} e^2(n) = \sum_{n=0}^{N-1} (x(n) - \hat{x}(n))^2 = \sum_{n=0}^{N-1} \left(x(n) + \sum_{k=1}^{p} \hat{a}_k\, x(n-k) \right)^2 \quad \textbf{[7.7.3.14]}$$

where $x(n)$ is the windowed data. The minimization is done by

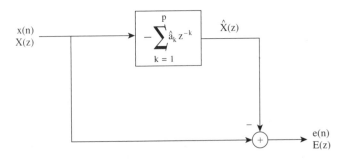

Figure 7.25   The inverse filter model

$$\frac{\partial \mathscr{E}}{\partial \hat{a}_i} = 0 \quad i = 1, 2, \ldots, p$$

which gives

$$\sum_{k=1}^{p} \hat{a}_k \sum_{n=0}^{N-1} x(n-k)\, x(n-i) = -\sum_{n=0}^{N-1} x(n)\, x(n-i) \;\text{ for } i = 1, 2, \ldots, p \qquad \textbf{[7.7.3.15]}$$

Quiz 7.11   Derive [7.7.3.15].

Note that $k = 0, 1, \ldots, p$. When these equations are derived using expectation they are known as the **normal equations,** and are also sometimes referred to as the **Yule–Walker equations** and the **Wiener–Hopf equations**. We will refer to these equations by the same names for the least square case as well. The equations can be expressed in a more compact form using the autocorrelation estimates as follows:

$$\sum_{k=1}^{p} \hat{a}_k \hat{R}_{XX}(i-k) = -\hat{R}_{XX}(i) \quad i = 1, 2, \ldots, p \qquad \textbf{[7.7.3.16]}$$

where

$$\hat{R}_{XX}(k) = \frac{1}{N} \sum_{n=0}^{N-1-|k|} x(n)\, x(n+|k|) \qquad \textbf{[7.7.3.17]}$$

Note that the $1/N$ term is not needed, as we mentioned previously. This is only a scale factor and does not affect the solution of the equations for the $\hat{a}_i$. Equation [7.7.3.16] is a set of p equations with p unknowns and can be solved using matrix techniques as follows:

$$\begin{bmatrix} \hat{R}_{XX}(0) & \hat{R}_{XX}(-1) & \vdots & \hat{R}_{XX}(-(p-1)) \\ \hat{R}_{XX}(1) & \hat{R}_{XX}(0) & \vdots & \hat{R}_{XX}(-(p-2)) \\ \vdots & \vdots & \vdots & \vdots \\ \hat{R}_{XX}(p-1) & \hat{R}_{XX}(p-2) & & \hat{R}_{XX}(0) \end{bmatrix} \begin{bmatrix} \hat{a}_1 \\ \hat{a}_2 \\ \vdots \\ \hat{a}_p \end{bmatrix} = - \begin{bmatrix} \hat{R}_{XX}(1) \\ \hat{R}_{XX}(2) \\ \vdots \\ \hat{R}_{XX}(p) \end{bmatrix} \qquad \textbf{[7.7.3.18]}$$

These equations can be solved by matrix inversion, but this is not as efficient as the Levinson–Durbin algorithm, which solves the equations for the $\hat{a}_i$ in a recursive manner. Algorithms for doing this are available in MATLAB and take advantage of the fact that the autocorrelation matrix is Toeplitz. MATLAB has a function called *lpc* that returns the $\hat{a}_i$ coefficients, given the data. Note that since the autocorrelation function is real and even, then the terms above the main diagonal in the correlation matrix in [7.7.3.18] can be replaced with terms with a positive argument.

The autocorrelation method is guaranteed to give a stable LP filter, namely, one such that the poles of $1/A(z)$ are all within the unit circle in the z-plane. Since we are assuming real data, the $\hat{a}_i$ coefficients are real, implying that the poles of $1/A(z)$ appear in complex conjugate pairs. Thus, for example, if p is even, then we will have an even number of coefficients and an even number of poles, with one-half of the poles being in the upper half of the unit circle in the z-plane and one-half of the poles being in the lower half. Of course, one or more pairs of poles could fall on the real line in the z-plane. If p is odd, then at least one root will be on the real line.

An additional equation is often added to the above equations for the $\hat{a}_i$, namely, the equation for the total squared error (prediction error), which from [7.7.3.13], [7.7.3.15], and [7.7.3.17] is

$$\mathscr{E} = \hat{R}_{XX}(0)\, a_0 + \sum_{k=1}^{p} \hat{a}_k \hat{R}_{XX}(-k) \qquad [7.7.3.19]$$

where $a_0 = 1$. Again, the estimates with negative arguments in [7.7.3.19] can be replaced with the corresponding estimates with positive arguments. This error will vary with the order p. The reason for introducing a_0 is that this is a convenience when the matrix equations are augmented for the additional unknown, $\mathscr{E}$ as follows:

$$\begin{bmatrix} \hat{R}_{XX}(0) & \hat{R}_{XX}(-1) & & \hat{R}_{XX}(-p) \\ \hat{R}_{XX}(1) & \hat{R}_{XX}(0) & \vdots & \hat{R}_{XX}(-(p-1)) \\ \vdots & \vdots & \vdots & \vdots \\ \hat{R}_{XX}(p) & \hat{R}_{XX}(p-1) & & \hat{R}_{XX}(0) \end{bmatrix} \begin{bmatrix} a_0 \\ \hat{a}_1 \\ \hat{a}_2 \\ \vdots \\ \hat{a}_p \end{bmatrix} = \begin{bmatrix} \mathscr{E} \\ 0 \\ \vdots \\ 0 \end{bmatrix} \qquad [7.7.3.20]$$

These equations are also often called the **extended or augmented normal equations**.

Quiz 7.12 Show that [7.7.3.20] is equivalent to [7.7.3.18] plus [7.7.3.19].

The **covariance method** for solving for the coefficients is similar to the autocorrelation method. The major difference is that the covariance method does not assume that the data are windowed, and that while N samples of the data are available, the error is windowed such that $N - p$ samples of the error are available. This affects the calculation of the "autocorrelation" values, since we now have

$$\mathscr{E} = \sum_{n=p}^{N-1} e^2(n) = \sum_{n=p}^{N-1} (x(n) - \hat{x}(n))^2 \qquad [7.7.3.21]$$

$$= \sum_{n=p}^{N-1} \left(x(n) + \sum_{k=1}^{p} \hat{a}_k\, x(n-k) \right)^2$$

The normal equations have the same form, namely:

$$\sum_{k=1}^{p} \hat{a}_k \hat{R}_{XX}(i-k) = -\hat{R}_{XX}(i) \qquad i = 1, 2, \dots, p \qquad [7.7.3.22]$$

However, the autocorrelation estimates are different, so a different notation is used to distinguish the two methods; that is:

$$C_{XX}(i, k) = \frac{1}{N-p} \sum_{n=p}^{N-1} x(n-i)\, x(n-k) \qquad [7.7.3.23]$$

and

$$C_{XX}(i, 0) = \frac{1}{N-p} \sum_{n=p}^{N-1} x(n-i)\, x(n) \qquad [7.7.3.24]$$

where $1 \leq i \leq p$, $0 \leq k \leq p$, the data record is N long. No window is applied to the data because we assume we have sufficient data to calculate the desired correlation values. The matrix equations have the same form, namely:

$$
\begin{bmatrix}
C_{XX}(1,1) & C_{XX}(1,2) & & C_{XX}(1,p) \\
C_{XX}(2,1) & C_{XX}(2,2) & \vdots & C_{XX}(2,p) \\
\vdots & \vdots & \vdots & \vdots \\
C_{XX}(p,1) & C_{XX}(p,2) & & C_{XX}(p,p)
\end{bmatrix}
\begin{bmatrix}
\hat{a}_1 \\ \hat{a}_2 \\ \vdots \\ \hat{a}_p
\end{bmatrix}
= -
\begin{bmatrix}
C_{XX}(1,0) \\ C_{XX}(2,0) \\ \vdots \\ C_{XX}(p,0)
\end{bmatrix}
\qquad \textbf{[7.7.3.25]}
$$

The correlation matrix is no longer Toeplitz, but has the properties of a covariance matrix, from which the name for this method is derived. The solution for this method does not use the Levinson–Durbin algorithm, but instead uses Cholesky decomposition (or other methods), which is also available in MATLAB.

The covariance method may yield estimates of the $\hat{a}_i$ coefficients such that the LP filter $1/A(z)$ does not have all of its poles inside the unit circle; that is, the filter may be unstable.

Return to [7.7.3.20] and note that all of the equations are prediction equations for the autocorrelation function. In particular the last equation can be written as

$$
\hat{R}_{XX}(p) + \hat{a}_1 \hat{R}_{XX}(p-1) + \cdots + \hat{a}_p \hat{R}_{XX}(0) = 0 \qquad \textbf{[7.7.3.26]}
$$

This equation can be considered a prediction equation for $\hat{R}_{XX}(p)$ using the past values of the autocorrelation function and the prediction coefficients. It can be shown that, for lag values greater than p,

$$
\hat{R}_{XX}(k) + \hat{a}_1 \hat{R}_{XX}(k-1) + \cdots + \hat{a}_p \hat{R}_{XX}(k-p) = 0 \qquad \textbf{[7.7.3.27]}
$$

for $k = p + 1, p + 2, \ldots$ Therefore, the linear prediction equations lead to a correlation prediction equation, whereby the correlation function can be extended. This is the basis for the maximum entropy spectral estimator mentioned earlier, which is considered further in the Problems.

7.7.4   POWER SPECTRAL ESTIMATION WITH LINEAR PREDICTION

Linear prediction is a data model. Consequently, it is frequently used to estimate the spectrum of data that are modeled using linear prediction techniques.

Definition 7.19. The **LP power spectral estimate** is the reciprocal of the square of the absolute value of the transform of the LP coefficients, namely:

$$
\hat{S}_{XX}(f) = \frac{1}{|A(z)|^2} = \frac{1}{\left| 1 + \displaystyle\sum_{i=1}^{p} \hat{a}_i z^{-i} \right|^2} \qquad \text{for } z = e^{j2\pi f} \qquad \textbf{[7.7.4.1]}
$$

where the $\hat{a}_i$ coefficients are the estimates obtained using the least squares method, above, and the number of coefficients p is the same as the number of poles of $1/A(z)$. Since $A(z)$ is a polynomial in z, the roots of this polynomial are the zeros of $A(z)$, which in turn are the poles of $1/A(z)$.

Why is [7.7.4.1] considered a good spectral estimate? We explain this as follows. The error can be expressed as

$$E(z) = A(z) X(z)$$

[7.7.4.2]

where the $A(z)$ in this equation represents the z-transform of the estimated coefficients. Then

$$|E(z)|^2 = |A(z)|^2 |X(z)|^2$$

[7.7.4.3]

and the true power spectrum is

$$S_{XX}(f) = |X(z)|^2 \quad \text{for } z = e^{j2\pi f}$$

[7.7.4.4]

The total squared error can be expressed as

$$\mathcal{E} = \frac{T}{2\pi} \int_{-\pi/T}^{\pi/T} |E(e^{j2\pi f})|^2 d\omega = \frac{T}{2\pi} \int_{-\pi/T}^{\pi/T} \frac{S_{XX}(f)}{\hat{S}_{XX}(f)} d\omega$$

[7.7.4.5]

where T is the sampling interval or $1/T$ is f_s, the sampling frequency. Now note that minimizing the error is equivalent to minimizing the integral of the ratio of the true power spectrum to the estimate. This ratio is positive. Both global and local errors are minimized by minimizing the integral. A local error may be thought of as an error at a particular frequency. Globally, the total error is determined by how well the true spectrum and the estimated spectrum match over the entire frequency range, regardless of the shape of the spectrum. Local errors are a measure of the difference between these two spectra at a given frequency. If the true spectrum is greater than the estimate (model), then the total error is larger than if the opposite is true.

Thus, after minimizing $\mathcal{E}$, we would expect the estimate to match the true spectrum better in those regions where the true spectrum is greater than the estimate. Consequently, the estimate, or model spectrum, should follow the true spectrum in the vicinity of the peaks, or local maxima. However, this is not necessarily the case in regions where minima (notches) occur, since the local error is already small and the emphasis is on reducing the largest errors. Thus, the estimate should be a good estimate of the spectral envelope of the true spectrum. Since it is usually the peaks in the spectrum that we want to estimate, the LP estimate is often used.

One problem with the LP method is the estimation of p, the number of coefficients to be used in the model. While there are criteria for this, it is still debated which is the best. One such criterion is the Akaike information criterion (AIC), which is defined as $AIC(p) = (N)\ln(\mathcal{E}) + 2p$, where p is the model order, N is the number of data points available, ln is the natural log, $\mathcal{E}$ is the total squared error for the pth order model given in [7.7.3.19]. The value of AIC can be plotted versus p to determine the best model order. A trial-and-error procedure is also often used, whereby the choice of p is determined by the value that gives the smallest error for reasonable variations in p. This is done by varying p and calculating the error for each value of p. Then we select the value of p that gives the least error. Another problem with the LP method is that it does

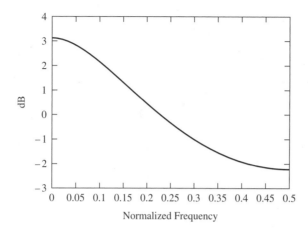

Figure 7.27   The spectrum for Example 7.28

the spectral plot for Example 6.33 appears to be bandpass, the peak in the spectrum in Figure 6.20 occurs at $f_s/2$, which is similar to Figure 7.21.

This example uses the function *lpc* in MATLAB to determine the power spectral estimate of the data shown in Figure 7.28, where the spectrum is also plotted. This algorithm uses the estimate for the biased autocorrelation function calculated using the data. The same results are obtained if one calculates the autocorrelation function, then calculates the LP coefficients, and then calculates the spectrum. So this MATLAB function is quite convenient to use. The reader is encouraged to examine this function carefully.

Example 7.29

7.8   THE SPECTROGRAM

The spectrogram provides a time history of the spectrum as shown in Figure 7.29 for the sentence "We were away a year ago" as spoken by a male. The amplitude of the spectrum is plotted in relative terms as variations in the gray level. This time history provides a time-frequency picture of the variations of the spectral resonances. Thus, we can view changes in the bandwidths of the resonances and changes in the resonances themselves as the spoken words change. Present-day procedures for calculating the spectrogram use FFT techniques. The power spectrum is estimated from a segment of data. The amplitude of the spectrum is quantized and mapped to an assigned gray level. The data segment is updated and the process repeated. The spectral estimates are then plotted versus time, as shown in Figure 7.29.

   The historical reason for this type of display is that some years ago, before digital techniques, the spectra and spectrogram were estimated using analog filters. For

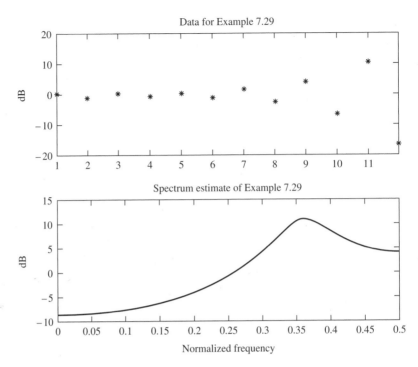

Figure 7.28   Results of *lpc* in MATLAB for the data shown

example, the spectrogram was estimated by repeatedly passing a tape recording of the signal through a bandpass filter, whose center frequency was shifted after each pass of the data. The tape recording of the data was made into a loop, which could be played over and over. The sweep of the bandpass filter was synchronized with the tape loop. The energy of the filter output for each pass of the tape loop controlled the heat of a stylus, which in turn burned a special paper. The more energy at the filter output, the darker the burn on the paper, thereby creating a gray level display of the energy of the signal in the filter band at that particular center frequency. The filter center frequency then shifted up in frequency and the taped data started a new loop. Figure 7.30 illustrates this process. It took approximately five minutes or so to plot the spectrogram of a one- or two-second record of speech. But this display has proven to be useful to speech researchers and is the reason it is still used today with digital techniques.

7.9   RANDOM NUMBER GENERATION

Often it is inconvenient, or costly, or impractical to perform a random experiment. Computer simulation of an experiment is usually more convenient, less costly, and

We were away a year ago

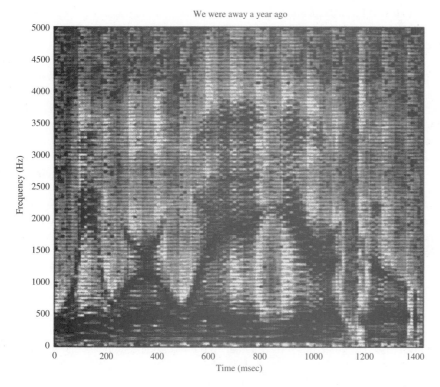

Figure 7.29   Spectrogram of the sentence "We were away a year ago"

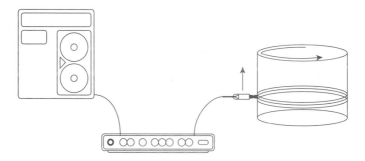

Figure 7.30   Illustration of analog spectrogram

quite practical. Computer simulation of random experiments often becomes a matter of generating a sequence of random numbers, such as a random sequence of zeros and ones to simulate the outcomes of successive flips of a coin. Other computer simulations may call for the generation of a sequence of random numbers that fall in the interval $[0, 1]$. Then by using a transformation of random variables, one can transform a uniform probability density function to a normal or other probability density function.

An illustration of a simple experiment is to estimate the area within the boundary of an irregularly shaped curve, as in Figure 7.31. One nonstatistical approach is to subdivide the rectangle enclosing the irregular curve into a grid and estimate the area by counting the number of squares within the irregular curve. Another approach is to select coordinates within the rectangle from a table of random numbers (or a random number generator) and note how these coordinates scatter within the rectangle. We then count those coordinates that fall within the irregular figure. The ratio of the points within the figure to the total number of points within the rectangle is an estimate of the ratio of the area of the figure to the area of the rectangle.

This procedure is referred to as the Monte Carlo Method and has a long history, since 1773 when it was used by the Frenchman Buffon to estimate π. The method became popular during World War II when mathematicians Ulam and von Neuman applied it to study neutron diffusion problems.

Numerous physical methods have been devised to generate random numbers. However, our interest is directed toward numerical procedures. These techniques typically use a recursive relationship that involves integers where each new number is generated from the previous one. The problem is to ensure that the numbers generated from the finite population of integers available are random in some sense. The recursion relationship must also be initiated in some manner. What if a number appears that has already been generated? Since the numbers are being generated by a recursion relationship, such an occurrence will cause the cycle to be repeated, that is, the sequence is generated again and again in an endless loop. The length of the generated sequence is called the period of the random number generator. The length of the period must usually be traded off against the computational complexity. Any sequence generated in this manner is deterministic, but we require that it satisfy certain statistical tests for randomness. Sequences of this sort are known as **pseudorandom sequences** since they are in fact deterministic, but do satisfy some randomness criteria.

Figure 7.31   Measuring area using a random
number generation approach

In the Fall 1995 *MATLAB News & Notes*, Cleve Moler, the president of Math Works Inc. wrote a short column about random numbers. He pointed out that in 1951 Berkeley Professor D. H. Lehmer defined randomness as the following:

> A random sequence is a vague notion . . . in which each term is unpredictable to the uninitiated and whose digits pass a certain number of tests traditional with statisticians.

Definition 7.20. One procedure for generating random numbers is the **mid-square method** where each new number generated is derived from the middle of n digits of the square of the previous n-digit number.

Consider the initial (seed) number to be $X_0 = 1782$. Then | **Example 7.30**

$$(x_0)^2 = 03175524 \rightarrow x_1 = 1755$$

$$(x_1)^2 = 03080025 \rightarrow x_2 = 0800$$

$$(x_3)^2 = 00640000 \rightarrow x_3 = 6400$$

$$\bullet \quad x_4 = 9600$$

$$\bullet \quad x_5 = 1600$$

$$\bullet \quad x_6 = 5600$$

$$x_7 = 3600$$

$$x_8 = 9600$$

$$x_9 = 1600$$

$$\bullet$$

$$\bullet$$

$$\bullet$$

An endless repetition is obtained and the period of the method with the seed value $x_0 = 1782$ is $N = 4$.

Even when the period is not as short as that in the above example, at some point in the sequence a previous number is generated and the sequence loops with a period usually considerably smaller than the largest machine integer. If a number ending with zeros is obtained, as above, the maximum period possible is very small. In fact, if any number in the sequence ends with 00, as above, the period cannot be greater than 99.

Quiz 7.13

Why is the last statement true?

Definition 7.21. The methods used today involve congruence and are of the form

$$x_{n+1} = ax_n + b \pmod{m} \qquad\qquad \text{[7.9.1]}$$

where $0 \le x_n \le m$. If $b = 0$, the method is known as the **multiplicative congruential method,** while if $b \neq 0$ it is called the **mixed congruential method**. Incidentally, Moler pointed out that Professor Lehmer was the inventor of these methods.

These methods are simple, can be computed rapidly, and can be analyzed theoretically.

Example 7.31   Consider [7.9.1] with $a = 5$ and $b = 2$ and $m = 13$ with the seed value $x_0 = 1$. Then

$$x_1 = (5)(1) + 2 \pmod{13} = 7$$

$$x_2 = (5)(7) + 2 \pmod{13} = 11$$

$$x_3 = (5)(11) + 2 \pmod{13} = 5$$

.

.

.

Note that the period cannot be greater than m. Therefore, m is usually selected to be one integer larger than the largest machine integer available.

Frequently, we desire the sequences generated to be bounded by zero and unity and to be uniformly distributed over this interval. This boundary requirement is easily accomplished by shifting the decimal point or scaling x_n. The constants a and b are selected to provide speed and good statistical properties. A summary of properties for programming [7.9.1] is presented below.

For the multiplicative congruential method, $b = 0$. For $m = 2^c$ ($c > 2$) the maximum period is $m/4$ and is achieved with x_0 odd and

$$a = 8s \pm 3 \text{ with } s = 1, 2, 3, \dots \qquad\qquad \text{[7.9.2]}$$

For $m = 10^d$ ($d > 3$) the maximum period is $m/20$. This is achieved with x_0 not divisible by 2 or 5 and with

$$a = 200s \pm r \text{ with } s = 1, 2, 3, \dots \text{ and} \qquad\qquad \text{[7.9.3]}$$

$$r = 3, 11, 13, 19, 21, 27, 29, 37, 53, 59, 61, 67, 69, 77, 83, \text{ or } 91$$

For the mixed congruential method $b \neq 0$. For $m = 2^c$ ($c > 2$) the maximum period is m and is achieved with any value for x_0 and with

$$a = 4s + 1 \text{ with } s = 1, 2, 3, \ldots \text{ and b odd} \qquad \textbf{[7.9.4]}$$

For $m = 10^d$ the maximum period is m and is achieved with any value for x_0 and b not divisible by 2 or 5 and

$$a = 20s + 1 \text{ with } s = 1, 2, 3, \ldots \qquad \textbf{[7.9.5]}$$

For good statistical behavior it is recommended that a be a value close to m. However, this does not always guarantee the desired performance, for it is possible for a sequence of numbers to pass a given set of tests for randomness yet still be unsatisfactory for a particular application.

Example 7.32

The repetition of patterns and the periodic nature of random number generators are illuminated by plotting the numbers as pairs in two dimensions. The multiplicative method $x_{n+1} = 11x_n$ (mod 64) with $x_0 = 1$, namely, $a = 11$ and $b = 0$, gives the sequence $\{x_n\} = 1, 11, 57, 51, 49, 27, 41, 3, 33, 43, 25, 19, 17, 59, 9, 35, 1, \ldots$

If the elements of the sequence are coupled in pairs as $(1, 11), (57, 51), \ldots$, then only eight pairs are obtained, which are plotted in Figure 7.32, where it can be seen that there is a linear relationship between the various pairs. The period is $m/4 = 64/4 = 16 = 2^4$.

Quiz 7.14   Repeat the above example with $x_0 = 11$ and plot the pairs. Is the relationship linear? Are the pairs of points related to the pairs of points in the last example?

We concluded that there are only a limited number of values that may be generated by this random number generator. However, even if the period is greatly increased, then linear patterns usually still exit.

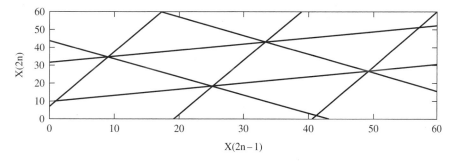

Figure 7.32   Linear relation between pairs of random numbers

Example 7.33 | For the multiplicative method let $m = 2^{17}$, so that the period is 2^{15}. Let $a = 11$ and $x_0 = 1$. In Figure 7.33 we plot x_n versus n instead of x_{2n} versus x_{2n-1} so that we might see another representation of the data. Here there are no distinct linear patterns, and the numbers appear to be uncorrelated. This is not always the case, however.

The procedures discussed above provide uniformly distributed random numbers over an interval. Frequently, Gaussianly distributed numbers are required. This distribution can be achieved in a two step procedure:

•   Compute r_n, where

$$r_n = \sqrt{2\sigma^2 \ln\left(\frac{1}{x_n}\right)} \qquad [7.9.6]$$

where x_n is the uniformly distributed random number over $[0, 1]$, ln is the natural logarithm, and σ is the desired variance for r_n. Then r_n has a Rayleigh distribution:

$$p_R(r) = \frac{r}{\sigma^2} e^{-\frac{r^2}{2\sigma^2}} \qquad [7.9.7]$$

•   Next, compute a pair of Gaussian random numbers, g_n and g_{n+1} with probability density

$$p_G(g) = \frac{1}{\sqrt{2\pi}\sigma} e^{-\frac{g^2}{2\sigma^2}} \qquad [7.9.8]$$

where

$$g_n = r_n \cos(2\pi x_{n+1}) \qquad [7.9.9a]$$

$$g_{n+1} = r_n \sin(2\pi x_{n+1}) \qquad [7.9.9b]$$

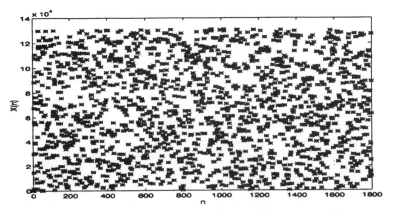

Figure 7.33   Relation between a random number and its sequence value

where the two numbers g_n and g_{n+1} are statistically independent. This technique produces Gaussianly distributed numbers from a uniform distribution.

MATLAB has two routines, *rand* and *randn*, for generating uniformly distributed and Gaussianly distributed random numbers, respectively, in a manner similar to that discussed here. The uniform random number generator, *rand*, is a multiplicative congruential generator with parameters $a = 7^5 = 16,807$, $b = 0$, and $m = 2^{31} - 1 = 2,147,483,647$.

The output of a random number generator typically has a frequency distribution that is approximately uniform over the frequency band, that is, is an approximation to white noise. We may bandlimit and spectral shape (or color, i.e., make nonwhite) the random number noise by digital filtering, such as with a lowpass, bandpass, or highpass filter. This is explored in the Problems.

We point out that according to Cleve Moler, future versions of MATLAB, starting with version 5, will use a new random number generator recommended by Professor George Marshall, of Florida State University. This new generator is not a multiplicative congruential method. There are no multiplications or divisions in the algorithm. It is designed to produce floating-point values. According to Moler there is no single seed value. Rather, the new generator has 35 words of internal memory or state. Thirty-two of these words form a cache of floating-point numbers z, between 0 and 1. The remaining three words contain an integer index i, which varies between 1 and 32, and single random integer j, and a "borrow" flag b. This entire state vector is built up a bit at a time during an initialization phase. Different initial states can be triggered by specifying different values of j. Additional details about the algorithm can be found in Moler's 1995 article. According to Moler, the algorithm is fast, producing a million random numbers per second on a 75 MHz Pentium laptop computer. The period is about 2^{1492}, which means that at 1 million numbers per second, it will take more than 10^{435} years before the generator repeats itself. The present multiplicative congruential generator used by MATLAB using the same laptop computer can exhaust the period in less than four hours, which is about 2 billion random numbers.

7.10   GENERATING CORRELATED SEQUENCES OF RANDOM VARIABLES

Suppose we have a random sequence X(n) of zero mean, unit variance, uncorrelated random variables. Express the sequence X(n) as a vector $\vec{X}$. In this section we will examine a method for generating a zero mean vector $\vec{Y}$ with a specified covariance matrix $\text{Cov}_{\vec{Y}\vec{Y}}$, where a valid covariance matrix is a real valued, symmetric matrix with non-negative eigenvalues. Suppose we let

$$\vec{Y} = [T]\,\vec{X} \qquad\qquad \textbf{[7.10.1]}$$

where $[T]$ is an $N \times N$ transformation matrix. The kth element of $\vec{Y}$ is

$$Y_k = \sum_{j=1}^{N} t_{kj}\, X_j \qquad\qquad \textbf{[7.10.2]}$$

where t_{kj} is the element in the kth row and jth column of $[T]$.

The expected value of $\vec{Y}$ is zero, since the elements of $\vec{X}$ are zero mean. The co-variance of the elements of $\vec{Y}$ are

$$E[Y_k\,Y_j] = E\left[\sum_{i=1}^{N} t_{ki}X_i \sum_{m=1}^{N} t_{jm}X_m\right] = \sum_{i=1}^{N}\sum_{m=1}^{N} t_{ki}t_{jm} E[X_i\,X_m] \qquad [7.10.3]$$

However, the X_i are zero mean, uncorrelated, and unit variance. Thus, $E[X_i\,X_m] = 1$ if $i = m$ and $E[X_i\,X_m] = 0$ otherwise. Therefore, we have

$$E[Y_k\,Y_j] = \sum_{i=1}^{N} t_{ki}t_{ji} \qquad [7.10.4]$$

This says that the kj element of the covariance matrix of $\vec{Y}$ is the dot product of the kth row of matrix [T] with the jth column of matrix [T]^T, which is the transpose of matrix [T]. Thus, the covariance matrix of $\vec{Y}$ is

$$\text{Cov}_{\vec{Y}\vec{Y}} = [T][T]^T \qquad [7.10.5]$$

In a typical situation we specify the covariance matrix and seek to determine the transformation matrix [T]. This can be done using the relation

$$\text{Cov}_{\vec{Y}\vec{Y}} = [P][D][P]^T \qquad [7.10.6]$$

where [D] is a diagonal matrix consisting of the eigenvalues of

$$\text{Cov}_{\vec{Y}\vec{Y}}$$

and [P] is a matrix with columns consisting of an orthonormal set of eigenvectors of

$$\text{Cov}_{\vec{Y}\vec{Y}}.$$

Then

$$[T] = [P][D]^{\frac{1}{2}} \qquad [7.10.7]$$

where $[D]^{1/2}$ is the diagonal matrix consisting of the square root of the elements of [D]. These matrix manipulations can be done using MATLAB.

Example 7.34

Let $\vec{X}$ contain two random variables as elements, each with zero mean, unit variance, and uncorrelated. Find [T] such that

$$\text{Cov}_{\vec{Y}\vec{Y}} = \begin{bmatrix} 1.0 & 0.3 \\ 0.3 & 1.0 \end{bmatrix}$$

Using MATLAB we find the eigenvalues and eigenvectors of $\text{Cov}_{\vec{Y}\vec{Y}}$ such that

$$[P] = \frac{1}{\sqrt{2}}\begin{bmatrix} 1 & 1 \\ -1 & 1 \end{bmatrix} \quad [D]^{\frac{1}{2}} = \begin{bmatrix} \sqrt{0.7} & 0 \\ 0 & \sqrt{1.3} \end{bmatrix}$$

$$[T] = \frac{1}{\sqrt{2}} \begin{bmatrix} \sqrt{0.7} & \sqrt{1.3} \\ -\sqrt{0.7} & \sqrt{1.3} \end{bmatrix}$$

Quiz 7.15   Verify that

$$\text{Cov}_{\vec{Y}\vec{Y}} = [T][T]^T$$

Note that the matrix $\text{Cov}_{\vec{Y}\vec{Y}}$ can be scaled to the desired variance.

7.11   ORTHOGONAL SERIES EXPANSIONS

If we have a periodic random process over an interval $-T/2$ to $T/2$, then it can be shown that the Fourier coefficients of a Fourier series expansion of the random process are uncorrelated. Furthermore, the Fourier series expansion of a periodic random process, $X_N(t)$, where N is the number of Fourier series coefficients, converges in the mean square to the random process, $X(t)$; that is:

$$\lim_{N \to \infty} E[|X(t) - X_N(t)|^2] = 0 \qquad \textbf{[7.11.1]}$$

For nonperiodic random processes a Fourier series expansion cannot, strictly speaking, be applied. However, we can assume that the nonperiodic random process is periodic with period T that goes to infinity.

For a general, nonperiodic random process these two properties (uncorrelated coefficients and convergence) may not hold. However, we can develop an orthogonal expansion over an arbitrary interval $T_1 \le t \le T_2$, which for convenience we express as $-T/2 \le t \le T/2$. We assume that such an expansion can be expressed for $-T/2 \le t \le T/2$ as

$$X(t) = \sum_{i=1}^{\infty} X_i \, \phi_i(t) \qquad \textbf{[7.11.2]}$$

where the $\phi_i(t)$ are a set of orthonormal basis functions such that

$$\int_{-T/2}^{T/2} \phi_i(t) \, \phi_j(t) \, dt = \delta_{ij} \qquad \textbf{[7.11.3]}$$

where δ_{ij} is zero for $i \ne j$ and is one for $i = j$.

The objective of this expansion is to determine the functions $\phi_i(t)$, such that the X_i random variables are uncorrelated, namely,

$$E[X_i X_j] = \lambda_i \, \delta_{ij} \qquad \textbf{[7.11.4]}$$

where

$$E[X_i^2] = \lambda_i \qquad \textbf{[7.11.5]}$$

We also have from [7.11.2] and [7.11.3] that

$$X_i = \int_{-T/2}^{T/2} X(t) \, \phi_i(t) \, dt \qquad \textbf{[7.11.6]}$$

Then

$$E[X_i X_j] = \int_{-T/2}^{T/2} \int_{-T/2}^{T/2} E[X(t) X(s)] \phi_i(t) \phi_j(s) \, dt \, ds$$

$$= \int_{-T/2}^{T/2} \int_{-T/2}^{T/2} R_{XX}(t-s) \phi_i(t) \phi_j(s) \, dt \, ds \qquad [7.11.7]$$

If we assume that the $\phi_i(t)$ are solutions to the integral equation

$$\lambda_i \phi_i(t) = \int_{-T/2}^{T/2} R_{XX}(t-s) \phi_i(s) \, ds \qquad [7.11.8]$$

then the solution is the set of functions $\phi_i(t)$, which are called the eigenfunctions, and the set of values λ_i are called the eigenvalues. In this integral equation the autocorrelation function $R_{XX}(t-s)$ is assumed known.

We can verify that [7.11.8] is the solution by substituting it into [7.11.7]; then

$$E[X_i X_j] = \lambda_i \int_{-T/2}^{T/2} \phi_i(t) \phi_j(t) \, dt = \lambda_i \delta_{ij} \qquad [7.11.9]$$

This shows that the X_i are uncorrelated if the orthogonal functions are the solutions to the integral equation. Furthermore, it can be shown that expansion [7.11.2] converges in the mean square to the random process X(t). This expansion is called the **Karhunen–Loeve** expansion and is used in decision theory, image processing and coding, detection theory, and pattern recognition. The idea is similar to that for linear prediction, in that the coefficients can be used as an efficient coding of the data since they are uncorrelated.

Example 7.35

For white noise the autocorrelation function is

$$R_{XX}(\tau) = \sigma_X^2 \delta(\tau)$$

or

$$R_{XX}(t_2 - t_1) = \sigma_X^2 \delta(t_2 - t_1)$$

Then the $\phi_i(t)$ satisfy

$$\lambda_i \phi_i(t_1) = \sigma_X^2 \int_{-T/2}^{T/2} \delta(t_2 - t_1) \phi_i(t_2) \, dt_2$$

or

$$\lambda_i \phi_i(t_1) = \sigma_X^2 \phi_i(t_1)$$

or

$$\lambda_i = \sigma_X^2$$

This says that the $\phi_i(t)$ functions can be any complete set with the eigenvalues equal to the variance.

It is generally difficult to solve the integral equation analytically for $\phi_i(t)$, given the autocorrelation function. Consequently, numerical techniques are often used. In this case an approximation is usually made, in that the series expansion for $X(t)$ is a finite series and is, therefore, an approximation or an estimate.

The development for discrete random sequences is similar to that given above. Equation [7.11.2] becomes a finite summation, since the data sequence is assumed to be finite from 1 to N. We expand the data sequence in a set of N orthonormal basis functions as

$$X(n) = \sum_{i=1}^{N} X_i\, \phi_i(n) \qquad [7.11.10]$$

where $i = 1, 2, \ldots, N$ and the $\phi_i(n)$ are a set of orthonormal functions such that

$$\sum_{n=1}^{N} \phi_i(n)\, \phi_j(n) = \delta_{ij} \qquad [7.11.11]$$

and

$$E[X_i\, X_j] = \lambda_i\, \delta_{ij} \qquad [7.11.12]$$

where

$$E[X_i^2] = \lambda_i \qquad [7.11.13]$$

We also have

$$X_i = \sum_{n=1}^{N} X(n)\, \phi_i(n) \qquad [7.11.14]$$

Then

$$E[X_i\, X_j] = \sum_{n=1}^{N} \sum_{k=1}^{N} E[X(n)\, X(k)]\, \phi_i(n)\, \phi_j(k) \qquad [7.11.15]$$

$$= \sum_{n=1}^{N} \sum_{k=1}^{N} R_{XX}(n-k)\, \phi_i(n)\, \phi_j(k)$$

If we assume that the $\phi_i(n)$ are solutions to the equation

$$\lambda_i\, \phi_i(n) = \sum_{k=1}^{N} R_{XX}(n-k)\, \phi_i(k) \qquad [7.11.16]$$

where $i = 1, 2, \ldots, N$, then similar to that above the solution is the set of functions $\phi_i(n)$, which are called the eigenfunctions and the set of values λ_i are called the eigenvalues. As before, the autocorrelation function $R_{XX}(n-k)$ is assumed known.

We can verify that [7.11.16] is the solution by substituting it into [7.11.15], then

$$E[X_i\, X_j] = \lambda_i \sum_{n=1}^{N} \phi_i(n)\, \phi_j(n) = \lambda_i \delta_{ij} \qquad [7.11.17]$$

This shows that the X_i are uncorrelated if the orthogonal functions are the solutions to [7.11.16], which is analogous to the integral equation [7.11.8].

Sometimes we may want to approximate the N orthonormal basis functions with a smaller subset of basis functions. In this case we would have

$$\hat{X}(n) = \sum_{i=1}^{L} X_i\, \phi_i(n) \qquad [7.11.18]$$

where $L < N$. Then in a manner analogous to linear prediction define an error such that

$$\mathcal{E} = \sum_{n=1}^{N} E^2(n) = \sum_{n=1}^{N} (X(n) - \hat{X}(n))^2 \qquad [7.11.19]$$

The error is the number of terms from $L+1$ to N; that is:

$$X(n) = \hat{X}(n) + E(n) = \sum_{i=1}^{L} X_i\, \phi_i(n) + \sum_{i=L+1}^{N} X_i\, \phi_i(n) \qquad [7.11.20]$$

The solution of [7.11.20] tells us that in order to minimize the error, we must select a special subset of the basis functions for the truncated expansion $\hat{X}(n)$. The basis functions to be selected are those that correspond to the eigenvectors with the largest eigenvalues of the autocorrelation matrix of the data. The error is the sum of the remaining eigenvalues, that is, the sum of the eigenvalues of the eigenvectors that are omitted.

In summary, the procedure is to estimate the autocorrelation matrix, find the eigenvalues and eigenvectors for the autocorrelation matrix, and then use all or some of the eigenvectors and corresponding eigenvalues to form an approximate Karhunen–Loeve expansion for the data. The procedure is to rank order the eigenvectors according to the values of the eigenvalues. The order is decreasing from the largest to the smallest. These eigenvectors become the $\phi_i(n)$, $i = 1, 2, \ldots$, with corresponding λ_i. For example, assume that the data is sufficient to allow the computation of three eigenvectors, and that the corresponding eigenvalues are $1, 0.4$, and 0.1. Now if we want to use only one eigenvector as an approximate expansion for the random process, we would select the eigenvector with the largest eigenvalue. The minimum mean square error for this case is the sum of the other two eigenvalues, in this case $0.4 + 0.1 = 0.5$. If we use two eigenvectors, then we would select those corresponding to the eigenvalues of 1 and 0.4, and the minimum mean square error is 0.1, and so on.

Example 7.36 | Suppose a random process has the following correlation matrix

$$\begin{bmatrix} 1.0 & 0.3 & 0.09 \\ 0.3 & 1.0 & 0.3 \\ 0.09 & 0.3 & 1.0 \end{bmatrix}$$

The eigenvalues of this matrix rank ordered from largest to smallest are

$$\begin{bmatrix} \lambda_1 & 0 & 0 \\ 0 & \lambda_2 & 0 \\ 0 & 0 & \lambda_3 \end{bmatrix} = \begin{bmatrix} 1.4716 & 0 & 0 \\ 0 & 0.9100 & 0 \\ 0 & 0 & 0.6184 \end{bmatrix}$$

and the corresponding eigenvectors are

$$[\vec{\phi}_1 \quad \vec{\phi}_2 \quad \vec{\phi}_3] = \begin{bmatrix} 0.5257 & -0.7071 & 0.4729 \\ 0.6688 & 0.0000 & -0.7435 \\ 0.5257 & 0.7071 & 0.4729 \end{bmatrix}$$

The eigenvectors are columns in the above matrix. Note that the eigenvector and eigenvalue functions in MATLAB return the values in the opposite order to that shown above; that is, the largest eigenvalue is at the lower right instead of the upper left, and the eigenvectors are correspondingly reversed.

Now suppose we want a Karhunen–Loeve expansion of the random process, where we have two samples of the random process available; namely, we seek to approximate X(t) with

$$\hat{X}(n) = X_1\,\phi_1(n) + X_2\,\phi_2(n)$$

then we would select $\phi_i(t)$, $i = 1, 2$, and the corresponding mean square error is 0.6184. Note that the values for X_1 and X_2 are determined using [7.11.14].

Quiz 7.16   If we wish to use only one eigenvector as an approximate expansion for the random process in the last example, which one should be selected? What is the mean square error for this approximation?

One of the Problems asks you to consider how the Karhunen–Loeve expansion is related to the method for generating correlated sequences of random variables.

7.12   MATLAB SOFTWARE

The software to be used for this chapter is the same as that provided for Chapter 6. Figure 7.34 shows the various menus, some of which were described in Chapter 6. The *time domain analysis* window has an option to calculate the energy and zero crossing rate for a data file. The *property* option for the *time analysis* menu lets the user change the analysis frame size and allows the user to select the option to overlap the frames if desired. Also included in the *time domain analysis* menu is an option to calculate the autocorrelation function using the biased estimator. Note that in the *property* window there is an option to allow an overlap of the successive data segments as the algorithm "slides" across the data record. This option can be set to zero overlap if desired, by moving the cursor to the number and typing in 0.

The *frequency domain analysis* window has options for LP, MA, and ARMA analysis, as well as the *spectra* option, discussed in Chapter 6. The *autocorrelation* option in the *linear prediction analysis* window calls the *lpc* function in MATLAB. The covariance method also uses MATLAB functions. The *property* option allows the user to specify the number of poles for the LP analysis.

Consider the following example using the software to calculate the LP spectrum of the vowel segment contained in the data file a.mat. As described in Chapter 6, we start the software, select *file*, select *load MATLAB*, select the data file a.mat, select *analysis* in the main menu window, select *frequency analysis*, select *LP analysis*, select *property* in the *linear prediction analysis* window. The *property* window shows that the default parameters are 512 for frame length, the number of poles is 14, and the data window is rectangular. You may change any or all of these selections, as described in Chapter 6. The *"between"* marks function is described in Chapter 6 as well. Suppose we leave the

334

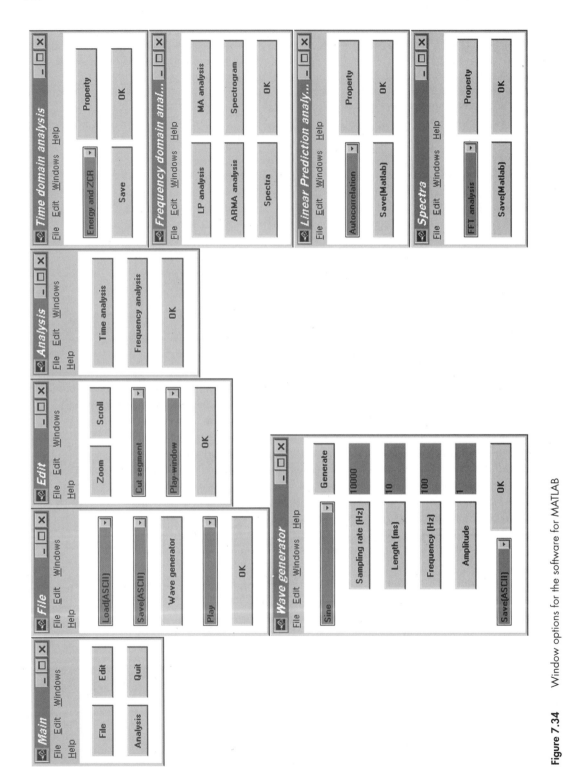

Figure 7.34 Window options for the software for MATLAB

settings as they are and click *ok*. The window will close. Now return to the *linear prediction analysis* window and select the *autocorrelation* button. A new window will open entitled *AR analysis (autocorrelation method)*. This window will display the FFT spectrum of the data file, a.mat. Superimposed on this FFT plot is a solid line representing the LP (or AR) spectrum for this data. To the right of the spectral plots is a pole-zero plot (in this case an all pole plot, since the data model is a linear prediction model). There are 14 poles, 6 in the upper half of the unit circle, 6 in the lower half, and 2 on the real line.

The MA option uses Durbin's technique, which is outlined in the text. The MA analysis option works in a manner similar to that for LP. However, this algorithm requires more computation time than the LP algorithm. There are four options for the ARMA spectrum calculation. These various algorithms are discussed more fully in advanced texts on spectral analysis. However, the user can still experiment with the ARMA techniques to obtain an intuitive feeling for the spectrum estimated by this method.

Note that there is also an option to calculate the spectrogram as well. This latter option calls the MATLAB function *specgram*. As described in the text, the spectrogram is useful for displaying a time varying spectrum of a long speech data file, such as the sentence "We were away a year ago" contained in the data file we.mat.

As a final example, consider using the *autocorrelation* option in the time domain analysis menu. Load the data file sine.mat. A sinewave containing 512 data points will be plotted. Select time domain analysis. Select property. Change the frame length to 1024. Click the ok button. Select the autocorrelation button in the *time domain analysis* window. A plot of the autocorrelation function will appear in the *time domain analysis autocorrelation (biased)* window. This plot is the same as that shown in Figure 6.24 in Chapter 6.

7.13   SUMMARY

In the previous chapters we focused on the ensemble properties of random processes. In this chapter we introduced concepts that provide a link between the properties of a member function of an ensemble and the ensemble itself. The first such concept dealt with ergodicity. Definitions were given for determining whether or not a wide sense stationary random process was ergodic in the mean and/or ergodic in the autocorrelation function. These concepts provide a method for estimating the mean and autocorrelation function by time averaging data measured from a member function.

The section on statistical inference considered point and interval estimators for parameters of a random process. This concept, in contrast to probability theory, considers how to use the data measured from an experiment a posteriori to make inferences about the properties of a random process. Three important properties of point estimators are the bias, the variance, and consistency. Interval estimators are concerned with confidence limits and the confidence level.

Several types of estimation procedures were examined, including mean square, maximum likelihood, and least squares.

Two estimators for the autocorrelation function were introduced, namely, the biased and unbiased estimators. We concluded that the biased estimator is the best.

The two major types of power spectral estimators are the parametric and nonparametric. The nonparametric spectral estimators include the periodogram and the Blackman–Tukey methods. These methods are often included in a class of classical estimators because they were among the first to be used. The parametric spectral estimators use data modeling methods and are generally considered superior to the classical methods. The parametric procedures require a means to estimate the parameters of the data model that is selected. We used the method of least squares, which requires no assumptions about the statistics of the data.

The spectrogram was briefly discussed, since it is used in many applications, including speech analysis.

Several approaches to random number generation were presented and related to software functions available in MATLAB.

One method for generating correlated sequences of random variables was described.

The chapter concluded with a discussion of the Karhunen–Loeve expansion, which is used in several application areas, including image processing and coding.

PROBLEMS

7.1   Consider the sine wave random process with fixed amplitude a, but with both random phase angle and frequency such that

$$X(t) = a \sin(\omega t + \theta)$$

$$p_X(\theta) = \frac{1}{2\pi}, \quad 0 \leq \theta \leq 2\pi$$

$$p_X(\omega) = \frac{1}{\omega_0}, \quad 0 \leq \omega \leq \omega_0$$

Assume that θ and ω are independent. Is this process ergodic in the mean? Is this process ergodic in the autocorrelation? Recall that this process is stationary in the wide sense.

7.2   We have considered wide sense stationary random processes of the form $R_{XX}(k) = (a)^{|k|}$, where $|a| < 1$. Assume this process has zero mean. Is the process ergodic in the mean?

7.3   Let $X(t)$ be a wide sense stationary random process that is ergodic in the mean and the autocorrelation. However, $X(t)$ is not zero mean. Let $Y(t) = CX(t)$, where C is a random variable independent of $X(t)$ and C is not zero mean. Show that $Y(t)$ is not ergodic in the mean or the autocorrelation.

7.4   Calculate the time average autocorrelation function for the periodic pulse train shown in Figure 7.35. Let $T > 2T_0$. Plot the result. Then calculate and plot the periodogram, and compare it with the Blackman–Tukey spectral estimate.

7.5   A random process has the autocorrelation function shown in Figure 7.36. Find the Blackman–Tukey spectral estimate analytically and then plot the result.

7.6   A random variable has a normal probability density of

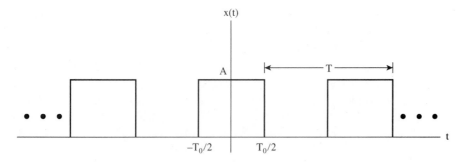

Figure 7.35

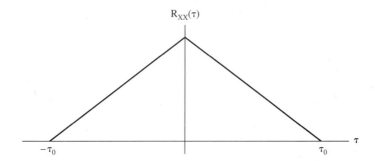

Figure 7.36

$$p_X(x) = \frac{1}{\sqrt{2\pi}}\, e^{-\frac{1}{2}(x-5)^2}$$

We measure 10 independent samples of the random variable.

    a. Determine the expected value of the sample mean.

    b. Determine the variance of the sample mean.

    c. Determine the expected value of the unbiased sample variance.

7.7   A company manufactures five-volt power supplies. However, since there are manufacturing tolerances, there are variations in the voltage design. The standard deviation in the design voltage is 5 percent. Using a 99 percent confidence level, determine whether or not the following samples fall within the confidence interval:

    a. 100 samples, $\hat{\mu}_X = 4.7$

    b. 100 samples, $\hat{\mu}_X = 4.9$

    c. 100 samples, $\hat{\mu}_X = 5.4$

Hint: consider [7.4.3.9].

7.8   Derive [7.4.2.10], [7.4.2.11], and [7.4.2.12].

7.9   Minimize [7.4.2.13] with respect to k to find $k = N + 1$.

7.10 You collect a sample size N_1 of data and find that N_1 just satisfies a 90 percent confidence level. What should the sample size N_2 be to increase the confidence level to 99.9 percent?

7.11 Company A manufactures computer applications boards. They are concerned with the mean time between failures (MTBF), which they regularly measure. Denote the sample MTBF as $\hat{\mu}_M$ and the true MTBF as μ_M. Determine the number of failures that must be measured before $\hat{\mu}_M$ lies within 20 percent of the true μ_M with a 90 percent probability. The probability density function is exponential, namely:

$$p_X(x) = \frac{1}{\mu_M} e^{-\frac{x}{\mu_M}}$$

7.12 Two independent samples of a random variable X are taken. Determine the expected value and variance of $\hat{\mu}_X$ if the probability density function is exponential; that is:

$$p_X(x) = e^{-x}$$

for $x \geq 0$ and zero otherwise.

7.13 The noise level in a room is measured N times. The error e for each measurement is independent of the others and is normally distributed with zero mean and standard deviation $\sigma_e = 0.1$. Determine the probability density of the sample mean $\hat{\mu}_X$ for $N = 100$.

7.14 Independent samples are taken of a random variable X. If the probability density of X is uniform, as in Figure 7.37, then approximate the density of the sample mean with a normal density, assuming the number of samples is large.

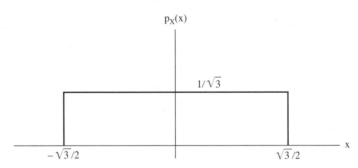

Figure 7.37

7.15 You are asked to analytically determine the maximum likelihood for the phase of a signal plus noise; that is:

$$X(n) = a \cos(2\pi f_0 nT + \theta) + N(n)$$

Let $n = 1, 2, 3, \ldots, N$. Assume the noise samples are independent and identically, Gaussianly distributed with zero mean and variance σ^2. The frequency f_0 is fixed, as is the amplitude a. The sampling interval is T. During the solution you will encounter some double frequency terms ($2f_0$); ignore these terms to arrive at a final solution.

7.16 A random process X(n) is to be approximated by a straight line using the estimate, $\hat{X}(n) = a + bn$. Determine the least squares estimates for a and b if N samples of the error and X(n) are available.

7.17 Show that correlation matrix is positive definite, namely:

$$[\hat{R}_{XX}(k)] = \frac{1}{N}[X]^T[X]$$

is positive definite.

7.18 Show that the expected value of the periodogram is the convolution of the true power spectrum with the power spectrum of the data window.

7.19 If you have available a random number generator that provides numbers uniformly distributed for the interval [0, 1], how would you transform this distribution to provide random numbers to be distributed over the interval [a, b]? Hint: If U(n) denotes the random numbers for the [0, 1] distribution and X(n) denotes the random numbers for the [a, b] distribution, how is X(n) related to U(n)? Simulate your result using *rand* in MATLAB.

7.20 The function *rand* in MATLAB gives you random numbers for the interval [0, 1]. Suppose you want to simulate an experiment involving the roll of a die, where the faces are equally likely. How would you do this? Simulate your approach using MATLAB. Calculate the sample mean for each face using the simulated data. Now suppose the faces are not equally likely; that is, the occurrence of each face has probability p_i, $i = 1, \ldots, 6$, and the sum of the p_i is one. How would you modify your approach? Simulate your approach using MATLAB. Calculate the sample mean for each face.

7.21 Prove [7.4.2.8].

7.22 This problem is to be completed using analytical methods so that you will gain some insight into the appropriate equations. Suppose you have a sample from a wide sense stationary random sequence as follows:

$$0, 1, 0, -1, 2$$

Determine $\hat{R}(0)$, $\hat{R}(1)$, and $\hat{R}(2)$ using the biased autocorrelation estimate. Next determine the correlation matrix for the autocorrelation method. Finally, determine the sample mean.

7.23 Suppose you are given the data sequence

$$0, 1, 0, -1, 2, -3, 5, 0, -7, 8$$

Determine the least square straight line fit to the data. Hint: Use the solution to Problem 7.16.

7.24 Suppose a zero mean random sequence X(n) has an autocorrelation function $R_{XX}(k) = c^{|k|}$. An estimate of X(n) is

$$\hat{X}(2) = -\hat{a}_1 X(1) - \hat{a}_2 X(0)$$

What is the linear prediction estimate for X(2)? What is the total squared error? Does the solution agree with the text examples?

7.25 Suppose the covariance matrix for generating correlated random variables is

$$\text{Cov}_{\vec{Y}\vec{Y}} = \begin{bmatrix} 5 & 1 \\ 1 & 2 \end{bmatrix}$$

Find the transformation matrix $[T]$.

7.26 A simple moving average filter processes a zero mean, unit variance random process $X(n)$ such that the filter output is $Y(n) = 1/2[X(n) + X(n-1)]$ for $n = 0, \ldots, N-1$, where $X(-1) = 0$ and $X(N) = 0$ and the $X(n)$ are independent, identically distributed random variables. Find the covariance (autocorrelation) matrix of $Y(n)$. Now let the variance for $X(n)$ be $(\sigma_X)^2$; find the autocorrelation function of $Y(n)$ and the power spectral density.

7.27 A simple moving average filter processes a zero mean, unit variance random process $X(n)$ such that the filter output is $Y(n) = [X(n) - X(n-1)]$ for $n = 0, \ldots, N-1$, where $X(-1) = 0$ and $X(N) = 0$ and the $X(n)$ are independent, identically distributed random variables. Find the covariance (autocorrelation) matrix of $Y(n)$. Now let the variance for $X(n)$ be σ_X^2. Find the autocorrelation function of $Y(n)$ and the power spectral density.

7.28 Problems 7.26 and 7.27 illustrate how a sequence can be generated whereby adjacent "pulses" (numbers) are correlated, but nonadjacent pulses are not correlated. Consequently, this problem is an extension of Problem 6.41. In Problem 6.41 let adjacent pulses be correlated in amplitude with correlation coefficient ρ_0 = constant. Nonadjacent pulses are independent with zero mean and uncorrelated. Find the power spectrum of the train of pulses.

7.29 Discuss how the method for generating correlated sequences of random variables is related to the Karhunen–Loeve expansion.

7.30 Let $R_{XX}(k) = (0.3)^{|k|}$ for $k = 0, 1, 2$. If we model the data with an LP model, we obtain $\hat{a}_1 = -0.3$, $\hat{a}_2 = 0$, $\hat{a}_3 = 0$. Consider the autocorrelation prediction equation $[7.7.3.27]$ and calculate $\hat{R}_{XX}(3)$. Discuss the implications of this result.

7.31 Company A has monthly earnings in millions of dollars as

Month	Earnings
1	67
2	85
3	89
4	78
5	97
6	105
7	93
8	112
9	88
10	117
11	115

Plot the data and calculate and plot the least square line fit to the data. See the solution to Problem 7.16. Use extrapolation to estimate the income for months 12 and 13. The true values are 113 and 85, respectively. How does the extrapolation using the least square line compare with these values? Now fit an LP model to the data given in the table, using *lpc* in MATLAB. Try model orders p = 1, 3, 5, 7, 9, and 11. Calculate and plot the total squared error versus p. For each model predict the income for months 12 and 13. Which value of p gives the best results? Does this agree with the error versus p results?

7.32   Derive the following impulse response for the first order $1/A(z)$ prediction filter:

$$h(n) = \delta(n) - \hat{a}_1 h(n-1)$$

where $\delta(n)$ is the unit pulse. Let $h(-1) = 0$. Let $\hat{a}_1 = -0.3$. Analytically generate 10 samples of $h(n)$. Now suppose you have a data sequence

$$0.2, 0.5, 1.1, 0.7, -0.1$$

Determine the error sequence. Calculate the correlation matrix using $\hat{a}_1$ only. (There are two unknowns and one equation. What can you do?) Repeat this problem for a second order filter, where

$$h(n) = \delta(n) - \hat{a}_1 h(n-1) - \hat{a}_2 h(n-2)$$

where $h(-1) = h(-2) = 0$ and $\hat{a}_1 = -0.625$ and $\hat{a}_2 = 0.25$.

MATLAB PROBLEMS

M7.1   Simulate Example 7.1 using the function *rand* in MATLAB; that is, generate several member functions of the ensemble. (Hint: The function *rand* is uniform for the interval [0, 1]. Map a portion of this interval to 1 and the other portion to −1.) Let the member functions contain at least 100 samples. Calculate the sample mean for each member function. Is the result of this calculation close to the true mean? If you increase the number of samples to 200, does the bias decrease? Estimate the autocorrelation function using one of the member functions you generated. Plot this estimate. Is the estimate biased? Does the estimate become less biased as the number of samples increases to 200?

M7.2   Calculate and plot the periodogram for each of the windows in MATLAB, namely, Bartlett, triangle, kaiser, hanning, hamming, chebyshev, boxcar (rectangular), and blackman. Which window has the lowest sidelobes? Which window has the narrowest main lobe? Which window has the widest main lobe?

M7.3   For the multiplicative method of generating random numbers, determine the sequence of numbers, for the following cases:

    a. mod 11, a = 3, $x_0 = 1$. What is the period?

    b. mod 11, a = 5, $x_0 = 1$. What is the period?

M7.4   Generate a 100-point data sequence using *randn* in MATLAB. Calculate the total squared error for a linear prediction model of the data for $p = 1, 2, \ldots, 10$. Plot the error versus p. What value of p has the smallest error? Compare your results with the Akaike information criterion.

M7.5   Calculate the spectrograms for the four words *hello, yes, no,* and *bye* that were provided on floppy disk in Chapter 1. These files are in the data subdirectory of the software package introduced in Chapter 6. The file names are dg_hello.d, and so on. Remember that these are ASCII files and sampled at 16 kHz. Can you identify the vowel regions?

M7.6   You have a random process with the following auto correlation matrix

$$\begin{bmatrix} 1.0 & 0.3 & 0.09 & 0.0027 \\ 0.3 & 1.0 & 0.3 & 0.09 \\ 0.09 & 0.3 & 1.0 & 0.3 \\ 0.0027 & 0.09 & 0.3 & 1 \end{bmatrix}$$

Generate a random sequence with the following covariance matrix

$$\begin{bmatrix} 1.0 & 0.1 & 0.2 & 0.3 \\ 0.1 & 1.0 & 0.1 & 0.2 \\ 0.2 & 0.1 & 1.0 & 0.1 \\ 0.3 & 0.2 & 0.1 & 1.0 \end{bmatrix}$$

Hint: Find the X_i for the Karhunen–Loeve expansion. Calculate T. Then calculate Y(n). Check your result by estimating the covariance values using the data you generate.

M7.7   Generate a 100-point random sequence using *rand* in MATLAB. Use a first order LP filter to filter this random sequence; that is, the filter is

$$A(z) = \frac{1}{1 + a_1 z^{-1}} = \frac{z}{z + a_1}$$

Let $a_1 = -0.1, -0.3,$ and -0.7. Calculate and compare the autocorrelation function for the output of the three filters. Do the results agree with the theory? Repeat this problem using *randn* in MATLAB. Are there any significant differences in your results?

M7.8   Suppose we have the following correlation matrix:

$$\begin{bmatrix} 1 & 0.3 \\ 0.3 & 1 \end{bmatrix}$$

Determine the first order LP model. Calculate $\hat{R}_{XX}(2)$ using the autocorrelation prediction equation [7.7.3.27]. Now suppose you are told the correlation matrix is

$$\begin{bmatrix} 1.0 & 0.3 & (0.3)^4 \\ 0.3 & 1.0 & 0.3 \\ (0.3)^4 & 0.3 & 1.0 \end{bmatrix}$$

Compare $\hat{R}_{XX}(2)$ to the true value. Now determine the second order LP model. Calculate $\hat{R}_{XX}(3)$ using [7.7.3.27]. Plot and compare the true values of the autocorrelation function with the predicted values.

M7.9   Construct a signal plus noise random sequence using 10 samples of the following:

$$X(n) = \cos(2\pi f_0 \, n \, T) + N(n)$$

where $N(n)$ is generated by *rand* in MATLAB, and f_0 is $(0.1)f_s = 0.1/T$. Calculate the periodogram of $X(n)$. Calculate the power spectrum for $X(n)$ using LP models with $p = 1, 2, 3$, and 5. Compare the LP spectra with the periodogram. In your opinion, which order is the best fit? Repeat the problem using 100 samples and compare your results.

M7.10 Construct a signal plus noise random sequence using 10 samples of the following:

$$X(n) = \cos(2\pi f_1 \, n \, T) + 10\cos(2\pi f_2 \, n \, T) + N(n)$$

where $N(n)$ is generated by *rand* in MATLAB, and f_1 is $(0.1)f_s = 0.1/T$ and f_2 is $(0.4)f_s = 0.4/T$. Calculate the periodogram of $X(n)$. Calculate the power spectrum for $X(n)$ using LP models with $p = 3, 4, 5, 6$, and 7. Compare the LP spectra with the periodogram. In your opinion, which order is the best fit? Repeat the problem using 100 samples and compare your results.

M7.11 Analyze a segment of the vowel in the data file ee.mat included with the software for this chapter. Use LP models with $p = 10, 11, 12, 13, 14$. Window the data with a hamming window prior to analysis. Calculate and plot the LP spectra and compare with the periodogram. Calculate and plot the total squared error versus the order p. The first three resonances for this vowel (/i/ as in see) occur at approximately, 270, 2290, and 3010 Hz. Which model order appears to give the best results? Does this agree with the periodogram results? Does this agree with the error versus p results? Now that you have the best LP model for this data, predict and plot the unwindowed data beyond the last data value in the file ee.mat. Comment on this prediction; for example, for how many samples does the prediction appear to work well? Repeat this problem for the vowel /a/ (as in Bach) in file a.mat. The first three resonances for this vowel occur at approximately 570, 840, and 2410 Hz.

M7.12 Apply a hamming window to the speech file ee.mat. Find the LP filter $1/A(z)$. Now inverse filter the speech signal and plot the data sequence, $e(n)$. Discuss your result; that is, discuss why the sequence has peaks where it does. Hint: Compare the location of the peaks in $e(n)$ with the speech data.

APPENDIX 7.1: MATLAB SOFTWARE FOR EXAMPLE 7.25

```
%mfile: Example 7.25
% 0. load the speech data
%%%%%%%%%%%%%%%%%%%%%%%%%%%
load ee.mat % the variable name for the speech data is "signal".
signal=signal(:)';
```

```
disp('play the speech signal . . . ');
sound([signal signal signal],10000)
lens=length(signal);
vmax=max(signal);
% 1. Segment the speech with different windows
%%%%%%%%%%%%%%%%%%%%%%%%%%%%%%%%%%%%%%%%%%%%
plot(1:lens,signal,'-',[ 1 1:lens lens],[0 1.1*vmax*boxcar(lens)' 0]);
axis([1-5 lens+5 -1.5*vmax 1.2*vmax]);
axis off;
title('speech Signal with a Rectangular Window');
pause(2)
signal1=signal.*hamming(lens)';
plot(1:lens,signal1,'-',1:lens,vmax*hamming(lens));
axis([1-5 lens+5 -1.5*vmax 1.1*vmax]);
axis off;
title('Speech Signal with a Hamming Window');
% 2. Calculate the periodogram
%%%%%%%%%%%%%%%%%%%%%%%%%%%%%
pause(2)
sigf=abs(fft(signal));
sigf=sigf.^2/lens;
sigf=fftshift(sigf);
plot(-0.5:1/(lens-1):0.5,10*log10(sigf));
    ylabel('dB');
    xlabel('Frequency');
    vmax=10*log10( max(abs(sigf)) );
    axis([-0.5 0.5 0 vmax]);
title('Periodogram of speech signal with rectangular window');
pause(2);
sigf1=abs(fft(signal1));
sigf1=sigf1.^2/lens;
sigf1=fftshift(sigf1);
plot(-0.5:1/(lens-1):0.5,10*log10(sigf1));
    ylabel('dB');
    xlabel('Frequency');
    vmax=10*log10( max(abs(sigf1)) );
    axis([-0.5 0.5 0 vmax]);
title('Periodogram of Speech signal with Hamming window');
% 3. Calculate the Autocorrelation function
%%%%%%%%%%%%%%%%%%%%%%%%%%%%%%%%%%%%%%%%%%%
lens=length(signal);
pause(2);
siga=xcorr(signal,'biased');
vmax=max(siga);
plot(-lens+1:lens-1,siga,'-',[ -lens+1 -lens+1:lens-1 lens-1], [0 1.1*vmax*boxcar(2*lens-1)' 0]);
axis([-lens-1 lens+1 -0.5*vmax 1.2*vmax]);
```

```
axis off;
title('Autocorrelation Function with a Rectangular Window');
pause(2)
siga1=xcorr(signal,'biased');
siga1=siga1.*hamming(2*lens−1);
vmax=max(siga1);
plot(−lens+1:lens−1,siga1,'-',-lens+1:lens−1,vmax*hamming(2*lens−1));
axis([−lens−1 lens+1 −0.5*vmax 1.2*vmax]);
axis off;
title('Autocorrelation Function with a Hamming Window');
% 4. Perform the Blackman-Tukey spectrum estimate
%%%%%%%%%%%%%%%%%%%%%%%%%%%%%%%%%%%%%%%%%%%%%%%
pause(2)
sigf=abs(fft(siga));
sigf=fftshift(sigf);
lens=length(sigf);
plot(−0.5:1/(lens−1):0.5,10*log10(sigf));
   ylabel('dB');
   xlabel('Frequency');
   vmax=10*log10( max(abs(sigf)) );
   axis([−0.5 0.5 0 vmax]);
title('Blackman-Tukey Spectrum with Rectangular window');
pause(2)
sigf1=abs(fft(siga1));
sigf1=fftshift(sigf1);
plot(−0.5:1/(lens−1):0.5,10*log10(sigf1));
   ylabel('dB');
   xlabel('Frequency');
   vmax=10*log10( max(abs(sigf1)) );
   axis([−0.5 0.5 0 vmax]);
title('Blackman-Tukey Spectrum with Hamming window').
```

Random Processes and Linear Systems

8.1 INTRODUCTION

In this chapter we consider the response of both continuous and discrete linear systems to random processes, such as a signal plus noise. The results include the derivation of the autocorrelation function and power spectral density for the output of a linear system when the input is a random process. We establish techniques that can be used to determine some of the statistical parameters of the output in terms of the linear system's impulse response or its corresponding frequency domain representation, that is, its frequency response. We demonstrate how, in some cases, we can optimize the system for certain conditions so that we can enhance the signal and suppress the noise. Several lengthy examples are considered, such as, the determination of the output statistics for a simple filter with a sine wave plus noise input, and a simplified PCM detection system. The results in this chapter use many of the concepts that have been developed in the previous chapters. It is assumed that the reader is generally familiar with the analysis of the response of linear systems to deterministic signals.

8.2 CONTINUOUS TIME LINEAR SYSTEMS

A summary of linear systems for continuous time is given here.

Definition 8.1. Let a system have an input $x(t)$ that is transformed by an operator $T[\ ]$ to produce an output $y(t)$; that is:

$$y(t) = T[x(t)] \tag{8.2.1}$$

The system is **linear** if it has the properties of **homogeneity** and **superposition,** namely, for arbitrary inputs $x_1(t)$ and $x_2(t)$ and arbitrary constants a and b, then

$$T[ax_1(t) + bx_2(t)] = aT[x_1(t)] + bT[x_2(t)] \tag{8.2.2}$$

Definition 8.2. A **time invariant system** is one that if

$$y(t) = T[x(t)]$$

then

$$y(t - t_0) = T[x(t - t_0)] \tag{8.2.3}$$

Definition 8.3. The **impulse response** of a linear, time invariant system is

$$y(t) = \int_{-\infty}^{\infty} \delta(s)\, h(t - s)\, ds = h(t) \tag{8.2.4}$$

This is the **convolution theorem**.

Definition 8.4. A linear system is **causal** if $h(t) = 0$ for $t < 0$. A system is said to be **physically realizable** if it is causal.

Definition 8.5. The **transfer function** is the Fourier transform of the impulse response, which is

$$H(f) = H(\omega) = H(j\omega) = \int_{-\infty}^{\infty} h(t)\, e^{-j\omega t}\, dt = \int_{-\infty}^{\infty} h(t)\, e^{-j2\pi ft}\, dt \tag{8.2.5}$$

The **transfer function** completely describes a linear, time invariant system. It is most useful as a descriptor of the frequency response of the system, since it characterizes the filtering action of the system, such as defining the passband and stopband regions of the system, as well as the phase response.

Definition 8.6. A linear system is **stable** if its response to any bounded input is bounded, that is, if $|x(t)| < M$, then $|y(t)| = |x(t)*h(t)| < Mc$, where M and c are constants.

We now let the input be a random process $X(t)$. Then $Y(t)$, the response, will also be a random process. While we can consider the calculation of the nth moment by ensemble averaging, we will generally only need the mean and the autocorrelation function.

Definition 8.7. The **mean** of the output of a linear system is

$$E[Y(t)] = \int_0^t E[X(s)]\, h(t - s)\, ds \tag{8.2.6}$$

Note that [8.2.6] will generally be time varying. A specific solution is impossible unless we stipulate some further conditions. However, before doing this, let us determine the autocorrelation function.

Definition 8.8. The **autocorrelation function** of the output of a linear system is given as

$$R_{YY}(t_1, t_2) = E[Y(t_1)Y(t_2)] = \int_0^{t_1}\int_0^{t_2} E[X(\tau)X(\alpha)]\, h(t_1 - \tau)\, h(t_2 - \alpha)\, d\tau\, d\alpha \tag{8.2.7}$$

Example 8.1 | Let the driving function (input) be a wide sense stationary white noise process with zero mean. The autocorrelation function is a delta function. Therefore:

$$E[X(t_1)X(t_2)] = R_{XX}(\tau) = N_0\delta(\tau) \qquad \text{[8.2.8]}$$

The mean of the output is zero, and the autocorrelation function is

$$R_{YY}(t_1, t_2) = E[Y(t_1)Y(t_2)] = N_0\int_0^{t_1} h(t_1 - s)\, h(t_2 - s)\, ds \qquad \text{[8.2.9]}$$

The development, so far, has provided general results. In the next section we become more specific.

8.3   THE OUTPUT AUTOCORRELATION FUNCTION

Now consider a system having zero initial conditions and with an input that is **wide sense stationary**; then the **output autocorrelation function** can be written as

$$R_{YY}(\tau) = \int_{-\infty}^{\infty}\int_{-\infty}^{\infty} E[X(t - \alpha)X(t + \tau - \beta)]\, h(\alpha)\, h(\beta)\, d\alpha\, d\beta \qquad \text{[8.3.1]}$$

Since

$$E[X(t - \alpha)X(t + \tau - \beta)] = R_{XX}(\tau - \beta + \alpha)$$

then

$$R_{YY}(\tau) = \int_{-\infty}^{\infty}\int_{-\infty}^{\infty} R_{XX}(\tau - \beta + \alpha)\, h(\beta)\, h(\alpha)\, d\beta\, d\alpha \qquad \text{[8.3.2]}$$

This is the output autocorrelation function expressed as a function of the impulse response of the system and the input autocorrelation function for a wide sense stationary random process.

Quiz 8.1   Derive [8.3.1] from [8.2.7].

Example 8.2 | Let the input be a white noise random process such that

$$R_{XX}(\tau) = N_0\delta(\tau) \qquad \text{[8.3.3]}$$

Then from [8.3.2] the output autocorrelation function is

$$R_{YY}(\tau) = \int_{-\infty}^{\infty}\int_{-\infty}^{\infty} N_0\,\delta(\tau + \alpha - \beta)\, h(\alpha)\, h(\beta)\, d\alpha\, d\beta \qquad \text{[8.3.4]}$$

$$= N_0\int_{-\infty}^{\infty} h(\alpha)\, h(\tau + \alpha)\, d\alpha$$

Definition 8.9. Define the **autocorrelation function of the system impulse response** to be

$$R_{hh}(\tau) = \int_{-\infty}^{\infty} h(\alpha)\, h(\tau + \alpha)\, d\alpha \qquad [8.3.5]$$

Then, completing Example 8.2, we have

$$R_{YY}(\tau) = N_0 R_{hh}(\tau) \qquad [8.3.6]$$

Quiz 8.2   Show that

$$R_{YY}(\tau) = \int_{-\infty}^{\infty} R_{hh}(s)\, R_{XX}(\tau + s)\, ds = \int_{-\infty}^{\infty} R_{hh}(t)\, R_{XX}(\tau - t)\, dt \qquad [8.3.7]$$

That is, the output autocorrelation function can be expressed as the autocorrelation obtained by time averaging the input autocorrelation function with the system autocorrelation function. Because the autocorrelation function is an even function, then the output autocorrelation function is also the convolution of the input autocorrelation function with the system autocorrelation function.

8.4   THE OUTPUT POWER SPECTRAL DENSITY

It is now rather easy to obtain an expression for the output power spectral density or the power spectrum. This is done by Fourier transforming [8.3.2].

Definition 8.10. The **output power spectrum** is defined as

$$S_{YY}(f) = \int_{-\infty}^{\infty} R_{YY}(\tau)\, e^{-j2\pi f\tau}\, d\tau$$

$$= \int_{-\infty}^{\infty} e^{-j2\pi f\tau}\, d\tau \left\{ \int_{-\infty}^{\infty}\int_{-\infty}^{\infty} R_{XX}(\tau + \alpha - \beta)\, h(\beta)\, h(\alpha)\, d\beta\, d\alpha \right\}$$

which can be expressed as

$$S_{YY}(f) = \int_{-\infty}^{\infty}\int_{-\infty}^{\infty}\int_{-\infty}^{\infty} R_{XX}(\tau + \alpha - \beta)\, e^{-j2\pi f(\tau - \beta + \alpha)}\, h(\beta)\, e^{-j2\pi f\beta}\, h(\alpha)\, e^{+j2\pi f\alpha}\, d\tau\, d\alpha\, d\beta \qquad [8.4.1]$$

$$= \int_{-\infty}^{\infty} h(\beta)\, e^{j2\pi f\beta}\, d\beta \int_{-\infty}^{\infty} h(\alpha)\, e^{-j2\pi f\alpha}\, d\alpha \int_{-\infty}^{\infty} R_{XX}(\tau + \alpha - \beta)\, e^{-j2\pi f(\tau + \alpha - \beta)}\, d\tau$$

$$= H^*(f)\, H(f)\, S_{XX}(f)$$

$$= |H(f)|^2\, S_{XX}(f)$$

Definition 8.11. The total **output power** can be obtained from [8.4.1] and is expressed as

$$P_0 = R_{YY}(0) = \int_{-\infty}^{\infty} S_{YY}(f)\, df = \frac{1}{2\pi} \int_{-\infty}^{\infty} S_{YY}(\omega)\, d\omega \qquad [8.4.2]$$

$$= \int_{-\infty}^{\infty} |H(f)|^2\, S_{XX}(f)\, df$$

Example 8.3 | Let the input spectrum consist of a delta function plus white noise and let the system impulse response be that for a lowpass RC network; that is:

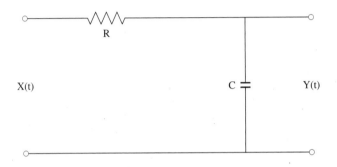

$$S_{XX}(f) = k\,\delta(f) + N_0$$

$$h(t) = \frac{1}{t_0}\, e^{-\frac{t}{t_0}}\, u(t), \qquad t_0 = RC$$

$$H(f) = \frac{\dfrac{1}{t_0}}{\dfrac{1}{t_0} + j(2\pi f)}$$

Then the output spectrum is

$$S_{YY}(f) = |H(f)|^2\, S_{XX}(f) = \frac{\left(\dfrac{1}{t_0}\right)^2}{\left(\dfrac{1}{t_0}\right)^2 + (2\pi f)^2}\, \{k\,\delta(f) + N_0\}$$

The output power is

$$P_0 = \int_{-\infty}^{\infty} S_{YY}(f)\, df = k + N_0 \int_{-\infty}^{\infty} \frac{\left(\dfrac{1}{t_0}\right)^2}{\left(\dfrac{1}{t_0}\right)^2 + (2\pi f)^2}\, df = k + \frac{N_0}{2RC}$$

8.5   THE RESPONSE OF LINEAR SYSTEMS TO SIGNAL PLUS NOISE

Often the input to a linear system will consist of signal plus noise, namely:

$$X(t) = S(t) + N(t) \qquad \text{[8.5.1]}$$

where the signal can be deterministic or a random process. If the signal and noise are independent random processes, and the noise has zero mean, then the output autocorrelation function is

$$R_{XX}(t_1, t_2) = \int_{-\infty}^{\infty}\int_{-\infty}^{\infty} R_{SS}(\beta, \alpha)\, h(t_1 - \beta)\, h(t_2 - \alpha)\, d\beta\, d\alpha \qquad \text{[8.5.2]}$$

$$+ \int_{-\infty}^{\infty}\int_{-\infty}^{\infty} R_{NN}(\beta, \alpha)\, h(t_1 - \beta)\, h(t_2 - \alpha)\, d\beta\, d\alpha$$

When the input is wide sense stationary, then we have

$$R_{YY}(\tau) = \int_{-\infty}^{\infty}\int_{-\infty}^{\infty} R_{SS}(\tau + \beta - \alpha)\, h(\beta)\, h(\alpha)\, d\beta\, d\alpha \qquad \text{[8.5.3]}$$

$$+ \int_{-\infty}^{\infty}\int_{-\infty}^{\infty} R_{NN}(\tau + \beta - \alpha)\, h(\beta)\, h(\alpha)\, d\beta\, d\alpha$$

This result says that the output autocorrelation function is the sum of the signal response and the noise response. This should not be surprising since we are dealing with linear systems. The output power spectrum is

$$S_{YY}(f) = |H(f)|^2 \{ S_{SS}(f) + S_{NN}(f) \} \qquad \text{[8.5.4]}$$

which is composed of two terms, namely, that due to the signal and that due to the noise. However, recall that the signal and noise were assumed to be independent so that no crossproduct terms between the signal and noise appear in the calculation of the output autocorrelation function.

Definition 8.12. The **signal-to-noise ratio** (S/N) is defined as the ratio of the variance of the signal to the variance of the noise. This is sometimes referred to as the power signal-to-noise ratio, while the square root of this ratio is sometimes called the voltage S/N. Both ratios are usually expressed in dB. The signal-to-noise ratio may be expressed as

$$\frac{S}{N} = \frac{R_{SS}(0) - E^2[S(t)]}{R_{NN}(0) - E^2[N(t)]} = \frac{\int_{-\infty}^{\infty} S_{SS}(f)\, df - E^2[S(t)]}{\int_{-\infty}^{\infty} S_{NN}(f)\, df - E^2[N(t)]} \qquad \text{[8.5.5]}$$

If the means are zero, we have

$$\frac{S}{N} = \frac{R_{SS}(0)}{R_{NN}(0)} = \frac{\int_{-\infty}^{\infty} S_{SS}(f)\, df}{\int_{-\infty}^{\infty} S_{NN}(f)\, df} \qquad [8.5.6]$$

This definition applies to either the input or output of a linear system.

One result that we will need in one of the following problems is that if the input to a linear system is a Gaussian random process, then the output is also a Gaussian random process. We do not prove this. However, the result is reasonable, since we have shown previously that a linear transformation of a Gaussian random process is also a Gaussian random process.

8.6   EXAMPLES

Here we consider four lengthy examples, which will help illustrate the previous theory.

Example 8.4   Consider the response of the RC circuit shown in Figure 8.1 to an input $X(t) = S(t)+N(t)$. Let the signal be a wide sense stationary random sine wave process

$$S(t) = A \sin(\omega_c t + \Theta)$$

where Θ is the only random variable, being uniformly distributed from 0 to 2π. The noise is white with zero mean and independent of S(t); that is:

$$R_{NN}(\tau) = N_0 \delta(\tau)$$

The output mean is zero and by [8.5.3] the output autocorrelation function is

$$R_{YY}(\tau) = \int_{-\infty}^{\infty}\int_{-\infty}^{\infty} \{R_{SS}(\tau + \beta - \alpha) + R_{NN}(\tau + \beta - \alpha)\}\, h(\beta)\, h(\alpha)\, d\beta\, d\alpha$$

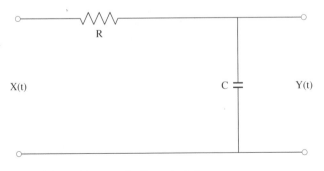

Figure 8.1   RC circuit for Example 8.4

We have previously shown that

$$R_{SS}(\tau) = \frac{A^2}{2} \cos \omega_c \tau$$

Therefore

$$R_{YY}(\tau) = \frac{A^2}{2t_0^2} \int_{-\infty}^{\infty}\int_{-\infty}^{\infty} \cos(\omega_c(\tau + \beta - \alpha))\, e^{-\frac{\beta}{t_0}}\, u(\beta)\, e^{-\frac{\alpha}{t_0}} u(\alpha)\, d\beta\, d\alpha$$

$$+ \frac{N_0}{t_0^2} \int_{-\infty}^{\infty}\int_{-\infty}^{\infty} \delta(\tau + \beta - \alpha)\, e^{-\frac{\beta}{t_0}} u(\beta)e^{-\frac{\alpha}{t_0}} u(\alpha)\, d\beta\, d\alpha$$

$$= \frac{\left(\frac{1}{t_0}\right)^2}{\left(\frac{1}{t_0}\right)^2 + \omega_c^2}\, \frac{A^2}{2} \cos \omega_c \tau + \frac{N_0}{2t_0}\, e^{-\frac{|\tau|}{t_0}}$$

where $t_0 = RC$ and

$$h(t) = \frac{1}{t_0}\, e^{-\frac{t}{t_0}}\, u(t)$$

is the impulse response of the RC circuit. Figure 8.2 illustrates the output autocorrelation function.

The output spectrum is obtained by taking the Fourier transform of the autocorrelation function and is

$$S_{YY}(f) = \frac{A^2}{4}\, \frac{\frac{1}{t_0^2}}{\frac{1}{t_0^2} + \omega_c^2}\, \{\delta(f + f_c) + \delta(f - f_c)\} + N_0 \frac{\frac{1}{t_0^2}}{\frac{1}{t_0^2} + \omega^2}$$

Figure 8.3 shows the output spectrum.

We next determine the output signal-to-noise ratio as a function of the filter parameters.

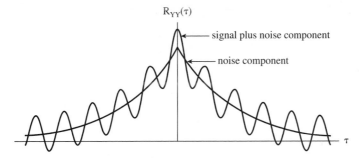

Figure 8.2   The autocorrelation function for Example 8.4

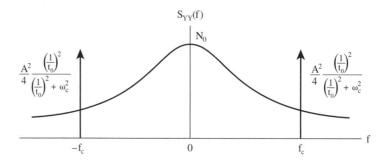

Figure 8.3   The spectrum for Example 8.4

$$\left(\frac{S}{N}\right)_0 = \frac{R_{SS}(0)\,|_{\text{output}}}{R_{NN}(0)\,|_{\text{output}}} = \frac{A^2}{2}\frac{\left(\frac{1}{t_0}\right)^2}{\dfrac{\left(\frac{1}{t_0}\right)^2 + \omega_c^2}{\dfrac{N_0}{2t_0}}} = \frac{A^2}{N_0}\frac{\left(\frac{1}{t_0}\right)}{\left(\frac{1}{t_0}\right)^2 + \omega_c^2}$$

It is possible to maximize the output signal-to-noise ratio with respect to the filter time constant. Set the partial derivative of $\left(\dfrac{S}{N}\right)_0$ with respect to t_0 to zero; that is:

$$\frac{\partial\left(\dfrac{S}{N}\right)_0}{\partial t_0} = 0 = \frac{A^2}{N_0}\frac{\left(-\dfrac{1}{t_0^2}\right)\left(\dfrac{1}{t_0^2} + \omega_c^2\right) + \dfrac{2}{t_0^4}}{\left(\dfrac{1}{t_0^2} + \omega_c^2\right)^2}$$

This leads to

$$t_0 = \frac{1}{\omega_c} = RC$$

Thus, in order to maximize the output signal-to-noise ratio, we set the time constant of the filter equal to the reciprocal of the frequency of the input sinusoid; that is, the 3dB point of the filter is the frequency of the input sine wave. This is reasonable since we are passing the signal and yet rejecting as much of the input white noise as possible.

Quiz 8.3   Verify the results given for $R_{YY}(\tau)$ in the above example.

Example 8.5 | We consider here an example similar to the last. However, in this case we let the input be nonstationary. This will allow us to demonstrate the techniques for nonstationary signals. We will make

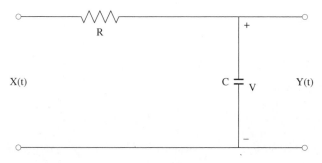

Figure 8.4   RC circuit for Example 8.5

several additional calculations as well. We will let the input noise be Gaussian, and we shall compute the complete time varying output probability density function.

The example is as follows. Let us consider a lowpass RC circuit with an initial condition
voltage V on the capacitor. This is shown in Figure 8.4.
The input is

$$X(t) = S(t) + N(t) = A \cos \omega_c t + N(t)$$

where N(t) is white, Gaussian noise with zero mean; that is:

$$S_{NN}(f) = N_0$$

$$R_{NN}(\tau) = N_0 \delta(\tau)$$

We will assume that the signal and noise are independent. We wish to determine the output probability density function as well as the RC time constant of the filter that will maximize the output
signal-to-noise ratio. Note that the signal for this example differs from that of the previous example since here there is no random variable. We proceed to the solution by determining some of the
statistical parameters of the input and output.

The mean value of the input is time varying, namely:

$$E[X(t)] = A \cos \omega_c t$$

$$< E[X(t)] > \ = 0$$

The input autocorrelation function is also time varying and is

$$R_{XX}(\tau,t) = A^2 \cos(\omega_c t) \cos(\omega_c(t + \tau)) + R_{NN}(\tau)$$

But

$$< R_{XX}(t,\tau) > \ = \frac{A^2}{2} \cos \omega_c \tau + R_{NN}(\tau)$$

We know the impulse response of the filter to be

$$h(t) = \frac{1}{t_0} e^{-\frac{t}{t_0}} u(t), \quad t_0 = RC$$

and the output is

$$Y(t) = \text{initial condition} + \int_{-\infty}^{\infty} X(\alpha)h(t - \alpha)d\alpha$$

$$= V e^{\frac{-t}{t_0}} + \int_{-\infty}^{\infty} \cos(\omega_c \alpha) \frac{1}{t_0} e^{-\frac{t-\alpha}{t_0}} u(t-\alpha) \, d\alpha + \int_{-\infty}^{\infty} N(\alpha) \, h(t-\alpha) \, d\alpha$$

$$= V e^{\frac{-t}{t_0}} + S(t)\big|_{\text{output}} + N(t)\big|_{\text{output}}$$

But the mean value of the output is

$$E[Y(t)] = V e^{\frac{-t}{t_0}} + S(t)\big|_{\text{output}}$$

The noise is stationary with zero mean.

Rather than compute the output autocorrelation function, let us determine the covariance function, which is

$$\text{Cov}_{YY}(\tau) = E[\{Y(t) - E[Y(t)]\}\{Y(t+\tau) - E[Y(t+\tau)]\}] = \rho_{YY}(\tau)\,\sigma_{Y_1}\sigma_{Y_2}$$

$$= E[N(t)\big|_{\text{output}} N(t+\tau)\big|_{\text{output}}] = N_0 \int_{-\infty}^{\infty} h(\alpha)\, h(\tau+\alpha)\, d\alpha$$

$$= \frac{N_0}{t_0^2} \int_{-\infty}^{\infty} e^{-\frac{\alpha}{t_0}} u(\alpha)\, e^{-\frac{(\tau+\alpha)}{t_0}} u(\tau+\alpha)\, d\alpha \; = \; \frac{N_0}{2t_0} e^{-\frac{|\tau|}{t_0}}$$

The output covariance depends only on the time difference τ, as does the output variance. However, the first and second output moments are time varying.

We now have enough data to construct the output probability density function, which will be a time varying, Gaussian probability density. Thus, the joint output probability density is

$$p_Y(y(t_1), y(t_2)) = \frac{1}{2\sigma_{Y_1}\sigma_{Y_2}\sqrt{1 - \rho_{YY}^2(\tau)}} \exp\left\{ -\frac{1}{2(1 - \rho_{YY}^2(\tau))}\left[\frac{(y_1 - E[y_1])^2}{\sigma_{Y_1}^2} \right.\right.$$

$$\left.\left. + \frac{(y_2 - E[y_2])^2}{\sigma_{Y_2}^2} - \frac{2\rho_{YY}(\tau)(y_1 - E[y_1])(y_2 - E[y_2])}{\sigma_{Y_1}\sigma_{Y_2}} \right] \right\}$$

where

$$p_Y(y(t_1), y(t_2)) = p_Y(y_1, y_2)$$

$$E[Y_1] = V e^{-\frac{t_1}{t_0}} + S(t_1)\big|_{\text{output}}$$

$$E[Y_2] = V e^{-\frac{t_2}{t_0}} + S(t_2)\big|_{\text{output}}$$

$$\sigma_{Y_1}^2 = \sigma_{Y_2}^2 = \frac{N_0}{2t_0}$$

$$\rho_{YY}(\tau)\sigma_{Y_1}\sigma_{Y_2} = \frac{N_0}{2t_0} e^{-\frac{|\tau|}{t_0}}$$

This is a complete statistical solution. Note that only the moments have been found, but since the system is linear and the input Gaussian, then the output is Gaussian and we need find only the first two moments and the correlation coefficient.

Note that $Y(t_1)$ and $Y(t_2)$ become uncorrelated (and independent since Gaussian) as $t \to \infty$ since $\rho(\tau) \to 0$. The initial condition also dies out. However, the sine wave input continues to oscillate, causing the mean of the output to vary with time.

The output autocorrelation function is given by

$$R_{YY}(t,\tau) = \rho_{YY}(\tau)\sigma_{Y_1}\sigma_{Y_2} + E[Y_1]E[Y_2]$$

$$= \frac{N_0}{2t_0}e^{-\frac{|\tau|}{t_0}} + \left\{Ve^{-\frac{t}{t_0}} + S(t)\big|_{output}\right\}\left\{Ve^{-\frac{(t+\tau)}{t_0}} + S(t+\tau)\big|_{output}\right\}$$

This reduces to the following as $t \to \infty$ since the transient terms due to the initial conditions decay:

$$R_{YY}(t,\tau) = \frac{N_0}{2t_0}e^{-\frac{|\tau|}{t_0}} + [S(t)\big|_{output}][S(t+\tau)\big|_{output}]$$

Taking the time averaging, we obtain

$$< R_{YY}(t,\tau) > = \frac{N_0}{2t_0}e^{-\frac{|\tau|}{t_0}} + \frac{A^2}{2}\frac{\frac{1}{t_0^2}}{\frac{1}{t_0^2} + \omega_c^2}\cos\omega_c\tau$$

This is the same result that we obtained in the previous example. Therefore, the output spectrum is the same, and the RC time constant that maximizes the output signal-to-noise ratio is the same.

Example 8.6

In this example we consider how to detect the presence of a periodic signal that is immersed in noise. We will not be able to extract the signal by this technique (it can be done another way), but we can detect its presence and determine its period.

Suppose we have

$$X(t) = S(t) + N(t)$$

where $S(t)$ is periodic and $N(t)$ is a wide sense stationary, white, Gaussian noise process with zero mean and $N(t)$ is independent of $S(t)$.

The autocorrelation function of $X(t)$ is

$$R_{XX}(\tau) = E[S(t)S(t+\tau)] + N_0\,\delta(\tau) = R_{SS}(\tau) + N_0\,\delta(\tau)$$

where $R_{SS}(\tau)$ is the autocorrelation function of the signal and is periodic with the same period as $S(t)$. As a specific example let

$$S(t) = A\sin(\omega_c t + \Theta)$$

where Θ is a random variable uniformly distributed from 0 to 2π. Then

$$R_{SS}(\tau) = \frac{A_2}{2}\cos\omega_c\tau$$

Then $R_{XX}(\tau)$ appears as shown in Figure 8.5

Since the noise is white and independent of the signal, its autocorrelation function is a delta function at the origin. Thus, the autocorrelation function of the signal is easily distinguished from the noise. This, of course, would work for nonperiodic signals as well. This property has been employed to the extent that commercial correlators are available to measure the period of periodic signals in noise. Note that the noise amplitude can be extremely large; for instance the S/N can be −10 dB, so that the signal may not appear to be present at all in an oscilloscope display of $S(t)+N(t)$. Yet the correlation functions are easily separated, and the period of the signal can be easily measured.

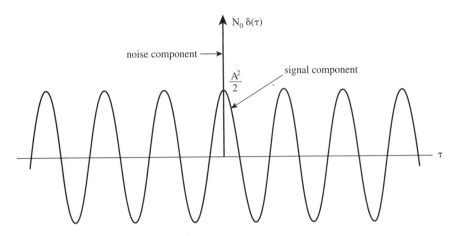

Figure 8.5   The autocorrelation function for a periodic signal plus noise

---

Example 8.7 In this example we determine the bit (binary digit) error probability at the output of a pulse code modulation (PCM) integrating detector. The system will be greatly simplified here for convenience. Therefore, our answer will not be optimum.

In a PCM-FM system the PCM signal frequency modulates (FMs) a carrier. Figure 8.6 shows the receiving system is in simplified form. Several of the key parts of the system are an IF (intermediate frequency) filter that is a band-pass filter in the receiver. This is followed by an FM discriminator, which converts frequency variations to voltage variations; that is, it recovers the modulating signal. This in turn is followed by a PCM detector, which we will assume to be an integrating detector; that is, it integrates the pulse plus noise for the period of the pulse. If at the end of a period of integration the voltage level is above a predetermined threshold, say one-half the height of a PCM pulse, it is decided that a PCM "one" is present. If the threshold is not exceeded, it is decided that a PCM "zero" is present.

It so happens that the noise spectrum at the output of the FM discriminator varies as the signal-to-noise ratio varies. We will not take this fact into account in our solution, however. We will determine the output of the integrating detector so that we can apply some of our previous results and yet not become too involved with the details of the receiver. Our problem, then, is to determine the bit error (or binary digit error) probability at the output of the integrating detector as a function of the input signal-to-noise ratio to the integrating detector.

We will make two assumptions: (1) that the integration period of the detector is sufficiently long so that no correlation exists between the output noise at the beginning of the integration period with that at the end; (2) the noise spectrum at the input to the integrating detector is flat and appears as in Figure 8.7, where B is the bandwidth of the IF filter and the variance of the noise is

$$\sigma_N^2 = N_0 B$$

or

$$N_0 = \frac{\sigma_N^2}{B}$$

We will also assume that the noise probability density function at the integrator input is Gaussian. (This is not true in general, but is a good approximation). Therefore, the noise is Gaussian at the integrator output. Thus, the variance of the output in terms of the input will completely specify the probability density of interest.

The variance of the detector output is

$$\sigma_{N_0}^2 = \int_{-\infty}^{\infty} |H(f)|^2 \, S_{NN}(f) \, df$$

where $H(f)$ is the integrator transfer function, $S_{NN}(f)$ is the input noise spectrum, and $\sigma_{N_0}^2$ is the variance of the noise output.

Let us assume the integrator is a simple passive RC integrator so that

$$H(f) = \frac{1}{1 + jt_0\,\omega}, \quad t_0 = RC$$

Then the output noise variance in terms of the input noise variance and the bandwidth is

$$\sigma_{N_0}^2 = \frac{\sigma_{N_i}^2}{B} \int_{-B/2}^{B/2} \frac{1}{1 + (\omega t_0)^2} \, df = 2\frac{\sigma_{N_i}^2}{B}\frac{1}{t_0^2} \int_0^{B/2} \frac{1}{\frac{1}{t_0^2} + \omega^2} \, df = \frac{\sigma_{N_i}^2}{B\,t_0\,\pi} \tan^{-1}(\pi\,B\,t_0)$$

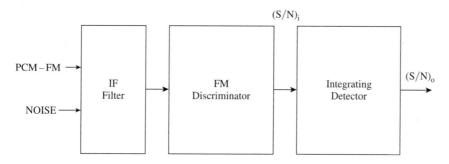

Figure 8.6   Simplified block diagram for a PCM-FM receiver

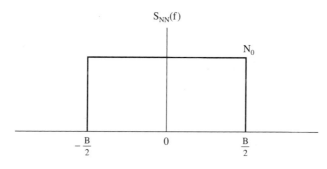

Figure 8.7   White noise

which can be approximated as

$$\sigma_{N_0}^2 \cong \frac{\sigma_{N_i}^2}{B\pi t_0} \left\{ \frac{\pi}{2} - \frac{1}{\pi B t_0} \right\}$$

The probability density function for the noise at the output of the integrator is Gaussian:

$$p_{N_0}(n_0) = \frac{1}{\sqrt{2\pi}\,\sigma_{N_0}} \, e^{-n_0^2 / 2\sigma_{N_0}^2}$$

The bit error probability is determined as follows. Two possible sources of error exist: (1) at the end of the integration period a "one" is indicated due to noise when actually a signal "zero" is present; (2) a "zero" is indicated when a signal one is present. Thus:

$$P(\text{error}) = P_E = P(\text{zero})\, P\left(N_0 > \frac{S_0}{2}\right) + P(\text{one})\, P\left(N_0 < -\frac{S_0}{2}\right)$$

where N_0 is the noise level at the integrator output and S_0 is the signal level at the integrator output when no noise is present. If $P(\text{one}) = P(\text{zero}) = 1/2$, then $S_0/2$ is the threshold level for making a decision that a "one" or "zero" is present.

It is not difficult to determine that for an RC integrator the output signal is approximately expressed as

$$S_0 = 0.4\, S_i$$

for a rectangular pulse, where it is assumed that the integration period is followed by dumping (a resetting of the integrator) and that the RC time constant is twice the integration period.

We have also assumed that the incoming signal (PCM wave train) is such that

$$P(\text{zero}) = P(\text{one}) = \frac{1}{2}$$

For a Gaussian probability density function:

$$P\left(N_0 > \frac{S_0}{2}\right) = P\left(N_0 < -\frac{S_0}{2}\right) = \frac{1}{2} - \int_0^{N_0 = S_0/2} p_{N_0}(n_0)\, dn_0$$

Then

$$P_E = \frac{1}{2} - \int_0^{N_0 = S_0/2} p_{N_0}(n_0)\, dn_0 = \frac{1}{2} - \int_0^{N_0 = 0.2 S_i} p_{N_0}(n_0)\, dn_0$$

Let

$$t = \frac{n_0}{\sigma_{N_0}}$$

Then

$$P_E = \frac{1}{2} - \int_0^{a} p(t)\, dt = \frac{1}{2} - \frac{1}{\sqrt{2\pi}} \int_0^{a} e^{-\frac{1}{2}t^2}\, dt$$

where

$$a = \frac{0.2 S_i}{\sigma_{N_0}} = \frac{S_i}{\sigma_{N_i}}\, 0.2 \frac{\sqrt{B t_0 \pi}}{\sqrt{\tan^{-1}\pi B t_0}} = 0.2 \frac{\sqrt{\pi B t_0}}{\sqrt{\left(\frac{\pi}{2} - \frac{1}{\pi B t_0}\right)}} \frac{S_i}{\sigma_{N_i}} = k \frac{S_i}{\sigma_{N_i}}$$

This equation is plotted in Figure 8.8. Here the bit error probability P_E is shown versus the input signal-to-noise ratio, where we have let the term $B t_0$ be several values to show how the bit error

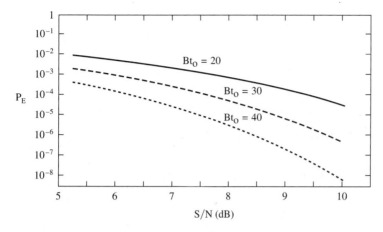

Figure 8.8   Bit error probability versus input S/N

probability varies with this quantity. This example illustrates the use of some of the results we have previously developed.

8.7   DISCRETE TIME LINEAR SYSTEMS

Discrete time systems satisfy the same properties as continuous time systems in that superposition is satisfied, as well as being time invariant and causal. The impulse response becomes the unit pulse response for discrete time systems. So for discrete deterministic systems we denote the input as $x(n)$, the output as $y(n)$, and the impulse response as $h(n)$. The system transfer function is $H(f)$, which is $H(z)$ with $z = \exp(j2\pi f)$. The convolution theorem becomes

$$y(n) = \sum_{-\infty}^{\infty} x(i)\, h(n - i) = x(n) * h(n) = \sum_{-\infty}^{\infty} h(i) x(n - i) = h(n) * x(n) \quad \text{[8.7.1]}$$

Determine the response of a discrete time linear system for an input $x(n) = a^n$ for $n \geq 0$ and $x(n) = 0$ for $n < 0$, where the unit pulse response is $h(n) = b^n$ for $n \geq 0$. The magnitudes of the constants a and b are less than one. From [8.7.1] we have | **Example 8.8**

$$y(n) = \sum_{-\infty}^{\infty} x(i)\, h(n - i) = \sum_{i=0}^{n} a^i\, b^{(n-i)} = b^n \sum_{i=0}^{n} a^i b^{-i} = b^n \sum_{i=0}^{n} \left(\frac{a}{b}\right)^i = b^n \left[\frac{1 - \left(\dfrac{a}{b}\right)^{n+1}}{1 - \left(\dfrac{a}{b}\right)}\right]$$

or

$$y(n) = \frac{b^{n+1} - a^{n+1}}{b - a}$$

where this result applies for $n \geq 0$ and $y(n) = 0$ for $n < 0$.

The results for the output of a discrete linear system are analogous to those for continuous time systems, which we state here for wide sense stationary random processes.

Definition 8.13. The **mean** of the output of a discrete time linear system is

$$E[Y(n)] = \sum_{i=0}^{n} E[X(i)] \, h(n - i) \tag{8.7.2}$$

Definition 8.14. The **autocorrelation** function of the output of a discrete time linear system is

$$R_{YY}(k) = \sum_{i=-\infty}^{\infty} \sum_{j=-\infty}^{\infty} R_{XX}(k - j + i) \, h(j) \, h(i) \tag{8.7.3}$$

Example 8.9   As for continuous time systems, let the input be a white noise random process such that

$$R_{XX}(k) = N_0 \, \delta(k)$$

Then the output autocorrelation function is

$$R_{YY}(k) = \sum_{i=-\infty}^{\infty} \sum_{i=-\infty}^{\infty} R_{XX}(k - j + i) \, h(j) \, h(j)$$

$$= N_0 \sum_{i=-\infty}^{\infty} h(i) \, h(k + i)$$

Definition 8.15. Define the **autocorrelation function of the system impulse response** to be

$$R_{hh}(k) = \sum_{i=-\infty}^{\infty} h(i) \, h(k + i) \tag{8.7.4}$$

Then, completing this example, we have

$$R_{YY}(k) = N_0 \, R_{hh}(k)$$

Quiz 8.4   As before, show that

$$R_{YY}(k) = \sum_{i=-\infty}^{\infty} R_{hh}(i) \, R_{XX}(k + i) = \sum_{i=-\infty}^{\infty} R_{hh}(i) \, R_{XX}(k - i) \tag{8.7.5}$$

That is, the output autocorrelation function can be expressed as the autocorrelation obtained by time averaging the input autocorrelation function with the system autocorrelation function. Because the autocorrelation function is an even function, the output autocorrelation function is also the convolution of the input autocorrelation function with the system autocorrelation function.

Definition 8.16. The **output power spectrum** is defined as

$$S_{YY}(f) = |H(f)|^2 \, S_{XX}(f) \qquad\qquad [8.7.6]$$

where the derivation follows that for continuous time systems. Equation $[8.7.6]$ is often expressed in z-transform notation as

$$S_{YY}(z) = |H(z)|^2 \, S_{XX}(z) \qquad\qquad [8.7.7]$$

Definition 8.17. The total **output power** is expressed as

$$P_0 = R_{YY}(0) = \int_{-f_s}^{f_s} S_{YY}(f) \, df = \int_{-f_s}^{f_s} |H(f)|^2 \, S_{XX}(f) \, df \qquad\qquad [8.7.8]$$

where f_s is the sampling frequency.

Definition 8.18. The **output power spectrum** for a wide sense stationary random signal plus noise at the input is

$$S_{YY}(f) = |H(f)|^2 \, \{ S_{ss}(f) + S_{NN}(f) \} \qquad\qquad [8.7.9]$$

where the signal and noise are independent random processes. Equation $[8.7.9]$ can also be written using z-transform notation.

The signal-to-noise ratio is the same as that defined previously in $[8.5.5]$ and $[8.5.6]$.

Suppose the unit pulse response for a discrete linear system is $h(n) = a^n$, $n \geq 0$, $h(n) = 0$ for $n < 0$, and $|a| < 1$. Let the input autocorrelation function be $\delta(k)$. Find the output autocorrelation function. We can use the results from Example 8.9. For $k \geq 0$ we have | **Example 8.10**

$$R_{YY}(k) = R_{hh}(k) = \sum_{i=-\infty}^{\infty} h(i) \, h(k+i) = \sum_{i=0}^{\infty} a^i \, a^{i+k} = \frac{a^k}{1-a^2}$$

Since the autocorrelation function is symmetric about k=0, then we have

$$R_{YY}(k) = \frac{a^{|k|}}{1-a^2}$$

Quiz 8.5   In the last example let the input autocorrelation function be $N_0 \, \delta(k)$ and $h(n) = ba^n$. Show that the output power is $N_0(b^2)/(1-a^2)$.

Find the transform of the autocorrelation function in the last example. Since the input autocorrelation function is $\delta(k)$, the z-transform is 1. The z-transform of $h(n)$ is $1/(1-az^{-1})$. Thus: | **Example 8.11**

$$S_{YY}(z) = S_{XX}(z)|H(z)|^2 = \frac{1}{1-az} \frac{1}{1-az^{-1}}$$

We measure a noisy signal transmitted over a wide band communication link. Thus, we have $Y(n) = X(n) + N(n)$, where $Y(n)$ is the measured value. Suppose we model the noise as white | **Example 8.12** noise with zero mean and standard deviation σ_N. The noise is independent of the signal. The power spectral density of the measurement is

$$S_{YY}(f) = S_{XX}(s) + S_{NN}(f) = S_{XX}(f) + \sigma_N^2 \delta(f)$$

Example 8.13 | Consider a first order linear prediction process $X(n) = -aX(n - 1) + E(n)$. Model $E(n)$ as white noise with zero mean and standard deviation σ_E. Find the power spectral density of $X(n)$. There are several ways to solve this problem. One approach is to determine the unit pulse response of the filter model, which is $h(n) = 0$ for $n < 0$, $h(0) = 1$, and $h(n) = (-a)^n$ for $n > 0$. Or $H(z) = X(z)/E(z) = 1/(1 + az^{-1})$, Then

$$S_{XX}(z) = S_{EE}(z) |H(z)|^2 = \sigma_E^2 \frac{1}{(1 + az)} \frac{1}{(1 + az^{-1})}$$

Quiz 8.6   Solve the last example by directly z-transforming the equation for the LP process.

8.8   TWO OPTIMUM LINEAR SYSTEMS

In this section we will consider two well-known optimum linear systems, also known as optimum linear filters. The first is called the matched filter, which is a correlation filter. The criterion used to derive this filter is the maximization of the output signal-to-noise ratio, which we do using continuous time theory.

The second filter is known as the Wiener filter, which is derived by formulating the least-mean-squared error filtering problem. The Wiener filter grew out of research conducted during World War II and is fundamentally a prediction and estimation filter; it can be used (1) to predict, (2) to predict and estimate, or (3) to estimate the signal in the presence of noise. We will derive the pure prediction filter using discrete time theory. However, the development for continuous time for all three cases is given in Appendix 5.

While the theory for these two linear filters was developed approximately 50 years ago, they are still in use for various applications. Furthermore, the theory provides insight to the algorithms that have been developed for Kalman filters, least square filters, recursive least square filters, and adaptive filters, which are discussed in other texts.

8.8.1   THE MATCHED FILTER

The assumptions for the matched filter are:

- The waveshape of the signal as well as the noise statistics at the filter input are known. Thus, we assume that the signal is deterministic.

- The filter is linear and time invariant.

- The output signal-to-noise ratio $\left(\frac{S}{N}\right)_0$ at time T is to be maximized; that is:

$$\max\left(\frac{S}{N}\right)_0 = \max\frac{s_0^2(T)}{E[N_0^2(T)]} \qquad \text{[8.8.1.1]}$$

The matched filter problem is to determine the impulse response of the filter that maximizes the output signal-to-noise as shown in Figure 8.9.

The solution to this problem is not difficult. The output signal is

$$s_0(T) = \int_{-\infty}^{T} s(\alpha)h(T-\alpha)d\alpha \qquad \text{[8.8.1.2]}$$

Similarly, the output noise is

$$N_0(T) = \int_{-\infty}^{T} N(\alpha)h(T-\alpha)d\alpha \qquad \text{[8.8.1.3]}$$

and

$$E[N_0^2(T)] = \int_{-\infty}^{T}\int_{-\infty}^{T} R_{NN}(\alpha,\sigma)h(T-\alpha)h(T-\sigma)d\alpha d\sigma \qquad \text{[8.8.1.4]}$$

Thus

$$\max\left(\frac{S}{N}\right)_0 = \max\frac{\left|\int_{-\infty}^{T} s(\alpha)h(T-\alpha)d\alpha\right|^2}{\int_{-\infty}^{T}\int_{-\infty}^{T} R_{NN}(\alpha,\sigma)h(T-\alpha)h(T-\sigma)d\alpha d\sigma} \qquad \text{[8.8.1.5]}$$

8.8.1.1 Matched Filter for White Noise   When the input noise is wide sense stationary and white, then the autocorrelation function becomes a delta function:

$$R_{NN}(\alpha,\sigma) = N_0\delta(\alpha-\sigma) \qquad \text{[8.8.1.1.1]}$$

where N_0 is the noise energy in watts/Hz, and is not to be confused with the noise output vs time. The denominator of [8.8.1.5] becomes

$$\int_{-\infty}^{T}\int_{-\infty}^{T} R_{NN}(\alpha,\sigma)\,h(T-\alpha)\,h(T-\sigma)\,d\alpha\,d\sigma = N_0\int_{-\infty}^{T} h^2\,(T-\alpha)\,d\alpha \qquad \text{[8.8.1.1.2]}$$

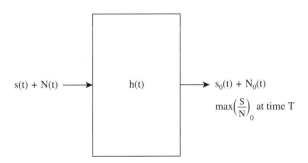

Figure 8.9   The matched filter

If the filter is linear and physically realizable, then we may let the limits on the integrals go to infinity and rewrite the equation [8.8.1.5] in the frequency domain as follows:

$$\max\left(\frac{S}{N}\right)_0 = \max \frac{\left|\int_{-\infty}^{\infty} S(f)\, H(f)\, e^{j2\pi f T}\, df\right|^2}{N_0 \int_{-\infty}^{\infty} |H(f)|^2\, df}$$ [8.8.1.1.3]

Recall **Schwarz's inequality** as

$$\left|\int_{-\infty}^{\infty} H(f) S(f) e^{j2\pi f T}\, df\right|^2 \leq \int_{-\infty}^{\infty} |H(f)|^2\, df \int_{-\infty}^{\infty} |S(f)|^2 df$$ [8.8.1.1.4]

where the equality is valid when

$$S(f)e^{j2\pi f T} = H^*(f)$$

Then

$$\max\left(\frac{S}{N}\right)_0 \leq \max \frac{1}{N_0} \int_{-\infty}^{\infty} |S(f)|^2 df$$ [8.8.1.1.5]

Note that the right side of [8.8.1.5] does not depend on $H(f)$, the filter frequency response. The signal-to-noise ratio is maximized when the equality in [8.8.1.4] is valid, in which case $H(f)$ becomes $H_0(f)$, the optimum filter frequency response; that is:

$$H(f)\, S(f)\, e^{j2\pi f T} = H_0(f)\, H_0(-f) = S(f)\, S(-f)$$ [8.8.1.1.6]

Note that we may use the integrands of [8.8.1.4] since they are positive functions. Equation [8.8.1.6] reduces to

$$H_0(f) = S(-f)e^{-j2\pi f T} = S^*(f)e^{-j2\pi f T}$$ [8.8.1.1.7]

And the impulse response becomes

$$h_0(t) = \int_{-\infty}^{\infty} s(-f)e^{-j2\pi f(T-t)}\, df$$ [8.8.1.1.8]

$$= s(T-t)$$

This says that the filter impulse response is **matched** to the input signal, namely, the filter impulse response is the input signal folded about the time T, as shown in Figure 8.10.

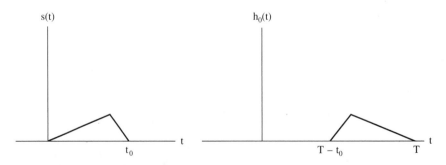

Figure 8.10   A matched filter example

Here we have assumed that the signal is deterministic and that we know its waveshape. However, matched filters can be designed for signals that are random processes.

When the filter is physically realizable, then

$$h_0(t) = 0 \quad t < 0 \qquad [8.8.1.1.9]$$

Thus

$$h_0(t) = \begin{cases} 0 & t < 0 \\ s(T - t) & t \ge 0 \end{cases} \qquad [8.8.1.1.10]$$

This implies that $s(t) = 0$, $t > t_0$, as in Figure 8.10. We can also see that to satisfy [8.8.1.1.9] and [8.8.1.1.10] the minimum value of T is the duration of the signal. Thus, we typically set T equal to the signal duration. Now note that the output signal is

$$s_0(t) = \int_{-\infty}^{t} s(\alpha)\, h_0(t - \alpha)\, d\alpha = \int_{-\infty}^{t} s(\alpha)\, s(\alpha - t + T)\, d\alpha \qquad [8.8.1.1.11]$$

Let $t = T - \tau$; then

$$s_0(\tau) = \int_{-\infty}^{T-\tau} s(\alpha)\, s(\alpha + \tau)\, d\alpha = R_{SS}(\tau) \qquad [8.8.1.1.12]$$

where $R_{SS}(\tau)$ is an energy autocorrelation function for the known signal. Thus, the matched filter is an autocorrelation filter. Equation [8.8.1.1.12] is a maximum when $\tau = 0$ and is the energy of the input signal, namely:

$$R_{SS}(0) = \int_{-\infty}^{T} s^2(\alpha)\, d\alpha = E \qquad [8.8.1.1.13]$$

Thus, the maximum output signal-to-noise ratio is

$$\max \left(\frac{S}{N}\right)_0 = \frac{E^2}{N_0 E} = \frac{E}{N_0} \qquad [8.8.1.1.14]$$

where E is given by [8.8.1.1.13] and N_0 is the noise power spectral density in watts per Hz.

8.8.1.2 Summary of Continuous Time Matched Filters Matched filters have two properties. First, the output of a matched filter at time T in response to **any signal** is the energy crosscorrelation between that signal and the signal to which the filter is matched. If the input signal is the signal to which the filter is matched, then the filter output is the energy autocorrelation function of the signal. We would expect to use a matched filter whenever the signal waveform is known and autocorrelation detection is desired.

The second important property of matched filters is that when the input consists of the signal to which the filter is matched plus stationary white noise, then the output signal-to-noise (at the optimum time) is greater than that obtainable by any other device. The maximum output signal-to-noise ratio is

$$\max \left(\frac{S}{N}\right)_0 = \frac{E}{N_0} \qquad [8.8.1.2.1]$$

In order to detect the presence of a desired signal, a threshold is often selected based on [8.8.1.2.1], say, 90 percent. Thus, if the threshold value is exceeded, then we decide the signal is present in the noise. However, it is quite possible that the threshold can be exceeded if the desired signal is not present or if the noise characteristics change. Some other signal, or even noise, with a large enough amplitude can

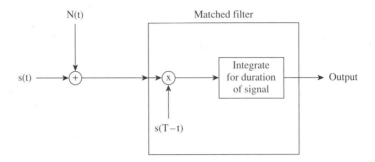

Figure 8.11   Implementation of matched filter

cause the threshold to be exceeded. Thus, one must be careful in interpreting the matched filter output.

The matched filter is easily implemented, as Figure 8.11 indicates.

Example 8.14 | Suppose the signal is a rectangular waveform of amplitude A and duration t_0. The signal is deterministic and will be denoted as s(t), and appears as

$s(t)$

A

t_0 t

Find the matched filter and maximum output signal-to-noise ratio when the input is a delayed version of the signal s(t), that is, when the input signal is s$(t - t_1)$, and the noise is white with a power spectral density level of N_0. Assume that the matched filter is designed for the signal s(t), not the delayed signal. When does the maximum signal-to-noise ratio occur?

By [8.8.1.1.8], the impulse response of the matched filter does not depend on t_1 and is

$$h_0(t) = s(T - t)$$

By [8.8.1.1.11]

$$s_0(t) = \int_{-\infty}^{t} s(\alpha - t_1)h_0(t - \alpha)\,d\alpha$$

$$= \int_{-\infty}^{t} s(\alpha - t_1)s(T - t + \alpha)\,d\alpha$$

$$= A^2\left[\int_{t_1}^{t-T+t_0} d\alpha + \int_{t-T}^{t_1+t_0} d\alpha\right]$$

$$= A^2[t - t_1 - T + t_0] \text{ for } t_1 + T - t_0 \le t \le t_1 + T$$

$$= A^2[t_1 + t_0 + T - t] \text{ for } t_1 + T \le t \le t_1 + t_0 + T$$

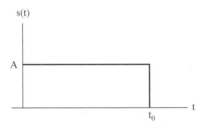

$s(\alpha - t_1)$

(t_1) $(t_0 + t_1)$ α

$s(T - t + \alpha) = s(\alpha - (t - T))$
for $t_1 - t_0 \le t - T \le t_1$
$(t - T)$ $(t - T + t_0)$ α

$s(T - t + \alpha) = s(\alpha - (t - T))$
for $t_1 \le t - T \le t_1 + t_0$
$(t - T)$ $(t - T + t_0)$ α

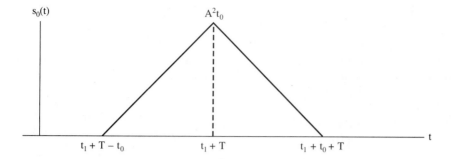

The output noise is given by N_0, while the peak signal energy is A^2t_0. So the maximum output signal-to-noise ratio is

$$\max \left(\frac{S}{N}\right)_0 = \frac{A^2 t_0}{N_0}$$

This maximum occurs at $t = t_1 + T$, which becomes $t = t_1 + t_0$ when we replace T with its minimum value of t_0. Thus, the matched filter output starts to build up at t_1, reaches its maximum value at $t_1 + t_0$, and then decays to its minimum value at $t_1 + 2t_0$. If the delay, t_1, is zero, then the triangle is shifted to the left so that it starts at the origin and builds to its maximum at t_0, then decays to zero at $2t_0$.

Example 8.15

Determine the matched filter for a truncated cosine, namely:

$$s(t) = \begin{cases} A \cos (\omega_0 t), & 0 \le t \le t_0 \\ 0 & , \quad \text{otherwise} \end{cases}$$

Let the noise be white with spectral density N_0. Find the maximum output signal-to-noise ratio. Consider letting t_0 become large so that the signal contains many cycles. What does the signal-to-noise ratio become?

$$h_0(t) = s(T - t) = A \cos(\omega_0 (T - t)) = A \cos(\omega_0 (t_0 - t))$$

where T has been replaced by its minimum value t_0. The maximum output signal-to-noise ratio is

$$\max \left(\frac{S}{N}\right)_0 = \frac{\int_0^{t_0} s^2(t)\,dt}{N_0} = \frac{A^2}{2N_0 \omega_0} [\omega_0 t_0 + \sin(\omega_0 t_0) \cos(\omega_0 t_0)]$$

As t_0 becomes large we may neglect the sine and cosine terms and the signal-to-noise ratio becomes

$$\max \left(\frac{S}{N}\right)_0 \cong \frac{A^2 \omega_0 t_0}{2N_0 \omega_0} = \frac{A^2 t_0}{2N_0}$$

which is one-half the signal-to-noise ratio of the previous example.

Quiz 8.7   Does the result in the last example seem reasonable? Give an explanation for the result.

The generalized matched filter is considered in Appendix 4, as well as the derivation for the physically unrealizable and physically realizable filter forms. Some additional examples appear there as well. The discrete time matched filter is obtained by using sampling theory as done previously. The derivation is similar to that presented next for the Wiener filter. The solution involves a vector representation for the optimum filter and the signal and a matrix representation for the noise.

8.8.1.3 Summary of Discrete Time Matched Filters   Let the vector representation for the sampled signal be given in the following reversed form:

$$\vec{s_R}(n) = [s(N-1), s(N-2), \cdots, s(0), 0, 0, \cdots,]^T \qquad \text{[8.8.1.3.1]}$$

The vector form for the optimum filter is given as

$$\vec{h_0}(n) = [h_0(0), h_0(1), h_0(2), \cdots, h_0(N-1)]^T \qquad \text{[8.8.1.3.2]}$$

The additive noise correlation matrix is $[R_{NN}(k)]$, which is found in a manner similar to that used in Chapter 7 for the linear prediction filter, or by using ensemble averaging, which is the manner to be used shortly for the Wiener filter. The optimum matched filter that maximizes the signal-to-noise ratio is then given as

$$\vec{h}_0(n) = [R_{NN}(k)]^{-1} \vec{s_R}(n) \qquad \text{[8.8.1.3.3]}$$

where it is assumed that the noise correlation matrix is invertible. The maximum signal-to-noise ratio is

$$\left(\frac{S}{N}\right)_0 = \vec{s_R}(n)^T [R_{NN}(k)]^{-1} \vec{s_R}(n) \qquad \text{[8.8.1.3.4]}$$

where, again, it is assumed that the noise correlation matrix is invertible. If the noise correlation matrix is not invertible, then a solution still exists that will maximize the signal-to-noise ratio; that is, the signal-to-noise ratio can be made infinite. The solution for this case is that if

$$[R_{NN}(k)] \vec{s_R}(n) = 0 \qquad \text{[8.8.1.3.5]}$$

then set

$$\vec{h}_0(n) = \vec{s_R}(n) \qquad \text{[8.8.1.3.6]}$$

Or if

$$[R_{NN}(k)] \vec{s_R}(n) \neq 0 \qquad \text{[8.8.1.3.7]}$$

then set the optimum filter vector such that it satisfies the following two conditions

$$\vec{h}_0(n)^T \vec{s_R}(n) \neq 0 \qquad \text{[8.8.1.3.8]}$$

and

$$[R_{NN}(k)] \vec{h}_0(n) = 0 \qquad \text{[8.8.1.3.9]}$$

Example 8.16 | In this example we illustrate the application of the above results for the discrete matched filter. The matrix operations are similar to those used in Chapter 7. Let the noise correlation matrix be

$$[R_{NN}(k)] = \begin{bmatrix} 1.0 & 0.3 & 0.09 \\ 0.3 & 1.0 & 0.3 \\ 0.09 & 0.3 & 1.0 \end{bmatrix}$$

and assume that the known reversed signal vector is

$$\vec{s_R}(n) = [3, 2, 1]^T$$

Then, using MATLAB, the optimum matched filter is

$$\vec{h}_0(n) = [R_{NN}(k)]^{-1} \vec{s_R}(n) = \begin{bmatrix} 1.0989 & -0.3297 & 0.0000 \\ -0.3297 & 1.1978 & -0.3297 \\ 0.0000 & -0.3297 & 1.0989 \end{bmatrix} \begin{bmatrix} 3 \\ 2 \\ 1 \end{bmatrix} = \begin{bmatrix} 2.6374 \\ 1.0769 \\ 0.4396 \end{bmatrix}$$

and the maximum signal-to-noise ratio is

$$\left(\frac{S}{N}\right)_0 = \vec{s_R}(n)^T [R_{NN}(k)]^{-1} \vec{s_R}(n) = [3\ 2\ 1] \begin{bmatrix} 1.0989 & -0.3297 & 0.0000 \\ -0.3297 & 1.1978 & -0.3297 \\ 0.0000 & -0.3297 & 1.0989 \end{bmatrix} \begin{bmatrix} 3 \\ 2 \\ 1 \end{bmatrix} = 10.5055$$

The discrete time matched filter can also be derived for the case when the signal is a discrete random sequence. In this case the maximum signal-to-noise ratio is

$$\left(\frac{S}{N}\right)_0 = \frac{\vec{h}_0(n)^T [R_{SS}(k)] \vec{h}_0(n)}{\vec{h}_0(n)^T [R_{NN}(k)] \vec{h}_0(n)} \qquad \text{[8.8.1.3.10]}$$

where $[R_{SS}(k)]$ is the signal correlation matrix, which can be estimated as in Chapter 7 or determined by ensemble averaging, and the optimum matched filter is given below. You are asked to derive [8.8.1.3.10] in one of the Problems. If we assume that the noise matrix is invertible, then the solution for the optimum matched filter in this case is the eigenvector corresponding to the largest eigenvalue of the matrix $[R_{NN}(k)]^{-1} [R_{SS}(k)]$. The largest eigenvalue is the maximum signal-to-noise ratio in [8.8.1.3.10]. If the noise correlation matrix is not invertible, then there exists a solution that will maximize the S/N. We do not discuss this further here.

8.8.2   THE DISCRETE TIME WIENER FILTER

The Wiener filter problem is outlined in Figure 8.12.

The purpose of the Wiener filter is to determine the least-mean-squared error estimate of the signal S(n), which is a random sequence. As for the matched filter, a delay n_0 can be designed into the solution. Three cases are usually considered:

1. Pure prediction. In this case the delay is $n_0 > 0$ and the noise is zero. The problem is to predict S(n) at some future time.

2. Prediction and estimation. Here the delay is $n_0 > 0$ and the noise is not zero. The problem is to both predict and estimate S(n) at some future time.

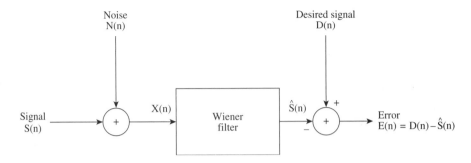

Figure 8.12   Formulation of the Wiener filter problem

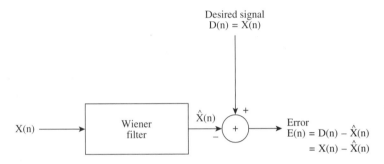

Figure 8.13   Wiener filter problem for the pure prediction case

3. Estimation. For this case the delay is $n_0 \leq 0$ and the noise is not zero. The problem is to estimate $S(n)$.

To solve these three cases, some assumptions are made, as follows. The input to the Wiener filter is additive, namely, signal plus noise. Both the signal and noise are discrete random sequences. Furthermore, both the signal and noise are stationary in the wide sense. A major problem is to determine a Wiener filter that is physically realizable. This is covered in Appendix 5 for the continuous time case. The error criterion is to minimize the mean-squared error: in other words,

$$E\,[E^2(n)] = E[\,(D(n) - \hat{S}(n))^2] = \text{minimum} \qquad \text{[8.8.2.1]}$$

where $D(n) = S\,(n - n_0)$ for cases (1) and (2) and $D(n) = S(n + n_0)$ for case (3).

8.8.2.1 The Discrete Time, Pure Prediction Wiener Filter   In Appendix 5 the continuous time solution for the Wiener filter is given along with several examples. Here we present only the solution for the pure prediction problem, namely, for case (1). For this case we modify Figure 8.12 as shown in Figure 8.13.

The form of the filter in Figure 8.13 is the same as that for Figure 7.25, that is, the inverse filter model. We are trying to estimate $X(n)$ by minimizing the error given by the difference between $X(n)$ and its estimate. We know from Chapter 7 that the form of the Wiener

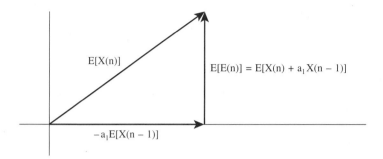

Figure 8.14   The principle of orthogonality. The data is orhtogonal to the error.

filter for this case will be an all zero (or MA) filter, since it is the inverse filter. However, we will show this below. In Chapter 7 we used the method of least squares. However, here we use ensemble averaging and minimize the mean squared error as follows:

$$\mathscr{E} = E\left[E^2(n)\right] = E\left[\left[X(n) - \hat{X}(n)\right]^2\right] \qquad \text{[8.8.2.1.1]}$$

$$= E\left[\left[X(n) + \sum_{k=1}^{p} a_k\, X(n-k)\right]^2\right]$$

Then

$$\hat{X}(n) = -\sum_{k=1}^{p} a_k\, X(n-k) \qquad \text{[8.8.2.1.2]}$$

Then minimizing the mean squared error with respect to an arbitrary a_i, we have

$$\frac{\partial \mathscr{E}}{\partial a_i} = 0 = 2\, E\left(\left[X(n) + \sum_{k=1}^{p} a_k\, X(n-k)\right]X(n-i)\right) \qquad \text{[8.8.2.1.3]}$$

Provided a minimum exists, then it follows that

$$E\left(\left[X(n) + \sum_{k=1}^{p} a_k\, X(n-k)\right]\, X(n-i)\right) = E[E(n)\, X(n-i)] = 0 \qquad \text{[8.8.2.1.4]}$$

where [8.8.2.1.4] is valid for $i = 1, 2, \ldots, p$. This last result, as we have seen in Chapter 7, is known as the **principle of orthogonality,** where the error is orthogonal to the data. This is shown again in Figure 8.14 for the case when $k = 1$ and $i = 1$.

As in Chapter 7, we can rewrite [8.8.2.1.4] such that

$$\sum_{k=1}^{p} a_k\, E[X(n-k)\, X(n-i)] = -E[X(n)\, X(n-i)] \qquad \text{[8.8.2.1.5]}$$

for $i = 1, 2, \ldots, p$. Then since

$$R_{XX}(i-k) = E[X(n-k)\, X(n-i)] \qquad \text{[8.8.2.1.6]}$$

we have

$$\sum_{k=1}^{p} a_k R_{XX}(i-k) = -R_{XX}(i) \quad \text{for } i = 1, 2, \ldots, p \qquad \text{[8.8.2.1.7]}$$

These equations are known by various names: the **Wiener–Hopf** equations, the **normal** equations, the **Yule–Walker** equations. The correlation functions and the a_k coefficients are not estimates, since they are determined by ensemble averaging. Thus, we see that the least square linear prediction filter is an estimate of the pure prediction Wiener filter. The filter coefficients derived by the least square method are estimates for the Wiener filter coefficients. As we did in Chapter 7, we can write [8.8.2.1.7] in matrix form as follows:

$$\begin{bmatrix} R_{XX}(0) & R_{XX}(-1) & \vdots & R_{XX}(-(p-1)) \\ R_{XX}(1) & R_{XX}(0) & \vdots & R_{XX}(-(p-2)) \\ \vdots & \vdots & \vdots & \vdots \\ R_{XX}(p-1) & R_{XX}(p-2) & & R_{XX}(0) \end{bmatrix} \begin{bmatrix} a_1 \\ a_2 \\ \vdots \\ a_p \end{bmatrix} = - \begin{bmatrix} R_{XX}(1) \\ R_{XX}(2) \\ \vdots \\ R_{XX}(p) \end{bmatrix} \qquad \text{[8.8.2.1.8]}$$

which can be expressed more concisely in matrix notation as

$$[R_{XX}]\vec{a} = -\vec{R}_{XX} \qquad \text{[8.8.2.1.9]}$$

This equation is to be compared with the integral equation solution in Appendix 5 for the continuous time Wiener filter.

The mean squared error is

$$\mathscr{E} = E[E^2(n)] = R_{XX}(0)\,a_0 + \sum_{k=1}^{p} a_k R_{XX}(k) \qquad \text{[8.8.2.1.10]}$$

where $a_0 = 1$. Then the **extended** or **augmented normal equations** become

$$\begin{bmatrix} R_{XX}(0) & R_{XX}(-1) & \vdots & R_{XX}(-p) \\ R_{XX}(1) & R_{XX}(0) & \vdots & R_{XX}(-(p-1)) \\ \vdots & \vdots & \vdots & \vdots \\ R_{XX}(p) & R_{XX}(p-1) & & R_{XX}(0) \end{bmatrix} \begin{bmatrix} a_0 \\ a_1 \\ a_2 \\ \vdots \\ a_p \end{bmatrix} = \begin{bmatrix} \mathscr{E} \\ 0 \\ \vdots \\ 0 \end{bmatrix} \qquad \text{[8.8.2.1.11]}$$

These equations are of the same form as those developed in Chapter 7 for the linear prediction filter. However, the above equations use ensemble averaging. The filter configuration is the same in Figure 8.15. In practice we use the estimation techniques we developed in Chapter 7.

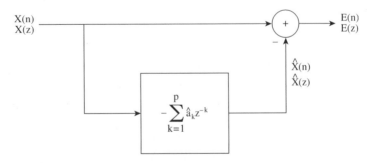

Figure 8.15   The Wiener filter for pure prediction

Note that the Wiener filter is not E(z)/X(Z); rather, it is expressed as

$$\frac{\vec{X}(z)}{X(z)} = H(z) = -\sum_{k=1}^{p} a_k z^{-k} \qquad \text{[8.8.2.1.12]}$$

where the a_k coefficients are the Wiener filter coefficients. This filter is an all zero filter. The Wiener filter usually allows an h(0), that is, an output proportional to X(n). Thus, we usually have

$$\text{Wiener}(z) = h(0) + h(1) z^{-1} + \cdots + h(p-1)z^{-(p-1)}$$

If we delay the Wiener filter, then we have

$$z^{-1}\,\text{Wiener}(z) = h(0)\, z^{-1} + h(1)\, z^{-2} + \cdots + h(p-1)z^{-p}$$

Now, comparing the coefficients of [8.8.2.1.12] with the delayed Wiener filter, we have

$$h(0) = -a_1, h(1) = -a_2, \cdots, h(p-1) = -a_p$$

This is the same as the inverse linear prediction filter, except that the feed forward term X(n) is not present. We shall call this the modified inverse linear prediction filter.

Figure 8.16 shows the relationships between the Wiener filter, the modified inverse linear prediction filter, and the delayed Wiener filter. Here it is easy to see how the Wiener filter is related to an MA filter and the inverse linear prediction filter.

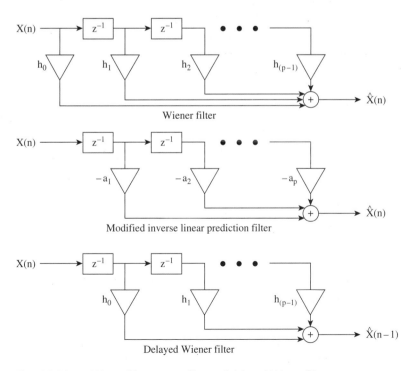

Figure 8.16   Wiener filter, inverse filter and delayed Wiener filter

The power spectral density of the Wiener filter is

$$S(f) = \left| -\sum_{k=1}^{P} a_k z^{-k} \right|^2 = \left| \sum_{k=1}^{P} a_k z^{-k} \right|^2 \quad \text{for } z = e^{j2\pi f} \qquad \textbf{[8.8.2.1.13]}$$

Example 8.17   Determine the discrete time pure prediction Wiener filter when the correlation matrix is given as

$$[R_{XX}(k)] = \begin{bmatrix} 1.0 & 0.25 & 0.0625 & 0.0039 \\ 0.25 & 1.0 & 0.25 & 0.0625 \\ 0.0625 & 0.25 & 1.0 & 0.25 \\ 0.0039 & 0.0625 & 0.25 & 1.0 \end{bmatrix}$$

The matrix equation to be solved is

$$[R_{XX}]\vec{a} = -\vec{R}_{XX}$$

where

$$\vec{R}_{XX} = [0.25\ 0.0625\ 0.0039\ 0.00001]^T$$

The solution for the vector of Wiener filter coefficients is

$$\vec{a} = [-0.25, -0.0031, 0.0130, -0.0021]^T$$

8.8.2.2 The Discrete Time, Estimation (Smoothing) Wiener Filter   Following the development in Appendix 5, one can show that the nonrealizable Wiener estimation (smoothing) filter is the following:

$$H(f) = \frac{S_{SS}(f)}{S_{SS}(f) + S_{NN}(f)} \qquad \textbf{[8.8.2.2.1]}$$

where we have assumed the input signal and noise are independent discrete time random sequences. This filter will generally not be causal. However, this result can be used to illustrate how the filter can be used to enhance the signal in the presence of noise. Note that the filter is such that it tends to enhance those frequencies where the ratio of the signal-to-noise power is large.

Example 8.18   Suppose we have the sum of two independent random sequences $X(n) = S(n) + N(n)$, and their power spectra are

$$S_{SS}(f) = \frac{4}{10 + \omega^2} \quad \text{and} \quad S_{NN}(f) = 1$$

Determine the nonrealizable Wiener smoothing filter and then filter the signal plus noise. By [8.8.2.2.1] we have

$$H(f) = \frac{\dfrac{4}{10 + \omega^2}}{1 + \dfrac{4}{10 + \omega^2}} = \frac{4}{14 + \omega^2}$$

Then filtering the power spectrum of the signal plus noise, we obtain

$$[S_{SS}(f) + S_{NN}(f)] H(f) = \left[1 + \frac{4}{10 + \omega^2}\right]\left[\frac{4}{14 + \omega^2}\right] = \frac{4}{10 + \omega^2}$$

Thus, the Wiener smoothing filter recovers the signal power spectrum from the signal plus noise power spectrum.

8.9   SUMMARY

The purpose of this chapter was to determine the response of linear systems to random processes, including signals plus noise. The output autocorrelation function was shown to be a function of the input autocorrelation function and the impulse response of the system. The output power spectral density was determined to be the product of the input power spectral density and the magnitude squared of the system transfer function. The examples illustrated how we could calculate the output autocorrelation function, the power spectral density, and the output probability density function. We also used the techniques of this chapter and the previous chapter to calculate the bit error probability for a simple PCM integrating detector.

Next we developed a similar set of equations for discrete time linear systems.

This chapter also briefly outlined two optimum filters, the matched filter and the Wiener filter. The matched filter was designed to maximize the output signal-to-noise ratio for a known input signal and a known input noise spectrum for continuous time systems. The matched filter was shown to be a correlation filter, which can be used to detect the presence of a signal in noise. The solution for the physically realizable, continuous time matched filter appears in Appendix 4. We briefly outlined the solution for the discrete time matched filter.

The Wiener filter was shown to be a least-mean-squared error filter. It may be used to predict a signal at some future time, to estimate the signal using a delay, or to predict and estimate the signal. In this chapter we determined the discrete time Wiener filter for pure prediction using ensemble averaging and showed how the solution is similar in form to that developed for the linear prediction inverse filter in Chapter 7. The solution for the continuous time Wiener filter is given in Appendix 5, along with several examples and the physically realizable solution.

A practice examination is available in Appendix 6 for Chapters 5 through 8.

PROBLEMS

8.1   Consider the nonlinear device $Y(t) = a X^2(t)$, where $X(t) = S(t) + N(t)$. Determine the mean of $Y(t)$ and the autocorrelation function for $Y(t)$ when the signal $S(t)$ and the noise $N(t)$ are both stationary with zero mean and $S(t)$ is independent of $N(t)$.

8.2   Calculate the spectrum for $Y(t)$ in Problem (8.1) if

$$S_{SS}(f) = \frac{A^2}{4}\{\delta(t + f_c) + \delta(f - f_c)\}$$

and

$$S_{NN}(f) = \begin{cases} N_0, & f_c - \dfrac{B}{2} \le f \le \dfrac{B}{2} + f_c \\ N_0, & -f_c - \dfrac{B}{2} \le f \le -f_c + \dfrac{B}{2} \\ 0, & \text{elsewhere} \end{cases}$$

8.3 Derive the crosscorrelation function between the input and output of a linear system with zero initial conditions and with an input that is a continuous time random process that is wide sense stationary. Show that when the input is white noise, then the crosscorrelation function is proportional to the impulse response of the system.

8.4 Find the equivalent noise bandwidth for a low pass RC network.

8.5 It is desired to learn the characteristics of a certain filter. A white noise source with an amplitude of 15 watts/Hz is connected to the input of the filter. The power spectrum of the filter output is measured and found to be $\dfrac{30}{\omega^2 + 10^2}$. What is the bandwidth (3 dB) of the filter? What is the attenuation (or gain) at zero frequency? What is the impulse response? Show a possible filter that satisfies these conditions.

8.6 Suppose we wish to detect PCM pulses in white noise, that is, we wish to determine the amplitude of each pulse as accurately as possible in a train of PCM pulses. One technique is to sample the pulse plus noise and measure the voltage of the sample. Show that filtering the PCM wave train plus noise before sampling improves the signal-to-noise ratio. Use a simple RC lowpass filter. Where would you suggest the 3 dB point of the filter be set? It is suggested that this problem first be worked by considering a duty cycle $\frac{t_0}{T_0} \ll 1$, where t_0 is the pulse width and T_0 is the period. Let the signal-to-noise ratio be defined as the peak amplitude of the output signal to the rms value of the output noise. Then express the output signal-to-noise ratio in terms of the pulse width and the equivalent noise bandwidth of the filter. Next determine the relationship between the pulse width and the equivalent noise bandwidth that maximizes the output signal-to-noise ratio. Then generalize these results.

8.7 For the high pass RC network shown in Figure 8.17, let $X(t) = A \sin((\omega_c t + \Theta) + N(t))$, where $N(t)$ is white, wide sense stationary Gaussian noise and Θ is a random variable uniformly distributed from 0 to 2π. Let the initial conditions be zero. Find the output mean, variance, and autocorrelation function. Find the output spectrum and the output signal-to-noise ratio. Plot the spectrum and autocorrelation function.

8.8 A parallel RLC network is driven by an input current source of $A \sin((\omega_c t + \Theta) + N(t))$, where $N(t)$ is white, wide sense stationary noise with zero mean. The output is the voltage across the network. The phase Θ is a random variable uniformly distributed from 0 to 2π. Find the output power spectrum by first computing the output autocorrelation function and then transforming. Then check this result by using [8.4.1]. Next, determine the output signal-to-noise

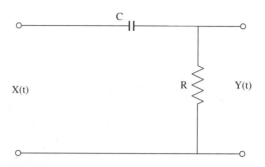

Figure 8.17   RC circuit for Problem 8.7

ratio and optimize the bandwidth to maximize the signal-to-noise ratio. Assume ω_c differs from the center frequency of the RLC filter. The autocorrelation function may have to be calculated as a function of t and τ and then let t go to infinity to find the steady state output. The filter may be overdamped, critically damped, or under damped. It may also have an initial voltage on the capacitor and a current through the inductor.

8.9 Suppose the signal autocorrelation function is

$$R_{SS}(\tau) = ae^{-b|\tau|} \quad a > 0 \text{ and } b > 0$$

and no noise is present. Determine the optimum prediction filter. Discuss the solution for $T < 0$ and $T > 0$. For $T > 0$ what is the form of the optimum prediction filter? Discuss a possible circuit implementation for this filter. Hint: See the solution in Appendix 5. How is the solution for this problem related to Example A5.1?

8.10 Suppose the signal spectrum is a constant $S_{SS}(f) = 1$ and the noise spectrum is a constant $S_{NN}(f) = 10$. Determine the optimum Wiener filter. (Hint: Consider Example 8.18 or Example A5.1.)

8.11 Find the matched filter when the signal is a triangular waveform

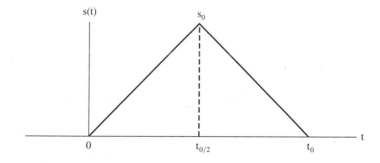

and the noise is stationary and white with a power spectrum of N_0.

8.12   Determine the realizable matched filter when the signal and noise are uncorrelated and given as

$$s(t) = e^{at} u(-t), \quad a > 0$$

$$R_{NN}(\tau) = e^{-b|\tau|}$$

(Hint: Don't make this problem difficult. Just do the solution in a straightforward manner. See Appendix 4 if you need help.)

8.13   In [8.8.1.3.10] the signal-to-noise ratio was given for the optimum matched filter. Derive this equation. First show that if $X(n)$ is a discrete random sequence applied to a linear filter with a unit pulse response $h(n)$, that the output power for the filter is

$$P_0 = E\left[\sum Y^2(n) \right] = E[\vec{Y}(n)^T \vec{Y}(n)] = \vec{h}(n)^T [R_{XX}(k)] \; \vec{h}(n)$$

where $Y(n)$ is the filter output. Hint: Write the filter output in vector form; that is, express the convolution theorem in vector form.

8.14   The output $Y(t)$ of a linear filter is c times the input $X(t)$. Show that $R_{YY}(\tau) = c^2 R_{XX}(\tau)$.

8.15   A random process is delayed as shown in Figure 8.18. The output $Y(t)$ is $Y(t) = X(t) + X(t - T) + X(t - 2T)$. Determine $R_{YY}(\tau)$ as a function of $R_{XX}(\tau)$. Find $E[(Y(t))^2]$.

8.16   Show that the crosscorrelation between an input $X(t)$ and the output $Y(t)$ of a linear filter with impulse response $h(t)$ is

$$R_{XY}(\tau) = \int_{-\infty}^{\infty} h(t) R_{XX}(\tau - t) \, dt$$

8.17   If the inputs to two linear filters $h_1(t)$ and $h_2(t)$ are $X_1(t)$ and $X_2(t)$, respectively, show that the crosscorrelation between the outputs $Y_1(t)$ and $Y_2(t)$ of the two filters is

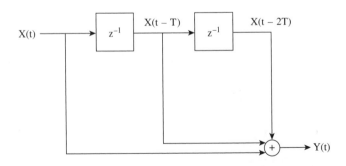

Figure 8.18

$$R_{Y_1 Y_2}(\tau) = \int_{-\infty}^{\infty} \int_{-\infty}^{\infty} h(\alpha) \, h(\beta) \, R_{X_1 X_2}(\tau + \alpha - \beta) \, d\alpha \, d\beta$$

8.18 If the input to a linear filter is a random telegraph process with c zero crossings per second and an amplitude A, determine the output power spectral density. The filter impulse response is $h(t) = b \exp(-at)$ for $t \geq 0$ and is zero for $t < 0$. Hint: See Problem 6.12 for the autocorrelation function for the random telegraph process.

8.19 If the input to a linear filter with impulse response $h(t) = b \exp(-at)$ for $t \geq 0$ and zero for $t < 0$ is white noise with power spectral density N_0, determine the autocorrelation function of the output. Hint: Consult the previous problem.

8.20 The input to a linear filter is a random process with the following autocorrelation function:

$$R_{XX}(\tau) = \frac{A\omega_0}{\pi} \frac{\sin(\omega_0 \tau)}{\omega_0 \tau}$$

The impulse response of the filter is of the same form and is

$$h(t) = \frac{\omega_1}{\pi} \frac{\sin(\omega_1 t)}{\omega_1 t}$$

Determine the autocorrelation function of the filter output for $\omega_0 \geq \omega_1$ and $\omega_0 < \omega_1$.

8.21 The power spectrum at the input to an ideal band-pass filter is

$$S_{XX}(f) = \frac{A}{1 + \left(\frac{\omega}{\omega_0}\right)^2}$$

Let the transfer function for the ideal band-pass filter be $H(f) = B$ for $\omega_1 < |\omega| < \omega_2$ and zero elsewhere. Sketch the input power spectrum and the band-pass filter. Determine the autocorrelation function of the output. You may have to make a reasonable approximation to obtain a simplified form. Assume that $\omega_1 \gg \omega_0$, $\omega_2 \gg \omega_0$, and $(\omega_2 - \omega_1)/\omega_2 \ll 1$

8.22 Determine the noise bandwidth for a filter with impulse response $h(t) = b \exp(-at)$ for $t \geq 0$ and zero for $t < 0$.

8.23 A filter has the following transfer function:

$$h(f) = \frac{4}{10 + j\omega}$$

Determine the ratio of the noise bandwidth for this filter to its 3-dB bandwidth.

8.24 Define a running average of a random process X(t) as

$$Y(t) = \frac{1}{T} \int_{t-T}^{t} X(\beta) \, d\beta$$

Find the power spectral density of Y(t) as a function of the power spectral density of X(t).

8.25 If the crosscorrelation function between the input X(n) and output Y(n) of a discrete time linear system h(n) is

$$R_{XY}(k) = E[X(n) Y(n + k)]$$

then show that

$$R_{XY}(k) = E[X(n) Y(n + k)] = \sum_{i=-\infty}^{\infty} h(i) R_{XX}(k - i)$$

8.26 A discrete random sequence X(n) is the input to a discrete linear filter h(n). The output is Y(n). Let $Z(n) = X(n + i) - Y(n)$. Find $E[(Z(n))^2]$ in terms of the autocorrelation functions for X(n) and Y(n) and the crosscorrelation function between X(n) and Y(n).

8.27 The unit pulse response of a discrete linear filter is $h(n) = a^n$ for $n \geq 0$ and is zero for $n < 0$, and $|a| < 1$. The autocorrelation function for the input random sequence is

$$R_{XX}(k) = 1 \quad \text{for} \quad k = 0 \text{ and is zero otherwise.}$$

Determine the crosscorrelation function between the input and output random sequences.

8.28 Find the power spectral density of a discrete random sequence with the following autocorrelation function:

$$R_{XX}(k) = a b^{|k|} \quad \text{where } |b| < 1$$

8.29 A discrete time linear filter has a unit pulse response h(n). The input to this filter is a random sequence with uncorrelated samples. Show that the output power spectral density is real and nonnegative.

8.30 Is the following function a valid autocorrelation function?

$$R_{XX}(0) = 1 \text{ and } R_{XX}(3) = R_{XX}(-3) = 0.75 \text{ and } R_{XX}(k) = 0 \quad \text{otherwise}$$

8.31 Suppose we have the sum of two independent random sequences with power spectra

$$S_{SS}(f) = \frac{2}{50 + \omega^2} \text{ and } S_{NN}(f) = 40$$

Determine the Wiener smoothing filter and then filter the signal plus noise power spectrum.

8.32 Determine the Wiener smoothing filter if the input random process is the sum of two independent random sequences S(n) + N(n), where the respective autocorrelation functions are

$$R_{SS}(k) = \frac{(\frac{1}{10})^{|k|}}{1 - (\frac{1}{10})^2} 10 \qquad R_{NN}(k) = \frac{(\frac{1}{4})^{|k|}}{1 - (\frac{1}{4})^2} 100$$

Determine the Wiener smoothing filter and then filter the signal plus noise power spectrum. Hint: See Example 6.33 for help on determining the power spectrum. What is the input S/N? Estimate the output S/N. Discuss whether or not the Wiener filter improves the S/N. Hint: Compare the spectra of the Wiener filter, the signal, and the noise by plotting each on the same graph.

MATLAB PROBLEMS

8.1M You have a random process with the following correlation matrix

$$
\begin{bmatrix}
1.0 & 0.3 & 0.09 & 0.0027 \\
0.3 & 1.0 & 0.3 & 0.09 \\
0.09 & 0.3 & 1.0 & 0.3 \\
0.0027 & 0.09 & 0.3 & 1
\end{bmatrix}
$$

Determine the pure prediction Wiener filter. Then determine the power spectrum of the Wiener filter. Are the results what you expected?

8.2M Generate a 100-point random sequence using *randn* in MATLAB. Use a first order LP filter to filter this random sequence; that is, the filter is

$$
A(z) = \frac{1}{1 + a_1 z^{-1}} = \frac{z}{z + a_1}
$$

Let $a_1 = -0.1$. Use the filtered data to obtain an estimate for the first order prediction Wiener filter. Compare the estimated filter coefficient with the true value.

8.3M Suppose we have the following correlation matrix:

$$
\begin{bmatrix}
1 & 0.3 \\
0.3 & 1
\end{bmatrix}
$$

Determine the first order Wiener prediction filter. Calculate $\hat{R}_{XX}(2)$ using the autocorrelation prediction equation given in Chapter 7, namely, [7.7.3.27]. Now suppose you are told the correlation matrix is

$$
\begin{bmatrix}
1.0 & 0.3 & (0.3)^4 \\
0.3 & 1.0 & 0.3 \\
(0.3)^4 & 0.3 & 1.0
\end{bmatrix}
$$

Compare $\hat{R}_{XX}(2)$ to the true value. Now determine the second order Wiener prediction filter. Calculate $\hat{R}_{XX}(3)$ using [7.7.3.27]. Plot and compare the true values of the autocorrelation function with the predicted values.

8.4M Construct a signal plus noise random sequence using 10 samples of the following:

$$
X(n) = \cos(2\pi f_0 n T) + N(n)
$$

where N(n) is generated by *rand* in MATLAB, and f_0 is $(0.1)f_s = 0.1/T$. Design a discrete time matched filter for the cosine signal. Filter the signal plus noise sequence with the matched filter. At what sample value does the filter output peak?

8.5M   Construct a signal plus noise random sequence using 10 samples of the following:

$$X(n) = \cos(2\pi f_1 n T) + 10 \cos(2\pi f_2 n T) + N(n)$$

where N(n) is generated by *rand* in MATLAB, and f_1 is $(0.1)f_s = 0.1/T$ and f_2 is $(0.4)f_s = 0.4/T$. Design a discrete time matched filter for the f_2 cosine signal. Filter the signal plus noise sequence with the matched filter. At what sample value does the filter output peak?

8.6M   Determine the discrete time matched filter for the following sampled signal:

$$\vec{s}(n) = [0, 0.2, 0.4, 0.6, 0.8, 1.0, 0.8, 0.6, 0.4, 0.2, 0]^T$$

Let the noise correlation matrix be

$$\begin{bmatrix} 1.0 & 0.3 & (0.3)^4 \\ 0.3 & 1.0 & 0.3 \\ (0.3)^4 & 0.3 & 1.0 \end{bmatrix}$$

which you may extend if needed. Also find the maximum S/N and the power spectrum of the filter and the signal. Plot the spectra.

8.7M   Determine the discrete time matched filter for the following sampled signal:

$$\vec{s}(n) = [0, 0.2, 0.4, 0.6, 0.8, 1.0]^T$$

Let the noise correlation matrix be

$$\begin{bmatrix} 1.0 & 0.3 & (0.3)^4 \\ 0.3 & 1.0 & 0.3 \\ (0.3)^4 & 0.3 & 1.0 \end{bmatrix}$$

which you may extend if needed. Also find the maximum S/N and the power spectrum of the filter and the signal. Plot the spectra.

8.8M   If the noise autocorrelation function is

$$R_{NN}(k) = (0.25)^{|k|}$$

and the signal vector is

$$\vec{s}(n) = [0.1, 0.3, 0.5]^T$$

then determine the discrete time matched filter, the maximum S/N, and the power spectrum of the noise, the filter, and the signal. Plot the spectra.

8.9M   If the noise autocorrelation function is

$$R_{NN}(k) = (0.5)^{|k|}$$

and the signal autocorrelation function is

$$R_{ss}(k) = 10 \ (0.8)^{|k|}$$

then determine the discrete time matched filter for the case when $k = 0, 1, 2, 3$. What is the maximum S/N? Determine and plot the power spectrum of the noise, signal, and the filter.

8.10M If a random sequence has the following autocorrelation function

$$R_{xx}(k) = 10 \ (0.8)^{|k|}$$

then find the discrete time, pure prediction Wiener filter. Determine and plot the power spectra for the random sequence and the filter.

8.11M Analyze a segment of the vowel in the data file ee.mat included with the software for Chapter 7. Window the data with a hamming window prior to analysis. Model the vowel data as an LP model of order 13. Use this LP model to calculate the power spectrum. Assume this is the signal power spectrum. Now take the original vowel data (not the modeled data) and add Gaussian noise to it using *randn* in MATLAB. Adjust the noise level to give you an approximate S/N of 1. Model this signal plus noise sequence using an LP model of order 13. Calculate the power spectrum of this signal plus noise model. Now design a Wiener smoothing filter using this data. Then filter the signal plus noise model with the Wiener filter. Filter the original signal plus noise data before it was modeled. Plot the various spectra and compare and discuss your results. When you design the Wiener filter, be sure to adjust your design for zero values of the spectrum that can occur in the filter denominator. Repeat the problem for a S/N = 0.1. The first three resonances for this vowel (/i/ as in see) occur at approximately, 270, 2290, and 3010 Hz. Repeat this problem for the vowel /a/ (as in Bach) in file a.mat. The first three resonances for this vowel occur at approximately 570, 840, and 2410 Hz.

1

UNIT STEP AND DELTA (IMPULSE) FUNCTIONS

A1.1   UNIT STEP FUNCTION

The unit step function is given as $u(t) = 1$ for $t \geq 0$ and $u(t) = 0$ for $t < 0$. This is illustrated in Figure A1.1.

The same definition applies to a unit step function in the frequency domain with t replaced by f and T replaced by f_0.

A1.2   DELTA (IMPULSE) FUNCTION

The Dirac delta function will be referred to here as simply the delta function. Note that the delta function is to be distinguished from the discrete time Kronecker delta function, which is $\delta_{ij} = 0$, $i \neq j$ and is $\delta_{ij} = 1$, $i = j$. The unit pulse function is a discrete time function that is often denoted as $\delta(n) = 1$, $n = 0$ and $\delta(n) = 0$, $n \neq 0$.

The delta function is defined as

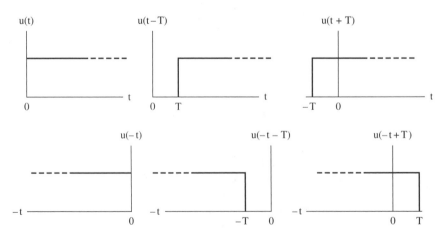

Figure A1.1   Unit step function for $T \geq 0$

$$\int_{-\infty}^{\infty} f(x)\, \delta(x)\, dx = f(0)$$

An alternate definition is

$$\int_{-\infty}^{\infty} \delta(x)\, dx = 1$$

where $\delta(x)$ is undefined for $x = 0$ and $\delta(x) = 0$ for $x \neq 0$. It is sometimes said that $\delta(x) = \infty$ for $x = 0$.

Another definition is

$$\delta(x) = \frac{1}{2\pi} \int_{-\infty}^{\infty} e^{-j\omega x}\, d\omega$$

Some delta function properties and identities include the following:

$$\delta(x) = \delta(-x)$$

$$\frac{d}{dx}\, \delta(x) = -\frac{d}{dx}\, \delta(-x)$$

$$x\delta(x) = 0$$

$$x\, \frac{d}{dx}\, \delta(x) = -\delta(x)$$

$$\delta(ax) = \frac{1}{|a|}\, \delta(x)$$

$$\delta(x^2 - a^2) = \frac{1}{2|a|}[\delta(x - a) + \delta(x + a)]$$

$$f(x)\delta(x - a) = f(a)\delta(x - a)$$

$$\delta[f(x)] = \sum_{n} \frac{1}{\left| \dfrac{d}{dx} f(x_n) \right|} \delta(x - x_n) \quad \text{where } f(x_n) = 0.$$

$$\delta(\vec{F}(\vec{r})) = \sum_{n} \frac{1}{|J(\vec{r}_n)|} \delta(\vec{r} - \vec{r}_n) \quad \text{where } \vec{F}(\vec{r}_n) = 0 \text{ and } d\vec{F} = J\, d\vec{r}$$

A useful identity is

$$\frac{1}{T_0} \sum_{n=-\infty}^{\infty} \delta\left(f - \frac{n}{T_0}\right) = \sum_{n=-\infty}^{\infty} e^{-j\omega n T_0}$$

Some limiting forms for the delta function include the following:

1. $\delta(x) = \lim_{\epsilon \to 0} f_\epsilon(x)$

where

$$f_\epsilon(x) = \frac{1}{\epsilon} \quad |x| < \frac{\epsilon}{2}$$

$$= 0 \quad |x| > \frac{\epsilon}{2}$$

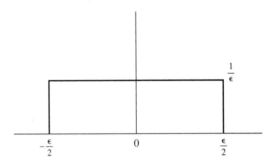

2. $\delta(x) = \lim\limits_{\epsilon \to 0} \dfrac{1}{\pi} \dfrac{\epsilon}{x^2 + \epsilon^2}$

3. $\delta(x) = \lim\limits_{\epsilon \to 0} \dfrac{1}{\sqrt{\pi}} \dfrac{1}{\epsilon} e^{-x^2/\epsilon^2}$

4. $\delta(x) = \dfrac{d}{dx} u(x) \qquad u(x) = 0 \quad x < 0$

$$= 1 \quad x > 0$$

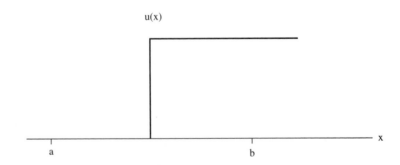

$$\int \frac{du(x)}{dx} dx = u(x) \bigg|_a^b = u(b) - u(a) = 1 - 0 = 1$$

5.

$$\delta(x) = \lim_{a \to \infty} \left[\frac{a}{\pi} \left(\frac{\sin ax}{ax} \right) \right]$$

$$\delta(t) = \lim_{\omega \to \infty} \left[\left(\frac{\sin \omega t}{\pi t} \right) \right]$$

$$\delta(\omega) = \lim_{t \to \infty} \left[\left(\frac{\sin \omega t}{\pi \omega} \right) \right]$$

$$\delta(f) = 2\pi \delta(\omega) = \lim_{t \to \infty} \left[\left(2 \frac{\sin \omega t}{\omega} \right) \right]$$

APPENDIX

2

SOME TYPICAL TIME FUNCTIONS AND SOME OF THEIR CHARACTERISTICS

A2.1   SOME TYPICAL TIME FUNCTIONS

The following figures illustrate some typical time functions and their corresponding autocorrelation functions, power spectral density, probability density, and cumulative probability functions. The MATLAB m-files for generating these characteristics are also included with the software for this book under subdirectory ap2. The names of each file are listed below. You can execute each of these files in MATLAB and view the various characteristics as sequential plots. The file genpdf.m is called by both psin.m and singausn.m. This file was created to reduce the amount of computation time.

Time Function	Name Of M-File
Sine wave	psin.m
Square wave	squarw.m
Pulse	pulse.m
Triangular	triangle.m
Sawtooth	saw.m
Wideband Gaussian noise	gausn.m
Bandlimited noise	blimitn.m
Sine wave plus Gaussian noise	singausn.m
Pseudo random binary sequence noise	pseqn.m

Typical Time Functions and Some of Their Characteristics

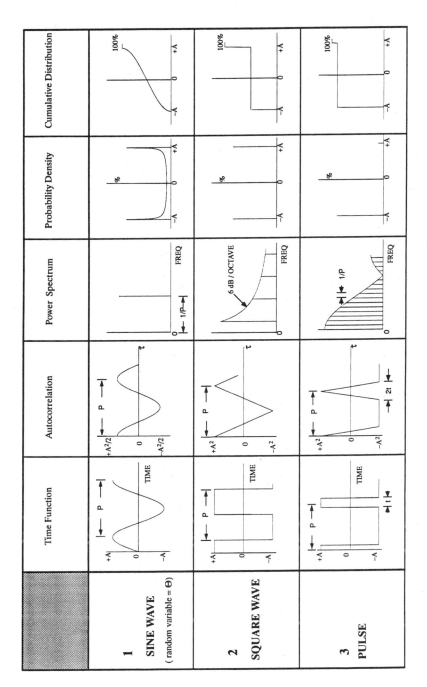

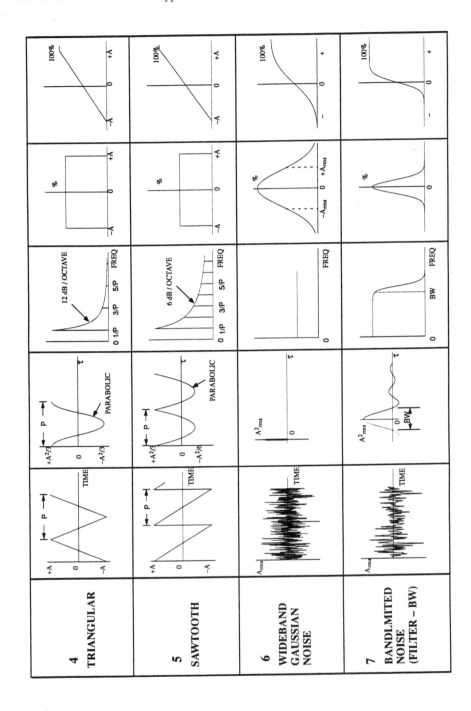

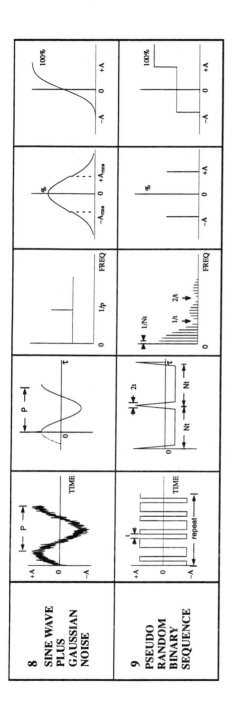

APPENDIX

3

SOME TOPICS IN FOURIER TRANSFORMS, Z-TRANSFORMS, AND SPECTRAL ANALYSIS

A3.1 INTRODUCTION

In this appendix we briefly review some topics in frequency analysis, including Fourier series, the Fourier transform, the Laplace transform, and the z-transform. Our review will focus on the analysis of deterministic signals.

A3.2 SIGNAL SPACE

This section presents highlights of signal space analysis. Very often it may be desirable, from a mathematical viewpoint, to express a specific function $x(t)$ as a function of other functions, say, as a series expansion. This summation may be finite or infinite. Such representations are often useful in that they may make certain properties of the original function more easily discerned, or the functions of the series expansion may be more easily operated upon by still other functions in a particular situation. Thus, we can represent a function as follows:

$$x(t) \cong \sum_n c_n g_n(t) \qquad\qquad \textbf{[A3.2.1]}$$

where we have used an approximation symbol rather than strict equality because equality may not always exist between the function $x(t)$ and the expansion in terms of the set of functions $\{g_n(t)\}$, which are selected as being suitable for a particular problem, and the $\{c_n\}$ are weighting factors. We may consider the function $x(t)$ as a vector in a **signal space** with coordinates $\{g_n(t)\}$. The c_n designate the distance that must be traversed along each coordinate, $\{g_n(t)\}$, to attain the final value of the vector, $x(t)$. We illustrate this idea in Figure A3.1 for two dimensions where $x(t) = c_1 g_1(t) + c_2 g_2(t)$.

If we know or specify the $\{g_n(t)\}$, how can we determine the $\{c_n\}$? Several techniques exist. One method that provides an approximation to $x(t)$ is to minimize the mean square error between $x(t)$ and the summation over some specified interval for which we wish the approximation to hold. Thus, we wish to minimize I, where

$$I = \frac{1}{b-a} \int_a^b [x(t) - \sum_n c_n g_n(t)]^2 \, dt \qquad\qquad \textbf{[A3.2.2]}$$

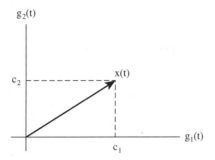

Figure A3.1   A simple two-dimensional
signal space

We determine from this equation the set of coefficients $\{c_n\}$ that minimize I. A necessary condition that can be used to accomplish this is

$$\frac{\partial I}{\partial c_i} = 0 \quad \text{for every i} \qquad \text{[A3.2.3]}$$

The set $\{c_n\}$ may not be unique, however. We shall not pursue this point here, but shall illustrate another method for determining the $\{c_n\}$. This method makes use of the concept of orthogonal functions.

Two nonzero functions $x(t)$ and $y(t)$ are said to be **orthogonal** on the interval (a,b) if and only if

$$\int_a^b x(t)y^*(t)dt = 0 \qquad \text{[A3.2.4]}$$

where the * denotes complex conjugate. In vector space terminology [A3.2.4] is called the **inner product of the functions**. Equation [A3.2.4] can be modified to include a set of functions $\{h_n(t)\}$ that are said to form an **orthogonal set** on (a,b) if and only if

$$\int_a^b h_i(t) \, h_j^*(t)dt = 0 \ \text{ for all } i \neq j \qquad \text{[A3.2.5]}$$

The set is said to be **orthonormal** if, in addition,

$$\int_a^b h_i(t)h_i^*(t)dt = 1 \quad \text{for all i} \qquad \text{[A3.2.6]}$$

Here each function in the set is orthogonal to every other function in the set, where not all the functions are zero.

It should be emphasized that the concept of orthogonality is related directly to a specified interval (a,b). Thus, a set of functions that is orthogonal on one interval may not be orthogonal on another interval.

A further generality is to include a **weighting function** w(t). Then

$$\int_a^b w(t)h_i(t)h_j^*(t)dt = 0, \quad i \neq j \qquad \text{[A3.2.7]}$$

This equation defines an orthogonal set on the interval (a,b) with respect to a weighting function w(t). The weighting function (or kernal) is usually specified as positive over the interval (a,b). Some typical weighting functions and their corresponding applicable intervals are: Legendre polynomials, $w(t) = 1, (-1,1)$; Hermite polynomials, $w(t) = e^{-t^2}, (-\infty, \infty)$; Laguerre polynomials, $w(t) = e^{-t}, (0, \infty)$; Chebyshev polynomials, $w(t) = \frac{1}{\sqrt{1-t^2}}, (-1, 1)$

If we select a set of orthogonal functions $\{h_n(t)\}$ over the interval (a,b) to approximate the function x(t) over the same interval, then

$$x(t) \cong \sum_n c_n h_n(t) \qquad \text{[A3.2.8]}$$

To determine the $\{c_n\}$, multiply both sides by $h_m^*(t)$ and integrate. Thus

$$\int_a^b x(t)h_m^*(t)dt \cong \int_a^b \sum c_n h_n(t)h_m^*(t)dt \qquad \text{[A3.2.9]}$$

$$\cong c_m \int_a^b h_n(t)h_m^*(t)dt, \quad m = n$$

$$\cong 0, \quad \text{otherwise}$$

Rearranging [A3.2.9], we have

$$c_n \cong \frac{\int_a^b x(t)h_n^*(t)dt}{\int_a^b h_n(t)h_n^*(t)dt} \qquad \text{[A3.2.10]}$$

for all n. These $\{c_n\}$ are known as the **generalized Fourier coefficients**. If the set of $\{h_n(t)\}$ are **orthonormal,** then

$$c_n \cong \int_a^b x(t)h_n^*(t)dt \qquad \text{[A3.2.11]}$$

One additional point should be mentioned, and that is the concept of **completeness,** which we explain as follows. Imagine that we have an ordinary three-dimensional space with an (x, y, z) orthogonal coordinate system. What happens if we approximate any three-dimensional vector using only the x and y coordinates? The approximation will be exact if the vector lies in the x-y plane. However, if the vector lies along the z-axis perpendicular to the x-y plane, then the best approximation in the minimum mean square error sense is the zero vector. Such an approximation is not very satisfactory, since we have tried to approximate a function (in this case a z-vector) with an incomplete set of coordinates, namely, the x-y coordinates. A **complete** set of coordinates or functions is known as the **basis** for the space.

An orthonormal set of functions $\{h_n(t)\}$ is said to be a **complete orthonormal set** if for all n

$$\int_a^b x(t)h_n^*(t)dt = 0 \qquad \text{[A3.2.12]}$$

implies that $x(t) = 0$.

A3.3   FOURIER SERIES

A particular example of an orthogonal expansion is the **Fourier series**. The set of orthogonal functions $\{h_n(t)\}$ is

$$\{1, \sin n\omega t, \cos n\omega t\}, \text{ for } n = 1, 2, 3, \ldots$$

Recall that the concept of orthogonality is directly related to a specified interval (a, b). How does this apply to the Fourier series? The frequency, ω, depends upon the interval; in fact, the interval is $T = \frac{2\pi}{\omega} = |b - a|$.

Thus, we can approximate a function $x(t)$ over the interval (a, b) by the use of [A3.2.8] as follows:

$$x(t) = a_0 + \sum_{n=1}^{\infty} [a_n \cos(n\omega t) + b_n \sin(n\omega t)] \qquad \text{[A3.3.1]}$$

where $\omega = \dfrac{2\pi}{T} = \dfrac{2\pi}{b-a}$ and by [A3.2.10] we have

$$a_n = \frac{\displaystyle\int_a^b x(t)\cos(n\omega t)\,dt}{\displaystyle\int_a^b \cos^2(n\omega t)\,dt} = \frac{2}{T}\int_a^b x(t)\cos(n\omega t)\,dt, \, n = 1, 2, \ldots \qquad \text{[A3.3.2]}$$

and

$$b_n = \frac{\displaystyle\int_a^b x(t)\sin(n\omega t)}{\displaystyle\int_a^b \sin^2(n\omega t)\,dt} = \frac{2}{T}\int_a^b x(t)\sin(n\omega t)\,dt, \, \, n = 1, 2, \ldots \qquad \text{[A3.3.3]}$$

$$a_0 = \frac{1}{T}\int_a^b x(t)\,dt \qquad \text{[A3.3.4]}$$

The function $x(t)$ need not be periodic to be expanded in a Fourier series over an interval (a, b). Furthermore, the expansion is not unique, because an innumerable number of functions exist that are the same over the interval (a, b) and they all have the same Fourier series expansion over the interval (a, b).

A sufficient condition for the Fourier series to converge everywhere in the interval is for $x(t)$ to be piecewise continuous in the closed interval $[a, b]$. What happens outside the interval? Here the series converges in the same manner, but to the periodic extension of $x(t)$. We will see this property again when we consider discrete data, the z-transform, and the discrete Fourier transform.

We may sketch the **line spectrum** of [A3.3.1], which illustrates the magnitude of each frequency component of $x(t)$. In general, two plots must be made: one for the coefficients a_n and one for the b_n, with a_0 being the dc term. However, there is another form known as the **complex Fourier series,** which allows us to plot the amplitude and phase of each frequency component. The complex Fourier series is

$$x(t) = \frac{1}{T} \sum_{-\infty}^{\infty} c_n e^{jn\omega t} \qquad \text{[A3.3.5]}$$

where

$$c_n = \int_a^b x(t) e^{-jn\omega t} dt \qquad \text{[A3.3.6]}$$

The c_n are complex numbers such that

$$\frac{c_n}{T} = \frac{1}{2} (a_n - j b_n) \qquad \text{[A3.3.7]}$$

The magnitude of c_n is the amplitude of the nth harmonic, while the phase of c_n is the phase of the nth harmonic. A plot of the magnitude of c_n is known as the **spectrum**.

Example A3.1

Find the complex Fourier series for the repetitive train of pulses of unit height shown in Figure A3.2.

$$c_n = \int_{-T/2}^{T/2} x(t) e^{-jn\omega t} dt = \int_{-\tau/2}^{\tau/2} (1) e^{-jn\omega t} dt = \tau \frac{\sin(\pi n \frac{\tau}{T})}{\pi n \frac{\tau}{T}} \qquad \text{[A3.3.8]}$$

where we let $\omega = \frac{2\pi}{T}$. The c_n are plotted in Fig. A3.2. The spacing between the c_n depends upon the reciprocal of the period of the pulse train T, while the first zero crossing of the envelope occurs at $\frac{2\pi}{\tau}$. Since the coefficients are real, the phase angle is zero. This also means that the c_n in [A3.3.8] are equal to the a_n given by [A3.3.2] and the b_n are zero. (The reader should verify this.) Note that the envelope of the spectrum is of the form $\frac{\sin(2\pi f)}{2\pi f}$.

A3.4   THE FOURIER TRANSFORM

The previous section illustrated how the Fourier series may be used as one signal space representation of a function that is defined on a finite interval. The function in that ex-

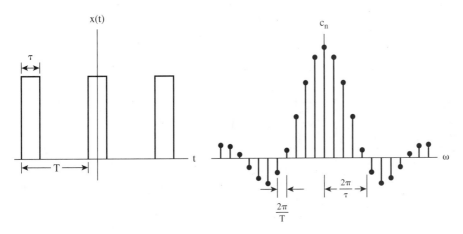

Figure A3.2   A train of pulses and its complex Fourier series

ample was periodic. What can be done when the function is not periodic? For example, aperiodic signals or transients cannot be represented by a Fourier series. However, there is an extension of the Fourier Series, known as the **Fourier transform,** that can be used for such signals.

Consider a function $x(t)$ that is defined on the interval $(-\infty, \infty)$. We will assume that over any finite interval, $x(t)$ can be represented by a Fourier series. Now we define a new function $y(t)$, such that

$$y(t) = x(t) \quad (a, b)$$

$$= 0 \quad \text{elsewhere} \tag{A3.4.1}$$

where $b - a = T$. Let us now represent $y(t)$ by a complex Fourier series, where

$$c_n = \int_a^b y(t) e^{-jn\omega t}\, dt = \int_a^b x(t)\, e^{-jn\omega t}\, dt = \int_{-\infty}^{\infty} y(t)\, e^{-jn\omega t}\, dt \tag{A3.4.2}$$

Then

$$y(t) = \frac{1}{T} \sum_{-\infty}^{\infty} c_n\, e^{jn\omega t} \tag{A3.4.3}$$

where $T = \frac{2\pi}{\omega}$ and ω is the fundamental radian frequency. Since $\omega = \Delta\omega = (n + 1)\omega - n\omega$, namely, $\Delta\omega$ is the incremental spacing between frequency components, then [A3.4.3] becomes

$$y(t) = \frac{1}{2\pi} \sum_{-\infty}^{\infty} c_n\, e^{jn\omega t}\, \Delta\omega \tag{A3.4.4}$$

If we take the limit of both sides of [A3.4.4] as $T \to \infty$ or $\Delta\omega \to 0$, then

$$x(t) = \lim_{T\to\infty} y(t) = \frac{1}{2\pi} \int_{-\infty}^{\infty} \left[\lim_{T\to\infty} c_n \right] e^{jn\omega t} \, d\omega \qquad \text{[A3.4.5]}$$

However, as $T\to\infty$, $n\omega\to\omega$, and c_n is such that it is defined for all frequencies, then

$$X(j\omega) = X(\omega) = X(f) = \lim_{T\to\infty} c_n \qquad \text{[A3.4.6]}$$

Therefore, [A3.4.5] becomes

$$x(t) = \frac{1}{2\pi} \int_{-\infty}^{\infty} X(j\omega) \, e^{j\omega t} \, d\omega \qquad \text{[A3.4.7]}$$

Note from [A3.4.2] that as $T\to\infty$

$$X(j\omega) = \lim_{T\to\infty} c_n = \int_{-\infty}^{\infty} x(t) \, e^{-j\omega t} \, dt \qquad \text{[A3.4.8]}$$

We have thus derived the **Fourier Transform pair**; that is, the **direct transform** is

$$X(j\omega) = \int_{-\infty}^{\infty} x(t) \, e^{-j\omega t} \, dt \qquad \text{[A3.4.9]}$$

and the **inverse transform** is

$$x(t) = \frac{1}{2\pi} \int_{-\infty}^{\infty} X(j\omega) \, e^{j\omega t} \, d\omega \qquad \text{[A3.4.10]}$$

Not all functions are Fourier transformable. For a function to be transformable the above limiting operations must converge properly. The sufficient conditions for the existence of the Fourier transform are:

1. $x(t)$ is absolutely integrable; namely,

$$\int_{-\infty}^{\infty} |x(t)| \, dt < \infty \qquad \text{[A3.4.11]}$$

2. $x(t)$ is representable by a Fourier series on every finite interval.

Example A3.2 | Find the Fourier transform of a single pulse shown in Figure A3.3.

$$X(j\omega) = \int_{-\infty}^{\infty} x(t) \, e^{-j\omega t} \, dt = \int_{-\tau/2}^{\tau/2} e^{-j\omega t} \, dt = \tau \, \frac{\sin\left(\omega \frac{\tau}{2}\right)}{\omega \frac{\tau}{2}} \qquad \text{[A3.4.12]}$$

If we compare this result with Figure A3.2, we find that [A3.4.12] is the envelope of the Fourier series shown in Figure A3.2. All frequencies are present; that is, [A3.4.12] is continuous while [A3.3.8] is discrete.

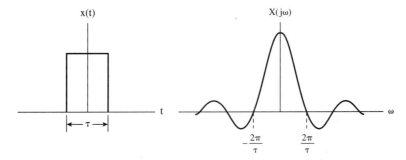

Figure A3.3   Fourier transform of a pulse

Find the Fourier transform for u(t), where u(t) is the unit step starting at t $= 0$. | **Example A3.3**

$$X(j\omega) = \int_0^\infty e^{-j\omega t}\, dt = \frac{1}{-j\omega} e^{-j\omega t}\Big|_0^\infty = \text{does not exist} \qquad \textbf{[A3.4.13]}$$

This is because the magnitude of $e^{-j\omega t}$ is unity. Thus, as $t \to \infty$, $e^{-j\omega t}$ does not converge to zero. Therefore, the transform does not exist. The reason this is so is that condition (1) (equation [A3.4.11]) is not satisfied. Note that the Laplace transform has a built-in convergence factor in $s = \sigma + j\omega$, where σ is referred to as the convergence factor. Thus the Laplace transform of u(t) exists.

This example considers the Fourier transform pair for the delta function. Since the transform does | **Example A3.4**
not actually satisfy [A3.4.11], we shall define the delta function as follows:

$$\delta(f) = 2\pi\, \delta(\omega) = \int_{-\infty}^\infty e^{-j\omega t}\, dt \qquad \textbf{[A3.4.14]}$$

where

$$1 = \frac{1}{2\pi} \int_{-\infty}^\infty \delta(f)\, e^{j\omega t}\, d\omega \qquad \textbf{[A3.4.15]}$$

A very useful relationship is the Fourier transform for $A\cos(\omega_0 t)$. This is found by using the results | **Example A3.5**
of Example A3.4 as follows:

$$X(j\omega) = \int_{-\infty}^\infty A\cos(\omega_0 t)\, e^{-j\omega t}\, dt = \frac{A}{2} \int_{-\infty}^\infty \left(e^{j\omega_0 t} + e^{-j\omega_0 t}\right) e^{-j\omega_0 t}\, dt$$

$$= \frac{A}{2} \int_{-\infty}^\infty e^{-j\,t(\omega-\omega_0)}\, dt + \frac{A}{2} \int_{-\infty}^\infty d^{-jt(\omega+\omega_0)}\, dt$$

$$= \frac{A}{2} \left[\delta(f - fo) + \delta(f + fo)\right] \qquad \textbf{[A3.4.16]}$$

We will use this result extensively in calculating the power spectral density of periodic signals, that is, for functions whose autocorrelation function is $\cos \omega_0 \tau$.

A3.5   ENERGY AND POWER

Consider any function x(t), such as voltage or current. The **total energy** is

$$\int_{-\infty}^{\infty} x^2(t) \, dt \qquad\qquad \text{[A3.5.1]}$$

The **average power** is found by time averaging the energy as follows:

$$\lim_{T \to \infty} \frac{1}{2T} \int_{-T}^{T} x^2(t) \, dt \qquad\qquad \text{[A3.5.2]}$$

The terms *energy* and *average power* have been used loosely here since the units do not necessarily have a direct relationship to physical energy or power. This is, however, often standard practice in communications and signal processing.

If the signal has finite energy, then the average power is zero since the infinite time average of a finite quantity is zero. Thus, if the power is not zero, then the energy is infinite. One example of this is a cosine wave which has infinite energy but finite power. In the frequency domain we shall represent such a signal by a delta function with an area equal to the power. The delta function denotes the fact that the energy is infinite but that the power is finite. We might also alter the definition in [A3.5.2] by removing the limit as T goes to infinity.

We can consider the Fourier transform of $x(t) = f^2(t)$ as follows:

$$X(j\omega) = \int_{-\infty}^{\infty} x(t) \, e^{-j\omega t} \, dt = \int_{-\infty}^{\infty} f^2(t) \, e^{-j\omega t} \, dt \qquad\qquad \text{[A3.5.3]}$$

Recall that the transform of the product of two functions in the time domain is the convolution of their respective transforms. Therefore:

$$X(j\omega) = \frac{1}{2\pi} \int_{-\infty}^{\infty} F(ju) \, F(j\omega - ju) \, du \qquad\qquad \text{[A3.5.4]}$$

If we equate [A3.5.3] and [A3.5.4] and let $\omega = 0$, then we have **Parseval's theorem**:

$$\int_{-\infty}^{\infty} f^2(t) dt = \frac{1}{2\pi} \int_{-\infty}^{\infty} |F(ju)|^2 \, du \qquad\qquad \text{[A3.5.5]}$$

which is the energy of f(t). Note that the left side of [A3.5.5] is also similar to the autocorrelation function of f(t) when $\tau = 0$. The autocorrelation function of f(t) estimated by time averaging is

$$\hat{R}_{FF}(\tau) = \lim_{T \to \infty} \frac{1}{2T} \int_{-T}^{T} f(t)\, f(t + \tau)\, dt \qquad \text{[A3.5.6]}$$

For $\tau = 0$ we obtain the average power.

A3.6   THE DISCRETE FOURIER TRANSFORM

The discrete Fourier transform is defined as

$$X(mf) = \sum_{n=0}^{N-1} x(nT)\, e^{-j\, 2\pi mfnT}$$

$$= \sum_{n=0}^{N-1} x(nT)\, W^{-mn} \qquad \text{[A3.6.1]}$$

where T is the interval between data samples, N is the total number of samples as well as the number of intervals, NT is the data record length, f is $1/(NT)$ and is the interval between frequency components, f_s is $1/T$ and is called the sampling frequency, and $W = e^{j2\pi fT}$.

Thus, we have the situation illustrated in Figure A3.4.

A3.7   RELATIONSHIP TO THE Z-TRANSFORM

Figure A3.5 shows the impulse sampling model, where the subscript s denotes the sampling operation.

The Laplace transform of the sampled signal is given as

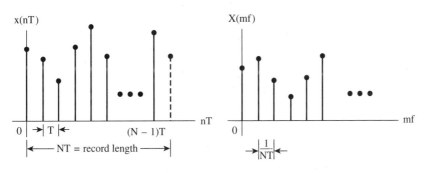

Figure A3.4   Illustration of sampling and the DFT

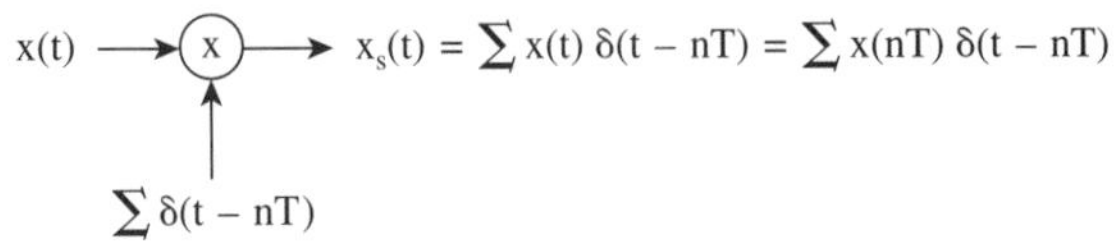

$$x(t) \longrightarrow \boxed{\times} \longrightarrow x_s(t) = \sum x(t)\, \delta(t - nT) = \sum x(nT)\, \delta(t - nT) \qquad \text{[A3.7.1]}$$

$$\sum \delta(t - nT)$$

Figure A3.5   Impulse sample model

$$X_s\,(s) = \int_0^\infty x_s(t)\, e^{-st}\, dt = \sum_0^\infty x\,(nT)\, e^{-snT} \qquad \text{[A3.7.2]}$$

The Fourier transform of the sampled signal is

$$X_s(j\omega) = \sum_0^\infty x\,(nT)\, e^{-j\omega nT} \qquad \text{[A3.7.3]}$$

And the z-transform of x(nT) is

$$X(z) = \sum_0^\infty x\,(nT)\, z^{-n} \qquad \text{[A3.7.4]}$$

If we let $z = e^{sT}$, then we have

$$X(z) = \sum_0^\infty x\,(nT)\, e^{-snT} = X_s(s) \qquad \text{[A3.7.5]}$$

If the unit circle is included in the region of convergence, then

$$X(z) = X_s(j\omega) \qquad \text{[A3.7.6]}$$

when $z = e^{j\omega T}$. Note that from [A3.7.2] we have

$$X_s\,(s + j\omega_s) = \sum_0^\infty x\,(nT)\, e^{-snT}\, e^{-j\omega_s nT} = \sum_0^\infty x\,(nT) e^{-snT} \qquad \text{[A3.7.7]}$$

where ω_s is the radian sampling frequency. Equation [A3.7.7] makes use of the fact that $e^{-j\omega_s nT} = e^{-2\frac{\pi}{T} nT} = 1$. Thus, $X_s(s)$ is periodically extended. Similarly we can show that the DFT is periodically extended, and that the DFT satisfies

$$X(mf) = X(z)|_{z = e^{j\omega T}}|_{\omega T = \frac{2\pi}{Nm}} \qquad \text{[A3.7.8]}$$

which says that the DFT is the z-transform sampled at discrete frequencies around the unit circle.

The s-plane for [A3.7.7] is partitioned into "strips," as shown in Figure A3.6, where the shaded strip is called the primary strip.

The spectrum of a sampled signal of finite duration would appear as shown in Figure A3.7.

Figure A3.7 illustrates that the spectrum about the origin in the primary strip is periodically extended beyond the primary strip to multiples of ω_s. This is the same interpretation as when the spectrum is determined from the z-transform with $z = e^{j\omega T}$. As ω varies from 0 to infinity multiple encirclements about the unit circle are made, thereby extending the spectrum for 0 to 2π (or 0 to f_s) to multiples of 2π (or multiples of f_s). This is illustrated in Figure A3.8. The DFT is a sampled spectrum, determined by taking samples of the z-transform around the unit circle, which is also illustrated in Figure A3.8.

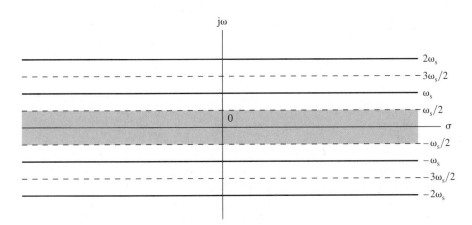

Figure A3.6   The periodic extension of $X_s(s)$

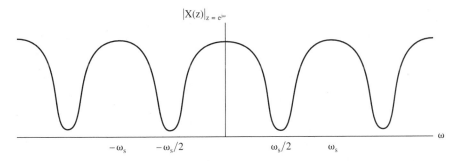

Figure A3.7   The spectrum across the "strips" in the s-plane for a sampled signal

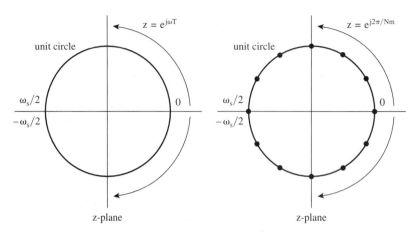

Figure A3.8 Spectrum on the unit circle

The inverse z-transform of the spectrum leads to a periodic extension in the time domain of the original sampled signal.

The fast Fourier transform (FFT) is an algorithm for rapidly calculating the DFT.

A3.8 WINDOWING

Figure A3.9 illustrates windowing the data. Windowing distorts the spectrum by "smearing" or "spreading" the true spectrum. This smearing is caused by convolving the spectrum of the window with the true spectrum. Another way to view this is that the window truncates the data, thereby broadening the spectrum. Windowing also reduces one's capability to resolve closely spaced spectral peaks. But if windowing the data distorts the spectrum, then why window the data? From a statistical point of view, it can be shown that windowing the data reduces the variance of the spectral estimate. Furthermore, if the transition regions (leading and trailing edges) of the window are smooth (not sharp), then the window will reduce the high frequency artifacts that can be introduced by windows with sharp leading and trailing edges. This high frequency artifact is sometimes called spectral splatter.

If the data window is rectangular and of the same length as the data record, then the convolution of the DFT of the data with the DFT of the window is the DFT of the data. This is because the DFT of the rectangular window has zeros at multiples of $f = 1/NT$, except at $f = 0$, where the magnitude of the DFT of the window is unity. This is shown in Figure A3.10, where we show the continuous spectrum of the rectangular window so that the zeros of the spectrum can be easily identified. Superimposed on the continuous spectrum are dots denoting the sample values of the DFT. Thus, the DFT is a unit pulse in the frequency domain. Other windows with smoother leading and trailing edges will generally have a wider main lobe, usually extending to $2/NT$, and will have zeros in the spectrum at multiples of $1/NT$ beyond this point. The properties of several data windows can be explored more thoroughly in MATLAB.

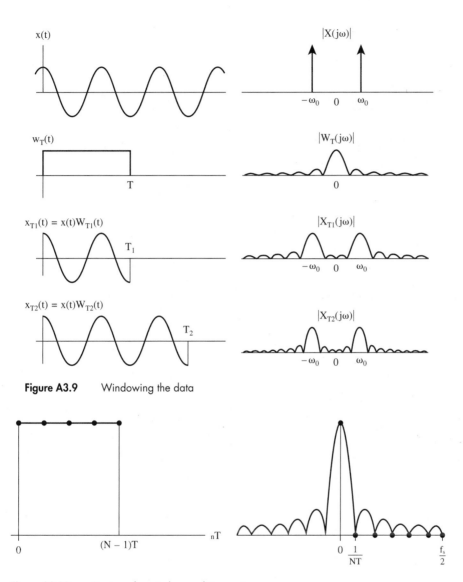

Figure A3.9   Windowing the data

Figure A3.10   Rectangular window and its spectrum

Appending zeros to increase the length of a data record does not increase the resolution of the spectral estimate, since no new information is added to the data record. However, the process of appending zeros increases the data record length, thereby increasing the value of NT to, say, MT. Then the value of 1/MT is less than 1/NT. This process generates new samples of the DFT that are more closely spaced in the frequency domain than the samples spaced at 1/NT. Thus, by appending zeros, we have increased the number of samples of the spectrum, which in turn provides a better interpretation of the spectral envelope (see Figure A3.11). However, since the sampling theorem was satisfied with the

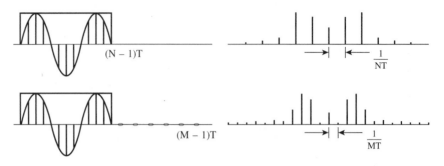

Figure A3.11   Appending zeros

original data record, the appending of zeros to the data record does not offer any increase in the resolution of the data over that provided by the sampling theorem.

A3.9   LEAKAGE

The spectrum of a data window typically has spectral sidelobes, as shown in Figure A3.9. This is a problem because these sidelobes can be misinterpreted as peaks in the spectrum of the data. The sidelobes in the spectrum are called leakage, since the energy in the spectrum has leaked from the main lobe into the sidelobes.

A kind of sidelobe can occur in the time domain as well. This is caused by filtering the spectrum with a filter with sharp transitions or sharp edges. The inverse transform of a spectrum that has been filtered by such a filter will have such sidelobes in the time domain, which in turn can be misinterpreted as being due to the data, when in fact they are introduced by the filter.

A3.10   DATA MODELING

A major purpose of data models is to increase the spectral resolution for short data records. One way to do this is to extend the autocorrelation function so that it has a longer record, thereby increasing the spectral resolution. Three typical data models are used frequently. They are autoregression, moving average, and autoregression–moving average. We discuss these models in Chapter 7. Many new spectral estimation procedures are based on data modeling techniques, which work well when the data and the model agree. If the data record is short, then the data modeling approach will generally provide a good spectral estimate, and the estimate will generally be better than the periodogram. If the data and the model do not fit well and the data record is reasonably long, then the periodogram will often provide a good spectral estimate. The periodogram is robust with respect to its ability to estimate the spectrum for a wide range of data types.

A3.11 STATISTICAL CONSIDERATIONS

In Chapter 7 we discuss various spectral estimators, along with methods for evaluating the value of a spectral estimator. The typical evaluation methods include estimating the mean and variance of the spectral estimator (also discussed in Chapter 7). Methods for reducing the variance of a spectral estimator include segmental averaging of the data and windowing the data.

Some statistical methods for estimating the spectrum will first estimate the autocorrelation function and then calculate the transform. The number of autocorrelation values is typically less than the data record length. Thus, these methods usually have less resolution than some nonstatistical spectral estimators. However, the spectral resolution of estimators that use the autocorrelation function can be improved. This is not done by appending zeros to the autocorrelation function, since this does not add new information beyond that already available. What is done is to predict the autocorrelation function and use the predicted values to extend the length of the autocorrelation function. Chapter 7 discusses methods for extrapolating the autocorrelation function using linear prediction techniques.

APPENDIX

4

THE MATCHED FILTER

A4.1 THE GENERALIZED MATCHED FILTER

If the noise is not white, then we have a more general result for the matched filter. Then it can be shown that the equation for a time invariant matched filter is

$$\int_{-\infty}^{T} R_{NN}(\tau - a)\, h_0(T - a)\, da = s(\tau) \qquad \text{[A4.1.1]}$$

for $-\infty < \tau < T$. This is an **integral equation**. Note that for the special case of stationary white noise, $R_{NN}(\tau - a) = N_0 \delta(\tau - a)$. Then, the optimum matched filter becomes

$$N_0 h_0 (T - \tau) = s(\tau)$$

or with a change of variables we have

$$h_0(t) = \frac{1}{N_0} s(T - t) \qquad \text{[A4.1.2]}$$

This is the same result as in Chapter 8 except for the N_0 term, which is a constant. The output signal-to-noise ratio is the same as before.

A4.2 THE UNREALIZABLE MATCHED FILTER

The integral equation [A4.1.1] can be solved by transform methods if we do not require that $h_0(t)$ be physically realizable; that is, we do not require that

$$h_0(t) = 0 \quad t < 0 \qquad \text{[A4.2.1]}$$

For this case we may take Fourier transforms of both sides of [A4.1.1] as follows:

$$\int_{-\infty}^{\infty} \left[\int_{-\infty}^{\infty} R_{NN}(\tau - a)\, h_0(T-a)\, da \right] e^{-j\omega\tau}\, d\tau = \int_{-\infty}^{\infty} s(\tau) e^{-j\omega\tau}\, d\tau = S(j\omega) \qquad \text{[A4.2.2]}$$

We may rewrite this equation by noting that

$$\int_{-\infty}^{\infty} \left[\int_{-\infty}^{\infty} R_{NN}\ (\tau - a)\ e^{-j\omega\tau}\ d\tau \right] h_0\ (T - a)\ da = \int_{-\infty}^{\infty} S_{NN}(j\omega)e^{-j\omega a}\ h_0(T - a)da$$

$$[\text{A4.2.3}]$$

By changing variables with $t = T - a$, we obtain

$$S(j\omega) = S_{NN}(\omega)e^{-j\omega T} \int_{-\infty}^{\infty} h_0(\tau)e^{j\omega\tau}\ d\tau \qquad [\text{A4.2.4}]$$

$$= S_{NN}(\omega)e^{-j\omega T}\left[H_0\ (-j\omega)\right]$$

Rearranging and conjugating, we have

$$H_0(j\omega) = \frac{S(-j\omega)}{S_{NN}\ (\omega)}\ e^{-j\omega T} \qquad [\text{A4.2.5}]$$

This is the transfer function for the unrealizable matched filter for an arbitrary noise power spectrum $S_{NN}(\omega)$. When the noise is white, then [A4.2.5] is the same as that in [A4.1.2].

A4.3   THE PHYSICALLY REALIZABLE MATCHED FILTER

Suppose we use the Laplace transform instead of the Fourier transform. Then we have $H_0(s)$, $S(s)$, and $S_{NN}(s)$. Now in general the noise power spectrum will consist of a numerator polynomial and denominator polynomial in s. We may factor these polynomials to find their roots. We will find a set of roots in the left-half-plane (LHP) and similar set in the right-half-plane (RHP). The roots appear in complex conjugate pairs, as well as in pairs reflected about the $j\omega$ axis. We may factor $S_{NN}(s)$ into two parts.

$$S_{NN}(s) = S_{NN}^{L}(s)\ S_{NN}^{R}(s) \qquad [\text{A4.3.1}]$$

where $S_{NN}^{L}(s)$ denotes the LHP portion of $S_{NN}(s)$ and $S_{NN}^{R}(s)$ denotes the RHP portion.
Now suppose we represent $H_0(s)$ as the cascade of two filters:

$$H_0(s) = H_1(s)H_2(s) \qquad [\text{A4.3.2}]$$

Let

$$H_1(s) = \frac{1}{S_{NN}^{L}\ (s)} \qquad [\text{A4.3.3}]$$

$H_1(s)$ is physically realizable since its roots are in the LHP. What must $H_2(s)$ be so that $H_0(s)$ is the optimum physically realizable matched filter? The output of $H_1(s)$ is

$$S_1(s) = H_1(s)S(s) = \frac{S(s)}{S_{NN}^{L}(s)} \qquad [\text{A4.3.4}]$$

Now let

$$H_3(s) = S_1(-s)e^{-sT} = \frac{S(-s)e^{-sT}}{S_{NN}^L(-s)} = \frac{S(-s)e^{-sT}}{S_{NN}^R(s)}$$ [A4.3.5]

which in general may have roots in the RHP.

Thus

$$h_3(t) = \frac{1}{2\pi j}\oint S_1(-s)e^{-sT}e^{st}\,ds$$ [A4.3.6]

which may not be zero for t < 0, and thus will not be physically realizable. (Note that if $S_{NN}^L(s)$ has a root in the upper LHP, then $S_{NN}^L(-s)$ will have a root in the lower RHP, while a root of $S_{NN}^L(s)$ in the lower LHP will be in the upper RHP for $S_{NN}^L(-s)$).

We may make this filter physically realizable by multiplying it by the unit step function:

$$h_2(t) = h_3(t)u(t)$$ [A4.3.7]

$$H_2(s) = \int_0^\infty h_3(t)e^{-st}\,dt = \int_0^\infty \left[\frac{1}{2\pi j}\oint \frac{S(-s)}{S_{NN}^R(s)}e^{s(t-T)}\,ds\right]e^{-st}\,dt$$ [A4.3.8]

The matched filter becomes

$$H_0(s) = H_1(s)H_2(s) = \frac{1}{S_{NN}^L(s)}\int_0^\infty \left[\frac{1}{2\pi j}\oint \frac{S(-s)}{S_{NN}^R(s)}e^{s(t-T)}\,ds\right]e^{-st}\,dt$$ [A4.3.9]

This solution is called the **prewhitening solution** for the generalized matched filter because $H_1(s)$, the first filter in the system, operates on the input signal plus noise to prewhiten the input. If only noise is present, then the filter output is white noise with roots only in the LHP, and the filter would be physically realizable. However, the signal is also present and this prewhitening operation distorts the input signal. We must then find the physically realizable matched filter for this distorted (prewhitened) signal. The solution for this is $H_2(s)$. The cascade of the two filters is the optimum physically realizable matched filter.

The integral equation for the generalized matched filter can be solved in a manner similar to that given above. The same solution is obtained.

Figure A4.1 is a summary of the generalized, physically realizable matched filter derived by prewhitening, where we have let $s = j\omega$ and assumed the contour integral converges.

Example A4.1 | Consider Example 8.4 in Chapter 8. We determined that the spectrum of the output of the lowpass RC filter was

$$S_{YY}(f) = \frac{A^2}{4}\frac{\frac{1}{t_0^2}}{\frac{1}{t_0^2}+\omega_c^2}\{\delta(f+f_c)+\delta(f-f_c)\} + N_0\frac{\frac{1}{t_0^2}}{\frac{1}{t_0^2}+\omega^2}$$

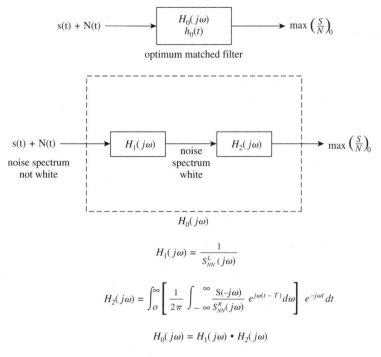

Figure A4.1   Summary of the generalized, physically realizable matched filter by prewhitening

$$= S_{SS}(f) + S_{NN}(f)$$

where $t_0 = RC$. Suppose this signal and noise are the input to a matched filter. Determine the unrealizable matched filter.

The equation for the unrealizable matched filter for signal plus noise is [A4.2.5]:

$$H_0(j\omega) = \frac{S(-j\omega)}{S_{NN}(\omega)} e^{-j\omega T}$$

We cannot use the equation for the power spectrum for the signal in the numerator of the above equation. We need the Fourier transform for the signal, which is

$$S(j\omega) = \frac{A}{2} \sqrt{\frac{\frac{1}{t_0^2}}{\frac{1}{t_0^2} + \omega_c^2}} \{\delta(f + f_c) + \delta(f - f_c)\}$$

$$= k\{\delta(f + f_c) + \delta(f - f_c)\} = S(-j\omega)$$

Now the unrealizable matched filter becomes

$$H_0(j\omega) = k\frac{\{\delta(f+f_c) + \delta(f-f_c)\}}{N_0 \frac{\frac{1}{t_0^2}}{\frac{1}{t_0^2} + \omega^2}} e^{-j\omega\tau}$$

$$= \frac{k\,t_0^2}{N_0}\{\delta\,(f + f_c) + \delta\,(f - f_c)\}\left(\frac{1}{t_0^2} + \omega^2\right)e^{-j\omega T}$$

The matched filter impulse response is the inverse Fourier transform of the above, which is

$$h_0(t) = \frac{kt_0^2}{N_0}\left(\frac{1}{t_0^2} + \omega_c^2\right)\{e^{-j\omega_c(t-T)} + e^{j\omega_c(t-T)}\}$$

$$= \frac{kt_0^2}{N_0}\left(\frac{1}{t_0^2} + \omega_c^2\right)2\{\cos\omega_c\,(t - T)\}$$

$$= \frac{A}{N_0}\cdot\frac{1}{\sqrt{\dfrac{\dfrac{1}{t_0^2}}{\dfrac{1}{t_0^2} + \omega_c^2}}}\cos\omega_c\,(t - T)$$

This filter is unrealizable because it is not zero for $t < 0$.

Example A4.2 | Suppose the signal spectrum is

$$S(j\omega) = \frac{1}{j\omega}$$

which is an integrator. Let the noise spectrum be

$$S_{NN}(\omega) = \frac{1 + \omega^2}{\omega^2} = \frac{1 + j\omega}{j\omega}\frac{1 - j\omega}{- j\omega}$$

$$= S_{NN}^L(j\omega)\,S_{NN}^R(j\omega)$$

Find the realizable matched filter.

$$H_1(j\omega) = \frac{1}{S_{NN}^L}(j\omega) = \frac{j\omega}{1 + j\omega}$$

$$S_1(j\omega) = S(j\omega)H_1(j\omega) = \frac{1}{1 + j\omega}$$

The unrealizable matched filter for $S_1(j\omega)$ is

$$H_3(j\omega) = S_1(-j\omega)\,e^{-j\omega T} = \frac{1}{1 - j\omega}e^{-j\omega T}$$

The impulse response is

$$h_3\,(t) = -e^{-(T-t)}\,u(T - t)$$

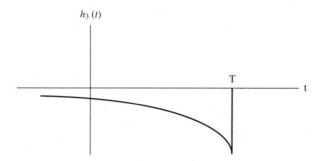

The realizable filter is

$$h_2(t) = h_3(t)u(t)$$

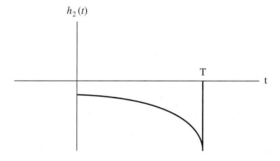

Then

$$H_2(j\omega) = \int_0^T h_2(t)e^{-j\omega t}\,dt = -\int_0^T e^{-(T-t)}e^{-j\omega t}\,dt$$

$$= \frac{e^{-T} - e^{-j\omega t}}{1 - j\omega}$$

Then the optimum matched filter is

$$H_0(j\omega) = H_1(j\omega)H_2(j\omega)$$

$$= \frac{j\omega}{1 + j\omega} \cdot \frac{e^{-T} - e^{-j\omega t}}{1 - j\omega}$$

$$= \frac{j\omega}{1 + \omega^2}\,(e^{-T} - e^{-j\omega t})$$

We may inverse transform this expression to obtain the impulse response.

APPENDIX

5

THE WIENER FILTER

A5.1 THE WIENER FILTER

The Wiener filter problem is outlined in Figure A5.1

The purpose of the Wiener filter is to determine the least-mean-squared error estimate $\hat{S}(t)$ for three cases of the desired signal.

1. Pure prediction. In this case $T > 0$ and $N(t)$ is zero. The problem is to predict $S(t)$ at some future time.

2. Prediction and estimation. Here $T > 0$ and $N(t)$ is not zero. The problem is to both predict and estimate $S(t)$ at some future time.

3. Estimation. For this case $T \leq 0$ and $N(t)$ is not zero. The problem is to estimate $S(t)$. We may use a time delay in the estimate.

To solve these three cases we make the following assumptions.

The input to the Wiener filter is additive, that is, signal plus noise. Both the signal and noise are random processes. Furthermore, both the signal and noise are at least stationary in the wide sense. The Wiener filter is to be physically realizable. The error criterion we shall use is the mean squared error:

$$E[E^2(t)] = E[(D(t) - \hat{S}(t))^2] = minimum \qquad \text{[A5.1.1]}$$

where $D(t) = S(t - T)$ or $D(t) = S(t + T)$ as the case may be.

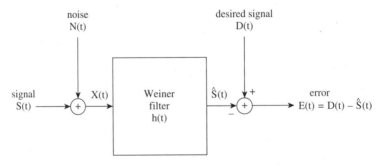

Figure A5.1   Formulation of the Wiener filter problem

We may solve $[A5.1.1]$ as follows:

$$E[E^2(t)] = E\left[S(t + T) - \int_0^\infty h(\tau)X(t - \tau)d\tau \right]^2 \qquad \textbf{[A5.1.2]}$$

$$= E\left[S(t + T)S(t + T) - 2S(t + T) \int_0^\infty h(\tau)X(t - \tau)d\tau \right.$$

$$\left. + \int_0^\infty \int_0^\infty X(t - a)X(t - \beta)h(a)h(\beta)da\ d\beta \right]$$

$$= R_{SS}(0) - 2\int_0^\infty R_{XS}(T + \tau)h(\tau)d\tau + \int_0^\infty \int_0^\infty R_{XX}(\beta - a)h(a)h(\beta)dad\beta$$

We want to find the optimum Wiener filter that minimizes $[A5.1.2]$. With the use of the calculus of variations, we obtain the following solution in the form of an integral equation.

$$\int_0^\infty R_{XX}(\tau - a)h_0(a)da = R_{XS}(\tau + T) \qquad \textbf{[A5.1.3]}$$

for $0 \le \tau < \infty$. The optimum Wiener filter is denoted by $h_0(t)$. Note that this integral equation, known as the **Wiener–Hopf equation,** is similar to that obtained for the matched filter. However, here we have autocorrelation and crosscorrelation functions for random processes, rather than a known signal waveform. Equation $[A5.1.3]$ depends only upon correlation functions or, equivalently, on the power spectra.

An important principle that arises from the derivation of the Wiener–Hopf integral equation is the **orthogonality principle,** which says that the mean squared error is minimized if the signal input to the Wiener filter is orthogonal (in the expectation sense) to the error signal, namely:

$$E[E(t)X(t - \tau)] = 0 \qquad \textbf{[A5.1.4]}$$

If we expand this equation, we have

$$E[(D(t) - \hat{S}(t)) X(t - \tau)] = E[(S(t + T) - \hat{S}(t)) X(t - \tau)]$$

$$= E\left\{ \left[S(t + T) - \int_0^\infty h_0(a)X(t - a)da \right] X(t - \tau) \right\}$$

$$= R_{XS}(\tau + T) - \int_0^\infty R_{XX}(\tau - a)h_0(a)da$$

$$= 0 \qquad \textbf{[A5.1.5]}$$

Rearranging the equation, we obtain

$$\int_0^\infty R_{XX}(\tau - a)h_0(a)da = R_{XS}(\tau + T) \qquad \textbf{[A5.1.6]}$$

which is once again [A5.1.3], the Wiener–Hopf integral equation.

We can interpret our signals as vectors in a signal space and illustrate the orthogonality principle in vector form as we did in Chapters 7 and 8.

A5.2   THE UNREALIZABLE WIENER FILTER

The unrealizable Wiener filter is found by relaxing the conditions on the Wiener–Hopf equation so that the filter impulse response is not restricted to be zero for negative time. When we do this the integral equation becomes

$$\int_{-\infty}^{\infty} R_{XX}\,(\tau - a)\,h_0\,(a)\,da = R_{XS}\,(\tau + T) \qquad \text{[A5.2.1]}$$

If we take the Fourier transform of [A5.2.1], as we did for the matched filter, we have

$$\int_{-\infty}^{\infty}\left[\int_{-\infty}^{\infty} R_{XX}\,(\tau - a)\,h_0(a)\,da\right] e^{-j\omega\tau}\,d\tau = \int_{-\infty}^{\infty} R_{XS}\,(\tau + t)\,e^{-j\omega\tau}\,d\tau \qquad \text{[A5.2.2]}$$

Then with a change of variable, we obtain

$$S_{XX}(\omega)H_0(j\omega) = S_{XS}(\omega)\,e^{j\omega T} \qquad \text{[A5.2.3]}$$

Solving for the transfer function for the optimum unrealizable Wiener filter, we have

$$H_0(j\omega) = \frac{S_{XS}(\omega)\,e^{j\omega T}}{S_{XX}(\omega)} \qquad \text{[A5.2.4]}$$

This result is similar to the one we obtained for the matched filter.

As a special case, we consider the signal S(t) to be independent of the noise N(t), so that

$$R_{XX}\,(\tau) = R_{SS}\,(\tau) + R_{NN}\,(\tau) \qquad \text{[A5.2.5]}$$

$$S_{XX}\,(\omega) = S_{SS}\,(\omega) + S_{NN}\,(\omega) \qquad \text{[A5.2.6]}$$

$$R_{XS}\,(\tau) = R_{SS}\,(\tau) \qquad \text{[A5.2.7]}$$

$$S_{XS}\,(\omega) = S_{SS}\,(\omega) \qquad \text{[A5.2.8]}$$

Then the optimum unrealizable Wiener filter becomes

$$H_0(j\omega) = \frac{S_{SS}\,(\omega)}{S_{SS}\,(\omega) + S_{NN}\,(\omega)}\,e^{j\omega T} \qquad \text{[A5.2.9]}$$

Now if the noise is zero, then

$$H_0\,(j\omega) = e^{j\omega T} \qquad \text{[A5.2.10]}$$

Thus, the optimum unrealizable Wiener filter becomes a pure **prediction filter,** which is unrealizable.

The expression for the mean squared error derived previously as [A5.1.2] may be simplified if we use [A5.2.1]. Then we obtain

$$\min E[E^2(t)] = R_{SS}(0) - \int_{-\infty}^{\infty} R_{XS}(T+a)h_0(a)\,da \qquad \text{[A5.2.11]}$$

We ask the reader to derive [A5.2.11]. The minimum mean squared error may also be expressed using the appropriate spectra as

$$\min E[E^2(t)] = \frac{1}{2\pi} \int_{-\infty}^{\infty} [S_{SS}(\omega) - S_{XS}(\omega)H_0(-j\omega)\,e^{j\omega T}]\,d\omega \qquad \text{[A5.2.12]}$$

If we substitute [A5.2.4] into [A5.2.12], we obtain

$$\min E[E^2(t)] = \frac{1}{2\pi} \int_{-\infty}^{\infty} \frac{S_{SS}(\omega)S_{XX}(\omega) - |S_{XS}(\omega)|^2}{S_{XX}(\omega)}\,d\omega \qquad \text{[A5.2.13]}$$

which becomes the following when the signal and noise are independent.

$$\min E[E^2(t)] = \frac{1}{2\pi} \int_{-\infty}^{\infty} \frac{S_{SS}(\omega)S_{NN}(\omega)}{S_{SS}(\omega) + S_{NN}(\omega)}\,d\omega \qquad \text{[A5.2.14]}$$

This is the same result we would obtain if we simply substituted [A5.2.9] into [A5.2.12].

A5.3   THE REALIZABLE WIENER FILTER

The equations for the realizable Wiener filter may be derived in a manner similar to that used for the prewhitening matched filter. By doing so we obtain

$$H_0(s) = \frac{1}{s_{XX}^L(s)} \cdot \int_0^{\infty} \left\{ \frac{1}{2\pi} \oint \frac{S_{XS}(s)}{S_{XX}^R(s)}\,e^{js\,(t+T)}ds \right\} e^{-st}\,d$$

$$= H_1(s) \cdot H_2(s) \qquad \text{[A5.3.1]}$$

The major differences between [A5.3.1] and [A4.3.9] are (1) in [A5.3.1] the spectrum $S_{XX}(s)$ that is to be factored is the spectrum of the signal plus noise and (2) the spectrum $S_{XS}(s)$ is the cross-spectrum of the signal plus noise with the signal and it is evaluated for positive s, not negative s.

Suppose the input to a Wiener filter is the sum of a signal and white noise that are uncorrelated. The power spectra are given as

Example A5.1

$$S_{SS}(\omega) = \frac{1}{1+\omega^2}, \quad S_{NN}(\omega) = N_0$$

Determine both the unrealizable and realizable Wiener filters. For this example we have

$$S_{XS}(\omega) = S_{SS}(\omega) = \frac{1}{1 + \omega^2}$$

$$S_{XX}(\omega) = S_{SS}(\omega) + S_{NN}(\omega)$$

$$= \frac{1}{1 + \omega^2} + N_0$$

$$= \frac{1 + N_0(1 + \omega^2)}{1 + \omega^2} = \frac{(1 + N_0) + N_0\omega^2}{1 + \omega^2}$$

$$= \frac{(\sqrt{1 + N_0} + \sqrt{N_0}\,j\omega)(\sqrt{1 + N_0} - \sqrt{N_0}\,j\omega)}{(1 + j\omega)(1 - j\omega)}$$

The unrealizable filter is given by [A5.2.9]:

$$H_0(j\omega) = \frac{\frac{1}{1+\omega^2}}{\frac{(1+N_0) + N_0\omega^2}{1+\omega^2}}\,e^{j\omega T} = \frac{1}{(1 + N_0) + N_0\omega^2}\,e^{j\omega T}$$

To find the realizable filter we have to use [A5.3.1] and factor the input spectrum.

$$H_1(j\omega) = \frac{1 + j\omega}{\sqrt{1 + N_0} + j\sqrt{N_0}\,\omega}$$

If we use the same notation as we did for the prewhitening matched filter, then the signal at the output of the prewhitening filter for the Wiener filter is

$$S_1(j\omega) = H_1(j\omega)\,S_{XS}(\omega)$$

$$= \frac{S_{XS}(\omega)}{S_{XX}^L(j\omega)}$$

and

$$H_3(j\omega) = S_1(-j\omega)\,e^{-j\omega T}$$

$$= \frac{S_{XS}(\omega)}{S_{XX}^R(j\omega)}\,e^{-j\omega T}$$

$$= \frac{1}{(1 + j\omega)(\sqrt{1 + N_0} - j\omega\sqrt{N_0})}\,e^{-j\omega T}$$

$$= \frac{1}{\sqrt{N_0} + \sqrt{1 + N_0}}\left[\frac{1}{1 + j\omega} + \frac{\sqrt{N_0}}{\sqrt{1 + N_0} - j\omega\sqrt{N_0}}\right]e^{-j\omega T}$$

The second term within the brackets is in the RHP (when we consider s as a complex variable), so it is ignored. Thus, the realizable filter becomes

$$H_2(j\omega) = \frac{e^{-j\omega T}}{\sqrt{N_0} + \sqrt{1 + N_0}}\frac{1}{1 + j\omega}$$

The impulse response is

$$h_2(t) = \frac{1}{\sqrt{N_0} + \sqrt{1 + N_0}} e^{-(t-T)} u(t - T)$$

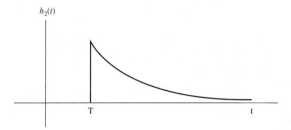

Finally the Wiener filter is

$$H_0(j\omega) = H_1(j\omega) H_2(j\omega)$$

$$= \frac{1 + j\omega}{\sqrt{1 + N_0} + j\sqrt{N_0}\,\omega} \cdot \frac{e^{-j\omega T}}{(\sqrt{N_0} + \sqrt{1 + N_0})(1 + j\omega)}$$

$$= \frac{e^{-j\omega T} \cdot}{\sqrt{1 + N_0} + \sqrt{N_0}} \cdot \frac{1}{\sqrt{1 + N_0} + j\sqrt{N_0}\,\omega}$$

The impulse response of this filter is

$$h_0(t) = \frac{\sqrt{N_0}}{\sqrt{1 + N_0} + \sqrt{N_0}} e^{-\frac{\sqrt{1+N_0}}{\sqrt{N_0}}(t-T)} u(t - T)$$

A6.1 PRACTICE EXAMINATIONS FOR CHAPTERS 1 THROUGH 4

EXAMINATION 1: CHAPTERS 1 THROUGH 4

Conditions: 1 hour and 30 minutes, open book.

1. (10) A set of seven digital voltmeters is monitoring seven mutually independent random data channels. The voltmeters have only a single digital display that may indicate 0 to 9 volts inclusive. The data on the channels may assume integer voltage levels of 0 to 9 inclusive. Each data level is equally likely to occur. What is the probability that a simultaneous reading of all the voltmeters will show seven volts on all channels?

2. (10) Two dice are thrown until the sum of the two faces showing is a seven. Find the most probable number of throws and the expected number of throws.

3. (20) You are given the opportunity to select tickets to a football game at your University in the following manner. One box contains two football tickets to game 1 and two football tickets to game 2. A second box contains two football tickets to game 1 and four football tickets to game 2. You select a box at random and withdraw two tickets without replacement from that box. What is the probability that both tickets are to the same game?

4. (20) Suppose 5 men out of 100 and 25 women out of 10,000 are color-blind. A color-blind person is chosen at random from a group that has twice as many males as females. What is the probability of that person's being a male?

5. (20) If there are two random variables X and Y and $Y = f(X)$ and X has a uniform probability density function for $1 \leq X \leq 2$, and $p_Y(y) = \exp(y)$ for $0 \leq Y \leq c$, then find c and $f(X)$. Assume $f(X)$ is monotonically increasing over the defined range.

6. (20) The amount of electricity (in hundreds of kilowatt-hours) that a certain power company is able to sell in a day is found to be a random variable with the following probability density function:

$$p_X(x) = Ax, \quad 0 \le X \le 5$$

$$= A(10 - x), \quad 5 \le X \le 10$$

$$= 0 \text{ otherwise}$$

a. Find A.

b. Graph $p_x(x)$.

c. What is the probability that the number of kilowatt-hours that will be sold tomorrow is more than 500? less than 500? between 250 and 750?

d. Denote respectively by R, S, and T the events that the number of kilowatt-hours sold in a day is greater than 500, less than 500, and between 250 and 750. Find $P(R \mid S)$ and $P(R \mid T)$. Are R and S independent events? Justify your answer. Are R and T independent events? Justify your answer.

EXAMINATION 2: CHAPTERS 1 THROUGH 4

Conditions: 1 hour, open book.

1. (15) A fair coin is tossed. The possible outcomes are heads and tails. Let the random variable be $X = 0$ for heads and $X = 1$ for tails. Find the characteristic function for this random variable.

2. (25) The cumulative probability distribution function for a random variable X is

$$P_X(X \le x) = (1 - e^{-2x}) u(x)$$

Find (a) the probability density function, (b) the probability that $X > 2$, (c) the probability that $-3 < X \le 4$, and (d) the mean and the variance.

3. (20) Two random variables X and Y have probability density functions given by

$$p_X(x) = 2e^{-2x} u(x) \quad \text{and} \quad p_Y(y) = 3e^{-3y} u(y)$$

Find the probability density function for the sum of $X + Y$.

4. (20) How long a series of digits, taken mutually independently and at random from the set of $\{0, 1, 2, \ldots, 9\}$, is necessary for a seven to appear in the series with probability of at least 9/10?

5. (20) Let the joint probability density function for two random variables be given as

$$p_{XY}(x, y) = c(xy + e^x)[u(x) - u(x - 1)][u(y) - u(y - 1)]$$

a. Find c.

b.   Find the marginal probability density for X.

c.   Determine whether or not X and Y are statistically independent.

A6.2 PRACTICE EXAMINATION FOR CHAPTERS 5 THROUGH 8

Conditions: 1.5 hours, open book.

1. (5) To perform a certain experiment you need a zero mean noise with a mean square value less than or equal to 100 $(\text{mv})^2$ (mv = millivolts). You have available a wide sense stationary white noise generator with the following power spectral density:

$$S_{NN}(f) = N_0 = 2 \times 10^{-5} \text{ volts}^2\text{-sec}$$

You also have a set of resistors, capacitors, and inductors. It occurs to you that you can design a lowpass filter to complete the experiment. What is the filter bandwidth and time constant? Draw two possible filter configurations that will work for this problem.

2. (15) A wide sense stationary random process S(t) is added to an independent wide sense stationary noise process N(t). Their power spectral densities are given below for two different cases:

I. $S_{SS}(f) = 1/(1 + \omega^2)$ $S_{NN}(f) = 4/(10 + \omega^2)$

II. $S_{SS}(f) = 3/(5 + \omega^2)$ $S_{NN}(f) = 2/(3 + \omega^2)$

The sum of these two random processes is the input to a simple lowpass filter. Determine the input signal-to-noise ratio (S/N) for both cases. For both cases determine whether or not the lowpass filter bandwidth can be adjusted to improve the S/N at the output. If so, determine the filter bandwidth. Tell how to calculate the output S/N.

3. (20) A wide sense stationary random process X(t) has the following autocorrelation function:

$$R_{XX}(\tau) = \exp(-2|\tau|) + 9$$

Determine the following for this random process:

a.   The mean value.

b.   The standard deviation.

c.   The correlation coefficient.

d. The power spectral density.

4. (20) It is desired to create a wide sense stationary random process with the following autocorrelation function and power spectral density:

$$R_{XX}(\tau) = \exp(-4|\tau|) \qquad S_{XX}(f) = 8/(16 + \omega^2)$$

Let $X(t) = A\cos(\omega\tau + \Theta)$, where A, f, and Θ are statistically independent random variables. Find the probability density functions for A, f, and Θ to give the specified autocorrelation function and power spectral density.

5. (20) The power spectral density of a signal plus noise is given as shown in the figure below. The signal and noise are independent and wide sense stationary. The signal is represented by the delta functions, the noise is represented by the rectangles. Find

a. The variance and mean of the signal.

b. The autocorrelation function of the signal.

c. The variance and mean of the noise.

d. The autocorrelation function of the noise.

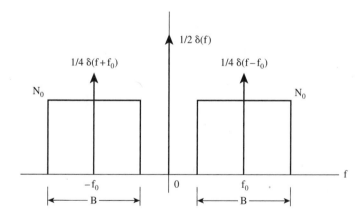

6. (20) You are to find an estimate of the power spectral density $S_{XX}(e^{j\omega})$ of an AR(2) random process that is

$$X(n) = -a_1 X(n-1) - a_2 X(n-2) + w(n)$$

where $w(n)$ is white noise with standard deviation $\sigma_w = 1$. However, you cannot measure $X(n)$. Instead you measure the noise corrupted process

$$Y(n) = X(n) + V(n)$$

where V(n) is uncorrelated with X(n) and is a moving average random process of order one; that is:

$$V(n) = b_0 Q(n) + b_1 Q(n-1)$$

where Q(n) is white noise with unit variance. Using your observations of Y(n), you estimate the following values for the autocorrelation function of Y(n)

$$R_{YY}(0) = 5, \ R_{YY}(1) = 2, \ R_{YY}(2) = 0, \ R_{YY}(3) = -1 \ R_{YY}(4) = 0.5$$

Based on measurements of the noise V(n), you estimate its power spectral density to be

$$S_{VV}(e^{j\omega}) = 3 + 2\cos(\omega)$$

Based on all of this information, estimate the power spectral density of X(n) using the linear prediction method.

BIBLIOGRAPHY

Brown, R. G. *Introduction to Random Signal Analysis and Kalman Filtering.* New York: John Wiley & Sons, 1983.

Cadzow, J. A. *Foundations of Digital Signal Processing and Data Analysis.* New York: Macmillan, 1987.

Candy, J. V. *Signal Processing: The Modern Approach.* New York: McGraw-Hill, 1988.

Childers, D. G. *Modern Spectrum Analysis.* New York: IEEE Press, 1978.

Childers, D. G., and A. Durling. *Digital Filtering and Signal Processing.* St. Paul: West Publishing, 1975.

Couch, L. W. *Digital and Analog Communication Systems.* 3rd ed. New York: Macmillan, 1990.

Davenport, W. B., and W. L. Root. *An Introduction to the Theory of Random Signals and Noise.* New York: McGraw-Hill, 1958.

Gardner, W. A. *Introduction to Random Processes.* 2nd ed. New York: McGraw-Hill, 1990.

Gibson, J. D. *Principles of Digital and Analog Communications.* 2nd ed. New York: Macmillan, 1993.

Kay, S. M. *Modern Spectral Estimation.* Englewood Cliffs, NJ: Prentice Hall, 1988.

———*Fundamentals of Statistical Signal Processing.* Englewood Cliffs, NJ: Prentice Hall, 1993.

Lawson, C. L., and R. J. Hanson. *Solving Least Squares Problems.* Englewood Cliffs, NJ: Prentice Hall, 1974.

Lee, Y. W. *Statistical Theory of Communication.* New York: John Wiley & Sons, 1960.

Leon-Garcia, A. *Probability and Random Processes for Electrical Engineering.* Reading, MA: Addison-Wesley Publishing, 1989.

Marple, S. L. Jr. *Digital Spectral Analysis with Applications.* Englewood Cliffs, NJ: Prentice Hall, 1987.

Mendenhall, W. *Introduction to Probability and Statistics.* 3rd ed. Belmont: Duxbury Press, 1971.

Mohanty, N. C. *Signal Processing: Signals, Filtering, and Detection.* New York: Van Nostrand Reinhold, 1987.

Oppenheim, A. V., and R. Schafer. *Discrete-Time Signal Processing.* Englewood Cliffs, NJ: Prentice Hall, 1975.

———*Digital Signal Processing.* Englewood Cliffs, NJ: Prentice Hall, 1989.

Orfanidis, S. J. *Introduction to Signal Processing.* Englewood Cliffs, NJ: Prentice Hall, 1996.

Papoulis, A. *Probability, Random Variables, and Stochastic Processes.* New York: McGraw-Hill, 1984.

Peebles, P. Z. Jr. *Probability, Random Variables and Random Signal Principles.* 2nd ed. New York: McGraw-Hill, 1987.

Scharf, L. L. *Statistical Signal Processing: Detection Estimation, and Time Series Analysis.* Reading, MA: Addison-Wesley Publishing, 1991.

Shanmugan, K. S., and A. M. Breipohl. *Random Signals: Detection, Estimation, and Data Analysis.* New York: John Wiley & Sons, 1988.

Srinath, M. D.; P. K. Rajasekaran; and R. Viswanathan. *Introduction to Statistical Signal Processing with Applications.* Englewood Cliffs, NJ: Prentice Hall, 1996.

Stark, H., and J. W. Woods. *Probability, Random Processes, and Estimation Theory for Engineers.* 2nd ed. Englewood Cliffs, NJ: Prentice Hall, 1994.

Therrien, C. W. *Discrete Random Signals and Statistical Signal Processing.* Englewood Cliffs, NJ: Prentice Hall, 1992.

Thomas, J. B. *An Introduction to Statistical Communication Theory.* New York: John Wiley & Sons, 1969.

Wozencraft, J. M., and I. M. Jacobs. *Principles of Communication Engineering.* New York: John Wiley & Sons, 1965.

INDEX

NAME & SUBJECT